P9-CQW-904

Student Solutions Manual

Volumes 2 & 3

Sears and
Zemansky's

UNIVERSITY PHYSICS

with Modern Physics

11th Edition

Young & Freedman

A. LEWIS FORD
Texas A&M University

PEARSON

Addison
Wesley

San Francisco • Boston • New York
Capetown • Hong Kong • London • Madrid • Mexico City
Montreal • Munich • Paris • Singapore • Sydney • Tokyo • Toronto

ISBN 0-8053-8696-3

Copyright © 2004 Pearson Education, Inc., publishing as Addison Wesley, 1301 Sansome St., San Francisco, CA 94111. All rights reserved. Manufactured in the United States of America. This publication is protected by Copyright and permission should be obtained from the publisher prior to any prohibited reproduction, storage in a retrieval system, or transmission in any form or by any means, electronic, mechanical, photocopying, recording, or likewise. For information regarding permission(s), write to: Rights and Permissions Department.

PEARSON
Addison
Wesley

7 8 9 10 - DOW - 07 06
www.aw.com/bc

CONTENTS

PREFACE

This *Student Solutions Manual*, Volumes 2 and 3, contains detailed solutions for approximately one third of the Exercises and Problems in Chapters 21 through 44 of the Eleventh Edition of *University Physics* by Hugh Young and Roger Freedman. The Exercises and Problems included in this manual are selected solely from the odd-numbered Exercises and Problems in the text (for which the answers are tabulated in the back of the textbook). The Exercises and Problems included were not selected at random but rather were carefully chosen to include at least one representative example of each problem type. The remaining Exercises and Problems, for which solutions are not given here, constitute an ample set of problems for you to tackle on your own. In addition, there are the Challenge Problems in the text for which no solutions are given here.

This manual greatly expands the set of worked-out examples that accompanies the presentation of physics laws and concepts in the text. This manual was written to provide you with models to follow in working physics problems. The problems are worked out in the manner and style in which you should carry out your own problem solutions.

The author will gratefully receive comments as to style, points of physics, errors, or anything else relating to this manual. The companion volume *Student Solutions Manual Volume 1* is also available from your college bookstore.

A. Lewis Ford
Physics Department
Texas A&M University
College Station, TX 77843
ford@physics.tamu.edu

CHAPTER 21
ELECTRIC CHARGE AND ELECTRIC FIELD

Exercises 1, 5, 7, 9, 17, 19, 23, 25, 27, 29, 31, 35, 39, 43, 45, 47, 57, 59, 61, 67
Problems 69, 71, 73, 75, 77, 81, 83, 85, 87, 95, 99, 101

Exercises

21.1 **a) IDENTIFY** and **SET UP:** Use the charge of one electron $(-1.602 \times 10^{-19} \text{ C})$ to find the number of electrons required to produce the net charge.

EXECUTE: The number of excess electrons needed to produce net charge q is

$$\frac{q}{-e} = \frac{-3.20 \times 10^{-9} \text{ C}}{-1.602 \times 10^{-19} \text{ C/electron}} = 2.00 \times 10^{10} \text{ electrons.}$$

b) IDENTIFY and **SET UP:** Use the atomic mass of lead to find the number of lead atoms in 8.00×10^{-3} kg of lead. From this and the total number of excess electrons, find the number of excess electrons per lead atom.

EXECUTE: The atomic mass of lead is 207×10^{-3} kg/mol, so the number of moles in 8.00×10^{-3} kg is

$$n = \frac{m_{\text{tot}}}{M} = \frac{8.00 \times 10^{-3} \text{ kg}}{207 \times 10^{-3} \text{ kg/mol}} = 0.03865 \text{ mol.}$$

N_A (Avogadro's number) is the number of atoms in 1 mole, so the number of lead atoms is $N = nN_A = (0.03865 \text{ mol})(6.022 \times 10^{23} \text{ atoms/mol}) = 2.328 \times 10^{22}$ atoms.

The number of excess electrons per lead atom is

$$\frac{2.00 \times 10^{10} \text{ electrons}}{2.328 \times 10^{22} \text{ atoms}} = 8.59 \times 10^{-13}.$$

EVALUATE: Even this small net charge corresponds to a large number of excess electrons. But the number of atoms in the sphere is much larger still, so the number of excess electrons per lead atom is very small.

21.5 **IDENTIFY** and **SET UP:** Use Avogadro's number to find the number of hydrogen atoms. There is one electron per atom.

EXECUTE: $N = nN_A = (1.80 \text{ mol})(6.022 \times 10^{23} \text{ atoms/mol}) = 1.084 \times 10^{24}$ atoms. There is 1 electron per hydrogen atom and each electron has charge $-e = -1.602 \times 10^{-19}$ C, so $Q = (-1.602 \times 10^{-19} \text{ C/electron})(1.084 \times 10^{24} \text{ electrons}) = -1.74 \times 10^5$ C.

EVALUATE: This is a large amount of charge. 1.8 moles of hydrogen atoms have a mass of 1.8 g. This small amount of material contains a huge amount of negative charge, but also an equal amount of positive charge.

21.7   **IDENTIFY:** Apply Coulomb's law.

SET UP: Consider the force on one of the spheres.

a) EXECUTE: $q_1 = q_2 = q$

$$F = \frac{1}{4\pi\epsilon_0} \frac{|q_1 q_2|}{r^2} = \frac{q^2}{4\pi\epsilon_0 r^2} \text{ so}$$

$$q = r\sqrt{\frac{F}{(1/4\pi\epsilon_0)}} = 0.150 \text{ m}\sqrt{\frac{0.220 \text{ N}}{8.988 \times 10^9 \text{ N} \cdot \text{m}^2/\text{C}^2}} = 7.42 \times 10^{-7} \text{ C (on each)}$$

b) $q_2 = 4q_1$

$$F = \frac{1}{4\pi\epsilon_0} \frac{|q_1 q_2|}{r^2} = \frac{4q_1^2}{4\pi\epsilon_0 r^2} \text{ so}$$

$$q_1 = r\sqrt{\frac{F}{4(1/4\pi\epsilon_0)}} = \tfrac{1}{2}r\sqrt{\frac{F}{(1/4\pi\epsilon_0)}} = \tfrac{1}{2}(7.42 \times 10^{-7} \text{ C}) = 3.71 \times 10^{-7} \text{ C.}$$

And then $q_2 = 4q_1 = 1.48 \times 10^{-6}$ C.

EVALUATE: The force on one sphere is the same magnitude as the force on the other sphere, whether the sphere have equal charges or not.

21.9   **IDENTIFY** and **SET UP:** Apply Coulomb's law. Set the magnitude of the electrical force exerted on the electron by the proton equal to the weight $m_e g$ of the electron and solve for the separation r between the two charges.

EXECUTE: The weight of an electron is $m_e g$. The nucleus of a hydrogen atom is a single proton with charge $+e$. The Coulomb force between the electron and the nucleus is $\dfrac{1}{4\pi\epsilon_0} \dfrac{e^2}{r^2}$.

Equating these two forces gives $m_e g = \dfrac{1}{4\pi\epsilon_0} \dfrac{e^2}{r^2}$.

$$r = e\sqrt{\frac{(1/4\pi\epsilon_0)}{m_e g}} = 1.602 \times 10^{-19} \text{ C}\sqrt{\frac{8.988 \times 10^9 \text{ N} \cdot \text{m}^2/\text{C}^2}{(9.109 \times 10^{-31} \text{ kg})(9.80 \text{ m/s}^2)}} = 5.08 \text{ m}$$

EVALUATE: The size of a hydrogen atom is many orders of magnitude smaller than this so in the atom the electrical force on the electron is much, much larger than its weight.

21.17   **IDENTIFY** and **SET UP:** Apply Coulomb's law to calculate the force exerted by q_2 and q_3 on q_1. Add these forces as vectors to get the net force. The target variable is the x-coordinate of q_3.

EXECUTE: $\vec{F}_2$ is in the $+x$-direction.

$F_2 = k\dfrac{|q_1 q_2|}{r_{12}^2} = 3.37$ N, so $F_{2x} = +3.37$ N

$F_x = F_{2x} + F_{3x}$ and $F_x = -7.00$ N

$F_{3x} = F_x - F_{2x} = -7.00$ N $- 3.37$ N $= -10.37$ N

For F_{3x} to be negative, q_3 must be on the $-x$-axis.

$F_3 = k\dfrac{|q_1 q_3|}{x^2}$, so $|x| = \sqrt{\dfrac{k|q_1 q_3|}{F_3}} = 0.144$ m, so $x = -0.144$ m

EVALUATE: q_2 attracts q_1 in the $+x$-direction so q_3 must attract q_1 in the $-x$-direction, and q_3 is at negative x.

21.19 **IDENTIFY:** Apply Coulomb's law to calculate the force each of the two charges exerts on the third charge. Add these forces as vectors.

SET UP: The three charges are placed as follows.

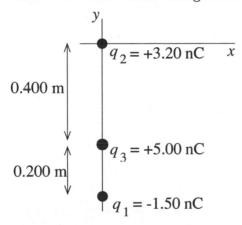

EXECUTE: Like charges repel and unlike attract, so the free-body diagram for q_3 is

$F_1 = \dfrac{1}{4\pi\epsilon_0}\dfrac{|q_1 q_3|}{r_{13}^2}$

$F_2 = \dfrac{1}{4\pi\epsilon_0}\dfrac{|q_2 q_3|}{r_{23}^2}$

$F_1 = (8.988 \times 10^9 \text{ N} \cdot \text{m}^2/\text{C}^2)\dfrac{(1.50 \times 10^{-9} \text{ C})(5.00 \times 10^{-9} \text{ C})}{(0.200 \text{ m})^2} = 1.685 \times 10^{-6}$ N

$F_2 = (8.988 \times 10^9 \text{ N} \cdot \text{m}^2/\text{C}^2)\dfrac{(3.20 \times 10^{-9} \text{ C})(5.00 \times 10^{-9} \text{ C})}{(0.400 \text{ m})^2} = 8.988 \times 10^{-7}$ N

The resultant force is $\vec{R} = \vec{F}_1 + \vec{F}_2$.

$R_x = 0$.

$R_y = F_1 + F_2 = 1.685 \times 10^{-6}$ N $+ 8.988 \times 10^{-7}$ N $= 2.58 \times 10^{-6}$ N.

The resultant force has magnitude 2.58×10^{-6} N and is in the $-y$-direction.

EVALUATE: The force between q_1 and q_3 is attractive and the force between q_2 and q_3 is repulsive.

21.23 IDENTIFY: Apply Coulomb's law to calculate the force exerted on one of the charges by each of the other three and then add these forces as vectors.

a) SET UP: The charges are placed as shown.

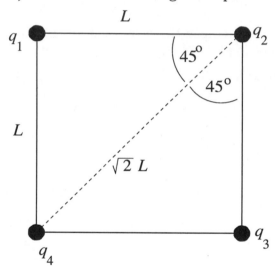

$$q_1 = q_2 = q_3 = q_4 = q$$

Consider forces on q_4. Take the y-axis to be parallel to the diagonal between q_2 and q_4 and let $+y$ be in the direction away from q_2. Then $\vec{F}_2$ is in the $+y$-direction.

EXECUTE:

$$F_3 = F_1 = \frac{1}{4\pi\epsilon_0}\frac{q^2}{L^2}$$

$$F_2 = \frac{1}{4\pi\epsilon_0}\frac{q^2}{2L^2}$$

$F_{1x} = -F_1 \sin 45° = -F_1/\sqrt{2}$
$F_{1y} = +F_1 \cos 45° = +F_1/\sqrt{2}$
$F_{3x} = +F_3 \sin 45° = +F_3/\sqrt{2}$
$F_{3y} = +F_3 \cos 45° = +F_3/\sqrt{2}$
$F_{2x} = 0, \ F_{2y} = F_2$

b) $R_x = F_{1x} + F_{2x} + F_{3x} = 0$

$$R_y = F_{1y} + F_{2y} + F_{3y} = (2/\sqrt{2})\frac{1}{4\pi\epsilon_0}\frac{q^2}{L^2} + \frac{1}{4\pi\epsilon_0}\frac{q^2}{2L^2} = \frac{q^2}{8\pi\epsilon_0 L^2}(1 + 2\sqrt{2})$$

$R = \dfrac{q^2}{8\pi\epsilon_0 L^2}(1 + 2\sqrt{2})$. Same for all four charges.

EVALUATE: In general the resultant force on one of the charges is directed away from the opposite corner. The forces are all repulsive since the charges are all the same. By symmetry the net force on one charge can have no component perpendicular to the diagonal of the square.

21.25 IDENTIFY: Use a constant acceleration equation to calculate a_x from the information given about the motion. Then use $\vec{F} = m\vec{a}$ to calculate $\vec{F}$ and Eq.(21.3) to calculate $\vec{E}$ from $\vec{F}$.

SET UP: Let $+x$-direction be to the right. Find a_x:

$v_{0x} = +1.50 \times 10^3$ m/s, $v_x = -1.50 \times 10^3$ m/s, $t = 2.65 \times 10^{-6}$ s, $a_x = ?$

EXECUTE: $v_x = v_{0x} + a_x t$ gives $a_x = -1.132 \times 10^9$ m/s^2

$F_x = ma_x = -7.516 \times 10^{-18}$ N

$\vec{F}$ is to the left ($-x$-direction), charge is positive, so $\vec{E}$ is to the left.

$E = F/q = (7.516 \times 10^{-18}$ N$)/[(2)(1.602 \times 10^{-19}$ C$)] = 23.5$ N/C

EVALUATE: The change in velocity is to the left so the acceleration and force are to the left. For a positive charge Eq.(21.3) says that $\vec{F}$ and $\vec{E}$ are in the same direction.

21.27 a) IDENTIFY: Eq.(21.4) relates the electric field, charge of the particle, and the force on the particle. If the particle is to remain stationary the net force on it must be zero.

SET UP: The weight is mg, downward. For the net force to be zero the force exerted by the electric field must be upward. The electric field is downward. Since the electric field and the electric force are in opposite directions the charge of the particle is negative.

$mg = |q|E$

EXECUTE: $|q| = \dfrac{mg}{E} = \dfrac{(1.45 \times 10^{-3} \text{ kg})(9.80 \text{ m/s}^2)}{650 \text{ N/C}} = 2.19 \times 10^{-5}$ C and

$q = -21.9 \ \mu$C

b) SET UP: The electrical force has magnitude $F_E = |q|E = eE$.
The weight of a proton is $w = mg$. $F_E = w$ so $eE = mg$

EXECUTE: $E = \dfrac{mg}{e} = \dfrac{(1.673 \times 10^{-27} \text{ kg})(9.80 \text{ m/s}^2)}{1.602 \times 10^{-19} \text{ C}} = 1.02 \times 10^{-7} \text{ N/C}.$
This is a very small electric field.

EVALUATE: In both cases $|q|E = mg$ and $E = (m/|q|)g$. In part (b) the $m/|q|$ ratio is much smaller ($\sim 10^{-8}$) than in part (a) ($\sim 10^{-2}$) so E is much smaller in (b). For subatomic particles gravity can usually be ignored compared to electric forces.

21.29 IDENTIFY: Use Eq.(21.3) to relate the field, force and charge.

a) SET UP: For a negative charge $\vec{F}$ and field $\vec{E}$ are in opposite directions. $\vec{F}$ is downward so $\vec{E}$ is upward.

q

E

F

EXECUTE:
$$E = \frac{F}{|q|} = \frac{6.20 \times 10^{-9} \text{ N}}{55.0 \times 10^{-6} \text{ C}} = 1.13 \times 10^{-4} \text{ N/C}$$

b) The copper nucleus has charge $+29e$. For a positive charge the field and force are in the same direction so $\vec{F}$ is upward when $\vec{E}$ is upward.
$F = |q|E = (29)(1.602 \times 10^{-19} \text{ C})(1.13 \times 10^{-4} \text{ N/C}) = 5.25 \times 10^{-22} \text{ N}$

EVALUATE: The copper nucleus of part (b) has a much smaller charge than the object so the force on it is much less. For the same electric field, the forces on negatively and positively charged objects are in opposite directions.

21.31 IDENTIFY: Eq.(21.3) gives the force on the particle in terms of its charge and the electric field between the plates. The force is constant and produces a constant acceleration. The motion is similar to projectile motion; use constant acceleration equations for the horizontal and vertical components of the motion.

a) SET UP:

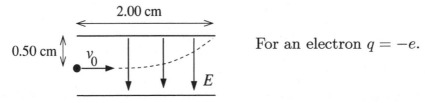

For an electron $q = -e$.

$\vec{F} = q\vec{E}$ and q negative gives that $\vec{F}$ and $\vec{E}$ are in opposite directions, so $\vec{F}$ is upward.

y

a

$F = eE$

x

EXECUTE:

$\sum F_y = ma_y$

$eE = ma$

Solve the kinematics to find the acceleration of the electron:

Just misses upper plate says that $x - x_0 = 2.00$ cm when $y - y_0 = +0.500$ cm.

x-component

$v_{0x} = v_0 = 1.60 \times 10^6$ m/s, $a_x = 0$, $x - x_0 = 0.0200$ m, $t = ?$

$x - x_0 = v_{0x}t + \frac{1}{2}a_x t^2$

$t = \dfrac{x - x_0}{v_{0x}} = \dfrac{0.0200 \text{ m}}{1.60 \times 10^6 \text{ m/s}} = 1.25 \times 10^{-8}$ s

In this same time t the electron travels 0.0050 m vertically:

y-component

$t = 1.25 \times 10^{-8}$ s, $v_{0y} = 0$, $y - y_0 = +0.0050$ m, $a_y = ?$

$y - y_0 = v_{0y}t + \frac{1}{2}a_y t^2$

$a_y = \dfrac{2(y - y_0)}{t^2} = \dfrac{2(0.0050 \text{ m})}{(1.25 \times 10^{-8} \text{ s})^2} = 6.40 \times 10^{13}$ m/s^2

(This analysis is very similar to that used in Chapter 3 for projectile motion, except that here the acceleration is upward rather than downward.)

This acceleration must be produced by the electric-field force:

$eE = ma$

$E = \dfrac{ma}{e} = \dfrac{(9.109 \times 10^{-31} \text{ kg})(6.40 \times 10^{13} \text{ m/s}^2)}{1.602 \times 10^{-19} \text{ C}} = 364$ N/C

Note that the acceleration produced by the electric field is <u>much</u> larger than g, the acceleration produced by gravity, so it is perfectly ok to neglect the gravity force on the electron in this problem.

b) $a = \dfrac{eE}{m_p} = \dfrac{(1.602 \times 10^{-19} \text{ C})(364 \text{ N/C})}{1.673 \times 10^{-27} \text{ kg}} = 3.49 \times 10^{10}$ m/s^2

This is much less than the acceleration of the electron in part (a) so the vertical deflection is less and the proton won't hit the plates.

The proton has the same initial speed, so the proton takes the same time $t = 1.25 \times 10^{-8}$ s to travel horizontally the length of the plates. The force on the proton is downward (in the same direction as $\vec{E}$, since q is positive), so the accleration is downward and $a_y = -3.49 \times 10^{10}$ m/s^2.

$y - y_0 = v_{0y}t + \frac{1}{2}a_y t^2 = \frac{1}{2}(-3.49 \times 10^{10}$ m/s$^2)(1.25 \times 10^{-8}$ s$)^2 = -2.73 \times 10^{-6}$ m.
The displacement is 2.73×10^{-6} m, downward.

c) **EVALUATE:** The displacements are in opposite directions because the electron has negative charge and the proton has positive charge. The electron and proton have the same magnitude of charge, so the force the electric field exerts has the same magnitude for each charge. But the proton has a mass larger by a factor of 1836 so its acceleration and its vertical displacement are smaller by this factor.

21.35   IDENTIFY and **SET UP:** The electric force is given by Eq.(21.3).
The gravitational force is $w_e = m_e g$. Compare these forces.
a) **EXECUTE:** $w_e = (9.109 \times 10^{-31}$ kg$)(9.80$ m/s$^2) = 8.93 \times 10^{-30}$ N

In Examples 21.7 and 21.8, $E = 1.00 \times 10^4$ N/C, so the electric force on the electron has magnitude

$F_E = |q|E = eE = (1.602 \times 10^{-19}$ C$)(1.00 \times 10^4$ N/C$) = 1.602 \times 10^{-15}$ N.

$\dfrac{w_e}{F_E} = \dfrac{8.93 \times 10^{-30} \text{ N}}{1.602 \times 10^{-15} \text{ N}} = 5.57 \times 10^{-15}$

The gravitational force is much smaller than the electric force and can be neglected.

b) $mg = |q|E$

$m = |q|E/g = (1.602 \times 10^{-19}$ C$)(1.00 \times 10^4$ N/C$)/(9.80$ m/s$^2) = 1.63 \times 10^{-16}$ kg

$\dfrac{m}{m_e} = \dfrac{1.63 \times 10^{-16} \text{ kg}}{9.109 \times 10^{-31} \text{ kg}} = 1.79 \times 10^{14}; \quad m = 1.79 \times 10^{14} m_e.$

EVALUATE: m is much larger than m_e. We found in part (a) that if $m = m_e$ the gravitational force is much smaller than the electric force. $|q|$ is the same so the electric force remains the same. To get w large enough to equal F_E, the mass must be made much larger.

c) The electric field in the region between the plates is uniform so the force it exerts on the charged object is independent of where between the plates the object is placed.

21.39   IDENTIFY and **SET UP:** Use $\vec{E}$ in Eq.(21.3) to calculate $\vec{F}$, $\vec{F} = m\vec{a}$ to calculate $\vec{a}$, and a constant acceleration equation to calculate the final velocity. Let $+x$ be east.
a) **EXECUTE:** $F_x = |q|E = (1.602 \times 10^{-19}$ C$)(1.50$ N/C$) = 2.403 \times 10^{-19}$ N

$a_x = F_x/m = (2.403 \times 10^{-19}$ N$)/(9.109 \times 10^{-31}$ kg$) = +2.638 \times 10^{11}$ m/s^2

$v_{0x} = +4.50 \times 10^5$ m/s, $a_x = +2.638 \times 10^{11}$ m/s^2, $x - x_0 = 0.375$ m, $v_x = ?$

$v_x^2 = v_{0x}^2 + 2a_x(x - x_0)$ gives $v_x = 6.33 \times 10^5$ m/s

EVALUATE: $\vec{E}$ is west and q is negative, so $\vec{F}$ is east and the electron speeds up.

b) EXECUTE:

$F_x = -|q|E = -(1.602 \times 10^{-19}\ \text{C})(1.50\ \text{N/C}) = -2.403 \times 10^{-19}\ \text{N}$

$a_x = F_x/m = (-2.403 \times 10^{-19}\ \text{N})/(1.673 \times 10^{-27}\ \text{kg}) = -1.436 \times 10^{8}\ \text{m/s}^2$

$v_{0x} = +1.90 \times 10^{4}\ \text{m/s},\ a_x = -1.436 \times 10^{8}\ \text{m/s}^2,\ x - x_0 = 0.375\ \text{m},\ v_x = ?$

$v_x^2 = v_{0x}^2 + 2a_x(x - x_0)$ gives $v_x = 1.59 \times 10^{4}\ \text{m/s}$

EVALUATE: $q > 0$ so $\vec{F}$ is west and the proton slows down.

21.43 IDENTIFY: Eq.(21.7) gives the electric field of each point charge. Use the principle of superposition and add the electric field vectors. In part (b) use Eq.(21.3) to calculate the force, using the electric field calculated in part (a).

a) SET UP:

The electric field of a point charge is directed away from the point charge if the charge is positive and toward the point charge if the charge is negative.

The magnitude of the electric field is $E = \dfrac{1}{4\pi\epsilon_0}\dfrac{|q|}{r^2}$, where r is the distance between the point where the field is calculated and the point charge.

(i) At point a the fields $\vec{E}_1$ of q_1 and $\vec{E}_2$ of q_2 are:

EXECUTE:

$E_1 = \dfrac{1}{4\pi\epsilon_0}\dfrac{|q_1|}{r_1^2} = (8.988 \times 10^{9}\ \text{N} \cdot \text{m}^2/\text{C}^2)\dfrac{2.00 \times 10^{-9}\ \text{C}}{(0.200\ \text{m})^2} = 449.4\ \text{N/C}$

$E_2 = \dfrac{1}{4\pi\epsilon_0}\dfrac{|q_2|}{r_2^2} = (8.988 \times 10^{9}\ \text{N} \cdot \text{m}^2/\text{C}^2)\dfrac{5.00 \times 10^{-9}\ \text{C}}{(0.600\ \text{m})^2} = 124.8\ \text{N/C}$

$E_{1x} = 449.4\ \text{N/C},\quad E_{1y} = 0$

$E_{2x} = 124.8\ \text{N/C},\quad E_{2y} = 0$

$E_x = E_{1x} + E_{2x} = +449.4\ \text{N/C} + 124.8\ \text{N/C} = +574.2\ \text{N/C}$

$E_y = E_{1y} + E_{2y} = 0$

The resultant field at point a has magnitude 574 N/C and is in the $+x$-direction.

(ii) **SET UP:** At point b the fields $\vec{E}_1$ of q_1 and $\vec{E}_2$ of q_2 are:

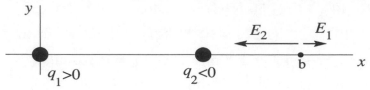

EXECUTE:

$$E_1 = \frac{1}{4\pi\epsilon_0}\frac{|q_1|}{r_1^2} = (8.988 \times 10^9 \text{ N} \cdot \text{m}^2/\text{C}^2)\frac{2.00 \times 10^{-9} \text{ C}}{(1.20 \text{ m})^2} = 12.5 \text{ N/C}$$

$$E_2 = \frac{1}{4\pi\epsilon_0}\frac{|q_2|}{r_2^2} = (8.988 \times 10^9 \text{ N} \cdot \text{m}^2/\text{C}^2)\frac{5.00 \times 10^{-9} \text{ C}}{(0.400 \text{ m})^2} = 280.9 \text{ N/C}$$

$E_{1x} = 12.5 \text{ N/C}, \quad E_{1y} = 0$

$E_{2x} = -280.9 \text{ N/C}, \quad E_{2y} = 0$

$E_x = E_{1x} + E_{2x} = +12.5 \text{ N/C} - 280.9 \text{ N/C} = -268.4 \text{ N/C}$

$E_y = E_{1y} + E_{2y} = 0$

The resultant field at point b has magnitude 268 N/C and is in the $-x$-direction.

(iii) **SET UP:** At point c the fields $\vec{E}_1$ of q_1 and $\vec{E}_2$ of q_2 are:

EXECUTE:

$$E_1 = \frac{1}{4\pi\epsilon_0}\frac{|q_1|}{r_1^2} = (8.988 \times 10^9 \text{ N} \cdot \text{m}^2/\text{C}^2)\frac{2.00 \times 10^{-9} \text{ C}}{(0.200 \text{ m})^2} = 449.4 \text{ N/C}$$

$$E_2 = \frac{1}{4\pi\epsilon_0}\frac{|q_2|}{r_2^2} = (8.988 \times 10^9 \text{ N} \cdot \text{m}^2/\text{C}^2)\frac{5.00 \times 10^{-9} \text{ C}}{(1.00 \text{ m})^2} = 44.9 \text{ N/C}$$

$E_{1x} = -449.4 \text{ N/C}, \quad E_{1y} = 0$

$E_{2x} = +44.9 \text{ N/C}, \quad E_{2y} = 0$

$E_x = E_{1x} + E_{2x} = -449.4 \text{ N/C} + 44.9 \text{ N/C} = -404.5 \text{ N/C}$

$E_y = E_{1y} + E_{2y} = 0$

The resultant field at point b has magnitude 404 N/C and is in the $-x$-direction.

b) SET UP: Since we have calculated $\vec{E}$ at each point the simplest way to get the force is to use $\vec{F} = -e\vec{E}$.

EXECUTE:

(i) $F = (1.602 \times 10^{-19} \text{ C})(574.2 \text{ N/C}) = 9.20 \times 10^{-17} \text{ N}$, $-x$-direction

(ii) $F = (1.602 \times 10^{-19} \text{ C})(268.4 \text{ N/C}) = 4.30 \times 10^{-17} \text{ N}$, $+x$-direction

(iii) $F = (1.602 \times 10^{-19} \text{ C})(404.5 \text{ N/C}) = 6.48 \times 10^{-17} \text{ N}$, $+x$-direction

EVALUATE: The general rule for electric field direction is away from positive charge and toward negative charge. Whether the field is in the $+x$- or $-x$-direction depends on where the field point is relative to the charge that produces the field. In part (a) the field magnitudes were added because the fields were in the same direction and in (b) and (c) the field magnitudes were subtracted because the two fields were in opposite directions. In part (b) we could have used Coulomb's law to find the forces on the electron due to the two charges and then added these force vectors, but using the resultant electric field is much easier.

21.45 IDENTIFY: The electric field of a positive charge is directed radially outward from the charge and has magnitude $E = \dfrac{1}{4\pi\epsilon_0}\dfrac{|q|}{r^2}$. The resultant electric field is the vector sum of the fields of the individual charges.

SET UP:

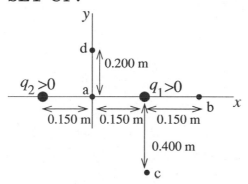

EXECUTE:

a)

$E_1 = E_2 = \dfrac{1}{4\pi\epsilon_0}\dfrac{|q|}{r^2}$ with $r = 0.150$ m.

$E = E_2 - E_1 = 0$; $E_x = 0$, $E_y = 0$

b)

$E = E_1 + E_2$, in the $+x$-direction

$E_1 = \dfrac{1}{4\pi\epsilon_0}\dfrac{|q_1|}{r_1^2} = (8.988 \times 10^9 \text{ N} \cdot \text{m}^2/\text{C}^2)\dfrac{6.00 \times 10^{-9} \text{ C}}{(0.150 \text{ m})^2} = 2396.8 \text{ N/C}$

$E_2 = \dfrac{1}{4\pi\epsilon_0}\dfrac{|q_2|}{r_2^2} = (8.988 \times 10^9 \text{ N} \cdot \text{m}^2/\text{C}^2)\dfrac{6.00 \times 10^{-9} \text{ C}}{(0.450 \text{ m})^2} = 266.3 \text{ N/C}$

$E = E_1 + E_2 = 2396.8 \text{ N/C} + 266.3 \text{ N/C} = 2660 \text{ N/C}; \; E_x = +2260 \text{ N/C}, \; E_y = 0$

c)

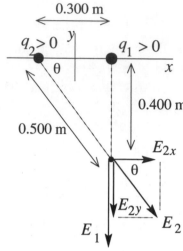

$\sin \theta = \dfrac{0.400 \text{ m}}{0.500 \text{ m}} = 0.800$

$\cos \theta = \dfrac{0.300 \text{ m}}{0.500 \text{ m}} = 0.600$

$E_1 = \dfrac{1}{4\pi\epsilon_0} \dfrac{|q_1|}{r_1^2}$

$E_1 = (8.988 \times 10^9 \text{ N} \cdot \text{m}^2/\text{C}^2) \dfrac{6.00 \times 10^{-9} \text{ C}}{(0.400 \text{ m})^2} = 337.1 \text{ N/C}$

$E_2 = \dfrac{1}{4\pi\epsilon_0} \dfrac{|q_2|}{r_2^2}$

$E_2 = (8.988 \times 10^9 \text{ N} \cdot \text{m}^2/\text{C}^2) \dfrac{6.00 \times 10^{-9} \text{ C}}{(0.500 \text{ m})^2} = 215.7 \text{ N/C}$

$E_{1x} = 0, \quad E_{1y} = -E_1 = -337.1 \text{ N/C}$

$E_{2x} = +E_2 \cos \theta = +(215.7 \text{ N/C})(0.600) = +129.4 \text{ N/C}$

$E_{2y} = -E_2 \sin \theta = -(215.7 \text{ N/C})(0.800) = -172.6 \text{ N/C}$

$E_x = E_{1x} + E_{2x} = +129 \text{ N/C}$

$E_y = E_{1y} + E_{2y} = -337.1 \text{ N/C} - 172.6 \text{ N/C} = -510 \text{ N/C}$

$E = \sqrt{E_x^2 + E_y^2} = \sqrt{(129 \text{ N/C})^2 + (-510 \text{ N/C})^2} = 526 \text{ N/C}$

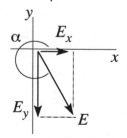

$\tan \alpha = \dfrac{E_y}{E_x}$

$\tan \alpha = \dfrac{-510 \text{ N/C}}{+129 \text{ N/C}} = -3.953$

$\alpha = 284°\text{C}$, counterclockwise from $+x$-axis

d)

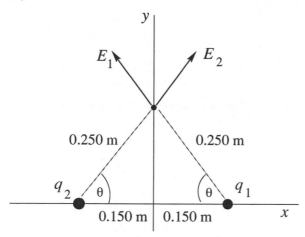

$$\sin \theta = \frac{0.200 \text{ m}}{0.250 \text{ m}} = 0.800$$

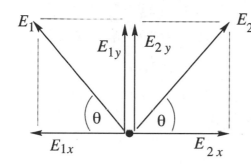

$$E_1 = E_2 = \frac{1}{4\pi\epsilon_0}\frac{|q|}{r^2}$$

$$E_1 = (8.988 \times 10^9 \text{ N} \cdot \text{m}^2/\text{C}^2)\frac{6.00 \times 10^{-9} \text{ C}}{(0.250 \text{ m})^2}$$

$$E_1 = E_2 = 862.8 \text{ N/C}$$

$E_{1x} = -E_1 \cos\theta, \quad E_{2x} = +E_2 \cos\theta$

$E_x = E_{1x} + E_{2x} = 0$

$E_{1y} = +E_1 \sin\theta, \ E_{2y} = +E_2 \sin\theta$

$E_y = E_{1y} + E_{2y} = 2E_{1y} = 2E_1 \sin\theta = 2(862.8 \text{ N/C})(0.800) = 1380 \text{ N/C}$

$E = 1380 \text{ N/C}$, in the $+y$-direction.

EVALUATE: Point a is symmetrically placed between identical charges, so symmetry tells us the electric field must be zero. Point b is to the right of both charges and both electric fields are in the $+x$-direction and the resultant field is in this direction. At point c both fields have a downward component and the field of q_2 has a component to the right, so the net $\vec{E}$ is in the 4th quadrant. At point d both fields have an upward component but by symmetry they have equal and opposite x-components so the net field is in the $+y$-direction. We can use this sort of reasoning to deduce the general direction of the net field before doing any calculations.

21.47 IDENTIFY: The resultant electric field is the vector sum of the field $\vec{E}_1$ of q_1 and $\vec{E}_2$ of q_2.

SET UP:

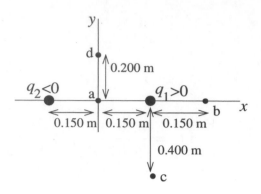

EXECUTE:

a)

$$E_1 = E_2 = \frac{1}{4\pi\epsilon_0}\frac{|q_1|}{r_1^2}$$

$$E_1 = (8.988 \times 10^9 \text{ N} \cdot \text{m}^2/\text{C}^2)\frac{6.00 \times 10^{-9} \text{ C}}{(0.150 \text{ m})^2}$$

$$E_1 = E_2 = 2397 \text{ N/C}$$

$E_{1x} = -2397$ N/C, $E_{1y} = 0$ $E_{2x} = -2397$ N/C, $E_{2y} = 0$

$E_x = E_{1x} + E_{2x} = 2(-2397 \text{ N/C}) = -4790$ N/C

$E_y = E_{1y} + E_{2y} = 0$

The resultant electric field at point a in the sketch has magnitude 4790 N/C and is in the $-x$-direction.

b)

$$E_1 = \frac{1}{4\pi\epsilon_0}\frac{|q_1|}{r_1^2} = (8.988 \times 10^9 \text{ N} \cdot \text{m}^2/\text{C}^2)\frac{6.00 \times 10^{-9} \text{ C}}{(0.150 \text{ m})^2} = 2397 \text{ N/C}$$

$$E_2 = \frac{1}{4\pi\epsilon_0}\frac{|q_2|}{r_2^2} = (8.988 \times 10^9 \text{ N} \cdot \text{m}^2/\text{C}^2)\frac{6.00 \times 10^{-9} \text{ C}}{(0.450 \text{ m})^2} = 266 \text{ N/C}$$

$E_{1x} = +2397$ N/C, $E_{1y} = 0$ $E_{2x} = -266$ N/C, $E_{2y} = 0$

$E_x = E_{1x} + E_{2x} = +2397 \text{ N/C} - 266 \text{ N/C} = +2130$ N/C

$E_y = E_{1y} + E_{2y} = 0$

The resultant electric field at point b in the sketch has magnitude 2130 N/C and is in the $+x$-direction.

c)

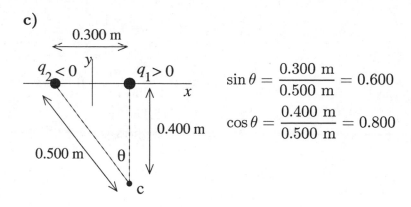

$$\sin \theta = \frac{0.300 \text{ m}}{0.500 \text{ m}} = 0.600$$

$$\cos \theta = \frac{0.400 \text{ m}}{0.500 \text{ m}} = 0.800$$

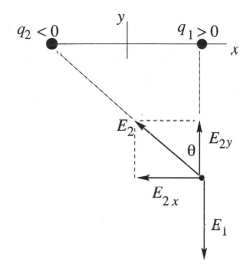

$$E_1 = \frac{1}{4\pi c_0} \frac{|q_1|}{r_1^2}$$

$$E_1 = (8.988 \times 10^9 \text{ N} \cdot \text{m}^2/\text{C}^2) \frac{6.00 \times 10^{-9} \text{ C}}{(0.400 \text{ m})^2}$$

$$E_1 = 337.0 \text{ N/C}$$

$$E_2 = \frac{1}{4\pi \epsilon_0} \frac{|q_2|}{r_2^2}$$

$$E_2 = (8.988 \times 10^9 \text{ N} \cdot \text{m}^2/\text{C}^2) \frac{6.00 \times 10^{-9} \text{ C}}{(0.500 \text{ m})^2}$$

$$E_2 = 215.7 \text{ N/C}$$

$E_{1x} = 0, \quad E_{1y} = -E_1 = -337.0 \text{ N/C}$

$E_{2x} = -E_2 \sin \theta = -(215.7 \text{ N/C})(0.600) = -129.4 \text{ N/C}$

$E_{2y} = +E_2 \cos \theta = +(215.7 \text{ N/C})(0.800) = +172.6 \text{ N/C}$

$E_x = E_{1x} + E_{2x} = -129 \text{ N/C}$

$E_y = E_{1y} + E_{2y} = -337.0 \text{ N/C} + 172.6 \text{ N/C} = -164 \text{ N/C}$

$E = \sqrt{E_x^2 + E_y^2} = 209 \text{ N/C}$

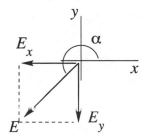

$$\tan \alpha = \frac{E_y}{E_x}$$

$$\tan \alpha = \frac{-164 \text{ N/C}}{-129 \text{ N/C}} = +1.271$$

$\alpha = 232°$, counterclockwise from $+x$-axis

d)

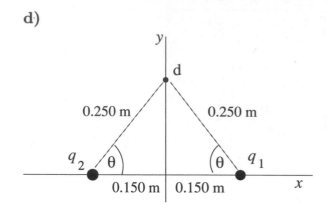

$$\sin \theta = \frac{0.200 \text{ m}}{0.250 \text{ m}} = 0.800$$

$$\cos \theta = \frac{0.150 \text{ m}}{0.250 \text{ m}} = 0.600$$

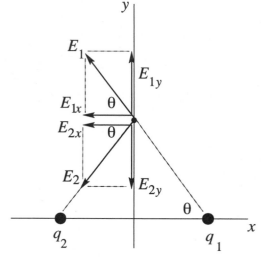

$$E_1 = E_2 = \frac{1}{4\pi\epsilon_0} \frac{|q|}{r^2}$$

$$E_1 = (8.988 \times 10^9 \text{ N} \cdot \text{m}^2/\text{C}^2) \frac{6.00 \times 10^{-9} \text{ C}}{(0.250 \text{ m})^2}$$

$$E_1 = 862.8 \text{ N/C}$$

$$E_2 = E_1 = 862.8 \text{ N/C}$$

$E_{1x} = -E_1 \cos \theta, \quad E_{2x} = -E_2 \cos \theta$

$E_x = E_{1x} + E_{2x} = -2(862.8 \text{ N/C})(0.600) = -1040 \text{ N/C}$

$E_{1y} = +E_1 \sin \theta, \; E_{2y} = -E_2 \sin \theta$

$E_y = E_{1y} + E_{2y} = 0$

$E = 1040 \text{ N/C}$, in the $-x$-direction.

EVALUATE: The electric field produced by a charge is toward a negative charge and away from a positive charge. As in Exercise 21.45, we can use this rule to deduce the direction of the resultant field at each point before doing any calculations.

21.57 IDENTIFY: Use symmetry to deduce the nature of the field lines.

a) SET UP: The only distinguishable direction is toward the line or away from the line, so the electric field lines are perpendicular to the line of charge.

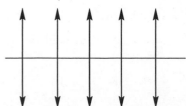   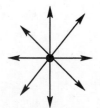

b) EXECUTE and EVALUATE: The magnitude of the electric field is inversely proportional to the spacing of the field lines. Consider a circle of radius r with the line of charge passing through the center.

The spacing of field lines is the same all around the circle, and in the direction perpendicular to the plane of the circle the lines are equally spaced, so E depends only on the distance r. The number of field lines passing out through the circle is independent of the radius of the circle, so the spacing of the field lines is proportional to the reciprocal of the circumference $2\pi r$ of the circle. Hence E is proportional to $1/r$.

21.59 a) IDENTIFY and SET UP: Use Eq.(21.14) to relate the dipole moment to the charge magnitude and the separation d of the two charges. The direction is from the negative charge toward the positive charge.

EXECUTE: $p = qd = (4.5 \times 10^{-9} \text{ C})(3.1 \times 10^{-3} \text{ m}) = 1.4 \times 10^{-11}$ C·m; The direction of $\vec{p}$ is from q_1 toward q_2.

b) IDENTIFY and SET UP: Use Eq.(21.15) to relate the magnitudes of the torque and field.

EXECUTE: $\tau = pE \sin\phi$ so

$$E = \frac{\tau}{p \sin\phi}$$

$$E = \frac{7.2 \times 10^{-9} \text{ N} \cdot \text{m}}{(1.4 \times 10^{-11} \text{ C} \cdot \text{m}) \sin 36.9°} = 860 \text{ N/C}$$

EVALUATE: Eq.(21.15) gives the torque about an axis through the center of the dipole. But the forces on the two charges form a couple (Problem 11.53) and the torque is the same for any axis parallel to this one. The force on each charge is $|q|E$ and the maximum moment arm for an axis at the center is $d/2$, so the maximum torque is $2(|q|E)(d/2) = 1.2 \times 10^{-8}$ N·m. The torque for the orientation of the dipole in the problem is less than this maximum.

21.61 a) IDENTIFY: The potential energy is given by Eq.(21.17).

SET UP: $U(\phi) = -\vec{p} \cdot \vec{E} = -pE \cos\phi$, where ϕ is the angle between $\vec{p}$ and $\vec{E}$.

EXECUTE:

parallel: $\phi = 0$ and $U(0°) = -pE$

perpendicular: $\phi = 90°$ and $U(90°) = 0$

$\Delta U = U(90°) - U(0°)) = pE = (5.0 \times 10^{-30} \text{ C} \cdot \text{m})(1.6 \times 10^{6} \text{ N/C}) = 8.0 \times 10^{-24}$ J.

b) $\frac{3}{2}kT = \Delta U$ so $T = \dfrac{2 \Delta U}{3k} = \dfrac{2(8.0 \times 10^{-24} \text{ J})}{3(1.381 \times 10^{-23} \text{ J/K})} = 0.39$ K

EVALUATE: Only at very low temperatures are the dipoles of the molecules aligned by a field of this strength. A much larger field would be required for alignment at room temperature.

21.67 **a) IDENTIFY:** Use Coulomb's law to calculate each force and then add them as vectors to obtain the net force. Torque is force times moment arm.

SET UP:

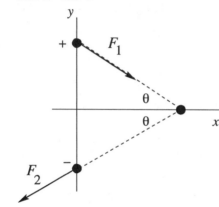

$\sin \theta = 1.50/2.00$ so $\theta = 48.6°$

Opposite charges attract and like charges repel.

$F_x = F_{1x} + F_{2x} = 0$

EXECUTE:

$F_1 = k\dfrac{|qq'|}{r^2} = k\dfrac{(5.00 \times 10^{-6} \text{ C})(10.0 \times 10^{-6} \text{ C})}{(0.0200 \text{ m})^2} = 1.124 \times 10^{3}$ N

$F_{1y} = -F_1 \sin \theta = -842.6$ N

$F_{2y} = -842.6$ N so $F_y = F_{1y} + F_{2y} = -1680$ N (in the direction from the $+5.00$-μC charge toward the -5.00-μC charge).

EVALUATE: The x-components cancel and the y-components add.

b) SET UP:

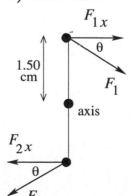

The y-components have zero moment arm and therefore zero torque.

F_{1x} and F_{2x} both produce clockwise torques.

EXECUTE: $F_{1x} = F_1 \cos\theta = 743.1$ N

$\tau = 2(F_{1x})(0.0150$ m$) = 22.3$ N $\cdot$ m, clockwise

EVALUATE: The electric field produced by the -10.00 μC charge is not unifrom so Eq.(21.15) does not apply.

Problems

21.69 a) IDENTIFY: Use Coulomb's law to calculate the force exerted by each Q on q and add these forces as vectors to find the resultant force. Make the approximation $x \gg a$ and compare the net force to $F = -kx$ to deduce k and then $f = (1/2\pi)\sqrt{k/m}$.

SET UP:

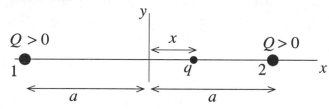

EXECUTE: Find the net force on q.

$F_x = F_{1x} + F_{2x}$ and
$F_{1x} = +F_1$, $F_{2x} = -F_2$

$$F_1 = \frac{1}{4\pi\epsilon_0}\frac{qQ}{(a+x)^2}, \quad F_2 = \frac{1}{4\pi\epsilon_0}\frac{qQ}{(a-x)^2}$$

$$F_x = F_1 - F_2 = \frac{qQ}{4\pi\epsilon_0}\left[\frac{1}{(a+x)^2} - \frac{1}{(a-x)^2}\right]$$

$$F_x = \frac{qQ}{4\pi\epsilon_0 a^2}\left[+\left(1+\frac{x}{a}\right)^{-2} - \left(1-\frac{x}{a}\right)^{-2}\right]$$

Since $x \ll a$ we can use the binomial expansion for $(1-x/a)^{-2}$ and $(1+x/a)^{-2}$ and keep only the first two terms: $(1+z)^n \approx 1 + nz$.

For $(1-x/a)^{-2}$, $z = -x/a$ and $n = -2$ so $(1-x/a)^{-2} \approx 1 + 2x/a$.

For $(1+x/a)^{-2}$, $z = +x/a$ and $n = -2$ so $(1+x/a)^{-2} \approx 1 - 2x/a$.

Then $F \approx \dfrac{qQ}{4\pi\epsilon_0 a^2}\left[\left(1-\dfrac{2x}{a}\right) - \left(1+\dfrac{2x}{a}\right)\right] = -\left(\dfrac{qQ}{\pi\epsilon_0 a^3}\right)x.$

For simple harmonic motion $F = -kx$ and the frequency of oscillation is $f = (1/2\pi)\sqrt{k/m}$. The net force here is of this form, with $k = qQ/\pi\epsilon_0 a^3$.

Thus $f = \dfrac{1}{2\pi}\sqrt{\dfrac{qQ}{\pi\epsilon_0 ma^3}}.$

b)

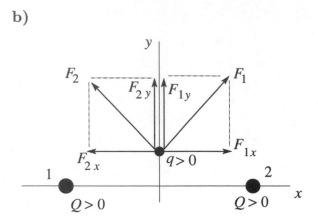

The x-components of the forces exerted by the two charges cancel, the y-components add, and the net force is in the $+y$-direction when $y > 0$ and in the $-y$-direction when $y < 0$. The charge moves away from the origin on the y-axis and never returns.

EVALUATE: The directions of the forces and of the net force depend on where q is located relative to the other two charges. In part (a), $F = 0$ at $x = 0$ and when the charge q is displaced in the $+x$- or $-x$-direction the net force is a restoring force, directed to return q to $x = 0$. The charge oscillates back and forth, similar to a mass on a spring.

21.71 IDENTIFY: Use Coulomb's law for the force that one sphere exerts on the other and apply the 1st condition of equilibrium to one of the spheres.

a) SET UP:

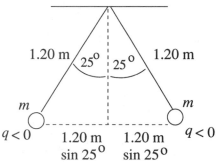

sphere on the left: sphere on the right:

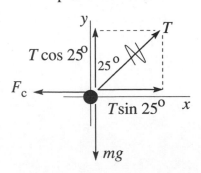   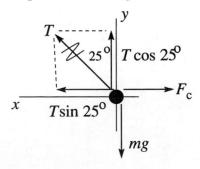

F_c is the repulsive Coulomb force exerted by one sphere on the other.

b) **EXECUTE:** From either force diagram in part (a):

$\sum F_y = ma_y$

$T\cos 25.0° - mg = 0$ and $T = \dfrac{mg}{\cos 25.0°}$

$\sum F_x = ma_x$

$T\sin 25.0° - F_c = 0$ and $F_c = T\sin 25.0°$

Use the first equation to eliminate T in the second:

$F_c = (mg/\cos 25.0°)(\sin 25.0°) = mg\tan 25.0°$

$F_c = \dfrac{1}{4\pi\epsilon_0}\dfrac{|q_1 q_2|}{r^2} = \dfrac{1}{4\pi\epsilon_0}\dfrac{q^2}{r^2} = \dfrac{1}{4\pi\epsilon_0}\dfrac{q^2}{[2(1.20\text{ m})\sin 25.0°]^2}$

Combine this with $F_c = mg\tan 25.0°$ and get

$mg\tan 25.0° = \dfrac{1}{4\pi\epsilon_0}\dfrac{q^2}{[2(1.20\text{ m})\sin 25.0°]^2}$

$q - (2.40\text{ m})\sin 25.0°\sqrt{\dfrac{mg\tan 25.0°}{(1/4\pi\epsilon_0)}}$

$q = (2.40\text{ m})\sin 25.0°\sqrt{\dfrac{(15.0\times 10^{-3}\text{ kg})(9.80\text{ m/s}^2)\tan 25.0°}{8.988\times 10^9\text{ N}\cdot\text{m}^2/\text{C}^2}} = 2.80\times 10^{-6}\text{ C}$

c) The separation between the two spheres is given by $2L\sin\theta$. $q = 2.80\ \mu\text{C}$ as found in part (b). $F_c = (1/4\pi\epsilon_0)q^2/(2L\sin\theta)^2$ and $F_c = mg\tan\theta$. Thus $(1/4\pi\epsilon_0)q^2/(2L\sin\theta)^2 = mg\tan\theta$.

$(\sin\theta)^2\tan\theta = \dfrac{1}{4\pi\epsilon_0}\dfrac{q^2}{4L^2 mq} =$

$(8.988\times 10^9\text{ N}\cdot\text{m}^2/\text{C}^2)\dfrac{(2.80\times 10^{-6}\text{ C})^2}{4(0.600\text{ m})^2(15.0\times 10^{-3}\text{ kg})(9.80\text{ m/s}^2)} = 0.3328.$

Solve this equation by trial and error. This will go quicker if we can make a good estimate of the value of θ that solves the equation. For θ small, $\tan\theta \approx \sin\theta$. With this approximation the equation becomes $\sin^3\theta = 0.3328$ and $\sin\theta = 0.6930$, so $\theta = 43.9°$. Now refine this guess:

θ	$\sin^2\theta\tan\theta$	
45.0°	0.5000	
40.0°	0.3467	
39.6°	0.3361	
39.5°	0.3335	
39.4°	0.3309	so $\theta = 39.5°$

EVALUATE: The expression in part (c) says $\theta \to 0$ as $L \to \infty$ and $\theta \to 90°$ as $L \to 0$. When L is decreased from the value in part (a), θ increases.

21.73 IDENTIFY and **SET UP:** Use Avogadro's number to find the number of Na^+ and Cl^- ions and the total positive and negative charge. Use Coulomb's law to calculate the electric force and $\vec{F} = m\vec{a}$ to calculate the acceleration.

a) EXECUTE: The number of Na^+ ions in 0.100 mol of NaCl is $N = nN_A$. The charge of one ion is $+e$, so the total charge is $q_1 = nN_A e =$

(0.100 mol)$(6.022 \times 10^{23}$ ions/mol)$(1.602 \times 10^{-19}$C/ion) $= 9.647 \times 10^3$ C

There are the same number of Cl^- ions and each has charge $-e$, so

$q_2 = -9.647 \times 10^3$ C.

$$F = \frac{1}{4\pi\epsilon_0} \frac{|q_1 q_2|}{r^2} = (8.988 \times 10^9 \text{ N} \cdot \text{m}^2/\text{C}^2)\frac{(9.647 \times 10^3 \text{ C})^2}{(0.0200 \text{ m})^2} = 2.09 \times 10^{21} \text{ N}$$

b) $a = F/m$. Need the mass of 0.100 mol of Cl^- ions. For Cl, $M = 35.453 \times 10^{-3}$ kg/mol, so $m = (0.100 \text{ mol})(35.453 \times 10^{-3} \text{ kg/mol}) = 35.45 \times 10^{-4}$ kg.

Then $a = \dfrac{F}{m} = \dfrac{2.09 \times 10^{21} \text{ N}}{35.45 \times 10^{-4} \text{ kg}} = 5.90 \times 10^{23} \text{ m/s}^2.$

c) EVALUATE: It is not reasonable to have such a huge force. The net charges of objects are rarely larger than 1 μC; a charge of 10^4 C is immense. A small amount of material contains huge amounts of positive and negative charges.

21.75 IDENTIFY: Use Coulomb's law to calculate the forces between pairs of charges and sum these forces as vectors to find the net charge.

a) SET UP:

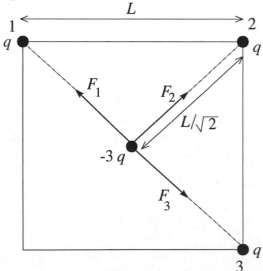

EXECUTE:

$\vec{F}_1 + \vec{F}_3 = \mathbf{0}$, so the net force is $\vec{F} = \vec{F}_2$.

$$F = \frac{1}{4\pi\epsilon_0}\frac{q(3q)}{(L/\sqrt{2})^2} = \frac{6q^2}{4\pi\epsilon_0 L^2},$$

away from the vacant corner.

b) SET UP:

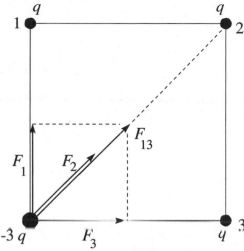

EXECUTE:

$$F_2 = \frac{1}{4\pi\epsilon_0} \frac{q(3q)}{(\sqrt{2}L)^2} = \frac{3q^2}{4\pi\epsilon_0(2L^2)}$$

$$F_1 = F_3 = \frac{1}{4\pi\epsilon_0} \frac{q(3q)}{L^2} = \frac{3q^2}{4\pi\epsilon_0 L^2}$$

The vector sum of F_1 and F_3 is
$F_{13} = \sqrt{F_1^2 + F_3^2}$.

$F_{13} = \sqrt{2}F_1 = \dfrac{3\sqrt{2}q^2}{4\pi\epsilon_0 L^2};$ $\vec{F}_{13}$ and $\vec{F}_2$ are in the same direction.

$F = F_{13} + F_2 = \dfrac{3q^2}{4\pi\epsilon_0 L^2}(\sqrt{2} + \dfrac{1}{2})$, and is directed toward the center of the square.

EVALUATE: By symmetry the net force is along the diagonal of the square. The net force is only slightly larger when the $-3q$ charge is at the center. Here it is closer to the charge at point 2 but the other two forces cancel.

21.77   IDENTIFY: Use Eq.(21.7) for the electric field produced by each point charge. Apply the principle of superposition and add the fields as vectors to find the net field.

a) SET UP:

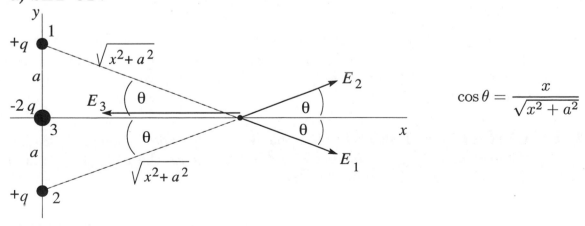

$$\cos\theta = \frac{x}{\sqrt{x^2 + a^2}}$$

EXECUTE:

$$E_1 = E_2 = \frac{1}{4\pi\epsilon_0}\left(\frac{q}{a^2 + x^2}\right)$$

$$E_3 = \frac{1}{4\pi\epsilon_0}\left(\frac{2q}{x^2}\right)$$

$E_{1y} = -E_1\sin\theta$, $E_{2y} = +E_2\sin\theta$ so $E_y = E_{1y} + E_{2y} = 0$.

$$E_{1x} = E_{2x} = +E_1\cos\theta = \frac{1}{4\pi\epsilon_0}\left(\frac{q}{a^2 + x^2}\right)\left(\frac{x}{\sqrt{x^2 + a^2}}\right), \quad E_{3x} = -E_3$$

$$E_x = E_{1x} + E_{2x} + E_{3x} = 2\left(\frac{1}{4\pi\epsilon_0}\left(\frac{q}{a^2 + x^2}\right)\left(\frac{x}{\sqrt{x^2 + a^2}}\right)\right) - \frac{2q}{4\pi\epsilon_0 x^2}$$

$$E_x = -\frac{2q}{4\pi\epsilon_0}\left(\frac{1}{x^2} - \frac{x}{(a^2 + x^2)^{3/2}}\right) = -\frac{2q}{4\pi\epsilon_0 x^2}\left(1 - \frac{1}{(1 + a^2/x^2)^{3/2}}\right)$$

Thus $E = \dfrac{2q}{4\pi\epsilon_0 x^2}\left(1 - \dfrac{1}{(1 + a^2/x^2)^{3/2}}\right)$, in the $-x$-direction.

b) $x \gg a$ implies $a^2/x^2 \ll 1$ and $(1 + a^2/x^2)^{-3/2} \approx 1 - 3a^2/2x^2$.

Thus $E \approx \dfrac{2q}{4\pi\epsilon_0 x^2}\left(1 - \left(1 - \dfrac{3a^2}{2x^2}\right)\right) = \dfrac{3qa^2}{4\pi\epsilon_0 x^4}$.

EVALUATE: $E \sim 1/x^4$. For a point charge $E \sim 1/x^2$ and for a dipole $E \sim 1/x^3$. The total charge is zero so at large distances the electric field should decrease faster with distance than for a point charge. By symmetry $\vec{E}$ must lie along the x-axis, which is the result we found in part (a).

21.81 IDENTIFY and **SET UP:** Use the density of copper to calculate the number of moles and then the number of atoms. Calculate the net charge and then use Coulomb's law to calculate the force.

EXECUTE:

a) $m = \rho V = \rho(\frac{4}{3}\pi r^3) = (8.9 \times 10^3 \text{ kg/m}^3)(\frac{4}{3}\pi)(1.00 \times 10^{-3} \text{ m})^3 = 3.728 \times 10^{-5}$ kg

$n = m/M = (3.728 \times 10^{-5} \text{ kg})/(63.546 \times 10^{-3} \text{ kg/mol}) = 5.867 \times 10^{-4}$ mol

$N = nN_A = 3.5 \times 10^{20}$ atoms

b) $N_e = (29)(3.5 \times 10^{20}) = 1.015 \times 10^{22}$ electrons and protons

$q_{net} = eN_e - (0.99900)eN_e = (0.100 \times 10^{-2})(1.602 \times 10^{-19} \text{ C})(1.015 \times 10^{22}) = 1.6 \text{ C}$

$F = k\dfrac{q^2}{r^2} = k\dfrac{(1.6 \text{ C})^2}{(1.00 \text{ m})^2} = 2.3 \times 10^{10} \text{ N}$

EVALUATE: The amount of positive and negative charge in even small objects is immense. If the charge of an electron and a proton weren't exactly equal, objects would have large net charges.

21.83 IDENTIFY: Eq.(21.3) gives the force exerted by the electric field. This force is constant since the electric field is uniform and gives the proton a constant acceleration. Apply the constant acceleration equations for the x- and y-components of the motion, just as for projectile motion.

a) SET UP: The electric field is upward so the electric force on the positively charged proton is upward and has magnitude $F = eE$. Use coordinates where positive y is downward. Then applying $\sum \vec{F} = m\vec{a}$ to the proton gives that $a_x = 0$ and $a_y = -eE/m$. In these coordinates the initial velocity has components $v_x = +v_0 \cos\alpha$ and $v_y = +v_0 \sin\alpha$.

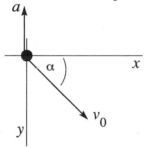

EXECUTE:

Finding h_{max}: At $y = h_{max}$ the y-component of the velocity is zero.

$v_y = 0, \quad v_{0y} = v_0 \sin\alpha, \quad a_y = -eE/m, \quad y - y_0 = h_{max} = ?$

$v_y^2 = v_{0y}^2 + 2a_y(y - y_0)$

$y - y_0 = \dfrac{v_y^2 - v_{0y}^2}{2a_y}$

$h_{max} = \dfrac{-v_0^2 \sin^2\alpha}{2(-eE/m)} = \dfrac{mv_0^2 \sin^2\alpha}{2eE}$

b) Use the vertical motion to find the time t:

$y - y_0 = 0, \quad v_{0y} = v_0 \sin\alpha, \quad a_y = -eE/m, \quad t = ?$

$y - y_0 = v_{0y}t + \tfrac{1}{2}a_y t^2$

With $y - y_0 = 0$ this gives $t = -\dfrac{2v_{0y}}{a_y} = -\dfrac{2(v_0 \sin\alpha)}{-eE/m} = \dfrac{2mv_0 \sin\alpha}{eE}$

Then use the x-component motion to find d:

$a_x = 0,\quad v_{0x} = v_0 \cos\alpha,\quad t = 2mv_0 \sin\alpha / eE,\quad x - x_0 = d = ?$

$x - x_0 = v_{0x}t + \frac{1}{2}a_x t^2$ gives

$$d = v_0 \cos\alpha \left(\frac{2mv_0 \sin\alpha}{eE} \right) = \frac{mv_0^2 2 \sin\alpha \cos\alpha}{eE} = \frac{mv_0^2 \sin 2\alpha}{eE}$$

c)

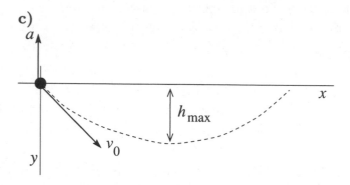

d) Use the expression in part (a):

$$h_{\text{max}} = \frac{[(4.00 \times 10^5 \text{ m/s})(\sin 30.0°)]^2 (1.673 \times 10^{-27} \text{ kg})}{2(1.602 \times 10^{-19} \text{ C})(500 \text{ N/C})} = 0.418 \text{ m}$$

Use the expression in part (b):

$$d = \frac{(1.673 \times 10^{-27} \text{ kg})(4.00 \times 10^5 \text{ m/s})^2 \sin 60.0°}{(1.602 \times 10^{-19} \text{ C})(500 \text{ N/C})} = 2.89 \text{ m}$$

EVALUATE: In part (a), $a_y = -eE/m = -4.8 \times 10^{10}$ m/s^2. This is much larger in magnitude than g, the acceleration due to gravity, so it is reasonable to ignore gravity. The motion is just like projectile motion, except that the acceleration is upward rather than downward and has a much different magntiude. h_{max} and d increase when α or v_0 increase and decrease when E increases.

21.85 IDENTIFY: Eq.(21.7) gives the electric field due to each charge. Use the principle of superposition and add the vector fields of each charge to obtain the resultant field.

SET UP:

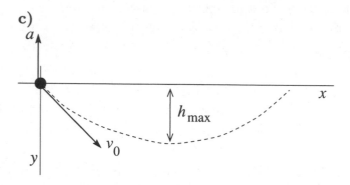

EXECUTE:

At point P the resultant field has magnitude 12.0 N/C and is in the +x-direction, so $E_x = +12.0$ N/C.

$\vec{E} = \vec{E}_1 + \vec{E}_2 + \vec{E}_3$ so $\vec{E}_2 = \vec{E} - \vec{E}_1 - \vec{E}_3$

$E_{2x} = E_x - E_{1x} - E_{3x}$; calculate E_{2x} and deduce the sign and magnitude of q_2.
The electric field $\vec{E}_1$ of q_1 at point P has magnitude

$$E_1 = \frac{1}{4\pi\epsilon_0}\frac{|q_1|}{r_1^2} = (8.988 \times 10^9 \text{ N} \cdot \text{m}^2/\text{C}^2)\frac{12.0 \times 10^{-9} \text{ C}}{(8.00 \text{ m})^2} = 1.685 \text{ N/C}$$

and is in the $+x$-direction. Thus $E_{1x} = +1.685$ N/C.

The electric field $\vec{E}_3$ of q_3 at point P has magnitude

$$E_3 = \frac{1}{4\pi\epsilon_0}\frac{|q_3|}{r_3^2} = (8.988 \times 10^9 \text{ N} \cdot \text{m}^2/\text{C}^2)\frac{16.0 \times 10^{-9} \text{ C}}{(3.00 \text{ m})^2} = 15.98 \text{ N/C}$$

and is in the $-x$-direction. Thus $E_{3x} = -15.98$ N/C.

Thus $E_{2x} = E_x - E_{1x} - E_{3x} - +12.0$ N/C $- 1.68$ N/C $(15.98$ N/C) $-$ $+26.30$ N/C.

Since E_{2x} is positive, $\vec{E}_2$ is in the $+x$-direction at P and q_2 is positive.

$$E_2 = \frac{1}{4\pi\epsilon_0}\frac{|q_2|}{r_2^2} \text{ so}$$

$$|q_2| = \frac{r_2^2 E_2}{(1/4\pi\epsilon_0)} = \frac{(5.00 \text{ m})^2(26.30 \text{ N/C})}{(8.988 \times 10^9 \text{ N} \cdot \text{m}^2/\text{C}^2)} = 7.32 \times 10^{-8} \text{ C}$$

$q_2 = +73.2$ nC

EVALUATE: The field of the negative charge q_3 is to the left and the field of the positive charge q_1 is to the right. $|q_3| > |q_1|$ and P is closest to $|q_3|$ so $|E_3| > |E_1|$ and q_2 must be positive to produce more field to the right.

21.87 a) IDENTIFY: Use Eq.(21.7) to calculate the electric field due to a small slice of the line of charge and integrate as in Example 21.11. Use Eq.(21.3) to calculate $\vec{F}$.

SET UP:

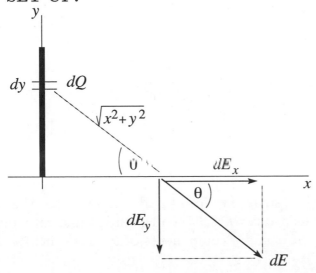

$$\sin\theta = \frac{y}{\sqrt{x^2 + y^2}}$$

$$\cos\theta = \frac{x}{\sqrt{x^2 + y^2}}$$

Slice the charge distribution up into small pieces of length dy. The charge dQ in each slice is $dQ = Q(dy/a)$. The electric field this produces at a distance x along the x-axis is dE. Calculate the components of $d\vec{E}$ and then integrate over the charge distribution to find the components of the total field.

EXECUTE:

$$dE = \frac{1}{4\pi\epsilon_0}\left(\frac{dQ}{x^2+y^2}\right) = \frac{Q}{4\pi\epsilon_0 a}\left(\frac{dy}{x^2+y^2}\right)$$

$$dE_x = dE\cos\theta = \frac{Qx}{4\pi\epsilon_0 a}\left(\frac{dy}{(x^2+y^2)^{3/2}}\right)$$

$$dE_y = -dE\sin\theta = -\frac{Q}{4\pi\epsilon_0 a}\left(\frac{y\,dy}{(x^2+y^2)^{3/2}}\right)$$

$$E_x = \int dE_x = \frac{Qx}{4\pi\epsilon_0 a}\int_0^a \frac{dy}{(x^2+y^2)^{3/2}} =$$

$$\frac{Qx}{4\pi\epsilon_0 a}\left[\frac{1}{x^2}\frac{y}{\sqrt{x^2+y^2}}\right]_0^a = \frac{Q}{4\pi\epsilon_0 x}\frac{1}{\sqrt{x^2+a^2}}$$

$$E_y = \int dE_y = -\frac{Q}{4\pi\epsilon_0 a}\int_0^a \frac{y\,dy}{(x^2+y^2)^{3/2}} =$$

$$-\frac{Q}{4\pi\epsilon_0 a}\left[-\frac{1}{\sqrt{x^2+y^2}}\right]_0^a = -\frac{Q}{4\pi\epsilon_0 a}\left(\frac{1}{x} - \frac{1}{\sqrt{x^2+a^2}}\right)$$

b) $\vec{F} = q_0\vec{E}$

$$F_x = -qE_x = \frac{-qQ}{4\pi\epsilon_0 x}\frac{1}{\sqrt{x^2+a^2}}; \quad F_y = -qE_y = \frac{qQ}{4\pi\epsilon_0 a}\left(\frac{1}{x} - \frac{1}{\sqrt{x^2+a^2}}\right)$$

c) For $x \gg a$, $\dfrac{1}{\sqrt{x^2+a^2}} = \dfrac{1}{x}\left(1+\dfrac{a^2}{x^2}\right)^{-1/2} = \dfrac{1}{x}\left(1 - \dfrac{a^2}{2x^2}\right) = \dfrac{1}{x} - \dfrac{a^2}{2x^3}$

$$F_x \approx -\frac{qQ}{4\pi\epsilon_0 x^2}, \quad F_y \approx \frac{qQ}{4\pi\epsilon_0 a}\left(\frac{1}{x} - \frac{1}{x} + \frac{a^2}{2x^3}\right) = \frac{qQa}{8\pi\epsilon_0 x^3}$$

EVALUATE: For $x \gg a$, $F_y \ll F_x$ and $F \approx |F_x| = \dfrac{qQ}{4\pi\epsilon_0 x^2}$ and $\vec{F}$ is in the $-x$-direction. For $x \gg a$ the charge distribution Q acts like a point charge.

21.95   IDENTIFY: Divide the charge distribution into small segments, use the point charge formula for the electric field due to each small segment and integrate over the charge distribution to find the x and y components of the total field.

SET UP:

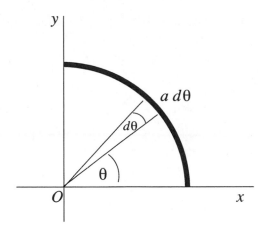

EXECUTE:
A small segment that subtends angle $d\theta$ has length $a\,d\theta$ and contains charge

$$dQ = \left(\frac{a\,d\theta}{\frac{1}{2}\pi a}\right) Q = \frac{2Q}{\pi}\,d\theta.$$

($\frac{1}{2}\pi a$ is the total length of the charge distribution.)

The charge is negative, so the field at the origin is directed toward the small segment. The small segment is located at angle θ as shown in the sketch.

$$dE = \frac{1}{4\pi\epsilon_0}\frac{|dQ|}{a^2}$$

$$dE = \frac{Q}{2\pi^2\epsilon_0 a^2}\,d\theta$$

$$dE_x = dE\cos\theta = (Q/2\pi^2\epsilon_0 a^2)\cos\theta\,d\theta$$

$$E_x = \int dE_x = \frac{Q}{2\pi^2\epsilon_0 a^2}\int_0^{\pi/2}\cos\theta\,d\theta = \frac{Q}{2\pi^2\epsilon_0 a^2}\left(\sin\theta\Big|_0^{\pi/2}\right) = \frac{Q}{2\pi^2\epsilon_0 a^2}$$

$$dE_y = dE\sin\theta = (Q/2\pi^2\epsilon_0 a^2)\sin\theta\,d\theta$$

$$E_y = \int dE_y = \frac{Q}{2\pi^2\epsilon_0 a^2}\int_0^{\pi/2}\sin\theta\,d\theta = \frac{Q}{2\pi^2\epsilon_0 a^2}\left(-\cos\theta\Big|_0^{\pi/2}\right) = \frac{Q}{2\pi^2\epsilon_0 a^2}$$

EVALUATE: Note that $E_x = E_y$, as expected from symmetry.

21.99 IDENTIFY and **SET UP:** For an infinite charge sheet $E = |\sigma|/2\epsilon_0$, the same at all points, and is directed away from the sheet if the sheet has positive charge and toward the sheet if it has negative charge.

Obtain the net electric field as the vector sum of the fields due to each sheet.

EXECUTE:
a)

$$E = E_I + E_{II} - E_{III}$$

$$E = (|\sigma_I| + |\sigma_{II}| - |\sigma_{III}|)/2\epsilon_0$$

$$E = (+0.0200\ \text{C/m}^2 + 0.0100\ \text{C/m}^2 - 0.0200\ \text{C/m}^2)/2\epsilon_0 =$$

$(+0.0100 \ \mathrm{C/m^2})/2(8.854 \times 10^{-12} \ \mathrm{C^2/N \cdot m^2}) = 5.65 \times 10^8 \ \mathrm{N/C}$, to left.

b)

$E = E_I + E_{III} - E_{II}$

$E = (|\sigma_I| + |\sigma_{III}| - |\sigma_{II}|)/2\epsilon_0$

$E = (+0.0200 \ \mathrm{C/m^2} + 0.0200 \ \mathrm{C/m^2} - 0.0100 \ \mathrm{C/m^2})/2\epsilon_0 =$
$(+0.0300 \ \mathrm{C/m^2})/2(8.854 \times 10^{-12} \ \mathrm{C^2/N \cdot m^2}) = 1.69 \times 10^9 \ \mathrm{N/C}$, to right.

c)

$E = E_I + E_{II} + E_{III}$

$E = (|\sigma_I| + |\sigma_{II}| + |\sigma_{III}|)/2\epsilon_0$

$E = (+0.0200 \ \mathrm{C/m^2} + 0.0100 \ \mathrm{C/m^2} + 0.0200 \ \mathrm{C/m^2})/2\epsilon_0 =$
$(+0.0500 \ \mathrm{C/m^2})/2(8.854 \times 10^{-12} \ \mathrm{C^2/N \cdot m^2}) = 2.82 \times 10^9 \ \mathrm{N/C}$, to right.

d)

$E = E_I + E_{II} - E_{III}$,

the same as at point P.

$E = 5.65 \times 10^8 \ \mathrm{N/C}$, to right.

EVALUATE: The direction of the electric field due to one of the sheets depends on the charge of the sheet and whether the field point is to the left or right of the sheet. The field is independent of the distance from the sheet, so at different field points the only change is the direction of the field due to each sheet.

21.101 IDENTIFY and **SET UP:** Example 21.12 gives the electric field due to one infinite sheet. Add the two fields as vectors.

EXECUTE: The electric field due to the first sheet, which is in the xy-plane, is $\vec{E}_1 = (\sigma/2\epsilon_0)\hat{k}$ for $z > 0$ and $\vec{E}_1 = -(\sigma/2\epsilon_0)\hat{k}$ for $z < 0$.

We can write this as $\vec{E}_1 = (\sigma/2\epsilon_0)(z/|z|)\hat{k}$, since $z/|z| = +1$ for $z > 0$ and $z/|z| = -z/z = -1$ for $z < 0$.

Similarly, we can write the electric field due to the second sheet as $\vec{E}_2 = -(\sigma/2\epsilon_0)(x/|x|)\hat{i}$, since its charge density is $-\sigma$.

The net field is $\vec{E} = \vec{E}_1 + \vec{E}_2 = (\sigma/2\epsilon_0)(- (x/|x|)\hat{i} + (z/|z|)\hat{k})$.

EVALUATE: The electric field is independent of the y-component of the field point since displacement in the $\pm y$-direction is parallel to both planes. The field depends on which side of each plane the field is located.

CHAPTER 22
GAUSS'S LAW

Exercises 1, 3, 5, 11, 17, 19, 21, 27
Problems 33, 35, 39, 43, 45, 47, 51, 53, 55, 57, 61, 63

Exercises

22.1   **a) IDENTIFY** and **SET UP:** $\Phi_E = \int E \cos \phi \, dA$, where ϕ is the angle between the normal to the sheet $\hat{n}$ and the electric field $\vec{E}$.

EXECUTE: In this problem E and $\cos \phi$ are constant over the surface so
$$\Phi_E = E \cos \phi \int dA = E \cos \phi A = (14 \text{ N/C})(\cos 60°)(0.250 \text{ m}^2) = 1.8 \text{ N} \cdot \text{m}^2/\text{C}.$$

b) EVALUATE: Φ_E is independent of the shape of the sheet as long as ϕ and E are constant at all points on the sheet.

c) EXECUTE: (i) $\Phi_E = E \cos \phi A$. Φ_E is largest for $\phi = 0°$, so $\cos \phi = 1$ and $\Phi_E = EA$.

(ii) Φ_E is smallest for $\phi - 90°$, so $\cos \phi = 0$ and $\Phi_E = 0$.

EVALUATE: Φ_E is 0 when the surface is parallel to the field so no electric field lines pass through the surface.

22.3   **IDENTIFY** and **SET UP:** Use Eq.(22.3) to calculate the flux. Identify the direction of the normal unit vector $\hat{n}$ for each surface.

EXECUTE:

a) $\vec{E} = -B\hat{i} + C\hat{j} - D\hat{k}$; $A = L^2$ face S_1:

$\hat{n} = -\hat{j}$

$\Phi_E = \vec{E} \cdot \vec{A} = \vec{E} \cdot (A\hat{n}) = (-B\hat{i} + C\hat{j} - D\hat{k}) \cdot (-A\hat{j}) = -CL^2.$

face S_2:

$\hat{n} = +\hat{k}$

$\Phi_E = \vec{E} \cdot \vec{A} = \vec{E} \cdot (A\hat{n}) = (-B\hat{i} + C\hat{j} - D\hat{k}) \cdot (A\hat{k}) = -DL^2.$

face S_3:

$\hat{n} = +\hat{j}$

$\Phi_E = \vec{E} \cdot \vec{A} = \vec{E} \cdot (A\hat{n}) = (-B\hat{i} + C\hat{j} - D\hat{k}) \cdot (A\hat{j}) = +CL^2.$

face S_4:

$\hat{n} = -\hat{k}$

$$\Phi_E = \vec{E} \cdot \vec{A} = \vec{E} \cdot (A\hat{n}) = (-B\hat{i} + C\hat{j} - D\hat{k}) \cdot (-A\hat{k}) = +DL^2.$$

face S_5:

$$\hat{n} = +\hat{i}$$

$$\Phi_E = \vec{E} \cdot \vec{A} = \vec{E} \cdot (A\hat{n}) = (-B\hat{i} + C\hat{j} - D\hat{k}) \cdot (A\hat{i}) = -BL^2.$$

face S_6:

$$\hat{n} = -\hat{i}$$

$$\Phi_E = \vec{E} \cdot \vec{A} = \vec{E} \cdot (A\hat{n}) = (-B\hat{i} + C\hat{j} - D\hat{k}) \cdot (-A\hat{i}) = +BL^2.$$

b) Add the flux through each of the six faces:

$$\Phi_E = -CL^2 - DL^2 + CL^2 + DL^2 - BL^2 + BL^2 = 0$$

The total electric flux through all sides is zero.

EVALUATE: All electric field lines that enter one face of the cube leave through another face. No electric field lines terminate inside the cube and the net flux is zero.

22.5   **a) IDENTIFY:** Use Eq.(22.5) to calculate the flux through the surface of the cylinder.

SET UP:

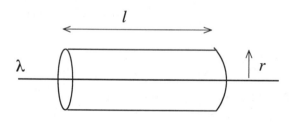 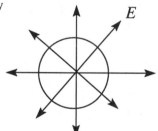

EXECUTE:

The area of the curved part of the cylinder is $A = 2\pi r l$.

The electric field is parallel to the end caps of the cylinder, so $\vec{E} \cdot \vec{A} = 0$ for the ends and the flux through the cylinder end caps is zero.

The electric field is normal to the curved surface of the cylinder and has the same magnitude $E = \lambda / 2\pi\epsilon_0 r$ at all points on this surface. Thus $\phi = 0°$ and

$$\Phi_E = EA\cos\phi = EA = (\lambda/2\pi\epsilon_0 r)(2\pi r l) = \frac{\lambda l}{\epsilon_0} = \frac{(6.00 \times 10^{-6} \text{ C/m})(0.400 \text{ m})}{8.854 \times 10^{-12} \text{ C}^2/\text{N} \cdot \text{m}^2} =$$

2.71×10^5 N $\cdot$ m^2/C

b) In the calculation in part (a) the radius r of the cylinder divided out, so the flux remains the same, $\Phi_E = 2.71 \times 10^5$ N $\cdot$ m^2/C.

c) $\Phi_E = \dfrac{\lambda l}{\epsilon_0} = \dfrac{(6.00 \times 10^{-6} \text{ C/m})(0.800 \text{ m})}{8.854 \times 10^{-12} \text{ C}^2/\text{N} \cdot \text{m}^2} = 5.42 \times 10^5 \text{ N} \cdot \text{m}^2/\text{C}$ (twice the flux calculated in parts (b) and (c)).

EVALUATE: The flux depends on the number of field lines that pass through the surface of the cylinder.

22.11 **a) IDENTIFY** and **SET UP:** It is rather difficult to calculate the flux directly from $\Phi = \oint \vec{E} \cdot d\vec{A}$ since the magnitude of $\vec{E}$ and its angle with $d\vec{A}$ varies over the surface of the cube. A much easier approach is to use Gauss's law to calculate the total flux through the cube. Let the cube be the Gaussian surface. The charge enclosed is the point charge.

EXECUTE: $\Phi_E = Q_{encl}/\epsilon_0 = \dfrac{9.60 \times 10^{-6} \text{ C}}{8.854 \times 10^{-12} \text{ C}^2/\text{N} \cdot \text{m}^2} = 1.084 \times 10^6 \text{ N} \cdot \text{m}^2/\text{C}.$

By symmetry the flux is the same through each of the six faces, so the flux through one face is $\frac{1}{6}(1.084 \times 10^6 \text{ N} \cdot \text{m}^2/\text{C}) = 1.81 \times 10^5 \text{ N} \cdot \text{m}^2/\text{C}.$

b) EVALUATE: In part (a) the size of the cube did not enter into the calculations. The flux through one face depends only on the amount of charge at the center of the cube. So the answer to (a) would not change if the size of the cube were changed.

22.17 **IDENTIFY** and **SET UP:** Example 22.5 derived that the electric field just outside the surface of a spherical conductor that has net charge q is $E = \dfrac{1}{4\pi\epsilon_0}\dfrac{q}{R^2}$. Calculate q and from this the number of excess electrons.

EXECUTE: $q = \dfrac{R^2 E}{(1/4\pi\epsilon_0)} = \dfrac{(0.160 \text{ m})^2(1150 \text{ N/C})}{8.988 \times 10^9 \text{ N} \cdot \text{m}^2/\text{C}^2} = 3.275 \times 10^{-9} \text{ C}.$

Each electron has a charge of magnitude $e = 1.602 \times 10^{-19}$ C, so the number of excess electrons needed is

$\dfrac{3.275 \times 10^{-9} \text{ C}}{1.602 \times 10^{-19} \text{ C}} = 2.04 \times 10^{10}.$

EVALUATE: The result we obtained for q is a typical value for the charge of an object. Such net charges correspond to a large number of excess electrons since the charge of each electron is very small.

22.19 **IDENTIFY:** Add the vector electric fields due to each line of charge. $E(r)$ for a line of charge is given by Example 22.6 and is directed toward a negative line of charge and away from a positive line.

SET UP:

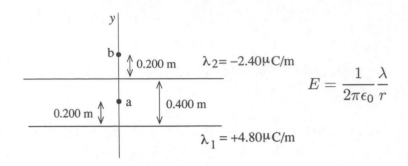

a) At point a, $\vec{E}_1$ and $\vec{E}_2$ are in the $+y$-direction (toward negative charge, away from positive charge).

$E_1 = (1/2\pi\epsilon_0)[(4.80 \times 10^{-6} \text{ C/m})/(0.200 \text{ m})] = 4.314 \times 10^5 \text{ N/C}$

$E_2 = (1/2\pi\epsilon_0)[(2.40 \times 10^{-6} \text{ C/m})/(0.200 \text{ m})] = 2.157 \times 10^5 \text{ N/C}$

$E = E_1 + E_2 = 6.47 \times 10^5 \text{ N/C}$, in the y-direction.

b) At point b, $\vec{E}_1$ is in the $+y$-direction and $\vec{E}_2$ is in the $-y$-direction.

$E_1 = (1/2\pi\epsilon_0)[(4.80 \times 10^{-6} \text{ C/m})/(0.600 \text{ m})] = 1.438 \times 10^5 \text{ N/C}$

$E_2 = (1/2\pi\epsilon_0)[(2.40 \times 10^{-6} \text{ C/m})/(0.200 \text{ m})] = 2.157 \times 10^5 \text{ N/C}$

$E = E_2 - E_1 = 7.2 \times 10^4 \text{ N/C}$, in the $-y$-direction.

EVALUATE: At point a the two fields are in the same direction and the magnitudes add. At point b the two fields are in opposite directions and the magnitudes subtract.

22.21 IDENTIFY: Add the vector fields due to each sphere.

SET UP: Outside each sphere the electric field is the same as if all the charge of the sphere were at its center, and the point where we are to calculate $\vec{E}$ is outside both spheres. $\vec{E}_1$ and $\vec{E}_2$ are both toward the sphere with negative charge.

$$E_1 = k\frac{|q_1|}{r_1^2} = k\frac{1.80 \times 10^{-6} \text{ C}}{(0.250 \text{ m})^2} = 2.591 \times 10^5 \text{ N/C}$$

$$E_2 = k\frac{|q_2|}{r_2^2} = k\frac{3.80 \times 10^{-6} \text{ C}}{(0.250 \text{ m})^2} = 5.471 \times 10^5 \text{ N/C}$$

$E = E_1 + E_2 = 8.06 \times 10^5 \text{ N/C}$, toward the negatively charged sphere.

EVALUATE: The two fields are in the same direction and their magnitudes add.

22.27 IDENTIFY: Apply Gauss's law to a Gaussian surface and calculate E.

a) SET UP: Consider the charge on a length l of the cylinder. This can be expressed as $q = \lambda l$. But since the surface area is $2\pi R l$ it can also be expressed as $q = \sigma 2\pi R l$. These two expressions must be equal, so $\lambda l = \sigma 2\pi R l$ and $\lambda = 2\pi R \sigma$.

b) Apply Gauss's law to a Gaussian surface that is a cylinder of length l, radius r, and whose axis coincides with the axis of the charge distribution.

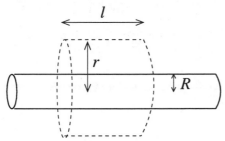

EXECUTE:
$$Q_{encl} = \sigma(2\pi Rl)$$

$$\Phi_E = 2\pi r l E$$

$$\Phi_E = \frac{Q_{encl}}{\epsilon_0} \text{ gives } 2\pi r l E = \frac{\sigma(2\pi Rl)}{\epsilon_0}$$

$$E = \frac{\sigma R}{\epsilon_0 r}$$

c) EVALUATE: Example 22.6 shows that the electric field of an infinite line of charge is $E = \lambda/2\pi\epsilon_0 r$.

$\sigma = \dfrac{\lambda}{2\pi R}$, so $E = \dfrac{\sigma R}{\epsilon_0 r} = \dfrac{R}{\epsilon_0 r}\left(\dfrac{\lambda}{2\pi R}\right) = \dfrac{\lambda}{2\pi\epsilon_0 r}$, the same as for an infinite line of charge that is along the axis of the cylinder.

Problems

22.33 a) IDENTIFY: Find the net flux through the parallelepiped surface and then use that in Gauss's law to find the net charge within. Flux out of the surface is positive and flux into the surface is negative.

SET UP: $\vec{E}_1$ gives flux out of the surface.

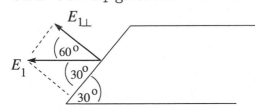

EXECUTE:
$$\Phi_1 = +E_{1\perp}A$$
$$A = (0.0600 \text{ m})(0.0500 \text{ m}) = 3.00\times 10^{-3} \text{ m}^2$$
$$E_{1\perp} = E_1 \cos 60° = (2.50\times 10^4 \text{ N/C})\cos 60°$$
$$E_{1\perp} = 1.25\times 10^4 \text{ N/C}$$

$$\Phi_{E_1} = +E_{1\perp}A = +(1.25\times 10^4 \text{ N/C})(3.00\times 10^{-3} \text{ m}^2) = 37.5 \text{ N}\cdot\text{m}^2/\text{C}$$

SET UP: $\vec{E}_2$ gives flux into the surface.

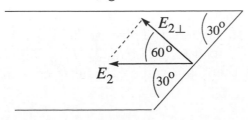

EXECUTE:
$$\Phi_2 = -E_{2\perp}A$$
$$A = (0.0600 \text{ m})(0.0500 \text{ m}) = 3.00\times 10^{-3} \text{ m}^2$$
$$E_{2\perp} = E_2 \cos 60° = (7.00\times 10^4 \text{ N/C})\cos 60°$$
$$E_{2\perp} = 3.50\times 10^4 \text{ N/C}$$

$$\Phi_{E_2} = -E_{2\perp}A = -(3.50 \times 10^4 \text{ N/C})(3.00 \times 10^{-3} \text{ m}^2) = -105.0 \text{ N} \cdot \text{m}^2/\text{C}$$

The net flux is $\Phi_E = \Phi_{E_1} + \Phi_{E_2} = +37.5 \text{ N·m}^2/\text{C} - 105.0 \text{ N·m}^2/\text{C} = -67.5 \text{ N·m}^2/\text{C}$. The net flux is negative (inward), so the net charge enclosed is negative.

Apply Gauss's law: $\Phi_E = \dfrac{Q_{encl}}{\epsilon_0}$

$$Q_{encl} = \Phi_E \epsilon_0 = (-67.5 \text{ N} \cdot \text{m}^2/\text{C})(8.854 \times 10^{-12} \text{ C}^2/\text{N} \cdot \text{m}^2) = -5.98 \times 10^{-10} \text{ C}.$$

b) EVALUATE: If there were no charge within the parallelpiped the net flux would be zero. This is not the case, so there is charge inside. The electric field lines that pass out through the surface of the parallelpiped must terminate on charges, so there also must be charges outside the parallelpiped.

22.35 IDENTIFY: Add the vector fields due to the sphere and due to the uniform sheet of charge. The electric field of the sphere is given by Example 22.9 and the electric field due to the infinite sheet is given by Example 22.7.

SET UP:

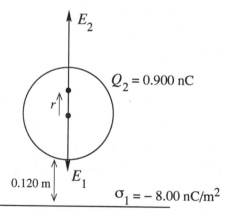

The electric field $\vec{E}_1$ of the sheet of charge is toward the sheet, so the electric field $\vec{E}_2$ of the sphere must be away from the sheet. This is true above the center of the sphere. Let r be the distance above the center of the sphere for the point where the electric field is zero.

EXECUTE: $E_1 = E_2$ so $\dfrac{|\sigma_1|}{2\epsilon_0} = \dfrac{1}{4\pi\epsilon_0}\dfrac{Q_2 r}{R^3}$

$$r = \frac{2\pi|\sigma_1|R^3}{Q_2} = \frac{2\pi(8.00 \times 10^{-9} \text{ C/m}^2)(0.120 \text{ m})^3}{0.900 \times 10^{-9} \text{ C}} = 0.097 \text{ m}$$

EVALUATE: The electric field of the sheet is $E = \sigma/2\varepsilon_0 = 452$ N/C and is directed upward above the sheet. Inside the sphere the electric field is away from the center and increases from zero at $r = 0$ to $E = (1/4\pi\epsilon_0)Q_2/R^2 = 562$ N/C at the surface of the sphere ($r = R$). Thus there is a value of r between $r = 0$ and $r = R$ where these two fields cancel.

22.39 **IDENTIFY:** Apply Gauss's law to a spherical Gaussian surface with radius r. Calculate the electric field at the surface of the Gaussian sphere.

a) SET UP:

(i) $r < a$

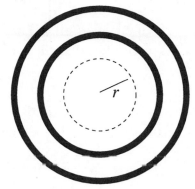

EXECUTE:
$$\Phi_E = EA = E(4\pi r^2)$$

$Q_{encl} = 0$; no charge is enclosed

$$\Phi_E = \frac{Q_{encl}}{\epsilon_0} \text{ says}$$

$E(4\pi r^2) = 0$ and $E = 0$.

(ii) $a < r < b$
Points in this region are in the conductor of the small shell, so $E = 0$.

(iii) **SET UP:** $b < r < c$
Apply Gauss's law to a spherical Gaussian surface with radius $b < r < c$.

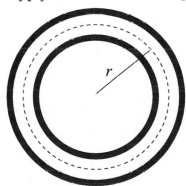

EXECUTE:
$$\Phi_E = EA = E(4\pi r^2)$$

The Gaussian surface encloses all of the small shell and none of the large shell, so $Q_{encl} = +2q$.

$\Phi_E = \dfrac{Q_{encl}}{\epsilon_0}$ gives $E(4\pi r^2) = \dfrac{2q}{\epsilon_0}$ so $E = \dfrac{2q}{4\pi\epsilon_0 r^2}$. Since the enclosed charge is positive the electric field is radially outward.

(iv) $c < r < d$
Points in this region are in the conductor of the large shell, so $E = 0$.

(v) **SET UP:** $r > d$
Apply Gauss's law to a spherical Gaussian surface with radius $r > d$.

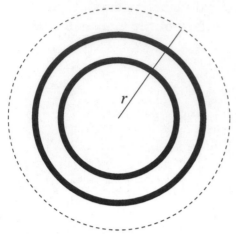

EXECUTE:
$$\Phi_E = EA = E(4\pi r^2)$$

The Gaussian surface encloses all of the small shell and all of the large shell, so $Q_{encl} = +2q + 4q = 6q$.

$$\Phi_E = \frac{Q_{encl}}{\epsilon_0} \text{ gives } E(4\pi r^2) = \frac{6q}{\epsilon_0}$$

$E = \dfrac{6q}{4\pi\epsilon_0 r^2}.$ Since the enclosed charge is positive the electric field is radially outward.

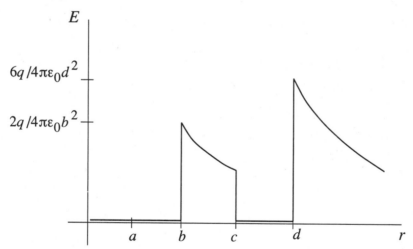

b) IDENTIFY and **SET UP:** Apply Gauss's law to a sphere that lies outside the surface of the shell for which we want to find the surface charge.

EXECUTE:

(i) charge on inner surface of the small shell:

Apply Gauss's law to a spherical Gaussian surface with radius $a < r < b$. This surface lies within the conductor of the small shell, where $E = 0$, so $\Phi_E = 0$. Thus by Gauss's law $Q_{encl} = 0$, so there is zero charge on the inner surface of the small shell.

(ii) charge on outer surface of the small shell:

The total charge on the small shell is $+2q$. We found in part (i) that there is zero charge on the inner surface of the shell, so all $+2q$ must reside on the outer surface.

(iii) charge on inner surface of large shell:

Apply Guass's law to a spherical Gaussian surface with radius $c < r < d$. The surface lies within the conductor of the large shell, where $E = 0$, so $\Phi_E = 0$. Thus by Gauss's law $Q_{\text{encl}} = 0$. The surface encloses the $+2q$ on the small shell so there must be charge $-2q$ on the inner surface of the large shell to make the total enclosed charge zero.

(iv) charge on outer surface of large shell

The total charge on the large shell is $+4q$. We showed in part (iii) that the charge on the inner surface is $-2q$, so there must be $+6q$ on the outer surface.

EVALUATE: The electric field lines for $b < r < c$ originate from the surface charge on the outer surface of the inner shell and all terminate on the surface charge on the inner surface of the outer shell. These surface charges have equal magnitude and opposite sign. The electric field lines for $r > d$ originate from the surface charge on the outer surface of the outer sphere.

22.43 IDENTIFY: Use Gauss's law to find the electric field $\vec{E}$ produced by the shell for $r < R$ and $r > R$ and then use $\vec{F} = q\vec{E}$ to find the force the shell exerts on the point charge.

a) SET UP: Apply Gauss's law to a spherical Gaussian surface that has radius $r > R$ and that is concentric with the shell.

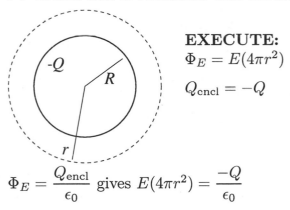

EXECUTE:
$\Phi_E = E(4\pi r^2)$

$Q_{\text{encl}} = -Q$

$\Phi_E = \dfrac{Q_{\text{encl}}}{\epsilon_0}$ gives $E(4\pi r^2) = \dfrac{-Q}{\epsilon_0}$

The magnitude of the field is $E = \dfrac{Q}{4\pi\epsilon_0 r^2}$ and it is directed toward the center of the shell.

Then $F = qE = \dfrac{qQ}{4\pi\epsilon_0 r^2}$, directed toward then center of the shell. (Since q is positive, $\vec{E}$ and $\vec{F}$ are in the same direction.)

b) SET UP: Apply Gauss's law to a spherical Gaussian surface that has radius $r < R$ and that is concentric with the shell.

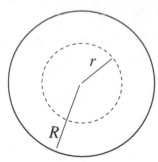

EXECUTE:

$$\Phi_E = E(4\pi r^2)$$

$$Q_{encl} = 0$$

$\Phi_E = \dfrac{Q_{encl}}{\epsilon_0}$ gives $E(4\pi r^2) = 0$

Then $E = 0$ so $F = 0$.

EVALUATE: Outside the shell the electric field and the force it exerts is the same as for a point charge $-Q$ located at the center of the shell. Inside the shell $E = 0$ and there is no force.

22.45 a) IDENTIFY: Apply Gauss's law to a Gaussian cylinder of length l and radius r, where $a < r < b$, and calculate E on the surface of the cylinder.

SET UP:

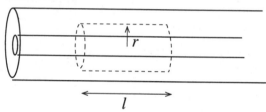

EXECUTE:

$$\Phi_E = E(2\pi rl)$$

$Q_{encl} = \lambda l$ (the charge on the length l of the inner conductor that is inside the Gaussian surface.

$\Phi_E = \dfrac{Q_{encl}}{\epsilon_0}$ gives $E(2\pi rl) = \dfrac{\lambda l}{\epsilon_0}$

$E = \dfrac{\lambda}{2\pi\epsilon_0 r}$. The enclosed charge is positive so the direction of $\vec{E}$ is radially outward.

b) SET UP: Apply Gauss's law to a Gaussian cylinder of length l and radius r, where $r > c$:

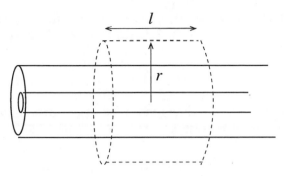

EXECUTE:

$\Phi_E = E(2\pi r l)$

$Q_{encl} = \lambda l$ (the charge on the length l of the inner conductor that is inside the Gaussian surface; the outer conductor carries no net charge.

$\Phi_E = \dfrac{Q_{encl}}{\epsilon_0}$ gives $E(2\pi r l) = \dfrac{\lambda l}{\epsilon_0}$

$E = \dfrac{\lambda}{2\pi \epsilon_0 r}$.   The enclosed charge is positive so the direction of $\vec{E}$ is radially outward.

c) $E = 0$ within a conductor. Thus $E = 0$ for $r < a$;

$E = \dfrac{\lambda}{2\pi \epsilon_0 r}$ for $a < r < b$; $E = 0$ for $b < r < c$;

$E = \dfrac{\lambda}{2\pi \epsilon_0 r}$ for $r > c$.

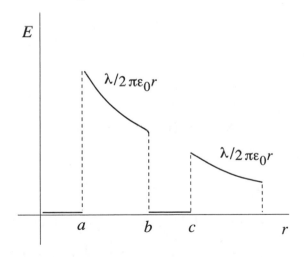

EVALUATE: Inside either conductor $E = 0$. Between the conductors and outside both conductors the electric field is the same as for a line of charge with linear charge density λ lying along the axis of the inner conductor.

d) IDENTIFY and **SET UP:** <u>inner surface</u>:

Apply Gauss's law to a Gaussian cylinder with radius r, where $b < r < c$. We know E on this surface; calculate Q_{encl}.

EXECUTE: This surface lies within the conductor of the outer cylinder, where $E = 0$, so $\Phi_E = 0$. Thus by Gauss's law $Q_{encl} = 0$. The surface encloses charge

λl on the inner conductor, so it must enclose charge $-\lambda l$ on the inner surface of the outer conductor. The charge per unit length on the inner surface of the outer cylinder is $-\lambda$.

<u>outer surface</u>:

The outer cylinder carries no net charge. So if there is charge per unit length $-\lambda$ on its inner surface there must be charge per unit length $+\lambda$ on the outer surface.

EVALUATE: The electric field lines between the conductors originate on the surface charge on the outer surface of the inner conductor and terminate on the surface charges on the inner surface of the outer conductor. These surface charges are equal in magnitude (per unit length) and opposite in sign. The electric field lines outside the outer conductor originate from the surface charge on the outer surface of the outer conductor.

22.47 a) IDENTIFY: Use Gauss's law to calculate $E(r)$.

(i) **SET UP:** $\underline{r < a}$: Apply Gauss's law to a cylindrical Gaussian surface of length l and radius r, where $r < a$.

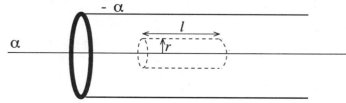

EXECUTE:
$\Phi_E = E(2\pi r l)$

$Q_{encl} = \alpha l$ (the charge on the length l of the line of charge)

$\Phi_E = \dfrac{Q_{encl}}{\epsilon_0}$ gives $E(2\pi r l) = \dfrac{\alpha l}{\epsilon_0}$

$E = \dfrac{\alpha}{2\pi\epsilon_0 r}$.   The enclosed charge is positive so the direction of $\vec{E}$ is radially outward.

(ii) $\underline{a < r < b}$: Points in this region are within the conducting tube, so $E = 0$.

(iii) **SET UP:** $\underline{r > b}$: Apply Gauss's law to a cylindrical Gaussian surface of length l and radius r, where $r > b$.

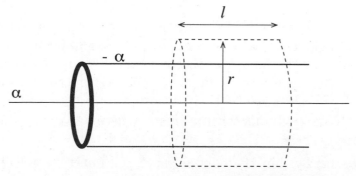

EXECUTE:
$\Phi_E = E(2\pi r l)$

$Q_{encl} = \alpha l$ (the charge on length l of the line of charge) $- \alpha l$ (the charge on length l of the tube)
Thus $Q_{encl} = 0$.

$\Phi_E = \dfrac{Q_{\text{encl}}}{\epsilon_0}$ gives $E(2\pi rl) = 0$ and $E = 0$.

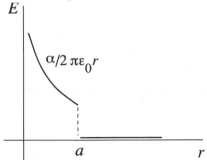

b) **IDENTIFY:** Apply Gauss's law to cylindrical surfaces that lie just outside the inner and outer surfaces of the tube. We know E so can calculate Q_{encl}.

(i) **SET UP:**

inner surface

Apply Gauss's law to a cylindrical Gaussian surface of length l and radius r, where $a < r < b$.

EXECUTE: This surface lies within the conductor of the tube, where $E = 0$, so $\Phi_E = 0$. Then by Gauss's law $Q_{\text{encl}} = 0$. The surface encloses charge αl on the line of charge so must enclose charge $-\alpha l$ on the inner surface of the tube. The charge per unit length on the inner surface of the tube is $-\alpha$.

(ii) outer surface

The net charge per unit length on the tube is $-\alpha$. We have shown in part (i) that this must all reside on the inner surface, so there is no net charge on the outer surface of the tube.

EVALUATE: For $r < a$ the electric field is due only to the line of charge. For $r > b$ the electric field of the tube is the same as for a line of charge along its axis. The fields of the line of charge and of the tube are equal in magnitude and opposite in direction and sum to zero. For $r < a$ the electric field lines originate on the line of charge and terminate on the surface charge on the inner surface of the tube. There is no electric field outside the tube and no surface charge on the outer surface of the tube.

22.51 IDENTIFY: There is a force on each electron due to the other electron and a force due to the sphere of charge. Use Coulomb's law for the force between the electrons. Example 22.9 gives E inside a uniform sphere and Eq.(21.3) gives the force.

SET UP:

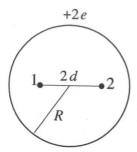

If the electrons are in equilibrium the net force on each one is zero.

EXECUTE: Consider the forces on electron 2. There is a repulsive force F_1 due to the other electron, electron 1.

$$F_1 = \frac{1}{4\pi\epsilon_0} \frac{e^2}{(2d)^2}$$

The electric field inside the uniform distribution of positive charge is

$$E = \frac{Qr}{4\pi\epsilon_0 R^3} \text{ (Example 22.9), where } Q = +2e. \text{ At the position of electron 2, } r = d.$$

The force F_{cd} exerted by the positive charge distribution is

$$F_{cd} = eE = \frac{e(2e)d}{4\pi\epsilon_0 R^3} \text{ and is attractive.}$$

The force diagram for electron 2 is

$$\overset{F_{cd}}{\longleftarrow} \quad \bullet \quad \overset{F_1}{\longrightarrow}$$

Net force equals zero implies $F_1 = F_{cd}$ and $\dfrac{1}{4\pi\epsilon_0} \dfrac{e^2}{4d^2} = \dfrac{2e^2 d}{4\pi\epsilon_0 R^3}$

Thus $(1/4d^2) = 2d/R^3$, so $d^3 = R^3/8$ and $d = R/2$.

EVALUATE: The electric field of the sphere is radially outward; it is zero at the center of the sphere and increases with distance from the center. The force this field exerts on one of the electrons is radially inward and increases as the electron is farther from the center. The force from the other electron is radially outward, is infinite when $d = 0$ and decreases as d increases. It is reasonable therefore for there to be a value of d for which these forces balance.

22.53 **IDENTIFY** and **SET UP:** Use the result of Example 22.9 to calculate $E(r)$ at each r. Eq.(21.3) then gives the force on the electron, and $\vec{F} = m\vec{a}$ gives $\vec{a}$.

EXECUTE: Example 22.9 shows that the electric field of a uniformly charged sphere is $E = \dfrac{Qr}{4\pi\epsilon_0 R^3}$ for $r < R$ and $E = \dfrac{Q}{4\pi\epsilon_0 r^2}$ for $r > R$.

The force on the electron has magnitude $F = qE = eE$. The acceleration has magnitude $a = F/m = eE/m$, where $e/m = (1.60 \times 10^{-19} \text{ C})/(9.109 \times 10^{-31} \text{ kg}) = 1.757 \times 10^{11}$ C/kg. The electric field is radially outward so the force and acceleration on the negatively-charged electron are both radially inward.

a) $\underline{r = 2R}$

$$E = \frac{Q}{4\pi\epsilon_0 r^2} = \frac{Q}{4\pi\epsilon_0 (2R)^2} = \frac{1}{4}\left(\frac{Q}{4\pi\epsilon_0 R^2}\right)$$

$$E = \frac{1}{4}\left(\frac{82e}{4\pi\epsilon_0 R^2}\right) = \frac{1}{4}\frac{(8.988 \times 10^9 \text{ N}\cdot\text{m}^2/\text{C}^2)(82)(1.602 \times 10^{-19} \text{ C})}{(7.1 \times 10^{-15} \text{ m})^2} =$$

$\frac{1}{4}(2.342 \times 10^{21} \text{ N/C}) = 5.855 \times 10^{20}$ N/C

$a = (e/m)E = (1.757 \times 10^{11} \text{ C/kg})(5.855 \times 10^{20} \text{ N/C}) = 1.0 \times 10^{32}$ m/s^2

b) $\underline{r = R}$

$$E = \frac{Q}{4\pi\epsilon_0 r^2} = \frac{Q}{4\pi\epsilon_0 R^2} = 2.342 \times 10^{21} \text{ N/C}.$$

$a = (e/m)E = (1.757 \times 10^{11} \text{ C/kg})(2.342 \times 10^{21} \text{ N/C}) = 4.1 \times 10^{32}$ m/s^2 (4 times larger than for $r = 2R$)

c) $\underline{r = R/2}$

$$E = \frac{Qr}{4\pi\epsilon_0 R^3} = \frac{Q(R/2)}{4\pi\epsilon_0 R^3} = \frac{1}{2}\left(\frac{Q}{4\pi\epsilon_0 R^2}\right) = \frac{1}{2}(2.342 \times 10^{21} \text{ N/C}) =$$

1.171×10^{21} N/C.

$a = (e/m)E = (1.757 \times 10^{11} \text{ C/kg})(1.171 \times 10^{21} \text{ N/C}) = 2.1 \times 10^{32}$ m/s^2 ($\frac{1}{2}$ the value at $r = R$)

d) At $r = 0$, $E = 0$ so $F = 0$ and $a = 0$.

EVALUATE: For $r \leq R$, $E(r)$ increases linearly as r increases so a increases linearly with r. For $r > R$, $E(r)$ decreases like $1/r$ as r increases so a decreases as $1/r$. Our numerical results reflect this behavior.

22.55 a) IDENTIFY and **SET UP:** Consider the direction of the field for x slightly greater than and slightly less than zero.

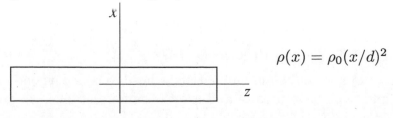

$$\rho(x) = \rho_0 (x/d)^2$$

EXECUTE: The charge distribution is symmetric about $x = 0$, so by symmetry $E(x) = E(-x)$. But for $x > 0$ the field is in the $+x$ direction and for $x < 0$ the field is in the $-x$ direction. At $x = 0$ the field can't be both in the $+x$ and $-x$ directions so must be zero. That is, $E_x(x) = -E_x(-x)$. At point $x = 0$ this gives $E_x(0) = -E_x(0)$ and this equation is satisfied only for $E_x(0) = 0$.

b) IDENTIFY and **SET UP:** $\underline{|x| > d}$ (outside the slab)

Apply Gauss's law to a cylindrical Gaussian surface whose axis is perpendicular to the slab and whose end caps have area A and are the same distance $|x| > d$ from $x = 0$.

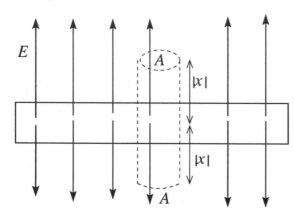

EXECUTE:

$\Phi_E = 2EA$

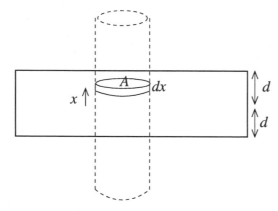

To find Q_{encl} consider a thin disk at coordinate x and with thickness dx. The charge within this disk is

$dq = \rho \, dV = \rho A \, dx = (\rho_0 A/d^2)x^2 \, dx$.

The total charge enclosed by the Gaussian cylinder is

$Q_{encl} = 2\int_0^d dq = (2\rho_0 A/d^2)\int_0^d x^2 \, dx = (2\rho_0 A/d^2)(d^3/3) = \frac{2}{3}\rho_0 Ad$.

Then $\Phi_E = \dfrac{Q_{encl}}{\epsilon_0}$ gives $2EA = 2\rho_0 Ad/3\epsilon_0$.

$E = \rho_0 d/3\epsilon_0$

$\vec{E}$ is directed away from $x = 0$, so $\vec{E} = (\rho_0 d/3\epsilon_0)(x/|x|)\hat{i}$.

IDENTIFY and **SET UP:** $\underline{|x| < d}$ (inside the slab)

Apply Gauss's law to a cylindrical Gaussian surface whose axis is perpendicular to the slab and whose end caps have area A and are the same distance $|x| < d$ from $x = 0$.

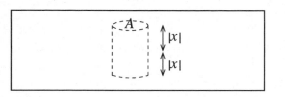

EXECUTE:

$\Phi_E = 2EA$

Q_{encl} is found as above, but now the integral on dx is only from 0 to x instead of 0 to d.

$Q_{\text{encl}} = 2\int_0^x dq = (2\rho_0 A/d^2)\int_0^x x^2\,dx = (2\rho_0 A/d^2)(x^3/3)$.

Then $\Phi_E = \dfrac{Q_{\text{encl}}}{\epsilon_0}$ gives $2EA = 2\rho_0 Ax^3/3\epsilon_0 d^2$.

$E = \rho_0 x^3/3\epsilon_0 d^2$

$\vec{E}$ is directed away from $x = 0$, so $\vec{E} = (\rho_0 x^3/3\epsilon_0 d^2)\hat{\imath}$.

EVALUATE: Note that $E = 0$ at $x = 0$ as stated in part (a). Note also that the expressions for $|x| > d$ and $|x| < d$ agree for $x = d$.

22.57 $\rho(r) = \rho_0(1 - r/R)$ for $r \le R$ where $\rho_0 = 3Q/\pi R^3$.
$\rho(r) = 0$ for $r > R$

a) IDENTIFY: The charge density varies with r inside the spherical volume. Divide the volume up into thin concentric shells, of radius r and thickness dr. Find the charge dq in each shell and integrate to find the total charge.

SET UP:

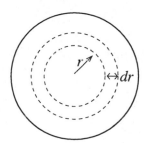

EXECUTE:
The volume of such a shell is
$dV = 4\pi r^2\,dr$

The charge contained within the shell is
$dq = \rho(r)\,dV = 4\pi r^2 \rho_0 (1 - r/R)\,dr$

The total charge Q in the charge distribution is obtained by integrating dq over all such shells into which the sphere can be subdivided:

$Q = \int dq = \int_0^R 4\pi r^2 \rho_0 (1 - r/R)\,dr = 4\pi\rho_0 \int_0^R (r^2 - r^3/R)\,dr$

$Q = 4\pi\rho_0 \left[\dfrac{r^3}{3} - \dfrac{r^4}{4R}\right]_0^R = 4\pi\rho_0 \left(\dfrac{R^3}{3} - \dfrac{R^4}{4R}\right) = 4\pi\rho_0 (R^3/12) =$
$4\pi(3Q/\pi R^3)(R^3/12) = Q$, as was to be shown.

b) IDENTIFY: Apply Gauss's law to a spherical surface of radius r, where $r > R$.

SET UP:

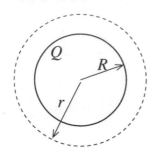

EXECUTE:

$$\Phi_E = \frac{Q_{encl}}{\epsilon_0}$$

$$E(4\pi r^2) = \frac{Q}{\epsilon_0}$$

$E = \dfrac{Q}{4\pi\epsilon_0 r^2}$; same as for point charge of charge Q.

c) IDENTIFY: Apply Gauss's law to a spherical surface of radius r, where $r < R$:
SET UP:

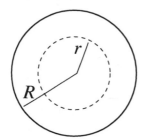

EXECUTE:

$$\Phi_E = \frac{Q_{encl}}{\epsilon_0}$$

$$\Phi_E = E(4\pi r^2)$$

To calculate the enclosed charge Q_{encl} use the same technique as in part (a), except integrate dq out to r rather than R. (We want the charge that is inside radius r.)

$$Q_{encl} = \int_0^r 4\pi r'^2 \rho_0 \left(1 - \frac{r'}{R}\right) dr' = 4\pi\rho_0 \int_0^r \left(r'^2 - \frac{r'^3}{R}\right) dr'$$

$$Q_{encl} = 4\pi\rho_0 \left[\frac{r'^3}{3} - \frac{r'^4}{4R}\right]_0^r = 4\pi\rho_0 \left(\frac{r^3}{3} - \frac{r^4}{4R}\right) = 4\pi\rho_0 r^3 \left(\frac{1}{3} - \frac{r}{4R}\right)$$

$\rho_0 = \dfrac{3Q}{\pi R^3}$ so $Q_{encl} = 12Q\dfrac{r^3}{R^3}\left(\dfrac{1}{3} - \dfrac{r}{4R}\right) = Q\left(\dfrac{r^3}{R^3}\right)\left(4 - 3\dfrac{r}{R}\right)$.

Thus Gauss's law gives $E(4\pi r^2) = \dfrac{Q}{\epsilon_0}\left(\dfrac{r^3}{R^3}\right)\left(4 - 3\dfrac{r}{R}\right)$

$$E = \frac{Qr}{4\pi\epsilon_0 R^3}\left(4 - \frac{3r}{R}\right), r \leq R$$

d)

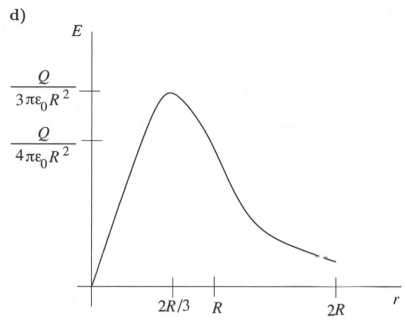

e) Where the electric field is a maximum, $\dfrac{dE}{dr} = 0$. Thus

$$\frac{d}{dr}\left(4r - \frac{3r^2}{R}\right) = 0 \text{ so } 4 - 6r/R = 0 \text{ and } r = 2R/3.$$

At this value of r, $E = \dfrac{Q}{4\pi\epsilon_0 R^3}\left(\dfrac{2R}{3}\right)\left(4 - \dfrac{3}{R}\dfrac{2R}{3}\right) = \dfrac{Q}{3\pi\epsilon_0 R^2}$

EVALUATE: Our expressions for $E(r)$ for $r < R$ and for $r > R$ agree at $r = R$. The results of part (e) for the value of r where $E(r)$ is a maximum agrees with the graph in part (d).

22.61 a) IDENTIFY: Use $\vec{E}(\vec{r})$ from Example (22.9) (inside the sphere) and relate the position vector of a point inside the sphere measured from the origin to that measured from the center of the sphere.

SET UP: For an insulating sphere of uniform charge density ρ and centered at the origin, the electric field inside the sphere is given by $E = Qr'/4\pi\epsilon_0 R^3$ (Example 22.9), where $\vec{r}'$ is the vector from the center of the sphere to the point where E is calculated.

But $\rho = 3Q/4\pi R^3$ so this may be written as $E = \rho r/3\epsilon_0$. And $\vec{E}$ is radially outward, in the direction of $\vec{r}'$, so $\vec{E} = \rho\vec{r}'/3\epsilon_0$.

For a sphere whose center is located by vector $\vec{b}$, a point inside the sphere and located by $\vec{r}$ is located by the vector $\vec{r}' = \vec{r} - \vec{b}$ relative to the center of the sphere.

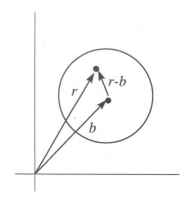

EXECUTE:

Thus $\vec{E} = \dfrac{\rho(\vec{r} - \vec{b})}{3\epsilon_0}$

EVALUATE: When $b = 0$ this reduces to the result of Example 22.9. When $\vec{r} = \vec{b}$, this gives $E = 0$, which is correct since we know that $E = 0$ at the center of the sphere.

b) IDENTIFY: The charge distribution can be represented as a uniform sphere with charge density ρ and centered at the origin added to a uniform sphere with charge density $-\rho$ and centered at $\vec{r} = \vec{b}$.

SET UP: $\vec{E} = \vec{E}_{\text{uniform}} + \vec{E}_{\text{hole}}$, where $\vec{E}_{\text{uniform}}$ is the field of a uniformly charged sphere with charge density ρ and $\vec{E}_{\text{hole}}$ is the field of a sphere located at the hole and with charge density $-\rho$. (Within the spherical hole the net charge density is $+\rho - \rho = 0$.)

EXECUTE:

$\vec{E}_{\text{uniform}} = \dfrac{\rho \vec{r}}{3\epsilon_0}$, where $\vec{r}$ is a vector from the center of the sphere.

$\vec{E}_{\text{hole}} = \dfrac{-\rho(\vec{r} - \vec{b})}{3\epsilon_0}$, at points inside the hole.

Then $\vec{E} = \dfrac{\rho \vec{r}}{3\epsilon_0} + \left(\dfrac{-\rho(\vec{r} - \vec{b})}{3\epsilon_0} \right) = \dfrac{\rho \vec{b}}{3\epsilon_0}$.

EVALUATE: $\vec{E}$ is independent of $\vec{r}$ so is uniform inside the hole. The direction of $\vec{E}$ inside the hole is in the direction of the vector $\vec{b}$, the direction from the center of the insulating sphere to the center of the hole.

22.63 IDENTIFY: The electric field at each point is the vector sum of the fields of the two charge distributions.

SET UP: Inside a sphere of uniform positive charge, $E = \dfrac{\rho r}{3\epsilon_0}$.

$\rho = \dfrac{Q}{\frac{4}{3}\pi R^3} = \dfrac{3Q}{4\pi R^3}$ so $E = \dfrac{Qr}{4\pi\epsilon_0 R^3}$, directed away from the center of the sphere.

Outside a sphere of uniform positive charge, $E = \dfrac{Q}{4\pi\epsilon_0 r^2}$, directed away from the center of the sphere.

EXECUTE:

a) $x = 0$ This point is inside sphere 1 and outside sphere 2.

$$E_1 = \frac{Qr}{4\pi\epsilon_0 R^3} = 0, \text{ since } r = 0.$$

$E_2 = \dfrac{Q}{4\pi\epsilon_0 r^2}$ with $r = 2R$ so $E_2 = \dfrac{Q}{16\pi\epsilon_0 R^2}$, in the $-x$-direction.

Thus $\vec{E} = \vec{E}_1 + \vec{E}_2 = -\dfrac{Q}{16\pi\epsilon_0 R^2}\hat{i}.$

b) $x = R/2$. This point is inside sphere 1 and outside sphere 2. Each field is directed away from the center of the sphere that produces it.

$$E_1 = \frac{Qr}{4\pi\epsilon_0 R^3} \text{ with } r = R/2 \text{ so}$$
$$E_1 = \frac{Q}{8\pi\epsilon_0 R^2}$$

$E_2 = \dfrac{Q}{4\pi\epsilon_0 r^2}$ with $r = 3R/2$ so $E_2 = \dfrac{Q}{9\pi\epsilon_0 R^2}$

$E = E_1 - E_2 = \dfrac{Q}{72\pi\epsilon_0 R^2}$, in the $+x$-direction and $\vec{E} = \dfrac{Q}{72\pi\epsilon_0 R^2}\hat{i}$

c) $x = R$. This point is at the surface of each sphere. The fields have equal magnitudes and opposite directions, so $E = 0$.

d) $x = 3R$. This point is outside both spheres. Each field is directed away from the center of the sphere that produces it.

$$E_1 = \frac{Q}{4\pi\epsilon_0 r^2} \text{ with } r = 3R \text{ so}$$
$$E_1 = \frac{Q}{36\pi\epsilon_0 R^2}$$

$E_2 = \dfrac{Q}{4\pi\epsilon_0 r^2}$ with $r = R$ so $E_2 = \dfrac{Q}{4\pi\epsilon_0 R^2}$

$E = E_1 + E_2 = \dfrac{5Q}{18\pi\epsilon_0 R^2}$, in the $+x$-direction and $\vec{E} = \dfrac{5Q}{18\pi\epsilon_0 R^2}\hat{i}$

EVALUATE: The field of each sphere is radially outward from the center of the sphere. We must use the correct expression for $E(r)$ for each sphere, depending on whether the field point is inside or outside that sphere.

CHAPTER 23
ELECTRIC POTENTIAL

Exercises 1, 3, 5, 9, 11, 13, 17, 21, 29, 31, 33, 35, 37, 39, 41, 43
Problems 49, 51, 55, 57, 59, 61, 63, 65, 69, 75, 79, 81, 83

Exercises

23.1 **IDENTIFY:** Apply Eq.(23.2) to calculate the work. The electric potential energy of a pair of point charges is given by Eq.(23.9).

SET UP: Let the initial position of q_2 be point a and the final position be point b.

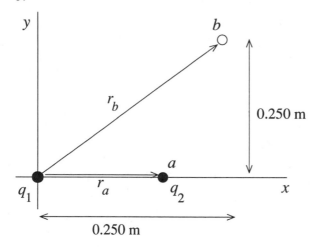

$$0.250 \text{ m} \qquad r_a = 0.150 \text{ m}$$
$$r_b = \sqrt{(0.250 \text{ m})^2 + (0.250 \text{ m})^2}$$
$$r_b = 0.3536 \text{ m}$$

EXECUTE: $W_{a \to b} = U_a - U_b$

$$U_a = \frac{1}{4\pi\epsilon_0} \frac{q_1 q_2}{r_a} = (8.988 \times 10^9 \text{ N} \cdot \text{m}^2/\text{C}^2) \frac{(+2.40 \times 10^{-6} \text{ C})(-4.30 \times 10^{-6} \text{ C})}{0.150 \text{ m}}$$

$$U_a = -0.6184 \text{ J}$$

$$U_b = \frac{1}{4\pi\epsilon_0} \frac{q_1 q_2}{r_b} = (8.988 \times 10^9 \text{ N} \cdot \text{m}^2/\text{C}^2) \frac{(+2.40 \times 10^{-6} \text{ C})(-4.30 \times 10^{-6} \text{ C})}{0.3536 \text{ m}}$$

$$U_b = -0.2623 \text{ J}$$

$$W_{a \to b} = U_a - U_b = -0.6184 \text{ J} - (-0.2623 \text{ J}) = -0.356 \text{ J}$$

EVALUATE: The attractive force on q_2 is toward the origin, so it does negative work on q_2 when q_2 moves to larger r.

23.3 **a) IDENTIFY:** Use conservation of energy:
$$K_a + U_a + W_{\text{other}} = K_b + U_b$$

U for the pair of point charges is given by Eq.(23.9).

SET UP:

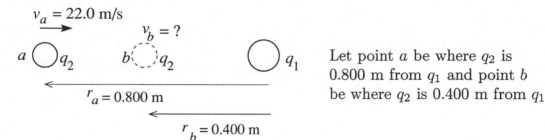

Let point a be where q_2 is 0.800 m from q_1 and point b be where q_2 is 0.400 m from q_1

EXECUTE:

Only the electric force does work, so $W_{\text{other}} = 0$ and $U = \dfrac{1}{4\pi\epsilon_0}\dfrac{q_1 q_2}{r}$.

$K_a - \frac{1}{2}mv_a^2 = \frac{1}{2}(1.50 \times 10^{-3}\ \text{kg})(22.0\ \text{m/s})^2 = 0.3630\ \text{J}$

$U_a = \dfrac{1}{4\pi\epsilon_0}\dfrac{q_1 q_2}{r_a} =$

$(8.988 \times 10^9\ \text{N}\cdot\text{m}^2/\text{C}^2)\dfrac{(-2.80 \times 10^{-6}\ \text{C})(-7.80 \times 10^{-6}\ \text{C})}{0.800\ \text{m}} = +0.2454\ \text{J}$

$K_b = \frac{1}{2}mv_b^2$

$U_b = \dfrac{1}{4\pi\epsilon_0}\dfrac{q_1 q_2}{r_b} =$

$(8.988 \times 10^9\ \text{N}\cdot\text{m}^2/\text{C}^2)\dfrac{(-2.80 \times 10^{-6}\ \text{C})(-7.80 \times 10^{-6}\ \text{C})}{0.400\ \text{m}} = +0.4907\ \text{J}$

The conservation of energy equation then gives $K_b = K_a + (U_a - U_b)$

$\frac{1}{2}mv_b^2 = +0.3630\ \text{J} + (0.2454\ \text{J} - 0.4907\ \text{J}) = 0.1177\ \text{J}$

$v_b = \sqrt{\dfrac{2(0.1177\ \text{J})}{1.50 \times 10^{-3}\ \text{kg}}} = 12.5\ \text{m/s}$

EVALUATE: The potential energy increases when the two positively charged spheres get closer together, so the kinetic energy and speed decrease.

b) IDENTIFY: Let point c be where q_2 has its speed momentarily reduced to zero. Apply conservation of energy to points a and c: $K_a + U_a + W_{\text{other}} = K_c + U_c$.

SET UP:

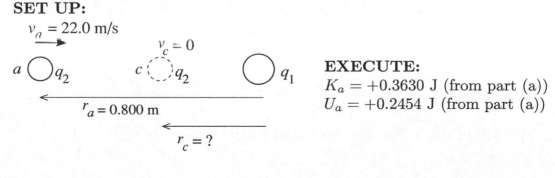

EXECUTE:

$K_a = +0.3630\ \text{J}$ (from part (a))

$U_a = +0.2454\ \text{J}$ (from part (a))

$K_c = 0$ (at distance of closest approach the speed is zero)

$$U_c = \frac{1}{4\pi\epsilon_0}\frac{q_1 q_2}{r_c}$$

Thus conservation of energy $K_a + U_a = U_c$ gives

$$\frac{1}{4\pi\epsilon_0}\frac{q_1 q_2}{r_c} = +0.3630\ \text{J} + 0.2454\ \text{J} = 0.6084\ \text{J}$$

$$r_c = \frac{1}{4\pi\epsilon_0}\frac{q_1 q_2}{0.6084\ \text{J}} =$$

$$(8.988 \times 10^9\ \text{N} \cdot \text{m}^2/\text{C}^2)\frac{(-2.80 \times 10^{-6}\ \text{C})(-7.80 \times 10^{-6}\ \text{C})}{+0.6084\ \text{J}} = 0.323\ \text{m}.$$

EVALUATE: $U \to \infty$ as $r \to 0$ so q_2 will stop no matter what its initial speed is.

23.5   **a) IDENTIFY** and **SET UP:** U is given by Eq.(23.9).

EXECUTE: $U = \dfrac{1}{4\pi\epsilon_0}\dfrac{qq'}{r}$

$$U = (8.988 \times 10^9\ \text{N} \cdot \text{m}^2/\text{C}^2)\frac{(+4.60 \times 10^{-6}\ \text{C})(+1.20 \times 10^{-6}\ \text{C})}{0.250\ \text{m}} = +0.198\ \text{J}$$

EVALUATE: The two charges are both of the same sign so their electric potential energy is positive.

b) IDENTIFY: Use conservation of energy: $K_a + U_a + W_{\text{other}} = K_b + U_b$

SET UP: Let point a be where q is released and point b be at its final position.

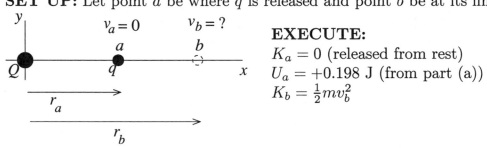

EXECUTE:
$K_a = 0$ (released from rest)
$U_a = +0.198\ \text{J}$ (from part (a))
$K_b = \frac{1}{2}mv_b^2$

Only the electric force does work, so $W_{\text{other}} = 0$ and $U = \dfrac{1}{4\pi\epsilon_0}\dfrac{qQ}{r}$.

(i) $r_b = 0.500\ \text{m}$

$$U_b = \frac{1}{4\pi\epsilon_0}\frac{qQ}{r} =$$

$$(8.988 \times 10^9\ \text{N} \cdot \text{m}^2/\text{C}^2)\frac{(+4.60 \times 10^{-6}\ \text{C})(+1.20 \times 10^{-6}\ \text{C})}{0.500\ \text{m}} = +0.0992\ \text{J}$$

Then $K_a + U_a + W_{\text{other}} = K_b + U_b$ gives $K_b = U_a - U_b$ and

$\frac{1}{2}mv_b^2 = U_a - U_b$ and $v_b = \sqrt{\dfrac{2(U_a - U_b)}{m}} = \sqrt{\dfrac{2(+0.198 \text{ J} - 0.0992 \text{ J})}{2.80 \times 10^{-4} \text{ kg}}} = 26.6 \text{ m/s}$.

(ii) $r_b = 5.00 \text{ m}$

r_b is now ten times larger than in (i) so U_b is ten times smaller:
$U_b = +0.0992 \text{ J}/10 = +0.00992 \text{ J}$.

$v_b = \sqrt{\dfrac{2(U_a - U_b)}{m}} = \sqrt{\dfrac{2(+0.198 \text{ J} - 0.00992 \text{ J})}{2.80 \times 10^{-4} \text{ kg}}} = 36.7 \text{ m/s}$.

(iii) $r_b = 50.0 \text{ m}$

r_b is now ten times larger than in (ii) so U_b is ten times smaller:
$U_b = +0.00992 \text{ J}/10 = +0.000992 \text{ J}$.

$v_b = \sqrt{\dfrac{2(U_a - U_b)}{m}} = \sqrt{\dfrac{2(+0.198 \text{ J} - 0.000992 \text{ J})}{2.80 \times 10^{-4} \text{ kg}}} = 37.5 \text{ m/s}$.

EVALUATE: The force between the two charges is repulsive and provides an acceleration to q. This causes the speed of q to increase as it moves away from Q.

23.9   **IDENTIFY:** Apply Eq.(23.2). The net work to bring the charges in from infinity is equal to the change in potential energy. The total potential energy is the sum of the potential energies of each pair of charges, calculated from Eq.(23.9).

SET UP: Let 1 be where all the charges are infinitely far apart. Let 2 be where the charges are at the corners of the triangle.

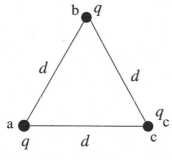

Let q_c be the third, unknown charge.

EXECUTE: $W = -\Delta U = -(U_2 - U_1)$

$U_1 = 0$

$U_2 = U_{ab} + U_{ac} + U_{bc} = \dfrac{1}{4\pi\epsilon_0 d}(q^2 + 2qq_c)$

Want $W = 0$, so $W = -(U_2 - U_1)$ gives $0 = -U_2$

$0 = \dfrac{1}{4\pi\epsilon_0 d}(q^2 + 2qq_c)$

$q^2 + 2qq_c = 0$ and $q_c = -q/2$.

EVALUATE: The potential energy for the two charges q is positive and for each q with q_c it is negative. There are two of the q, q_c terms so must have $q_c < q$.

23.11 IDENTIFY: Apply conservation of energy (Eq.23.3). The initial electric potential energy can be calculated from Eq.(23.11), with all three pairs of charges included.

SET UP: The three pairs are are one proton-proton and two proton-alpha particle pairs. Let 1 refer to when the charges are in the triangle and 2 to when they are far apart, where $U = 0$.

EXECUTE: $K_1 + U_1 = K_2 + U_2$; $K_1 = U_2 = 0$ so $K_2 = U_1$

$$U_1 = \frac{e^2}{4\pi\epsilon_0}\left(\frac{1}{r} + \frac{2}{r} + \frac{2}{r}\right) = \frac{1}{4\pi\epsilon_0}\frac{5e^2}{r}, \text{ with } r = 8.00 \times 10^{-10} \text{ m}$$

$U_1 = 1.44 \times 10^{-18} \text{ J} = 9.00 \text{ eV}$

EVALUATE: We found the total kinetic energy of the three charges when they are far apart, but our calculation doesn't tell us how this energy is shared between the particles.

23.13 IDENTIFY and SET UP: Apply conservation of energy to points A and B.

EXECUTE: $K_A + U_A = K_B + U_B$

$U = qV$, so $K_A + qV_A = K_B + qV_B$

$K_B = K_A + q(V_A - V_B) = 0.00250 \text{ J} + (-5.00 \times 10^{-6} \text{ C})(200 \text{ V} - 800 \text{ V}) = 0.00550 \text{ J}$

$v_B = \sqrt{2K_B/m} = 7.42 \text{ m/s}$

EVALUATE: It is faster at B; a negative charge gains speed when it moves to higher potential.

23.17 IDENTIFY: Apply the equation that preceeds Eq.(23.17): $W_{a \to b} = q' \int_a^b \vec{E} \cdot d\vec{l}$.

SET UP: Use coordinates where $+y$ is upward and $+x$ is to the right. Then $\vec{E} = E\hat{j}$ with $E = 4.00 \times 10^4$ N/C.

a)

$d\vec{l} = dx\hat{i}$

EXECUTE: $\vec{E} \cdot d\vec{l} = (E\hat{j}) \cdot (dx\hat{i}) = 0$ so $W_{a \to b} = q' \int_a^b \vec{E} \cdot d\vec{l} = 0$.

EVALUATE: The electric force on the positive charge is upward (in the direction of the electric field) and does no work for a horizontal displacement of the charge.

b) SET UP:

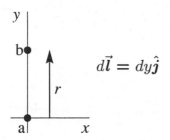

EXECUTE: $\vec{E} \cdot d\vec{l} = (E\hat{j}) \cdot (dy\hat{j}) = E \, dy$

$W_{a \to b} = q' \int_a^b \vec{E} \cdot d\vec{l} = q'E \int_a^b dy = q'E(y_b - y_a)$

$y_b - y_a = +0.670$ m, positive since the displacement is upward and we have taken $+y$ to be upward.

$W_{a \to b} = q'E(y_b - y_a) = (+28.0 \times 10^{-9} \text{ C})(1.00 \times 10^4 \text{ N/C})(+0.670 \text{ m})$
$= +7.50 \times 10^{-4}$ J.

EVALUATE: The electric force on the positive charge is upward so it does positive work for an upward displacement of the charge.

c) SET UP:

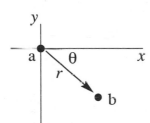

$y_a = 0$

$y_b = -r \sin \theta = -(2.60 \text{ m}) \sin 45° = -1.838$ m
The vertical component of the 2.60 m displacement is 1.838 m downward.

EXECUTE: $d\vec{l} = dx\hat{i} + dy\hat{j}$ (The displacement has both horizontal and vertical components.)

$\vec{E} \cdot d\vec{l} = (E\hat{j}) \cdot (dx\hat{i} + dy\hat{j}) = E \, dy$ (Only the vertical component of the displacement contributes to the work.)

$W_{a \to b} = q' \int_a^b \vec{E} \cdot d\vec{l} = q'E \int_a^b dy = q'E(y_b - y_a)$

$W_{a \to b} = q'E(y_b - y_a) = (+28.0 \times 10^{-9} \text{ C})(4.00 \times 10^4 \text{ N/C})(-1.838 \text{ m})$
$= -2.06 \times 10^{-3}$ J.

EVALUATE: The electric force on the positive charge is upward so it does negative work for a displacement of the charge that has a downward component.

23.21 IDENTIFY: $V = \dfrac{1}{4\pi\epsilon_0} \sum_i \dfrac{q_i}{r_i}$

SET UP:

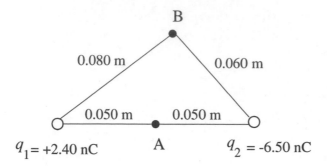

$q_1 = +2.40$ nC   A $q_2 = -6.50$ nC

EXECUTE:

a) $V_A = \dfrac{1}{4\pi\epsilon_0}\left(\dfrac{q_1}{r_{A1}} + \dfrac{q_2}{r_{A2}}\right)$

$V_A = (8.988 \times 10^9 \text{ N} \cdot \text{m}^2/\text{C}^2)\left(\dfrac{+2.40 \times 10^{-9} \text{ C}}{0.050 \text{ m}} + \dfrac{-6.50 \times 10^{-9} \text{ C}}{0.050 \text{ m}}\right) = -737 \text{ V}$

b) $V_B = \dfrac{1}{4\pi\epsilon_0}\left(\dfrac{q_1}{r_{B1}} + \dfrac{q_2}{r_{B2}}\right)$

$V_B = (8.988 \times 10^9 \text{ N} \cdot \text{m}^2/\text{C}^2)\left(\dfrac{+2.40 \times 10^{-9} \text{ C}}{0.080 \text{ m}} + \dfrac{-6.50 \times 10^{-9} \text{ C}}{0.060 \text{ m}}\right) = -704 \text{ V}$

c) **IDENTIFY** and **SET UP:** Use Eq.(23.13) and the results of parts (a) and (b) to calculate W.

EXECUTE: $W_{B \to A} = q'(V_B - V_A) = (2.50 \times 10^{-9} \text{ C})(-704 \text{ V} - (-737 \text{ V})) = +8.2 \times 10^{-8} \text{ J}$

EVALUATE: The electric force does positive work on the positive charge when it moves from higher potential (point B) to lower potential (point A).

23.29 a) **IDENTIFY** and **SET UP:** The direction of $\vec{E}$ is always from high potential to low potential so point b is at higher potential.

b) Apply Eq.(23.17) to relate $V_b - V_a$ to E.

EXECUTE: $V_b - V_a = -\int_a^b \vec{E} \cdot d\vec{l} = \int_a^b E\,dx = E(x_b - x_a)$.

$E = \dfrac{V_b - V_a}{x_b - x_a} = \dfrac{+240 \text{ V}}{0.90 \text{ m} - 0.60 \text{ m}} = 800 \text{ V/m}$

c) $W_{b \to a} = q(V_b - V_a) = (-0.200 \times 10^{-6} \text{ C})(+240 \text{ V}) = -4.80 \times 10^{-5} \text{ J}$.

EVALUATE: The electric force does negative work on a negative charge when the negative charge moves from high potential (point b) to low potential (point a).

23.31 **IDENTIFY** and **SET UP:** Apply conservation of energy, Eq.(23.3). Use Eq.(23.12) to express U interms of V.

a) EXECUTE: $K_1 + qV_1 = K_2 + qV_2$

$q(V_1 - V_2) = K_2 - K_1; \qquad q = -1.602 \times 10^{-19}$ C

$K_1 = \frac{1}{2} m_e v_1^2 = 4.099 \times 10^{-18}$ J; $\qquad K_2 = \frac{1}{2} m_e v_2^2 = 2.915 \times 10^{-17}$ J

$V_1 - V_2 = \dfrac{K_2 - K_1}{q} = -156$ V

EVALUATE: The electron gains kinetic energy when it moves to higher potential.

b) EXECUTE: Now $K_1 = 2.915 \times 10^{-17}$ J, $K_2 = 0$

$V_1 - V_2 = \dfrac{K_2 - K_1}{q} = +182$ V

EVALUATE: The electron loses kinetic energy when it moves to lower potential.

23.33 **a) IDENTIFY** and **SET UP:** The electric field on the ring's axis is calculated in Example 21.10. The force on the electron exerted by this field is given by Eq.(21.3).

EXECUTE: When the electron is on either side of the center of the ring, the ring exerts an attractive force directed toward the center of the ring. This restoring force produces oscillatory motion of the electron along the axis of the ring, with amplitude 30.0 cm. The force on the electron is _not_ of the form $F = -kx$ so the oscillatory motion is not simple harmonic motion.

b) IDENTIFY: Apply conservation of energy to the motion of the electron.

SET UP: $K_a + U_a = K_b + U_b$ with a at the initial position of the electron and b at the center of the ring. From Example 23.11, $V = \dfrac{1}{4\pi\epsilon_0} \dfrac{Q}{\sqrt{x^2 + R^2}}$, where R is the radius of the ring.

EXECUTE: $x_a = 30.0$ cm, $x_b = 0$.

$K_a = 0$ (released from rest), $K_b = \frac{1}{2}mv^2$

Thus $\frac{1}{2}mv^2 = U_a - U_b$

And $U = qV = -eV$ so $v = \sqrt{\dfrac{2e(V_b - V_a)}{m}}$.

$V_a = \dfrac{1}{4\pi\epsilon_0} \dfrac{Q}{\sqrt{x_a^2 + R^2}} = (8.988 \times 10^9 \text{ N} \cdot \text{m}^2/\text{C}^2) \dfrac{24.0 \times 10^{-9} \text{ C}}{\sqrt{(0.300 \text{ m})^2 + (0.150 \text{ m})^2}}$

$V_a = 643$ V

$$V_b = \frac{1}{4\pi\epsilon_0} \frac{Q}{\sqrt{x_b^2 + R^2}} = (8.988 \times 10^9 \ \text{N} \cdot \text{m}^2/\text{C}^2)\frac{24.0 \times 10^{-9} \ \text{C}}{0.150 \ \text{m}} = 1438 \ \text{V}$$

$$v = \sqrt{\frac{2e(V_b - V_a)}{m}} = \sqrt{\frac{2(1.602 \times 10^{-19} \ \text{C})(1438 \ \text{V} - 643 \ \text{V})}{9.109 \times 10^{-31} \ \text{kg}}} = 1.67 \times 10^7 \ \text{m/s}$$

EVALUATE: The positively charged ring attracts the negatively charged electron and accelerates it. The electron has its maximum speed at this point. When the electron moves past the center of the ring the force on it is opposite to its motion and it slows down.

23.35 IDENTIFY and **SET UP:** Use the result of Example 23.9 to relate the electric field between the plates to the potential difference between them and their separation. The force this field exerts on the particle is given by Eq.(21.3). Use the equation that precedes Eq.(23.17) to calculate the work.

EXECUTE:

a) From Example 23.9, $E = \dfrac{V_{ab}}{d} = \dfrac{360 \ \text{V}}{0.0450 \ \text{m}} = 8000 \ \text{V/m}$

b) $F = |q|E = (2.40 \times 10^{-9} \ \text{C})(8000 \ \text{V/m}) = +1.92 \times 10^{-5} \ \text{N}$

c)

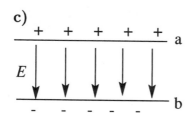

The plate with positive charge (plate a) is at higher potential. The electric field is directed from high potential toward low potential (or, $\vec{E}$ is from + charge toward − charge), so $\vec{E}$ points from a to b. Hence the force that $\vec{E}$ exerts on the positive charge is from a to b, so it does positive work.

$W = \int_a^b \vec{F} \cdot d\vec{l} = Fd$, where d is the separation between the plates.

$W = Fd = (1.92 \times 10^{-5} \ \text{N})(0.0450 \ \text{m}) = +8.64 \times 10^{-7} \ \text{J}$

d) $V_a - V_b = +360 \ \text{V}$ (plate a is at higher potential)

$\Delta U = U_b - U_a = q(V_b - V_a) = (2.40 \times 10^{-9} \ \text{C})(-360 \ \text{V}) = -8.64 \times 10^{-7} \ \text{J}.$

EVALUATE: We see that $W_{a \to b} = -(U_b - U_a) = U_a - U_b$.

23.37 IDENTIFY and **SET UP:** Use the result of Example 23.9 to relate the electric field between the plates to the potential difference between them and their separation. The force this field exerts on the particle is given by Eq.(21.3). Use the equation that precedes Eq.(23.17) to calculate the work. Example 23.9 also relates

E or V_{ab} to the surface charge density σ.

EXECUTE:

a) $E = \dfrac{V_{ab}}{d}$ gives that

$$d = \frac{V_{ab}}{E} = \frac{4.75 \times 10^3 \text{ V}}{3.00 \times 10^6 \text{ N/C}} = 1.58 \times 10^{-3} \text{ m} = 1.58 \text{ mm}.$$

b) $E = \sigma/\epsilon_o$

$\sigma = E\epsilon_0 = (3.00 \times 10^6 \text{ V/m})(8.854 \times 10^{-12} \text{ C}^2/\text{N} \cdot \text{m}^2) = 2.66 \times 10^{-5} \text{ C/m}^2.$

EVALUATE: As d becomes smaller, E becomes larger.

23.39 IDENTIFY and **SET UP:** Consider the electric field outside and inside the shell and use that to deduce the potential.

EXECUTE:

a) The electric field outside the shell is the same as for a point charge at the center of the shell, so the potential outside the shell is the same as for a point charge:

$$V = \frac{q}{4\pi\epsilon_0 r} \text{ for } r > R.$$

The electric field is zero inside the shell, so no work is done on a test charge as it moves inside the shell and all points inside the shell are at the same potential as the surface of the shell: $V = \dfrac{q}{4\pi\epsilon_0 R}$ for $r \leq R$.

b) $V = \dfrac{kq}{R}$ so $q = \dfrac{RV}{k} = \dfrac{(0.15 \text{ m})(-1200 \text{ V})}{k} = -20 \text{ nC}$

c) EVALUATE: No, the amount of charge on the sphere is very small. Since $U = qV$ the total amount of electric energy stored on the balloon is only (20 nC)(1200 V) = 2.4×10^{-5} J.

23.41 IDENTIFY and **SET UP:** Use Eq.(23.19) to calculate the components of $\vec{E}$.

EXECUTE: $V = Axy - Bx^2 + Cy$

a) $E_x = -\dfrac{\partial V}{\partial x} = -Ay + 2Bx$

$E_y = -\dfrac{\partial V}{\partial y} = -Ax - C$

$E_z = -\dfrac{\partial V}{\partial z} = 0$

b) $E = 0$ requires that $E_x = E_y = E_z = 0$.

$E_z = 0$ everywhere.

$E_y = 0$ at $x = -C/A$.

And E_x is also equal zero for this x, any value of z, and

$y = 2Bx/A = (2B/A)(-C/A) = -2BC/A^2$.

EVALUATE: V doesn't depend on z so $E_z = 0$ everywhere.

23.43 a) IDENTIFY and **SET UP:** V is independent of x and y so

$$E_x = -\frac{\partial V}{\partial x} = 0 \text{ and } E_y = -\frac{\partial V}{\partial y} = 0.$$

$$E_z = -\frac{\partial V}{\partial z}$$

EXECUTE:

For $z < 0$, $V = 0$ so $E_z = 0$. $E_x = E_y = E_z = 0$ so $E = 0$.

For $0 < z < d$, $V = Cz$ so $E_z = -C$. $\vec{E} = -C\hat{k}$.

For $z > d$, $V = Cd$ which is constant and has no z-dependence, so $E_z = 0$. $E_x = E_y = E_z = 0$ so $E = 0$.

b) EVALUATE: There is a uniform electric field in the $-z$-direction for z between 0 and d and zero field elsewhere. This is the field of two infinite sheets of charge parallel to the xy-plane, one with charge $+\sigma$ at $z = d$ and one with charge $-\sigma$ at $z = 0$.

For this charge distribution $E = \sigma/\epsilon_0$ between the plates, with direction from the positive plate toward the negative plate, and $E = 0$ outside the plates.

To have $E = C$ between the plates need $C = \sigma/\epsilon_0$, so $\sigma = C\epsilon_0$.

Problems

23.49 a) IDENTIFY: Apply the work-energy theorem, Eq.(6.6).

SET UP:

EXECUTE: $W_{\text{tot}} = \Delta K = K_b - K_a = K_b = 4.35 \times 10^{-5}$ J

The electric force F_E and the additional force F both do work, so that $W_{\text{tot}} =$

$W_{F_E} + W_F$.

$W_{F_E} = W_{\text{tot}} - W_F = 4.35 \times 10^{-5}\ \text{J} - 6.50 \times 10^{-5}\ \text{J} = -2.15 \times 10^{-5}\ \text{J}$

EVALUATE:

$$\overset{F_E}{\underset{\longleftarrow}{}} \quad \overset{q}{\bullet} \quad \overset{F}{\underset{\longrightarrow}{}}$$

The electric force is to the left (in the direction of the electric field since the particle has positive charge). The displacement is to the right, so the electric force does negative work. The additional force F is in the direction of the displacement, so it does positive work.

b) IDENTIFY and SET UP: For the work done by the electric force, $W_{a \to b} = q(V_a - V_b)$

EXECUTE: $V_a - V_b = \dfrac{W_{a \to b}}{q} = \dfrac{-2.15 \times 10^{-5}\ \text{J}}{7.60 \times 10^{-9}\ \text{C}} = -2.83 \times 10^3\ \text{V}$.

EVALUATE: The starting point (point a) is at 2.83×10^3 V lower potential than the ending point (point b). We know that $V_b > V_a$ because the electric field always points from high potential toward low potential.

c) IDENTIFY: Calculate E from $V_a - V_b$ and the separation d between the two points.

SET UP: Since the electric field is uniform and directed opposite to the displacement

$W_{a \to b} = -F_E d = -qEd$, where $d = 8.00$ cm is the displacement of the particle.

EXECUTE: $E = -\dfrac{W_{a \to b}}{qd} = -\dfrac{V_a - V_b}{d} = -\dfrac{-2.83 \times 10^3\ \text{V}}{0.0800\ \text{m}} = 3.54 \times 10^4\ \text{V/m}$.

EVALUATE: In part (a), W_{tot} is the total work done by both forces. In parts (b) and (c) $W_{a \to b}$ is the work done just by the electric force.

23.51 IDENTIFY and SET UP: Calculate the components of $\vec{E}$ from Eq.(23.19). Eq.(21.3) gives $\vec{F}$ from $\vec{E}$.

EXECUTE:

a) $V = Cx^{4/3}$

$C = V/x^{4/3} = 240\ \text{V}/(13.0 \times 10^{-3}\ \text{m})^{4/3} = 7.85 \times 10^4\ \text{V/m}^{4/3}$

b) $E_x = -\dfrac{\partial V}{\partial x} = -\dfrac{4}{3}Cx^{1/3} = -(1.05 \times 10^5\ \text{V/m}^{4/3})x^{1/3}$

The minus sign means that E_x is in the $-x$-direction, which says that $\vec{E}$ points from the positive anode toward the negative cathode.

c) $\vec{F} = q\vec{E}$ so $F_x = -eE_x = \frac{4}{3}eCx^{1/3}$

Halfway between the electrodes means $x = 6.50 \times 10^{-3}$ m.

$F_x = \frac{4}{3}(1.602 \times 10^{-19} \text{ C})(7.85 \times 10^4 \text{ V/m}^{4/3})(6.50 \times 10^{-3} \text{ m})^{1/3} = 3.13 \times 10^{-15}$ N

F_x is positive, so the force is directed toward the positive anode.

EVALUATE: V depends only on x, so $E_y = E_z = 0$. $\vec{E}$ is directed from high potential (anode) to low potential (cathode). The electron has negative charge, so the force on it is directed opposite to the electric field.

23.55 a) IDENTIFY: Use Eq.(23.10) for the electron and each proton.

SET UP:

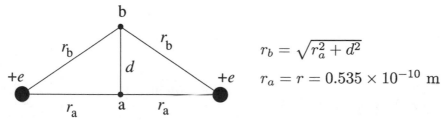

+e   - e   +e

●————————●————————● $r = (1.07 \times 10^{-10} \text{ m})/2 = 0.535 \times 10^{-10}$ m

    r r

EXECUTE: The potential energy of interaction of the electron with each proton is

$$U = \frac{1}{4\pi\epsilon_0}\frac{(-e^2)}{r}, \text{ so the total potential energy is}$$

$$U = -\frac{2e^2}{4\pi\epsilon_0 r} = -\frac{2(8.988 \times 10^9 \text{ N}\cdot\text{m}^2/\text{C}^2)(1.60 \times 10^{-19} \text{ C})^2}{0.535 \times 10^{-10} \text{ m}} = -8.60 \times 10^{-18} \text{ J}$$

$U = -8.60 \times 10^{-18} \text{ J}(1 \text{ eV}/1.602 \times 10^{-19} \text{ J}) = -53.7$ eV

EVALUATE: The electron and proton have charges of opposite signs, so the potential energy of the system is negative.

b) IDENTIFY and SET UP:

$r_b = \sqrt{r_a^2 + d^2}$

$r_a = r = 0.535 \times 10^{-10}$ m

Apply $K_a + U_a + W_{\text{other}} = K_b + U_b$ with point a midway between the protons and point b where the electron instantaneously has $v = 0$ (at its maximum displacement d from point a).

EXECUTE: Only the Coulomb force does work, so $W_{\text{other}} = 0$.

$U_a = -8.60 \times 10^{-18}$ J (from part (a)

$K_a = \frac{1}{2}mv^2 = \frac{1}{2}(9.109 \times 10^{-31} \text{ kg})(1.50 \times 10^6 \text{ m/s})^2 = 1.025 \times 10^{-18}$ J

$K_b = 0$

$U_b = -2ke^2/r_b$

Then $U_b = K_a + U_a - K_b = 1.025 \times 10^{-18}$ J $- 8.60 \times 10^{-18}$ J $=$ -7.575×10^{-18} J.

$$r_b = -\frac{2ke^2}{U_b} = -\frac{2(8.988 \times 10^9 \text{ N} \cdot \text{m}^2/\text{C}^2)(1.60 \times 10^{-19} \text{ C})^2}{-7.575 \times 10^{-18} \text{ J}} = 6.075 \times 10^{-11} \text{ m}$$

Then $d = \sqrt{r_b^2 - r_a^2} = \sqrt{(6.075 \times 10^{-11} \text{ m})^2 - (5.35 \times 10^{-11} \text{ m})^2} = 2.88 \times 10^{-11}$ m.

EVALUATE: The force on the electron pulls it back toward the midpoint. The transverse distance the electron moves is about 0.27 times the separation of the protons.

23.57 a) IDENTIFY: The potential at any point is the sum of the potentials due to each of the two charged conductors.

SET UP: From Example 23.10, for a conducting cylinder with charge per unit length λ the potential outside the cylinder is given by $V = (\lambda/2\pi\epsilon_0) \ln(r_0/r)$ where r is the distance from the cylinder axis and r_0 is the distance from the axis for which we take $V = 0$. Inside the cylinder the potential has the same value as on the cylinder surface. The electric field is the same for a solid conducting cylinder or for a hollow conducting tube so this expression for V applies to both. This problem says to take $r_0 = b$.

EXECUTE: For the hollow tube of radius b and charge per unit length $-\lambda$: outside $V = -(\lambda/2\pi\epsilon_0)\ln(b/r)$;   inside $V = 0$ since $V = 0$ at $r = b$.

For the metal cylinder of radius a and charge per unit length λ: outside $V = (\lambda/2\pi\epsilon_0)\ln(b/r)$, inside $V = (\lambda/2\pi\epsilon_0)\ln(b/a)$, the value at $r = a$.

(i) $r < a$; inside both $V = (\lambda/2\pi\epsilon_0)\ln(b/a)$

(ii) $a < r < b$; outside cylinder, inside tube $V = (\lambda/2\pi\epsilon_0)\ln(b/r)$

(iii) $r > b$; outside both The potentials are equal in magnitude and opposite in sign so $V = 0$.

b) For $r = a$, $V_a = (\lambda/2\pi\epsilon_0)\ln(b/a)$.
For $r = b$, $V_b = 0$.
Thus $V_{ab} = V_a - V_b = (\lambda/2\pi\epsilon_0)\ln(b/a)$.

c) IDENTIFY and **SET UP:** Use Eq.(23.23) to calculate E.

EXECUTE: $E = -\dfrac{\partial V}{\partial r} = -\dfrac{\lambda}{2\pi\epsilon_0}\dfrac{\partial}{\partial r}\ln\left(\dfrac{b}{r}\right) = -\dfrac{\lambda}{2\pi\epsilon_0}\left(\dfrac{r}{b}\right)\left(-\dfrac{b}{r^2}\right) = \dfrac{V_{ab}}{\ln(b/a)}\dfrac{1}{r}$.

d) The electric field between the cylinders is due only to the inner cylinder, so V_{ab} is not changed, $V_{ab} = (\lambda/2\pi\epsilon_0)\ln(b/a)$.

EVALUATE: The electric field is not uniform between the cylinders, so $V_{ab} \neq E(b-a)$.

23.59 **IDENTIFY** and **SET UP:** Use Eq.(21.3) to calculate $\vec{F}$ and then $\vec{F} = m\vec{a}$ gives $\vec{a}$.

EXECUTE:

a) $\vec{F}_E = q\vec{E}$. Since $q = -e$ is negative $\vec{F}_E$ and $\vec{E}$ are in opposite directions; $\vec{E}$ is upward so $\vec{F}_E$ is downward. The magnitude of F_E is

$F_E = |q|E = eE = (1.602 \times 10^{-19}\text{ C})(1.10 \times 10^3\text{ N/C}) = 1.76 \times 10^{-16}\text{ N}$.

b) Calculate the acceleration of the electron produced by the electric force:

$$a = \frac{F}{m} = \frac{1.76 \times 10^{-16}\text{ N}}{9.109 \times 10^{-31}\text{ kg}} = 1.93 \times 10^{14}\text{ m/s}^2$$

EVALUATE: This is much larger than $g = 9.80\text{ m/s}^2$, so the gravity force on the electron can be neglected. $\vec{F}_E$ is downward, so $\vec{a}$ is downward.

c) IDENTIFY and **SET UP:** The acceleration is constant and downward, so the motion is like that of a projectile. Use the horizontal motion to find the time and then use the time to find the vertical displacement.

EXECUTE:

x-component

$v_{0x} = 6.50 \times 10^6\text{ m/s};\quad a_x = 0;\quad x - x_0 = 0.060\text{ m};\quad t = ?$

$x - x_0 = v_{0x}t + \frac{1}{2}a_x t^2$ and the a_x term is zero, so

$$t = \frac{x - x_0}{v_{0x}} = \frac{0.060\text{ m}}{6.50 \times 10^6\text{ m/s}} = 9.231 \times 10^{-9}\text{ s}$$

y-component

$v_{0y} = 0;\quad a_y = 1.93 \times 10^{14}\text{ m/s}^2;\quad t = 9.231 \times 10^{-9}\text{ m/s};\quad y - y_0 = ?$

$y - y_0 = v_{0y}t + \frac{1}{2}a_y t^2$

$y - y_0 == \frac{1}{2}(1.93 \times 10^{14}\text{ m/s}^2)(9.231 \times 10^{-9}\text{ s})^2 = 0.00822\text{ m} = 0.822\text{ cm}$

d)

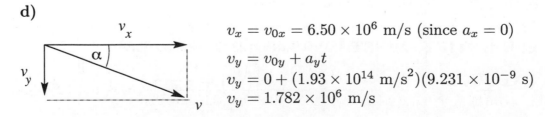

$v_x = v_{0x} = 6.50 \times 10^6\text{ m/s}$ (since $a_x = 0$)

$v_y = v_{0y} + a_y t$

$v_y = 0 + (1.93 \times 10^{14}\text{ m/s}^2)(9.231 \times 10^{-9}\text{ s})$

$v_y = 1.782 \times 10^6\text{ m/s}$

$$\tan \alpha = \frac{v_y}{v_x} = \frac{1.782 \times 10^6 \text{ m/s}}{6.50 \times 10^6 \text{ m/s}} = 0.2742 \text{ so } \alpha = 15.3°.$$

EVALUATE: The greater the electric field or the smaller the initial speed the greater the downward deflection.

e) IDENTIFY and **SET UP:** Consider the motion of the electron after it leaves the region between the plates. Outside the plates there is no electric field, so $a = 0$. (Gravity can still be neglected since the electron is traveling at such high speed and the times are small.) Use the horizontal motion to find the time it takes the electron to travel 0.120 m horizontally to the screen. From this time find the distance downward that the electron travels.

EXECUTE:

x-component

$v_{0x} = 6.50 \times 10^6$ m/s; $a_x = 0$; $x - x_0 = 0.120$ m; $t - ?$

$x - x_0 = v_{0x}t + \frac{1}{2}a_x t^2$ and the a_x term is zero, so

$$t = \frac{x - x_0}{v_{0x}} = \frac{0.120 \text{ m}}{6.50 \times 10^6 \text{ m/s}} = 1.846 \times 10^{-8} \text{ s}$$

y-component

$v_{0y} = 1.782 \times 10^6$ m/s (from part (b)); $a_y = 0$; $t = 1.846 \times 10^{-8}$ m/s;

$y - y_0 = ?$

$y - y_0 = v_{0y}t + \frac{1}{2}a_y t^2 = (1.782 \times 10^6 \text{ m/s})(1.846 \times 10^{-8} \text{ s}) = 0.0329 \text{ m} = 3.29 \text{ cm}$

EVALUATE: The electron travels downward a distance 0.822 cm while it is between the plates and a distance 3.29 cm while traveling from the edge of the plates to the screen. The total downward deflection is 0.822 cm + 3.29 cm = 4.11 cm.

The horizontal distance between the plates is half the horizontal distance the electron travels after it leaves the plates. And the vertical velocity of the electron increases as it travels between the plates, so it makes sense for it to have greater downward displacement during the motion after it leaves the plates.

23.61 a) IDENTIFY and **SET UP:** Problem 23.57 derived that $E = \dfrac{V_{ab}}{\ln(b/a)} \dfrac{1}{r}$, where a is the radius of the inner cylinder (wire) and b is the radius of the outer hollow cylinder. The potential difference between the two cylinders is V_{ab}. Use this expression to calculate E at the specified r

EXECUTE: Midway between the wire and the cylinder wall is at a radius of $r = (a+b)/2 = (90.0 \times 10^{-6} \text{ m} + 0.140 \text{ m})/2 = 0.07004 \text{ m}.$

$$E = \frac{V_{ab}}{\ln(b/a)} \frac{1}{r} = \frac{50.0 \times 10^3 \text{ V}}{\ln(0.140 \text{ m}/90.0 \times 10^{-6} \text{ m})(0.07004 \text{ m})} = 9.71 \times 10^4 \text{ V/m}$$

b) **IDENTIFY** and **SET UP:** The electric force is given by Eq.(21.3). Set this equal to ten times the weight of the particle and solve for $|q|$, the magnitude of the charge on the particle.

EXECUTE: $F_E = 10mg$

$$|q|E = 10mg \text{ and } |q| = \frac{10mg}{E} = \frac{10(30.0 \times 10^{-9} \text{ kg})(9.80 \text{ m/s}^2)}{9.71 \times 10^4 \text{ V/m}} = 3.03 \times 10^{-11} \text{ C}$$

EVALUATE: It requires only this modest net charge for the electric force to be much larger than the weight.

23.63 a) **IDENTIFY:** Calculate the potential due to each thin ring and integrate over the disk to find the potential. V is a scalar so no components are involved.

SET UP: Consider a thin ring of radius y and width dy. The ring has area $2\pi y \, dy$ so the charge on the ring is $dq = \sigma(2\pi y \, dy)$.

EXECUTE: The result of Example 23.11 then says that the potential due to this thin ring at the point on the axis at a distance x from the ring is

$$dV = \frac{1}{4\pi\epsilon_0} \frac{dq}{\sqrt{x^2 + y^2}} = \frac{2\pi\sigma}{4\pi\epsilon_0} \frac{y \, dy}{\sqrt{x^2 + y^2}}$$

$$V = \int dV = \frac{\sigma}{2\epsilon_0} \int_0^R \frac{y \, dy}{\sqrt{x^2 + y^2}} = \frac{\sigma}{2\epsilon_0} \left[\sqrt{x^2 + y^2} \right]_0^R = \frac{\sigma}{2\epsilon_0} (\sqrt{x^2 + R^2} - x)$$

EVALUATE: For $x \gg R$ this result should reduce to the potential of a point charge with $Q = \sigma\pi R^2$.

$\sqrt{x^2 + R^2} = x(1 + R^2/x^2)^{1/2} \approx x(1 + R^2/2x^2)$ so $\sqrt{x^2 + R^2} - x \approx R^2/2x$

Then $V \approx \dfrac{\sigma}{2\epsilon_o} \dfrac{R^2}{2x} = \dfrac{\sigma\pi R^2}{4\pi\epsilon_0 x} = \dfrac{Q}{4\pi\epsilon_0 x}$, as expected.

b) **IDENTIFY** and **SET UP:** Use Eq.(23.19) to calculate E_x.

EXECUTE: $E_x = -\dfrac{\partial V}{\partial x} = -\dfrac{\sigma}{2\epsilon_0} \left(\dfrac{x}{\sqrt{x^2 + R^2}} - 1 \right) = \dfrac{\sigma x}{2\epsilon_0} \left(\dfrac{1}{x} - \dfrac{1}{\sqrt{x^2 + R^2}} \right)$.

EVALUATE: Our result agrees with Eq.(21.11) in Example 21.12.

23.65 a) **IDENTIFY:** Use $V_a - V_b = \int_a^b \vec{E} \cdot d\vec{l}$.

SET UP: From Problem 22.48, $E(r) = \dfrac{\lambda r}{2\pi\epsilon_0 R^2}$ for $r \leq R$ (inside the cylindrical charge distribution) and

$E(r) = \dfrac{\lambda}{2\pi\epsilon_0 r}$ for $r \geq R$. Let $V = 0$ at $r = R$ (at the surface of the cylinder).

EXECUTE: $r > R$

Take point a to be at R and point b to be at r, where $r > R$. Let $d\vec{l} = d\vec{r}$. $\vec{E}$ and $d\vec{r}$ are both radially outward, so $\vec{E} \cdot d\vec{r} = E\,dr$. Thus $V_R - V_r = \int_R^r E\,dr$. Then $V_R = 0$ gives $V_r = -\int_R^r E\,dr$. In this interval $(r > R)$, $E(r) = \lambda/2\pi\epsilon_0 r$, so

$$V_r = -\int_R^r \frac{\lambda}{2\pi\epsilon_0 r}\,dr = -\frac{\lambda}{2\pi\epsilon_o}\int_R^r \frac{dr}{r} = -\frac{\lambda}{2\pi\epsilon_0}\ln\left(\frac{r}{R}\right).$$

EVALUATE: This expression gives $V_r = 0$ when $r = R$ and the potential decreases (becomes a negative number of larger magnitude) with increasing distance from the cylinder.

EXECUTE: $r < R$

Take point a at r, where $r < R$, and point b at R. $\vec{E} \cdot d\vec{r} = E\,dr$ as before. Thus $V_r - V_R = \int_r^R E\,dr$. Then $V_R = 0$ then gives $V_r = \int_r^R E\,dr$. In this interval $(r < R)$, $E(r) = \lambda r/2\pi\epsilon_0 R^2$, so

$$V_r = \int_r^R \frac{\lambda r}{2\pi\epsilon_0 R^2}\,dr = \frac{\lambda}{2\pi\epsilon_o R^2}\int_r^R r\,dr = \frac{\lambda}{2\pi\epsilon_0 R^2}\left(\frac{R^2}{2} - \frac{r^2}{2}\right).$$

$$V_r = \frac{\lambda}{4\pi\epsilon_0}\left(1 - \left(\frac{r}{R}\right)^2\right).$$

EVALUATE: This expression also gives $V_r = 0$ when $r = R$. The potential is $\lambda/4\pi\epsilon_0$ at $r = 0$ and decreases with increasing r.

b) EXECUTE:

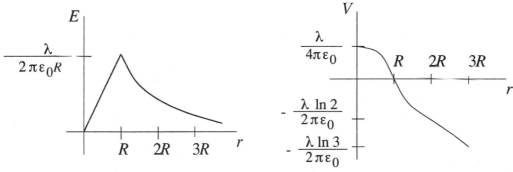

EVALUATE: E at any r is the negative of the slope of $V(r)$ at that r (Eq.23.23).

23.69 IDENTIFY and **SET UP:** Use Eq.(23.17) to calculate the potential differences. Problem 22.30 gives that $\vec{E} = (-5.00 \text{ N/C} \cdot \text{m})x\hat{i} + (3.00 \text{ N/C} \cdot \text{m})z\hat{k}$

EXECUTE:

a) S_1 and S_3 are parallel to the xz-plane; S_1 is at $y_1 = 0$ and S_3 is at $y_3 = L$.

$$V_1 - V_3 = \int_1^3 \vec{E} \cdot d\vec{l}; \quad dl = dy\hat{j} \quad \text{so } \vec{E} \cdot d\vec{l} = 0 \text{ so } V_1 - V_3 = 0.$$

b) S_2 and S_4 are parallel to the xy-plane; S_4 is at $z_4 = 0$ and S_2 is at $z_2 = L$.

$$V_4 - V_2 = \int_4^2 \vec{E} \cdot d\vec{l}; \quad dl = dz\hat{k} \quad \text{so} \quad \vec{E} \cdot d\vec{l} = (3.00 \text{ N/C} \cdot \text{m})z \, dz.$$

$$V_4 - V_2 = (3.00 \text{ N/C} \cdot \text{m}) \int_{z_4}^{z_2} z \, dz = (3.00 \text{ N/C} \cdot \text{m})(\tfrac{1}{2}z^2|_0^L) = (1.50 \text{ N/C} \cdot \text{m})L^2$$

$V_4 - V_2 = (1.50 \text{ N/C} \cdot \text{m})(0.300 \text{ m})^2 = 0.135 \text{ V}; \, V_4 - V_2$ is positive.

Thus S_4 is at higher potential. ($\vec{E}$ points from high potential toward low potential.)

c) S_5 and S_6 are parallel to the yz-plane; S_6 is at $x_6 = 0$ and S_5 is at $x_5 = L$.

$$V_6 - V_5 = \int_6^5 \vec{E} \cdot d\vec{l}; \quad dl = dx\hat{i} \quad \text{so} \quad \vec{E} \cdot d\vec{l} = (-5.00 \text{ N/C} \cdot \text{m})x \, dx.$$

$$V_6 - V_5 = (-5.00 \text{ N/C·m}) \int_{x_6}^{x_5} x \, dx = (-5.00 \text{ N/C·m})(\tfrac{1}{2}x^2|_0^L) = (-2.50 \text{ N/C·m})L^2$$

$V_6 - V_5 = (-2.50 \text{ N/C} \cdot \text{m})(0.300 \text{ m})^2 = -0.225 \text{ V}; \, V_6 - V_5$ is negative so S_5 is at higher potential. ($\vec{E}$ points from high potential toward low potential.)

EVALUATE: In each case where V_{ab} is nonzero, $\vec{E}$ is in the direction of decreasing potential.

23.75 IDENTIFY: Use Eq.(23.17) to calculate V_{ab}.

SET UP: From Problem 22.37, for $R \le r \le 2R$ (between the sphere and the shell) $E = Q/4\pi\epsilon_0 r^2$

Take a at R and b at $2R$.

EXECUTE: $V_{ab} = V_a - V_b = \displaystyle\int_R^{2R} E \, dr = \frac{Q}{4\pi\epsilon_0} \int_R^{2R} \frac{dr}{r^2} = \frac{Q}{4\pi\epsilon_0}\left[-\frac{1}{r}\right]_R^{2R} = \frac{Q}{4\pi\epsilon_0}\left(\frac{1}{R} - \frac{1}{2R}\right)$

$$V_{ab} = \frac{Q}{8\pi\epsilon_0 R}$$

EVALUATE: The electric field is radially outward and points in the direction of decreasing potential, so the sphere is at higher potential than the shell.

23.79 IDENTIFY: Slice the rod into thin slices and use Eq.(23.14) to calculate the potential due to each slice. Integrate over the length of the rod to find the total potential at each point.

a) SET UP:

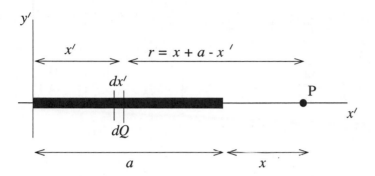

Use coordinates with the origin at the left-hand end of the rod and one axis along the rod. Call the axes x' and y' so as not to confuse them with the distance x given in the problem.

EXECUTE: Slice the charged rod up into thin slices of width dx'. Each slice has charge $dQ = Q(dx'/a)$ and a distance $r = x + a - x'$ from point P. The potential at P due to the small slice dQ is

$$dV = \frac{1}{4\pi\epsilon_0}\left(\frac{dQ}{r}\right) = \frac{1}{4\pi\epsilon_0}\frac{Q}{a}\left(\frac{dx'}{x+a-x'}\right).$$

Compute the total V at P due to the entire rod by integrating dV over the length of the rod ($x' = 0$ to $x' = a$):

$$V = \int dV = \frac{Q}{4\pi\epsilon_0 a}\int_0^a \frac{dx'}{(x+a-x')} = \frac{Q}{4\pi\epsilon_0 a}\left[-\ln(x+a-x')\right]_0^a =$$

$$\frac{Q}{4\pi\epsilon_0 a}\ln\left(\frac{x+a}{x}\right).$$

EVALUATE: As $x \to \infty$, $V \to \dfrac{Q}{4\pi\epsilon_0 a}\ln\left(\dfrac{x}{x}\right) = 0.$

b) SET UP:

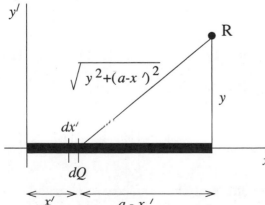

$dQ = (Q/a)dx'$ as in part (a)

Each slice dQ is a distance $r = \sqrt{y^2 + (a - x')^2}$ from point R.

EXECUTE: The potential dV at R due to the small slice dQ is

$$dV = \frac{1}{4\pi\epsilon_0}\left(\frac{dQ}{r}\right) = \frac{1}{4\pi\epsilon_0}\frac{Q}{a}\frac{dx'}{\sqrt{y^2 + (a - x')^2}}.$$

$$V = \int dV = \frac{Q}{4\pi\epsilon_0 a}\int_0^a \frac{dx'}{\sqrt{y^2 + (a - x')^2}}.$$

In the integral make the change of variable $u = a - x'$; $du = -dx'$

$$V = -\frac{Q}{4\pi\epsilon_0 a}\int_a^0 \frac{du}{\sqrt{y^2 + u^2}} = -\frac{Q}{4\pi\epsilon_0 a}\left[\ln(u + \sqrt{y^2 + u^2}\right]_a^0$$

$$V = -\frac{Q}{4\pi\epsilon_0 a}[\ln y - \ln(a + \sqrt{y^2 + a^2})] = \frac{Q}{4\pi\epsilon_0 a}\left[\ln\left(\frac{a + \sqrt{a^2 + y^2}}{y}\right)\right].$$

(The expression for the integral was found in appendix B.)

EVALUATE: As $y \to \infty$, $V \to \dfrac{Q}{4\pi\epsilon_0 a}\ln\left(\dfrac{y}{y}\right) = 0$.

c) **SET UP:** <u>part (a)</u>: $V = \dfrac{Q}{4\pi\epsilon_0 a}\ln\left(\dfrac{x + a}{x}\right) = \dfrac{Q}{4\pi\epsilon_0 a}\ln\left(1 + \dfrac{a}{x}\right)$.

From Appendix B, $\ln(1 + u) = u - u^2/2\ldots$, so $\ln(1 + a/x) = a/x - a^2/2x^2$ and this becomes a/x when x is large.

EXECUTE: Thus $V \to \dfrac{Q}{4\pi\epsilon_0 a}\left(\dfrac{a}{x}\right) = \dfrac{Q}{4\pi\epsilon_0 x}$. For large x, V becomes the potential of a point charge.

<u>part (b)</u>: $V = \dfrac{Q}{4\pi\epsilon_0 a}\left[\ln\left(\dfrac{a + \sqrt{a^2 + y^2}}{y}\right)\right] = \dfrac{Q}{4\pi\epsilon_0 a}\ln\left(\dfrac{a}{y} + \sqrt{1 + \dfrac{a^2}{y^2}}\right)$.

From the binomial theorem (Appendix B), $\sqrt{1 + a^2/y^2} = (1 + a^2/y^2)^{1/2} = 1 + a^2/2y^2 + \ldots$

Thus $a/y + \sqrt{1 + a^2/y^2} \to 1 + a/y + a^2/2y^2 + \ldots \to 1 + a/y$. And then using $\ln(1 + u) \approx u$ gives

$$V \to \frac{Q}{4\pi\epsilon_0 a}\ln(1 + a/y) \to \frac{Q}{4\pi\epsilon_0 a}\left(\frac{a}{y}\right) = \frac{Q}{4\pi\epsilon_0 y}.$$

EVALUATE: For large y, V becomes the potential of a point charge.

23.81 a) **IDENTIFY** and **SET UP:** The potential at the surface of a charged conducting sphere is given by Example 23.8: $V = \dfrac{1}{4\pi\epsilon_0}\dfrac{q}{R}$. For spheres A and B this gives

$$V_A = \frac{Q_A}{4\pi\epsilon_0 R_A} \text{ and } V_B = \frac{Q_B}{4\pi\epsilon_0 R_B}.$$

EXECUTE: $V_A = V_B$ gives $Q_A/4\pi\epsilon_0 R_A = Q_B/4\pi\epsilon_0 R_B$ and $Q_B/Q_A = R_B/R_A$. And then $R_A = 3R_B$ implies $Q_B/Q_A = 1/3$.

b) IDENTIFY and **SET UP:** The electric field at the surface of a charged conducting sphere is given in Example 22.5:

$$E = \frac{1}{4\pi\epsilon_0}\frac{|q|}{R^2}.$$

EXECUTE: For spheres A and B this gives

$$E_A = \frac{|Q_A|}{4\pi\epsilon_0 R_A^2} \text{ and } E_B = \frac{|Q_B|}{4\pi\epsilon_0 R_B^2}.$$

$$\frac{E_B}{E_A} = \left(\frac{|Q_B|}{4\pi\epsilon_0 R_B^2}\right)\left(\frac{4\pi\epsilon_0 R_A^2}{|Q_A|}\right) = |Q_B/Q_A|(R_A/R_B)^2 = (1/3)(3)^2 = 3.$$

EVALUATE: The sphere with the larger radius needs more net charge to produce the same potential. We can write $E = V/R$ for a sphere, so with equal potentials the sphere with the smaller R has the larger V.

23.83 IDENTIFY and **SET UP:** The potential at the surface is given by Example 23.8 and the electric field at the surface is given by Example 22.5. The charge initially on sphere 1 spreads between the two spheres such as to bring them to the same potential.

EXECUTE:

a) $E_1 = \frac{1}{4\pi\epsilon_0}\frac{Q_1}{R_1^2}, \quad V_1 = \frac{1}{4\pi\epsilon_0}\frac{Q_1}{R_1} = R_1 E_1$

b) Two conditions must be met:

1) Let q_1 and q_2 be the final charges on each sphere. Then $q_1 + q_2 = Q_1$ (charge conservation)

2) Let V_1 and V_2 be the final potentials of each sphere. All points of a conductor are at the same potential, so $V_1 = V_2$.

$V_1 = V_2$ requires that $\frac{1}{4\pi\epsilon_0}\frac{q_1}{R_1} = \frac{1}{4\pi\epsilon_0}\frac{q_2}{R_2}$ and then $q_1/R_1 = q_2/R_2$

$q_1 R_2 = q_2 R_1 = (Q_1 - q_1)R_1$

This gives $q_1 = (R_1/[R_1 + R_2])Q_1$ and $q_2 = Q_1 - q_1 = Q_1(1 - R_1/[R_1 + R_2]) = Q_1(R_2/[R_1 + R_2])$

c) $V_1 = \frac{1}{4\pi\epsilon_0}\frac{q_1}{R_1} = \frac{Q_1}{4\pi\epsilon_0(R_1 + R_2)}$ and

$$V_2 = \frac{1}{4\pi\epsilon_0}\frac{q_2}{R_2} = \frac{Q_1}{4\pi\epsilon_0(R_1+R_2)}, \text{ which equals } V_1 \text{ as it should.}$$

d) $E_1 = \dfrac{V_1}{R_1} = \dfrac{Q_1}{4\pi\epsilon_0 R_1(R_1+R_2)}$

$E_2 = \dfrac{V_2}{R_2} = \dfrac{Q_1}{4\pi\epsilon_0 R_2(R_1+R_2)}$

EVALUATE: Part (a) says $q_2 = q_1(R_2/R_1)$. The sphere with the larger radius needs more charge to produce the same potential at its surface. When $R_1 = R_2$, $q_1 = q_2 = Q_1/2$. The sphere with the larger radius has the smaller electric field at its surface.

CHAPTER 24
CAPACITANCE AND DIELECTRICS

Exercises 3, 11, 13, 15, 17, 23, 25, 29, 35, 37, 39, 41, 45, 49
Problems 51, 57, 59, 61, 63, 65, 67, 69, 71

Exercises

24.3 **IDENTIFY** and **SET UP:** It is a parallel-plate air capacitor, so we can apply the equations of Sections 24.1.

EXECUTE:

a) $C = \dfrac{Q}{V_{ab}}$ so $V_{ab} = \dfrac{Q}{C} = \dfrac{0.148 \times 10^{-6} \text{ C}}{245 \times 10^{-12} \text{ F}} = 604 \text{ V}$

b) $C = \dfrac{\epsilon_0 A}{d}$ so

$A = \dfrac{Cd}{\epsilon_0} = \dfrac{(245 \times 10^{-12} \text{ F})(0.328 \times 10^{-3} \text{ m})}{8.854 \times 10^{-12} \text{ C}^2/\text{N} \cdot \text{m}^2} = 9.08 \times 10^{-3} \text{ m}^2 = 90.8 \text{ cm}^2$

c) $V_{ab} = Ed$ so $E = \dfrac{V_{ab}}{d} = \dfrac{604 \text{ V}}{0.328 \times 10^{-3} \text{ m}} = 1.84 \times 10^{6} \text{ V/m}$

d) $E = \dfrac{\sigma}{\epsilon_0}$ so

$\sigma = E\epsilon_0 = (1.84 \times 10^6 \text{ V/m})(8.854 \times 10^{-12} \text{ C}^2/\text{N} \cdot \text{m}^2) = 1.63 \times 10^{-5} \text{ C/m}^2$

EVALUATE: We could also calculate σ directly as Q/A.

$\sigma = \dfrac{Q}{A} = \dfrac{0.148 \times 10^{-6} \text{ C}}{9.08 \times 10^{-3} \text{ m}^2} = 1.63 \times 10^{-5} \text{ C/m}^2$, which checks.

24.11 **IDENTIFY** and **SET UP:** Use the expression for C/L derived in Example 24.4. Then use Eq.(24.1) to calculate Q.

EXECUTE:

a) From Example 24.4, $\dfrac{C}{L} = \dfrac{2\pi\epsilon_0}{\ln(r_b/r_a)}$

$\dfrac{C}{L} = \dfrac{2\pi(8.854 \times 10^{-12} \text{ C}^2/\text{N} \cdot \text{m}^2)}{\ln(3.5 \text{ mm}/1.5 \text{ mm})} = 6.57 \times 10^{-11} \text{ F/m} = 66 \text{ pF/m}$

b) $C = (6.57 \times 10^{-11} \text{ F/m})(2.8 \text{ m}) = 1.84 \times 10^{-10} \text{ F}$.
$Q = CV = (1.84 \times 10^{-10} \text{ F})(350 \times 10^{-3} \text{ V}) = 6.4 \times 10^{-11} \text{ C} = 64 \text{ pC}$

The conductor at higher potential has the positive charge, so there is +64 pC on the inner conductor and −64 pC on the outer conductor.

EVALUATE: C depends only on the dimensions of the capacitor. Q and V are proportional.

24.13 **IDENTIFY** and **SET UP:** Use the expressions derived in Example 24.3.
EXECUTE:

a) $C = 4\pi\epsilon_0 \dfrac{r_a r_b}{r_b - r_a}$

$C = 4\pi(8.854 \times 10^{-12} \text{ C}^2/\text{N}\cdot\text{m}^2)\left(\dfrac{(0.148 \text{ m})(0.125 \text{ m})}{0.148 \text{ m} - 0.125 \text{ m}}\right) = 8.95 \times 10^{-11}$ F = 89.5 pF

b) $E = Q/4\pi\epsilon_0 r^2$ between the spheres.

$C = Q/V$ so $Q = CV = (89.5 \times 10^{-12} \text{ F})(120 \text{ V}) = 1.074 \times 10^{-8}$ C

$E = Q/4\pi\epsilon_0 r^2 = (8.988 \times 10^9 \text{ N}\cdot\text{m}^2/\text{C}^2)(1.074 \times 10^{-8} \text{ C})/r^2 = (96.53 \text{ N}\cdot\text{m}^2/\text{C})/r^2$

For $r = 0.126$ m, $E = \dfrac{96.53 \text{ N}\cdot\text{m}^2/\text{C}}{(0.126 \text{ m})^2} = 6.08 \times 10^3$ V/m

c) For $r = 0.147$ m, $E = \dfrac{96.53 \text{ N}\cdot\text{m}^2/\text{C}}{(0.147 \text{ m})^2} = 4.47 \times 10^3$ V/m

d) **EVALUATE:** No, the results of parts (b) and (c) show that E is not uniform in the region between the spheres.

24.15 **IDENTIFY:** Replace series and parallel combinations of capacitors by their equivalents. In each equivalent network apply the rules for Q and V for capacitors in series and parallel; start with the simplest network and work back to the original circuit.

SET UP: Do parts (a) and (b) together.

$C_1 = C_2 = C_3 = C_4 = 4.00 \ \mu\text{F}$

$V_{ab} = 28.0$ V

EXECUTE:
Simplify the circuit by replacing the capacitor combinations by their equivalents:

$$\frac{1}{C_{12}} = \frac{1}{C_1} + \frac{1}{C_2}$$

$$C_{12} = \frac{C_1 C_2}{C_1 + C_2} = \frac{(4.00 \times 10^{-6} \text{ F})(4.00 \times 10^{-6} \text{ F})}{4.00 \times 10^{-6} \text{ F} + 4.00 \times 10^{-6} \text{ F}} = 2.00 \times 10^{-6} \text{ F}$$

$$C_{123} = C_{12} + C_3$$
$$C_{123} = 2.00 \times 10^{-6} \text{ F} + 4.00 \times 10^{-6} \text{ F}$$
$$C_{123} = 6.00 \times 10^{-6} \text{ F}$$

$$\frac{1}{C_{1234}} = \frac{1}{C_{123}} + \frac{1}{C_4}$$

$$C_{1234} = \frac{C_{123} C_4}{C_{123} + C_4} = \frac{(6.00 \times 10^{-6} \text{ F})(4.00 \times 10^{-6} \text{ F})}{6.00 \times 10^{-6} \text{ F} + 4.00 \times 10^{-6} \text{ F}} = 2.40 \times 10^{-6} \text{ F}$$

The circuit is equivalent to

$$V_{1234} = V = 28.0 \text{ V}$$

$$Q_{1234} = C_{1234} V = (2.40 \times 10^{-6} \text{ F})(28.0 \text{ V}) = 67.2 \ \mu\text{C}$$

Now build back up the original circuit, step by step:

$$Q_{123} = Q_4 = Q_{1234} = 67.2 \ \mu\text{C}$$
(charge same for capacitors in series)

Then $V_{123} = \dfrac{Q_{123}}{C_{123}} = \dfrac{67.2 \ \mu\text{C}}{6.00 \ \mu\text{F}} = 11.2 \text{ V}$

$V_4 = \dfrac{Q_4}{C_4} = \dfrac{67.2 \ \mu\text{C}}{4.00 \ \mu\text{F}} = 16.8 \text{ V}$

Note that $V_4 + V_{123} = 16.8 \text{ V} + 11.2 \text{ V} = 28.0 \text{ V}$, as it should.

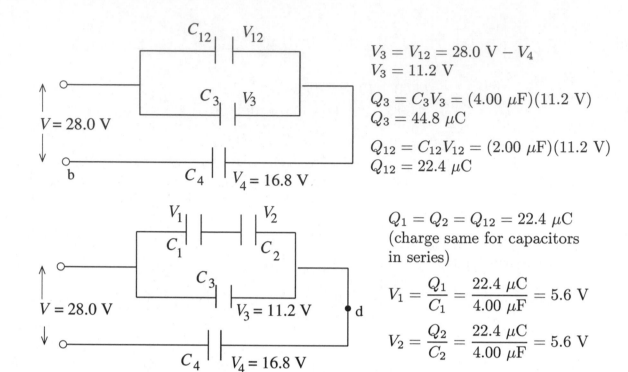

$V_3 = V_{12} = 28.0 \text{ V} - V_4$
$V_3 = 11.2 \text{ V}$

$Q_3 = C_3 V_3 = (4.00 \ \mu\text{F})(11.2 \text{ V})$
$Q_3 = 44.8 \ \mu\text{C}$

$Q_{12} = C_{12} V_{12} = (2.00 \ \mu\text{F})(11.2 \text{ V})$
$Q_{12} = 22.4 \ \mu\text{C}$

$Q_1 = Q_2 = Q_{12} = 22.4 \ \mu\text{C}$
(charge same for capacitors
in series)

$V_1 = \dfrac{Q_1}{C_1} = \dfrac{22.4 \ \mu\text{C}}{4.00 \ \mu\text{F}} = 5.6 \text{ V}$

$V_2 = \dfrac{Q_2}{C_2} = \dfrac{22.4 \ \mu\text{C}}{4.00 \ \mu\text{F}} = 5.6 \text{ V}$

Note that $V_1 + V_2 = 11.2 \text{ V}$, which equals V_3 as it should.
Summary:
$Q_1 = 22.4 \ \mu\text{C}, \quad V_1 = 5.6 \text{ V}$
$Q_2 = 22.4 \ \mu\text{C}, \quad V_2 = 5.6 \text{ V}$
$Q_3 = 44.8 \ \mu\text{C}, \quad V_3 = 11.2 \text{ V}$
$Q_4 = 67.2 \ \mu\text{C}, \quad V_4 = 16.8 \text{ V}$

c) $V_{ad} = V_3 = 11.2 \text{ V}$

EVALUATE: $V_1 + V_2 + V_4 = V$, or $V_3 + V_4 = V$. $Q_1 = Q_2$, $Q_1 + Q_3 = Q_4$ and $Q_4 = Q_{1234}$.

24.17 IDENTIFY: The two capacitors are in parallel so the voltage is the same on each, and equal to the applied voltage V_{ab}.

SET UP: Do parts (a) and (b) together.

EXECUTE:
$V_1 = V_2 = V$
$V_1 = 52.0 \text{ V}$
$V_2 = 52.0 \text{ V}$

$C = Q/V$ so $Q = CV$
$Q_1 = C_1 V_1 = (3.00 \ \mu\text{F})(52.0 \text{ V}) = 156 \ \mu\text{C}$

$Q_2 = C_2 V_2 = (5.00 \ \mu\text{F})(52.0 \ \text{V}) = 260 \ \mu\text{C}$

EVALUATE: To produce the same potential difference, the capacitor with the larger C has the larger Q.

24.23 IDENTIFY and **SET UP:** Use the rules for V for capacitors in series and parallel: for capacitors in parallel the voltages are the same and for capacitors in series the voltages add.

EXECUTE: $V_1 = Q_1/C_1 = (150 \ \mu\text{C})/(3.00 \ \mu\text{F}) = 50 \ \text{V}$

C_1 and C_2 are in parallel, so $V_2 = 50 \ \text{V}$

$V_3 = 120 \ \text{V} - V_1 = 70 \ \text{V}$

EVALUATE: Now that we know the voltages, we could also calculate Q for the other two capacitors.

24.25 IDENTIFY and **SET UP:** The energy density is given by Eq.(24.11): $u = \frac{1}{2}\epsilon_0 E^2$. Use $V = Ed$ to solve for E.

EXECUTE: Calculate E: $E = \dfrac{V}{d} = \dfrac{400 \ \text{V}}{5.00 \times 10^{-3} \ \text{m}} = 8.00 \times 10^4 \ \text{V/m}$.

Then $u = \frac{1}{2}\epsilon_0 E^2 = \frac{1}{2}(8.854 \times 10^{-12} \ \text{C}^2/\text{N} \cdot \text{m}^2)(8.00 \times 10^4 \ \text{V/m})^2 = 0.0283 \ \text{J/m}^3$

EVALUATE: E is smaller than the value in Example 24.8 by about a factor of 6 so u is smaller by about a factor of $6^2 = 36$.

24.29 IDENTIFY and **SET UP:** Combine Eqs.(24.9) and (24.2) to write the stored energy in terms of the separation between the plates.

EXECUTE:

a) $U = \dfrac{Q^2}{2C}$; $C = \dfrac{\epsilon_0 A}{x}$ so $U = \dfrac{x Q^2}{2\epsilon_0 A}$

b) $x \to x + dx$ gives $U = \dfrac{(x + dx)Q^2}{2\epsilon_0 A}$

$dU = \dfrac{(x + dx)Q^2}{2\epsilon_0 A} - \dfrac{x Q^2}{2\epsilon_0 A} = \left(\dfrac{Q^2}{2\epsilon_0 A}\right) dx$

c) $dW = F \, dx = dU$, so $F = \dfrac{Q^2}{2\epsilon_0 A}$

d) **EVALUATE:**

$E = \dfrac{\sigma}{\epsilon_0} = \dfrac{Q}{\epsilon_0 A}$

$F = \frac{1}{2}QE$, not QE

The reason for the difference is that E is the field due to <u>both</u> plates. If we consider the positive plate only and calculate its electric field using Gauss's law:

$$\oint \vec{E} \cdot d\vec{A} = \frac{Q_{encl}}{\epsilon_0}$$

$$2EA = \frac{\sigma A}{\epsilon_0}$$

$$E = \frac{\sigma}{2\epsilon_0} = \frac{Q}{2\epsilon_0 A}$$

The force this field exerts on the other plate, that has charge $-Q$, is $F = \dfrac{Q^2}{2\epsilon_0 A}$.

24.35 a) IDENTIFY and **SET UP:** Apply Eq.(24.11) with the electric field values calculated in Exercise 24.13.

EXECUTE:

From Exercise 24.13, $E = 6.08 \times 10^3$ V/m at $r = 12.6$ cm. $u = \frac{1}{2}\epsilon_0 E^2 = \frac{1}{2}(8.854 \times 10^{-12}$ C^2/N $\cdot$ m$^2)(6.08 \times 10^3$ V/m$)^2 = 1.64 \times 10^{-4}$ J/m^3

b) From Exercise 24.13, $E = 4.47 \times 10^3$ V/m at $r = 14.7$ cm.

$u = \frac{1}{2}\epsilon_0 E^2 = \frac{1}{2}(8.854 \times 10^{-12}$ C^2/N $\cdot$ m$^2)(4.47 \times 10^3$ V/m$)^2 = 8.85 \times 10^{-5}$ J/m^3

c) EVALUATE: No, the results of parts (a) and (b) show that the energy density is not uniform in the region between the spheres. E decreases as r increases so u decreases also.

24.37 IDENTIFY: Use the rules for series and for parallel capacitors to express the voltage for each capacitor in terms of the applied voltage. Express U, Q, and E in terms of the capacitor voltage.

SET UP: Let the applied voltage be V. Let each capacitor have capacitance C. $U = \frac{1}{2}CV^2$ for a single capacitor with voltage V.

EXECUTE:

a) series

Voltage across each capacitor is $V/2$. The total energy stored is
$U_s = 2(\frac{1}{2}C[V/2]^2) = \frac{1}{4}CV^2$

parallel

Voltage across each capacitor is V. The total energy stored is
$U_p = 2(\frac{1}{2}CV^2) = CV^2$

$U_p = 4U_s$

b) $Q = CV$ for a single capacitor with voltage V.

$$Q_s = 2(C[V/2]) = CV; \qquad Q_p = 2(CV) = 2CV; \qquad Q_p = 2Q_s$$

c) $E = V/d$ for a capacitor with voltage V

$$E_s = V/2d; \qquad E_p = V/d; \qquad E_p = 2E_s$$

EVALUATE: The parallel combination stores more energy and more charge since the voltage for each capacitor is larger for parallel. More energy stored and larger voltage for parallel means larger electric field in the parallel case.

24.39 **IDENTIFY** and **SET UP:** Q is constant so we can apply Eq.(24.14). The charge density on each surface of the dielectric is given by Eq.(24.16).

EXECUTE: $E = \dfrac{E_0}{K}$ so $K = \dfrac{E_0}{E} = \dfrac{3.20 \times 10^5 \text{ V/m}}{2.50 \times 10^5 \text{ V/m}} = 1.28$

a) $\sigma_i = \sigma(1 - 1/K)$

$\sigma = \epsilon_0 E_0 = (8.854 \times 10^{-12} \text{ C}^2/\text{N} \cdot \text{m}^2)(3.20 \times 10^5 \text{ N/C}) = 2.833 \times 10^{-6} \text{ C/m}^2$

$\sigma_i = (2.833 \times 10^{-6} \text{ C/m}^2)(1 - 1/1.28) = 6.20 \times 10^{-7} \text{ C/m}^2$

b) As calculated above, $K = 1.28$.

EVALUATE: The surface charges on the dielectric produce an electric field that partially cancels the electric field produced by the charges on the capacitor plates.

24.41 **IDENTIFY** and **SET UP:** For a parallel-plate capacitor with a dielectric we can use the equation $C = K\epsilon_0 A/d$. Minimum A means smallest possible d. d is limited by the requirement that E be less than 1.60×10^7 V/m when V is as large as 5500 V.

EXECUTE: $V = Ed$ so $d = \dfrac{V}{E} = \dfrac{5500 \text{ V}}{1.60 \times 10^7 \text{ V/m}} = 3.44 \times 10^{-4}$ m

Then $A = \dfrac{Cd}{K\epsilon_0} = \dfrac{(1.25 \times 10^{-9} \text{ F})(3.44 \times 10^{-4} \text{ m})}{(3.60)(8.854 \times 10^{-12} \text{ C}^2/\text{N} \cdot \text{m}^2)} = 0.0135 \text{ m}^2$.

EVALUATE: The relation $V = Ed$ applies with or without a dielectric present. A would have to be larger if there were no dielectric.

24.45 **a) IDENTIFY** and **SET UP:** Since the capacitor remains connected to the power supply the potential difference doesn't change when the dielectric is inserted. Use Eq.(24.9) to calculate V and combine it with Eq.(24.12) to obtain a relation between the stored energies and the dielectric constant and use this to calculate K.

EXECUTE: Before the dielectric is inserted $U_0 = \frac{1}{2}C_0 V^2$ so

$$V = \sqrt{\frac{2U_0}{C_0}} = \sqrt{\frac{2(1.85 \times 10^{-5} \text{ J})}{360 \times 10^{-9} \text{ F}}} = 10.1 \text{ V}$$

b) $K = C/C_0$

$U_0 = \frac{1}{2}C_0 V^2$, $U = \frac{1}{2}CV^2$ so $C/C_0 = U/U_0$

$$K = \frac{U}{U_0} = \frac{1.85 \times 10^{-5} \text{ J} + 2.32 \times 10^{-5} \text{ J}}{1.85 \times 10^{-5} \text{ J}} = 2.25$$

EVALUATE: K increases the capacitance and then from $U = \frac{1}{2}CV^2$, with V constant an increase in C gives an increase in U.

24.49 IDENTIFY: Apply Eq.(24.23) to calculate E. $V = Ed$ and $C = Q/V$ apply whether there is a dielectric between the plates or not.

a) **SET UP:** Apply Eq.(24.23) to the dashed surface:

EXECUTE:

$$\oint K\vec{E} \cdot d\vec{A} = \frac{Q_{\text{encl-free}}}{\epsilon_0}$$

$$\oint K\vec{E} \cdot d\vec{A} = KEA'$$

since $E = 0$ outside the plates

$$Q_{\text{encl-free}} = \sigma A' = (Q/A)A'$$

Thus $KEA' = \dfrac{(Q/A)A'}{\epsilon_0}$ and $E = \dfrac{Q}{\epsilon_0 AK}$

b) $V = Ed = \dfrac{Qd}{\epsilon_0 AK}$

c) $C = \dfrac{Q}{V} = \dfrac{Q}{(Qd/\epsilon_0 AK)} = K\dfrac{\epsilon_0 A}{d} = KC_0.$

EVALUATE: Our result shows that $K = C/C_0$, which is Eq.(24.12).

Problems

24.51 IDENTIFY and SET UP: If the capacitor remains connected to the battery, the battery keeps the potential difference between the plates constant by changing the charge on the plates.

EXECUTE:

a) $C = \dfrac{\epsilon_0 A}{d}$

$$C = \frac{(8.854 \times 10^{-12} \text{ C}^2/\text{N} \cdot \text{m}^2)(0.16 \text{ m})^2}{9.4 \times 10^{-3} \text{ m}} = 2.4 \times 10^{-11} \text{ F} = 24 \text{ pF}$$

b) Remains connected to the battery says that V stays 12 V.

$Q = CV = (2.4 \times 10^{-11} \text{ F})(12 \text{ V}) = 2.9 \times 10^{-10} \text{ C}$

c) $E = \dfrac{V}{d} = \dfrac{12 \text{ V}}{9.4 \times 10^{-3} \text{ m}} = 1.3 \times 10^3 \text{ V/m}$

d) $U = \frac{1}{2}QV = \frac{1}{2}(2.9 \times 10^{-10} \text{ C})(12.0 \text{ V}) = 1.7 \times 10^{-9} \text{ J}$

EVALUATE: Increasing the separation decreases C. With V constant, this means that Q decreases and U decreases. Q decreases and $E = Q/\varepsilon_0 A$ so E decreases. We come to the same conclusion from $E = V/d$.

24.57 a) IDENTIFY: For capacitors in parallel, the voltages are the same and equal to the applied voltage. Eq.(24.1) gives Q.

SET UP:

EXECUTE:

$V_1 = V_2 = 660 \text{ V}$

$Q_1 = C_1 V_1 = (4.00 \times 10^{-6} \text{ F})(660 \text{ V})$
$Q_1 = 2.64 \times 10^{-3} \text{ C}$

$Q_2 = C_2 V_2 = (6.00 \times 10^{-6} \text{ F})(660 \text{ V}) = 3.96 \times 10^{-3} \text{ C}$

EVALUATE: The capacitor with larger C has larger Q.

b) IDENTIFY: The + and $-$ charges combine. The charge that is left distributes between the two capacitors to make the potentials across each capacitor the same.

SET UP:

EXECUTE:
Conservation of charge gives
$q_1 + q_2 = Q_2 - Q_1$ (since
terminals of unlike sign are connected)

$q_1 + q_2 = 3.96 \times 10^{-3} \text{ C} - 2.64 \times 10^{-3} \text{ C} = 1.32 \times 10^{-3} \text{ C}$

From the circuit diagram we can see that $v_1 = v_2$.

$v_1 = v_2$ says that $q_1/C_1 = q_2/C_2$ and $q_2 = (C_2/C_1)q_1 = (6.00 \ \mu\text{F}/4.00 \ \mu\text{F})q_1 = 1.50q_1$

Use this result in the equation $q_1 + q_2 = 1.32 \times 10^{-2}$ C and get $2.50q_1 = 1.32 \times 10^{-3}$ C

$q_1 = 5.28 \times 10^{-4} \text{ C}, \ q_2 = 7.92 \times 10^{-4} \text{ C}$

$v_1 = \dfrac{q_1}{C_1} = \dfrac{5.28 \times 10^{-4} \text{ C}}{4.00 \times 10^{-6} \text{ F}} = 132 \text{ V} \qquad v_2 = \dfrac{q_2}{C_2} = \dfrac{7.92 \times 10^{-4} \text{ C}}{6.00 \times 10^{-6} \text{ F}} = 132 \text{ V}$

EVALUATE: We do have $v_1 = v_2$. The capacitor with the larger C has the larger q.

24.59 **a) IDENTIFY:** Replace series and parallel combinations of capacitors by their equivalents.

SET UP:

$$C_1 = C_5 = 8.4 \ \mu F$$
$$C_2 = C_3 = C_4 = 4.2 \ \mu F$$

EXECUTE:

Simplify the circuit by replacing the capacitor combinations by their equivalents:

$$\frac{1}{C_{34}} = \frac{1}{C_3} + \frac{1}{C_4}$$

$$\frac{1}{C_{34}} = \frac{C_3 + C_4}{C_3 C_4}$$

$$C_{34} = \frac{C_3 C_4}{C_3 + C_4} = \frac{(4.2 \ \mu F)(4.2 \ \mu F)}{4.2 \ \mu F + 4.2 \ \mu F} = 2.1 \ \mu F$$

$$C_{234} = C_2 + C_{34}$$
$$C_{234} = 4.2 \ \mu F + 2.1 \ \mu F$$
$$C_{234} = 6.3 \ \mu F$$

$$\frac{1}{C_{eq}} = \frac{1}{C_1} + \frac{1}{C_5} + \frac{1}{C_{234}}$$

$$\frac{1}{C_{eq}} = \frac{2}{8.4 \ \mu F} + \frac{1}{6.3 \ \mu F}$$

$$C_{eq} = 2.5 \ \mu F$$

EVALUATE: For capacitors in series the equivalent capacitor is smaller than any of those in series. For capacitors in parallel the equivalent capacitance is larger than any of those in parallel.

b) IDENTIFY and **SET UP:** In each equivalent network apply the rules for Q and V for capacitors in series and parallel; start with the simplest network and work back to the original circuit.

EXECUTE:

$$Q_{eq} = C_{eq} V$$
$$Q_{eq} = (2.5 \ \mu F)(220 \ V) = 550 \ \mu C$$

$Q_1 = Q_5 = Q_{234} = 550 \ \mu C$ (capacitors in series have same charge)

$$V_1 = \frac{Q_1}{C_1} = \frac{550 \ \mu C}{8.4 \ \mu F} = 65 \ V$$

$$V_5 = \frac{Q_5}{C_5} = \frac{550 \ \mu C}{8.4 \ \mu F} = 65 \ V$$

$$V_{234} = \frac{Q_{234}}{C_{234}} = \frac{550 \ \mu C}{6.3 \ \mu F} = 87 \ V$$

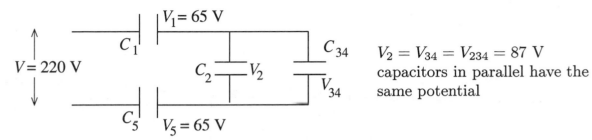

$V_2 = V_{34} = V_{234} = 87 \ V$
capacitors in parallel have the
same potential

$$Q_2 = C_2 V_2 = (4.2 \ \mu F)(87 \ V) = 370 \ \mu C$$
$$Q_{34} = C_{34} V_{34} = (2.1 \ \mu F)(87 \ V) = 180 \ \mu C$$

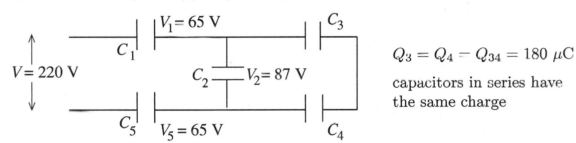

$Q_3 = Q_4 = Q_{34} = 180 \ \mu C$

capacitors in series have
the same charge

$$V_3 = \frac{Q_3}{C_3} = \frac{180 \ \mu C}{4.2 \ \mu F} = 43 \ V$$

$$V_4 = \frac{Q_4}{C_4} = \frac{180 \ \mu C}{4.2 \ \mu F} = 43 \ V$$

Summary:

$Q_1 = 550 \ \mu C, \quad V_1 = 65 \ V$

$Q_2 = 370 \ \mu C, \quad V_2 = 87 \ V$

$Q_3 = 180 \ \mu C, \quad V_3 = 43 \ V$

$Q_4 = 180 \ \mu C, \quad V_4 = 43 \ V$

$Q_5 = 550 \ \mu C, \quad V_5 = 65 \ V$

EVALUATE: $V_3 + V_4 = V_2$ and $V_1 + V_2 + V_5 = 220 \ V$ (apart from some small rounding error)

$Q_1 = Q_2 + Q_3$ and $Q_5 = Q_2 + Q_4$

24.61 a) IDENTIFY: Replace the three capacitors in series by their equivalent.
The charge on the equivalent capacitor equals the charge on each of the original

capacitors.

SET UP:

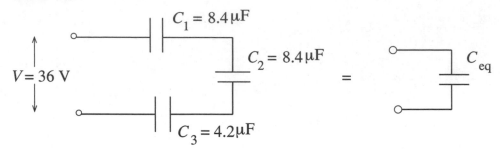

EXECUTE:

$C_3 = C_1/2$ so $\dfrac{1}{C_{eq}} = \dfrac{1}{C_1} + \dfrac{1}{C_2} + \dfrac{1}{C_3} = \dfrac{4}{8.4\ \mu F}$ and $C_{eq} = 8.4\ \mu F/4 = 2.1\ \mu F$

$Q = C_{eq}V = (2.1\ \mu F)(36\ V) = 76\ \mu C$

The three capacitors are in series so they each have the same charge:

$Q_1 = Q_2 = Q_3 = 76\ \mu C$

EVALUATE: The equivalent capacitance for capacitors in series is smaller than each of the original capacitors.

b) IDENTIFY and **SET UP:** Use $U = \frac{1}{2}QV$. We know each Q and we know that $V_1 + V_2 + V_3 = 36$ V.

EXECUTE: $U = \frac{1}{2}Q_1V_1 + \frac{1}{2}Q_2V_2 + \frac{1}{2}Q_3V_3$

But $Q_1 = Q_2 = Q_3 = Q$ so $U = \frac{1}{2}Q(V_1 + V_2 + V_3)$

But also $V_1 + V_2 + V_3 = V = 36$ V, so $U = \frac{1}{2}QV = \frac{1}{2}(76\ \mu C)(36\ V) = 1.4 \times 10^{-3}$ J.

EVALUATE: We could also use $U = Q^2/2C$ and calculate U for each capacitor.

c) IDENTIFY: The charges on the plates redistribute to make the potentials across each capacitor the same.

SET UP:

$$
C_1\bigg|_+ \qquad C_2\bigg|_+ \qquad C_3\bigg|_+ \qquad\qquad C_1\bigg|_+ \;\; C_2\bigg|_+ \;\; C_3\bigg|_+
$$

$$
Q_{01}\bigg|_- \qquad Q_{02}\bigg|_- \qquad Q_{03}\bigg|_- \qquad \longrightarrow \qquad Q_1\bigg|_-\,V_1 \;\; Q_2\bigg|_-\,V_2 \;\; Q_3\bigg|_-\,V_3
$$

EXECUTE: The total positive charge that is available to be distributed on the upper plates of the three capacitors is $Q_0 = Q_{01} + Q_{02} + Q_{03} = 3(76\ \mu C) = 228\ \mu C$. Thus $Q_1 + Q_2 + Q_3 = 228\ \mu C$.

After the circuit is completed the charge distributes to make $V_1 = V_2 = V_3$.

$V = Q/C$ and $V_1 = V_2$ so $Q_1/C_1 = Q_2/C_2$ and then $C_1 = C_2$ says $Q_1 = Q_2$.

$V_1 = V_3$ says $Q_1/C_1 = Q_3/C_3$ and $Q_1 = Q_3(C_1/C_3) = Q_3(8.4\ \mu\text{F}/4.2\ \mu\text{F}) = 2Q_3$
Using $Q_2 = Q_1$ and $Q_1 = 2Q_3$ in the above equation gives $2Q_3 + 2Q_3 + Q_3 = 228\ \mu\text{C}$.
$5Q_3 = 228\ \mu\text{C}$ and $Q_3 = 45.6\ \mu\text{C}$, $Q_1 = Q_2 = 91.2\ \mu\text{C}$

Then $V_1 = \dfrac{Q_1}{C_1} = \dfrac{91.2\ \mu\text{C}}{8.4\ \mu\text{F}} = 11\ \text{V}$, $V_2 = \dfrac{Q_2}{C_2} = \dfrac{91.2\ \mu\text{C}}{8.4\ \mu\text{F}} = 11\ \text{V}$, and

$V_3 = \dfrac{Q_3}{C_3} = \dfrac{45.6\ \mu\text{C}}{4.2\ \mu\text{F}} = 11\ \text{V}.$

The voltage across each capacitor in the parallel combination is 11 V.

d) $U = \frac{1}{2}Q_1V_1 + \frac{1}{2}Q_2V_2 + \frac{1}{2}Q_3V_3.$
But $V_1 = V_2 = V_3$ so $U = \frac{1}{2}V_1(Q_1 + Q_2 + Q_3) = \frac{1}{2}(11\ \text{V})(228\ \mu\text{C}) = 1.3 \times 10^{-3}\ \text{J}.$
EVALUATE: This is less than the original energy of 1.4×10^{-3} J. The stored energy has decreased, as in Example 24.7.

24.63 IDENTIFY: Replace series and parallel combinations of capacitors by their equivalents. In each equivalent network apply the rules for Q and V for capacitors in series and parallel; start with the simplest network and work back to the original circuit.

a) SET UP:

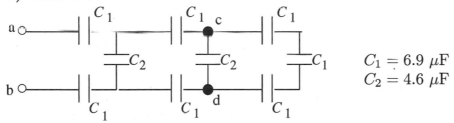

$C_1 = 6.9\ \mu\text{F}$
$C_2 = 4.6\ \mu\text{F}$

EXECUTE: Simplify the network by replacing the capacitor combinations by their equivalents.

$\dfrac{1}{C_{eq}} = \dfrac{3}{C_1}$

$C_{eq} = \dfrac{C_1}{3} = \dfrac{6.9\ \mu\text{F}}{3} = 2.3\ \mu\text{F}$

$C_{eq} = 2.3\ \mu\text{F} + C_2$
$C_{eq} = 2.3\ \mu\text{F} + 4.6\ \mu\text{F} = 6.9\ \mu\text{F}$

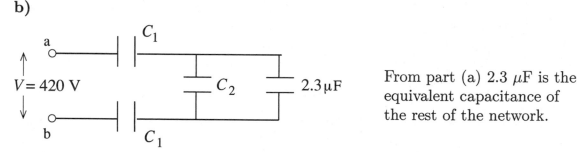

$$\frac{1}{C_{eq}} = \frac{2}{C_1} + \frac{1}{6.9 \ \mu F} = \frac{3}{6.9 \ \mu F}$$

$$C_{eq} = 2.3 \ \mu F$$

$$C_{eq} = C_2 + 2.3 \ \mu F = 4.6 \ \mu F + 2.3 \ \mu F$$

$$C_{eq} = 6.9 \ \mu F$$

$$\frac{1}{C_{eq}} = \frac{2}{C_1} + \frac{1}{6.9 \ \mu F} = \frac{3}{6.9 \ \mu F}$$

$$C_{eq} = 2.3 \ \mu F$$

b)

From part (a) 2.3 μF is the equivalent capacitance of the rest of the network.

The equivalent network is

series, so all three capacitors have the same Q.

But here all three have the same C, so by $V = Q/C$ all three must have the same V. The three voltages must add to 420 V, so each capacitor has $V = 140$ V. The 6.9 μF to the right is the equivalent of C_2 and the 2.3 μF capacitor in parallel, so $V_2 = 140$ V. (Capacitors in parallel have the same potential difference.)

Hence $Q_1 = C_1 V_1 = (6.9 \ \mu F)(140 \ V) = 9.7 \times 10^{-4}$ C

and $Q_2 = C_2 V_2 = (4.6 \ \mu F)(140 \ V) = 6.4 \times 10^{-4}$ C.

c) From the potentials deduced in part (b) we have

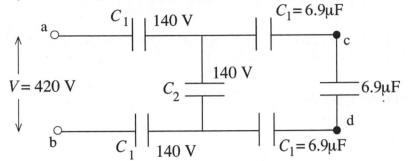

From part (a) 6.9 μF is the equivalent capacitance of the rest of the network.

The three right-most capacitors are in series and therefore have the same charge. But their capacitances are also equal, so by $V = Q/C$ they each have the same potential difference. Their potentials must sum to 140 V, so the potential across each is 47 V and $V_{cd} = 47$ V.

EVALUATE: In each capacitor network the rules for combining V for capacitors in series and parallel are obeyed. Note that $V_{cd} < V$, in fact $V - 2(140 \text{ V}) - 2(47 \text{ V}) = V_{cd}$.

24.65 a) IDENTIFY and SET UP: Q is constant. $C = KC_0$; use Eq.(24.1) to relate the dielectric constant K to the ratio of the voltages without and with the dielectric.

EXECUTE:

with the dielectric: $V = Q/C = Q/(KC_0)$

without the dielectric: $V_0 = Q/C_0$

$V_0/V = K$, so $K = (45.0 \text{ V})/(11.5 \text{ V}) = 3.91$

EVALUATE: Our analysis agrees with Eq.(24.13).

b) IDENTIFY: The capacitor can be treated as equivalent to two capacitors C_1 and C_2 in parallel, one with area $2A/3$ and air between the plates and one with area $A/3$ and dielectric between the plates.

SET UP:

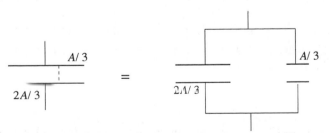

EXECUTE: Let $C_0 = \epsilon_0 A/d$ be the capacitance with only air between the plates. $C_1 = KC_0/3$, $C_2 = 2C_0/3$; $C_{eq} = C_1 + C_2 = (C_0/3)(K + 2)$

$$V = \frac{Q}{C_{eq}} = \frac{Q}{C_0}\left(\frac{3}{K+2}\right) = V_0\left(\frac{3}{K+2}\right) = (45.0 \text{ V})\left(\frac{3}{5.91}\right) = 22.8 \text{ V}$$

EVALUATE: The voltage is reduced by the dielectric. The voltage reduction is less when the dielectric doesn't completely fill the volume between the plates.

24.67 a) IDENTIFY: The conductor can be at some potential V, where $V = 0$ far from the conductor. This potential depends on the charge Q on the conductor so we can define $C = Q/V$ where C will not depend on V or Q.

b) SET UP: Use the expression for the potential at the surface of the sphere in the analysis on part (a).

EXECUTE: For any point on a solid conducting sphere $V = Q/4\pi\epsilon_0 R$ if $V = 0$ at $r \to \infty$.

$$C = \frac{Q}{V} = Q\left(\frac{4\pi\epsilon_0 R}{Q}\right) = 4\pi\epsilon_0 R$$

c) $C = 4\pi\epsilon_0 R = 4\pi(8.854 \times 10^{-12} \text{ F/m})(6.38 \times 10^6 \text{ m}) = 7.10 \times 10^{-4} \text{ F} = 710 \ \mu\text{F}.$

EVALUATE: The capacitance of the earth is about seven times larger than the largest capacitances in this range. The capacitance of the earth is quite small, in view of its large size.

24.69 IDENTIFY: Use $E(r)$ from Example 22.9 in Eq.(24.11).

SET UP: $E = \dfrac{1}{4\pi\epsilon_0}\dfrac{Qr}{R^3}$ for $r < R$ and $E = \dfrac{1}{4\pi\epsilon_0}\dfrac{Q}{r^2}$ for $r > R$.

EXECUTE:

a) $u = \frac{1}{2}\epsilon_0 E^2 = \frac{1}{2}\epsilon_0\left(\dfrac{1}{4\pi\epsilon_0}\dfrac{Qr}{R^3}\right)^2 = \dfrac{1}{4\pi\epsilon_0}\dfrac{Q^2 r^2}{8\pi R^6}$

b) $u = \frac{1}{2}\epsilon_0 E^2 = \frac{1}{2}\epsilon_0\left(\dfrac{1}{4\pi\epsilon_0}\dfrac{Q}{r^2}\right)^2 = \dfrac{1}{4\pi\epsilon_0}\dfrac{Q^2}{8\pi r^4}$

c) IDENTIFY and **SET UP:** $dU = u\,dV$ where $dV = 4\pi r^2\,dr$ is the volume of a thin spherical shell of radius r and thickness dr. Integrate this expression over all space to find the total electric field energy.

EXECUTE:

For $r < R$, $U = \displaystyle\int_0^R u4\pi r^2\,dr = \dfrac{1}{4\pi\epsilon_0}\dfrac{Q^2}{2R^6}\int_0^R r^4\,dr = \dfrac{1}{4\pi\epsilon_0}\dfrac{Q^2}{2R^6}\left(\dfrac{R^5}{5}\right) = \dfrac{1}{4\pi\epsilon_0}\dfrac{Q^2}{10R}.$

For $r > R$, $U = \displaystyle\int_R^\infty u4\pi r^2\,dr = \dfrac{1}{4\pi\epsilon_0}\dfrac{Q^2}{2}\int_R^\infty \dfrac{dr}{r^2} = \dfrac{1}{4\pi\epsilon_0}\dfrac{Q^2}{2}\left(-\dfrac{1}{r}\Big|_R^\infty\right) = \dfrac{1}{4\pi\epsilon_0}\dfrac{Q^2}{2R}.$

The total electric field energy is

$$U = \frac{1}{4\pi\epsilon_0} \frac{Q^2}{10R} + \frac{1}{4\pi\epsilon_0} \frac{Q^2}{2R} = \frac{1}{4\pi\epsilon_0} \frac{Q^2}{R} \left(\frac{1}{10} + \frac{1}{2} \right) = \frac{1}{4\pi\epsilon_0} \frac{3Q^2}{5R}.$$

EVALUATE: $U = Q^2/2C$ gives $C = 10\pi\varepsilon_0 R/3$. Compare this to C for a solid conducting sphere found in Problem 24.67.

24.71 IDENTIFY: $C = Q/V$, so we need to calculate the effect of the dielectrics on the potential difference between the plates.

SET UP: Let the potential of the positive plate be V_a, the potential of the negative plate be V_c, and the potential midway between the plates where the dielectrics meet be V_b.

$$C = \frac{Q}{V_a - V_c} = \frac{Q}{V_{ac}}.$$

$$V_{ac} = V_{ab} + V_{bc}.$$

EXECUTE: The electric field in the absence of any dielectric is $E_0 = \dfrac{Q}{\epsilon_0 A}$. In the first dielectric the electric field is reduced to

$$E_1 = \frac{E_0}{K_1} = \frac{Q}{K_1\epsilon_0 A} \text{ and } V_{ab} = E_1 \left(\frac{d}{2} \right) = \frac{Qd}{K_1 2\epsilon_0 A}.$$

In the second dielectric the electric field is reduced to

$$E_2 = \frac{E_0}{K_2} = \frac{Q}{K_2\epsilon_0 A} \text{ and } V_{bc} = E_2 \left(\frac{d}{2} \right) = \frac{Qd}{K_2 2\epsilon_0 A}.$$

Thus $V_{ac} = V_{ab} + V_{bc} = \dfrac{Qd}{K_1 2\epsilon_0 A} + \dfrac{Qd}{K_2 2\epsilon_0 A} = \dfrac{Qd}{2\epsilon_0 A} \left(\dfrac{1}{K_1} + \dfrac{1}{K_2} \right)$

$$V_{ac} = \frac{Qd}{2\epsilon_0 A} \left(\frac{K_1 + K_2}{K_1 K_2} \right).$$

This gives $C = \dfrac{Q}{V_{ac}} = Q \left(\dfrac{2\epsilon_0 A}{Qd} \right) \left(\dfrac{K_1 K_2}{K_1 + K_2} \right) = \dfrac{2\epsilon_0 A}{d} \left(\dfrac{K_1 K_2}{K_1 + K_2} \right).$

EVALUATE: An equivalent way to calculate C is to consider the capacitor to be two in series, one with dielectric constant K_1 and the other with dielectric constnat K_2 and both with plate separation $d/2$. (Can imagine inserting a thin conducting plate between the dielectic slabs.)

$$C_1 = K_1 \frac{\varepsilon_0 A}{d/2} = 2K_1 \frac{\varepsilon_0 A}{d}$$

$$C_2 = K_2 \frac{\varepsilon_0 A}{d/2} = 2K_2 \frac{\varepsilon_0 A}{d}$$

Since they are in series the total capacitance C is given by

$$\frac{1}{C} = \frac{1}{C_1} + \frac{1}{C_2} \text{ so } C = \frac{C_1 C_2}{C_1 + C_2} = \frac{2\varepsilon_0 A}{d} \left(\frac{K_1 K_2}{K_1 + K_2} \right)$$

CHAPTER 25
CURRENT, RESISTANCE, AND ELECTROMOTIVE FOR

Exercises

25.3 **IDENTIFY** and **SET UP:** Use Eq.(25.3) to calculate the drift speed and then use that to find the time to travel the length of the wire.

EXECUTE:

a) Calculate the drift speed v_d:

$$J = \frac{I}{A} = \frac{I}{\pi r^2} = \frac{4.85 \text{ A}}{\pi (1.025 \times 10^{-3} \text{ m})^2} = 1.469 \times 10^6 \text{ A/m}^2$$

$$v_d = \frac{J}{n|q|} = \frac{1.469 \times 10^6 \text{ A/m}^2}{(8.5 \times 10^{28}/\text{m}^3)(1.602 \times 10^{-19} \text{ C})} = 1.079 \times 10^{-4} \text{ m/s}$$

$$t - \frac{L}{v_d} = \frac{0.710 \text{ m}}{1.079 \times 10^{-4} \text{ m/s}} = 6.58 \times 10^3 \text{ s} = 110 \text{ min.}$$

b) $v_d = \dfrac{I}{\pi r^2 n|q|}$

$$t = \frac{L}{v_d} = \frac{\pi r^2 n|q| L}{I}$$

t is proportional to r^2 and hence to d^2 where $d = 2r$ is the wire diameter.

$$t = (6.58 \times 10^3 \text{ s}) \left(\frac{4.12 \text{ mm}}{2.05 \text{ mm}}\right)^2 = 2.66 \times 10^4 \text{ s} = 440 \text{ min.}$$

c) **EVALUATE:** The drift speed is proportional to the current density and therefore it is inversely proportional to the square of the diameter of the wire. Increasing the diameter by some factor decreases the drift speed by the square of that factor.

25.5 **IDENTIFY** and **SET UP:** Use Eq.(25.3) to set up a ratio.

EXECUTE: $J = n|q|v_d$, so $J/v_d = n|q|$ is constant.

$J_1/v_{d1} = J_2/v_{d2}$,

$v_{d2} = v_{d1}(J_2/J_1) = v_{d1}(I_2/I_1) = (1.20 \times 10^{-4} \text{ m/s})(6.00/1.20) = 6.00 \times 10^{-4} \text{ m/s}$

EVALUATE: When I increases by a factor of 5 then v_d increases by a factor of 5.

25.9 **IDENTIFY** and **SET UP:** Apply Eq.(25.1) to find the charge dQ in time dt.

Integrate to find the total charge in the whole time interval.

EXECUTE:

a) $dQ = I\,dt$

$$Q = \int_0^{8.0\text{ s}} (55\text{ A} - (0.65\ \text{A/s}^2)t^2)\,dt = \left[(55\text{ A})t - (0.217\ \text{A/s}^2)t^3\right]_0^{8.0\text{ s}}$$

$$Q = (55\text{ A})(8.0\text{ s}) - (0.217\ \text{A/s}^2)(8.0\text{ s})^3 = 330\text{ C}$$

b) $I = \dfrac{Q}{t} = \dfrac{330\text{ C}}{8.0\text{ s}} = 41\text{ A}$

EVALUATE: The current decreases from 55 A to 13.4 A during the interval. The decrease is not linear and the average current is not equal to $(55\text{A} + 13.4\text{ A})/2$.

25.15 **IDENTIFY** and **SET UP:** Use Eq.(25.10) to calculate A. Find the volume of the wire and use the density to calculate the mass.

EXECUTE: Find the volume of one of the wires:

$$R = \frac{\rho L}{A}\quad\text{so}\quad A = \frac{\rho L}{R}\quad\text{and}$$

$$\text{volume} = AL = \frac{\rho L^2}{R} = \frac{(1.72 \times 10^{-8}\ \Omega\cdot\text{m})(3.50\text{ m})^2}{0.125\ \Omega} = 1.686 \times 10^{-6}\text{ m}^3$$

$$m = (\text{density})V = (8.9 \times 10^3\text{ kg/m}^3)(1.686 \times 10^{-6}\text{ m}^3) = 15\text{ g}$$

EVALUATE: The mass we calculated is reasonable for a wire.

25.21 **IDENTIFY** and **SET UP:** Apply Eq.(25.8) with $A = \pi r^2$ and solve for r.

EXECUTE: $\dfrac{V}{L} = \rho\left(\dfrac{I}{\pi r^2}\right)$ where $\rho = 2.75 \times 10^{-8}\ \Omega\cdot\text{m}$ (Table 25.1).

$$r = \sqrt{\frac{\rho I L}{\pi V}} = \sqrt{\frac{(2.75 \times 10^{-8}\ \Omega\cdot\text{m})(6.00\text{ A})(1.20\text{ m})}{\pi(1.50\text{ V})}} = 0.205\text{ mm}$$

EVALUATE: This is on the order of a typical wire radius. (See Example 25.2.) The smaller r is the greater are R and V for a given length of wire.

25.23 **IDENTIFY** and **SET UP:** Eq.(25.5) relates the electric field that is given to the current density. $V = EL$ gives the potential difference across a length L of wire and Eq.(25.11) allows us to calculate R.

EXECUTE:

a) Eq.(25.5): $\rho = E/J$ so $J = E/\rho$

From Table 25.1 the resistivity for gold is $2.44 \times 10^{-8}\ \Omega\cdot\text{m}$.

$$J = \frac{E}{\rho} = \frac{0.49\text{ V/m}}{2.44 \times 10^{-8}\ \Omega\cdot\text{m}} = 2.008 \times 10^7\text{ A/m}^2$$

$$I = JA = J\pi r^2 = (2.008 \times 10^7 \text{ A/m}^2)\pi(0.41 \times 10^{-3} \text{ m})^2 = 11 \text{ A}$$

b) $V = EL = (0.49 \text{ V/m})(6.4 \text{ m}) = 3.1 \text{ V}$

c) We can use Ohm's law (Eq.(25.11): $V = IR$.

$$R = \frac{V}{I} = \frac{3.1 \text{ V}}{11 \text{ A}} = 0.28 \text{ }\Omega$$

EVALUATE: We can also calculate R from the resistivity and the dimensions of the wire (Eq.25.10):

$$R = \frac{\rho L}{A} = \frac{\rho L}{\pi r^2} = \frac{(2.44 \times 10^{-8} \text{ }\Omega \cdot \text{m})(6.4 \text{ m})}{\pi(0.42 \times 10^{-3} \text{ m})^2} = 0.28 \text{ }\Omega, \text{ which checks.}$$

25.25 **IDENTIFY** and **SET UP:** Use $V = EL$ to calculate E and then $\rho = E/J$ to calculate ρ.
EXECUTE:
a) $E = \dfrac{V}{L} = \dfrac{0.938 \text{ V}}{0.750 \text{ m}} = 1.25 \text{ V/m}$

b) $E = \rho J$ so $\rho = \dfrac{E}{J} = \dfrac{1.25 \text{ V/m}}{4.40 \times 10^7 \text{ A/m}^2} = 2.84 \times 10^{-8} \text{ }\Omega \cdot \text{m}$

EVALUATE: This value of ρ is similar to that for the good metallic conductors in Table 25.1.

25.27 **IDENTIFY:** Apply $R = R_0[1 + \alpha(T - T_0)]$ to calculate the resistance at the second temperature.
a) **SET UP:** $\alpha = 0.0004 \text{ (C}°)^{-1}$ (Table 25.1). Let T_0 be $0.0°$C and T be $11.5°$C.
EXECUTE: $R_0 = \dfrac{R}{1 + \alpha(T - T_0)} = \dfrac{100.0 \text{ }\Omega}{1 + (0.0004 \text{ (C}°)^{-1}(11.5°\text{C}))} = 99.54 \text{ }\Omega$

b) **SET UP:** $\alpha = -0.0005 \text{ (C}°)^{-1}$ (Table 25.2). Let $T_0 = 0.0°$C and $T = 25.8°$C.
EXECUTE:
$R = R_0[1 + \alpha(T - T_0)] = 0.0160 \text{ }\Omega[1 + (-0.0005 \text{ (C}°)^{-1})(25.8 \text{ C}°)] = 0.0158 \text{ }\Omega$
EVALUATE: Nichrome, like most metallic conductors, has a positive α and its resistance increases with temperature. For carbon, α is negative and its resistance decreases as T increases.

25.35 **IDENTIFY:** The voltmeter reads the potential difference V_{ab} between the terminals of the battery.

SET UP: <u>open circuit</u> $I = 0$

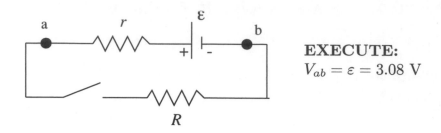

EXECUTE:
$V_{ab} = \varepsilon = 3.08$ V

SET UP: <u>switch closed</u>

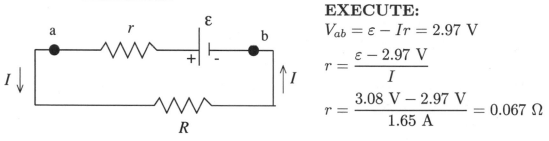

EXECUTE:
$V_{ab} = \varepsilon - Ir = 2.97$ V

$$r = \frac{\varepsilon - 2.97 \text{ V}}{I}$$

$$r = \frac{3.08 \text{ V} - 2.97 \text{ V}}{1.65 \text{ A}} = 0.067 \ \Omega$$

And $V_{ab} = IR$ so $R = \dfrac{V_{ab}}{I} = \dfrac{2.97 \text{ V}}{1.65 \text{ A}} = 1.80 \ \Omega$.

EVALUATE: When current flows through the battery there is a voltage drop across its internal resistance and its terminal voltage V is less than its emf.

25.37 a) IDENTIFY and **SET UP:** Assume that the current is clockwise.

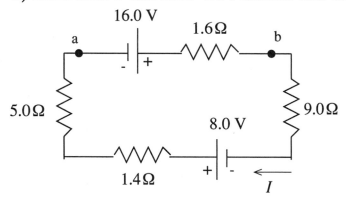

Add up the potential rises and drops as travel clockwise around the circuit.

EXECUTE: $16.0 \text{ V} - I(1.6 \ \Omega) - I(9.0 \ \Omega) + 8.0 \text{ V} - I(1.4 \ \Omega) - I(5.0 \ \Omega) = 0$

$$I = \frac{16.0 \text{ V} + 8.0 \text{ V}}{9.0 \ \Omega + 1.4 \ \Omega + 5.0 \ \Omega + 1.6 \ \Omega} = \frac{24.0 \text{ V}}{17.0 \ \Omega} = 1.41 \text{ A, clockwise}$$

EVALUATE: The 16.0 V battery drives the current clockwise more strongly than the 8.0 V batttery does in the opposite direction.

b) IDENTIFY and **SET UP:** Start at point a and travel through the battery to point b, keeping track of the potential changes. At point b the potential is V_b.

EXECUTE: $V_a + 16.0 \text{ V} - I(1.6 \ \Omega) = V_b$

$V_a - V_b = -16.0 \text{ V} + (1.41 \text{ A})(1.6 \ \Omega)$

$V_{ab} = -16.0 \text{ V} + 2.3 \text{ V} = -13.7 \text{ V}$ (point a is at lower potential; it is the negative terminal)

EVALUATE: Could also go counterclockwise from a to b:

$V_a + (1.41 \text{ A})(5.0 \ \Omega) + (1.41 \text{ A})(1.4 \ \Omega) - 8.0 \text{ V} + (1.41 \text{ A})(9.0 \ \Omega) = V_b$

$V_{ab} = -13.7 \text{ V}$, which checks.

c) IDENTIFY and **SET UP:** Start at point a and travel through the battery to point c, keeping track of the potential changes.

EXECUTE: $V_a + 16.0 \text{ V} - I(1.6 \ \Omega) - I(9.0 \ \Omega) = V_c$

$V_a - V_c = -16.0 \text{ V} + (1.41 \text{ A})(1.6 \ \Omega + 9.0 \ \Omega)$

$V_{ac} = -16.0 \text{ V} + 15.0 \text{ V} = -1.0 \text{ V}$ (point a is at lower potential than point c)

EVALUATE: Could also go counterclockwise from a to c:

$V_a + (1.41 \text{ A})(5.0 \ \Omega) + (1.41 \text{ A})(1.4 \ \Omega) - 8.0 \text{ V} = V_c$

$V_{ac} = -1.0 \text{ V}$, which checks.

d) Call the potential zero at point a. Travel clockwise around the circuit.

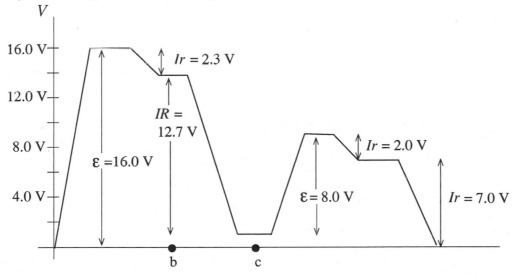

25.41 a) IDENTIFY: The potential rise across the emf and the drop across the internal resistance r sum to zero.

SET UP:

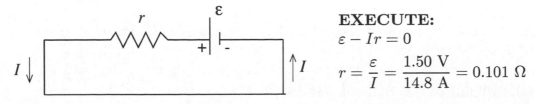

EXECUTE:

$\varepsilon - Ir = 0$

$r = \dfrac{\varepsilon}{I} = \dfrac{1.50 \text{ V}}{14.8 \text{ A}} = 0.101 \ \Omega$

b) $r = \dfrac{\varepsilon}{I} = \dfrac{1.50 \text{ V}}{6.8 \text{ A}} = 0.22 \ \Omega$

c) $r = \dfrac{\varepsilon}{I} = \dfrac{12.6 \text{ V}}{1000 \text{ A}} = 0.0126 \ \Omega$

EVALUATE: The smaller r is, the greater the short-circuit current.

25.45 IDENTIFY and **SET UP:** By definition $p = \dfrac{P}{LA}$. Use $P = VI$, $E = VL$ and $I = JA$ to rewrite this expression in terms of the specified varaibles.

EXECUTE:

a) E is related to V and J is related to I, so use $P = VI$. This gives $p = \dfrac{VI}{LA}$

$\dfrac{V}{L} = E$ and $\dfrac{I}{A} = J$ so $p = EJ$

b) J is related to I and ρ is related to R, so use $P = IR^2$. This gives $p = \dfrac{I^2 R}{LA}$.

$I = JA$ and $R = \dfrac{\rho L}{A}$ so $p = \dfrac{J^2 A^2 \rho L}{LA^2} = \rho J^2$

c) E is related to V and ρ is related to R, so use $P = V^2/R$. This gives $p = \dfrac{V^2}{RLA}$.

$V = EL$ and $R = \dfrac{\rho L}{A}$ so $p = \dfrac{E^2 L^2}{LA}\left(\dfrac{A}{\rho L}\right) = \dfrac{E^2}{\rho}$.

EVALUATE: For a given material (ρ constant), p is proportional to J^2 or to E^2.

25.47 a) IDENTIFY and **SET UP:** $P = VI$ and energy $=$ (power)X(time).

EXECUTE: $P = VI = (12 \text{ V})(60 \text{ A}) = 720 \text{ W}$

The battery can provide this for 1.0 h, so the energy the battery has stored is
$U = Pt = (720 \text{ W})(3600 \text{ s}) = 2.6 \times 10^6 \text{ J}$

b) IDENTIFY and **SET UP:** For gasoline the heat of combustion is $L_c = 46 \times 10^6$ J/kg. Solve for the mass m required to supply the energy calculated in part (a) and use density $\rho = m/V$ to calculate V.

EXECUTE: The mass of gasoline that supplies 2.6×10^6 J is $m = \dfrac{2.6 \times 10^6 \text{ J}}{46 \times 10^6 \text{ J/kg}} = 0.0565$ kg.

The volume of this mass of gasoline is

$$V = \frac{m}{\rho} = \frac{0.0565 \text{ kg}}{900 \text{ kg/m}^3} = 6.3 \times 10^{-5} \text{ m}^3 \left(\frac{1000 \text{ L}}{1 \text{ m}^3} \right) = 0.063 \text{ L}$$

c) IDENTIFY and **SET UP:** Energy = (power)X(time); the energy is that calculated in part (a).

EXECUTE: $U = Pt$, $t = \dfrac{U}{P} = \dfrac{2.6 \times 10^6 \text{ J}}{450 \text{ W}} = 5800 \text{ s} = 97 \text{ min} = 1.6 \text{ h}$.

EVALUATE: The battery discharges at a rate of 720 W (for 60 A) and is charged at a rate of 450 W, so it takes longer to charge than to discharge.

25.49 IDENTIFY: Solve for the current I in the circuit. Apply Eq.(25.17) to the specified circuit elements to find the rates of energy conversion.

SET UP:

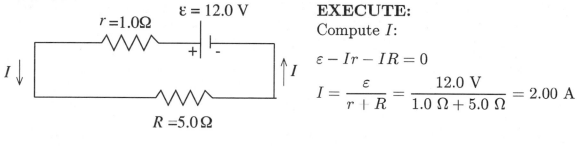

EXECUTE:
Compute I:

$$\varepsilon - Ir - IR = 0$$

$$I = \frac{\varepsilon}{r + R} = \frac{12.0 \text{ V}}{1.0 \text{ }\Omega + 5.0 \text{ }\Omega} = 2.00 \text{ A}$$

a) The rate of conversion of chemical energy to electrical energy in the emf of the battery is $P = \varepsilon I = (12.0 \text{ V})(2.00 \text{ A}) = 24.0 \text{ W}$.

b) The rate of dissipation of electrical energy in the internal resistance of the battery is $P = I^2 r = (2.00 \text{ A})^2 (1.0 \text{ }\Omega) = 4.0 \text{ W}$.

c) The rate of dissipation of electrical energy in the external resistor R is $P = I^2 R = (2.00 \text{ A})^2 (5.0 \text{ }\Omega) = 20.0 \text{ W}$.

EVALUATE: The rate of production of electrical energy in the circuit is 24.0 W. The total rate of consumption of electrical energy in the circuit is 4.00 W + 20.0 W = 24.0 W. Equal rate of production and consumption of electrical energy are required by energy conservation.

Problems

25.53 a) IDENTIFY and **SET UP:** Use $R = \dfrac{\rho L}{A}$.

EXECUTE: $\rho = \dfrac{RA}{L} = \dfrac{(0.104 \text{ }\Omega)\pi(1.25 \times 10^{-3} \text{ m})^2}{14.0 \text{ m}} = 3.65 \times 10^{-8} \text{ }\Omega \cdot \text{m}$

EVALUATE: This value is similar to that for good metallic conductors in Table 25.1.

b) IDENTIFY and **SET UP:** Use $V = EL$ to calculate E and then Ohm's law gives I.

EXECUTE: $V = EL = (1.28 \text{ V/m})(14.0 \text{ m}) = 17.9 \text{ V}$

$$I = \frac{V}{R} = \frac{17.9 \text{ V}}{0.104 \text{ }\Omega} = 172 \text{ A}$$

EVALUATE: We could do the calculation another way:

$$E = \rho J \text{ so } J = \frac{E}{\rho} = \frac{1.28 \text{ V/m}}{3.65 \times 10^{-8} \text{ }\Omega \cdot \text{m}} = 3.51 \times 10^7 \text{ A/m}^2$$

$I = JA = (3.51 \times 10^7 \text{ A/m}^2)\pi(1.25 \times 10^{-3} \text{ m})^2 = 172 \text{ A}$, which checks

c) IDENTIFY and **SET UP:** Calculate $J = I/A$ or $J = E/\rho$ and then use Eq.(25.3) for the target variable v_d.

EXECUTE: $J = n|q|v_d = nev_d$

$$v_d = \frac{J}{ne} = \frac{3.51 \times 10^7 \text{ A/m}^2}{(8.5 \times 10^{28} \text{ m}^{-3})(1.602 \times 10^{-19} \text{ C})} = 2.58 \times 10^{-3} \text{ m/s} = 2.58 \text{ mm/s}$$

EVALUATE: Even for this very large current the drift speed is small.

25.55 IDENTIFY and **SET UP:** With the voltmeter connected across the terminals of the battery there is no current through the battery and the voltmeter reading is the battery emf; $\varepsilon = 12.6 \text{ V}$.

With a wire of resistance R connected to the battery current I flows and $\varepsilon - Ir - IR = 0$, where r is the internal resistance of the battery. Apply this equation to each piece of wire to get two equations in the two unknowns.

EXECUTE: Call the resistance of the 20.0-m piece R_1; then the resistance of the 40.0-m piece is $R_2 = 2R_1$.

$\varepsilon - I_1 r - I_1 R_1 = 0$; $12.6 \text{ V} - (7.00 \text{ A})r - (7.00 \text{ A})R_1 = 0$

$\varepsilon - I_2 r - I_2(2R_1) = 0$; $12.6 \text{ V} - (4.20 \text{ A})r - (4.20 \text{ A})(2R_1) = 0$

Solving these two equations in two unknowns gives $R_1 = 1.20 \text{ }\Omega$. This is the resistance of 20.0 m, so the resistance of one meter is $[1.20 \text{ }\Omega/(20.0 \text{ m})](1.00 \text{ m}) = 0.060 \text{ }\Omega$

EVALUATE: We can also solve for r and we get $r = 0.600 \text{ }\Omega$. When measuring small resistances, the internal resistance of the battery has a large effect.

25.59 a) IDENTIFY: Apply Eq.(25.10) to calculate the resistance of each thin disk and then integrate over the truncated cone to find the total resistance.

SET UP:

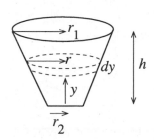

EXECUTE:
The radius of a truncated cone a distance y above the bottom is given by

$$r = r_2 + (y/h)(r_1 - r_2) = r_2 + y\beta$$
with $\beta = (r_1 - r_2)/h$

Consider a thin slice a distance y above the bottom. The slice has thickness dy and radius r. The resistance of the slice is

$$dR = \frac{\rho\, dy}{A} = \frac{\rho\, dy}{\pi r^2} = \frac{\rho\, dy}{\pi (r_2 + \beta y)^2}$$

The total resistance of the cone is obtained by integrating over these thin slices:

$$R = \int dR = \frac{\rho}{\pi} \int_0^h \frac{dy}{(r_2 + \beta y)^2} = \frac{\rho}{\pi}\left[-\frac{1}{\beta}(r_2 + y\beta)^{-1}\right]_0^h = -\frac{\rho}{\pi\beta}\left[\frac{1}{r_2 + h\beta} - \frac{1}{r_2}\right]$$

But $r_2 + h\beta = r_1$

$$R = \frac{\rho}{\pi\beta}\left[\frac{1}{r_2} - \frac{1}{r_1}\right] = \frac{\rho}{\pi}\left(\frac{h}{r_1 - r_2}\right)\left(\frac{r_1 - r_2}{r_1 r_2}\right) = \frac{\rho h}{\pi r_1 r_2}$$

b) **EVALUATE:** Let $r_1 = r_2 = r$. Then $R = \rho h/\pi r^2 = \rho L/A$ where $A = \pi r^2$ and $L = h$. This agrees with Eq.(25.10).

25.61 IDENTIFY and **SET UP:** Use $E = \rho J$ to calculate the current density between the plates. Let A be the area of each plate; then $I = JA$.

EXECUTE: $J = \dfrac{E}{\rho}$ and $E = \dfrac{\sigma}{K\epsilon_0} = \dfrac{Q}{KA\epsilon_0}$

Thus $J = \dfrac{Q}{KA\epsilon_0 \rho}$ and $I = JA = \dfrac{Q}{K\epsilon_0 \rho}$, as was to be shown.

EVALUATE: $C = K\epsilon_0 A/d$ and $V = Q/C = Qd/K\epsilon_0 A$ so the result can also be written as $I = VA/d\rho$. The resistance of the dielectric is $R = V/I = d\rho/A$, which agrees with Eq.(25.10).

25.65 IDENTIFY: In each case write the terminal voltage in terms of ε, I, and r. Since I is known, this gives two equations in the two unknowns ε and r.

SET UP:

$V_{ab} = 8.4$ V
$V_{ab} = \varepsilon - Ir$
$\varepsilon - (1.50\ \text{A})r = 8.4$ V

$I = 1.50$ A

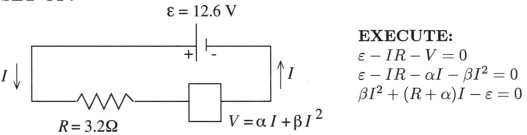

$$V_{ab} = 9.4 \text{ V}$$
$$V_{ab} = \varepsilon + Ir$$
$$\varepsilon + (3.50 \text{ A})r = 9.4 \text{ V}$$

$I = 3.50$ A

EXECUTE:

a) Solve the first equation for ε and use that result in the second equation:

$\varepsilon = 8.4 \text{ V} + (1.50 \text{ A})r$

$8.4 \text{ V} + (1.50 \text{ A})r + (3.50 \text{ A})r = 9.4 \text{ V}$

$(5.00 \text{ A})r = 1.0 \text{ V}$ so $r = \dfrac{1.0 \text{ V}}{5.00 \text{ A}} = 0.20 \text{ }\Omega$

b) Then $\varepsilon = 8.4 \text{ V} + (1.50 \text{ A})r = 8.4 \text{ V} + (1.50 \text{ A})(0.20 \text{ }\Omega) = 8.7 \text{ V}$

EVALUATE: When the current passes through the emf in the direction from $-$ to $+$, the terminal voltage is less than the emf and when it passes through from $+$ to $-$, the terminal voltage is greater than the emf.

25.69 IDENTIFY: Set the sum of the potential rises and drops around the circuit equal to zero and solve for I.

SET UP:

$\varepsilon = 12.6$ V

$I \downarrow$ $\quad$ $\uparrow I$

$R = 3.2\Omega$ $\qquad$ $V = \alpha I + \beta I^2$

EXECUTE:
$$\varepsilon - IR - V = 0$$
$$\varepsilon - IR - \alpha I - \beta I^2 = 0$$
$$\beta I^2 + (R + \alpha)I - \varepsilon = 0$$

The quadratic formula gives $I = (1/2\beta)[-(R + \alpha) \pm \sqrt{(R + \alpha)^2 + 4\beta\varepsilon}]$

I must be positive, so take the $+$ sign

$I = (1/2\beta)[-(R + \alpha) + \sqrt{(R + \alpha)^2 + 4\beta\varepsilon}]$

$I = -2.692 \text{ A} + 4.116 \text{ A} = 1.42 \text{ A}$

EVALUATE: For this I the voltage across the thermistor is 8.0 V. The voltage across the resistor must then be 12.6 V $-$ 8.0 V $=$ 4.6 V, and this agrees with Ohm's law for the resistor.

25.71 IDENTIFY: The ammeter acts as a resistance in the circuit loop. Set the sum of the potential rises and drops around the circuit equal to zero.

a) SET UP: With the ammeter in the circuit.

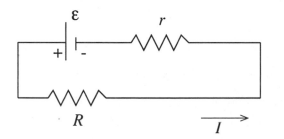

EXECUTE:

$$I_A = \frac{\varepsilon}{r + R + R_A}$$

$$\varepsilon = I_A(r + R + R_A)$$

SET UP: With the ammeter removed

EXECUTE:

$$I = \frac{\varepsilon}{R + r}$$

Combining the two equations gives

$$I = \left(\frac{1}{R+r}\right) I_A(r + R + R_A) = I_A\left(1 + \frac{R_A}{r + R}\right)$$

b) Want $I_A = 0.990I$. Use this in the result for part (a).

$$I = 0.990I\left(1 + \frac{R_A}{r + R}\right)$$

$$0.010 = 0.990\left(\frac{R_A}{r + R}\right)$$

$$R_A = (r + R)(0.010/0.990) = (0.45 \ \Omega + 3.80 \ \Omega)(0.010/0.990) = 0.0429 \ \Omega$$

c) $I - I_A = \dfrac{\varepsilon}{r + R} - \dfrac{\varepsilon}{r + R + R_A}$

$$I - I_A = \varepsilon\left(\frac{r + R + R_A - r - R}{(r + R)(r + R + R_A)}\right) = \frac{\varepsilon R_A}{(r + R)(r + R + R_A)}.$$

EVALUATE: The difference between I and I_A increases as R_A increases. If R_A is larger than the value calculated in part (b) then I_A differs from I by more than 1.0%.

25.75 a) IDENTIFY: Set the sum of the potential rises and drops around the circuit equal to zero and solve for the resulting equation for the current I. Apply Eq.(25.17) to each circuit element to find the power associated with it.

SET UP:

EXECUTE:

$$\varepsilon_1 - \varepsilon_2 - I(r_1 + r_2 + R) = 0$$

$$I = \frac{\varepsilon_1 - \varepsilon_2}{r_1 + r_2 + R}$$

$$I = \frac{12.0 \text{ V} - 8.0 \text{ V}}{1.0 \ \Omega + 1.0 \ \Omega + 8.0 \ \Omega}$$

$$I = 0.40 \text{ A}$$

b) $P = I^2 R + I^2 r_1 + I^2 r_2 = I^2 (R + r_1 + r_2) = (0.40 \text{ A})^2 (8.0 \ \Omega + 1.0 \ \Omega + 1.0 \ \Omega)$

$P = 1.6 \text{ W}$

c) Chemical energy is converted to electrical energy in a battery when the current goes through the battery from the negative to the positive terminal, so the electrical energy of the charges increases as the current passes through. This happens in the 12.0 V battery, and the rate of production of electrical energy is $P = \varepsilon_1 I = (12.0 \text{ V})(0.40 \text{ A}) = 4.8 \text{ W}$.

d) Electrical energy is converted to chemical energy in a battery when the current goes through the battery from the positive to the negative terminal, so the electrical energy of the charges decreases as the current passes through. This happens in the 8.0 V battery, and the rate of consumption of electrical energy is $P = \varepsilon_2 I = (8.0 \text{ V})(0.40 \text{ A}) = 3.2 \text{ W}$.

e) EVALUATE: Total rate of production of electrical energy $= 4.8$ W.

Total rate of consumption of electrical energy $= 1.6$ W $+ 3.2$ W $= 4.8$ W, which equals the rate of production, as it must.

25.77 IDENTIFY: Apply $\vec{F} = m\vec{a}$ with $\vec{F} = |q|\vec{E}$ and use $V_{bc} = EL$ to relate a and V_{bc}.

a) SET UP:

EXECUTE:

$$\sum \vec{F} = m\vec{a}$$

$|q|E = ma$ and then $|q|/m = a/E$

b) $V_{bc} = EL$ so $E = V_{bc}/L$

Using this in the expression from part (a) gives $|q|/m = aL/V_{bc}$

c) SET UP:

EXECUTE: If the acceleration is to the right the force on the free charges must be to the right. For a negative charge the force and electric field are in opposite directions, so $\vec{E}$ is to the left.

b● ←——— E ●c

$\vec{E}$ points from high potential so point c is at higher potential.

d) From part (b),

$$a = \frac{V_{bc}}{L}\frac{|q|}{m} = \left(\frac{1.00 \times 10^{-3} \text{ V}}{0.50 \text{ m}}\right)\left(\frac{1.60 \times 10^{-19} \text{ C}}{9.11 \times 10^{-31} \text{ kg}}\right) = 3.5 \times 10^8 \text{ m/s}^2.$$

e) EVALUATE: The acceleration required in part (d) is quite large. The rotating spool with many turns allows for a very large length L of wire. From $V_{bc} = aL(m/|q|)$ this increases V_{bc} and makes it easier to measure.

CHAPTER 26

DIRECT-CURRENT CIRCUITS

Exercises

26.5 **IDENTIFY:** Eq.(26.2) gives the equivalent resistance of the three resistors in parallel. For resistors in parallel, the voltages are the same and the currents add.

a) SET UP:

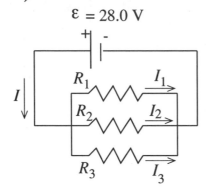

$\mathcal{E} = 28.0$ V

R_1 I_1

R_2 I_2

R_3 I_3

EXECUTE:
parallel

$$\frac{1}{R_{eq}} = \frac{1}{R_1} + \frac{1}{R_2} + \frac{1}{R_3}$$

$$\frac{1}{R_{eq}} = \frac{1}{1.60 \ \Omega} + \frac{1}{2.40 \ \Omega} + \frac{1}{4.80 \ \Omega}$$

$$R_{eq} = 0.800 \ \Omega$$

b) For resistors in parallel the voltage is the same across each and equal to the applied voltage; $V_1 = V_2 = V_3 = \varepsilon = 28.0$ V

$$V = IR \text{ so } I_1 = \frac{V_1}{R_1} = \frac{28.0 \text{ V}}{1.60 \ \Omega} = 17.5 \text{ A}$$

$$I_2 = \frac{V_2}{R_2} = \frac{28.0 \text{ V}}{2.40 \ \Omega} = 11.7 \text{ A and } I_3 = \frac{V_3}{R_3} = \frac{28.0 \text{ V}}{4.8 \ \Omega} = 5.8 \text{ A}$$

c) The currents through the resistors add to give the current through the battery:
$I = I_1 + I_2 + I_3 = 17.5 \text{ A} + 11.7 \text{ A} + 5.8 \text{ A} = 35.0 \text{ A}$

EVALUATE: Alternatively, we can use the equivalent resistance R_{eq}:

$\mathcal{E} = 28.0$ V

$R_{eq} = 0.800 \Omega$

$$\varepsilon - IR_{eq} = 0$$

$$I = \frac{\varepsilon}{R_{eq}} = \frac{28.0 \text{ V}}{0.800 \ \Omega} = 35.0 \text{ A},$$
which checks

d) As shown in part (b), the voltage across each resistor is 28.0 V.

e) IDENTIFY and **SET UP:** We can use any of the three expressions for P: $P = VI = I^2R = V^2/R$. They will all give the same results, if we keep enough significant figures in intermediate calculations.

EXECUTE: Using $P = V^2/R$,

$$P_1 = V_1^2/R_1 = \frac{(28.0 \text{ V})^2}{1.60 \text{ } \Omega} = 490 \text{ W}, \quad P_2 = V_2^2/R_2 = \frac{(28.0 \text{ V})^2}{2.40 \text{ } \Omega} = 327 \text{ W, and}$$

$$P_3 = V_3^2/R_3 = \frac{(28.0 \text{ V})^2}{4.80 \text{ } \Omega} = 163 \text{ W}$$

EVALUATE: The total power dissipated is $P_{\text{out}} = P_1 + P_2 + P_3 = 980 \text{ W}$. This is the same as the power $P_{\text{in}} = \varepsilon I = (28.0 \text{ V})(35.0 \text{ A}) = 980 \text{ W}$ delivered by the battery.

f) $P = V^2/R$. The resistors in parallel each have the same voltage, so the power P is largest for the one with the least resistance.

26.7   IDENTIFY and **SET UP:** Use Eq.(25.18).
EXECUTE:

a) $P = V_{ab}^2/R$, so $V_{ab} = \sqrt{PR} = \sqrt{(5.0 \text{ W})(15 \times 10^3 \text{ } \Omega)} = 270 \text{ V}$.

b) $P = \dfrac{V_{ab}^2}{R} = \dfrac{(120 \text{ V})^2}{9.0 \times 10^3 \text{ } \Omega} = 1.6 \text{ W}$

EVALUATE: For a given R, smaller voltage gives smaller P. For a given voltage, smaller R gives larger P.

26.9   IDENTIFY: Replace the series combinations of resistors by their equivalents. In the resulting parallel network the battery voltage is the voltage across each resistor.

SET UP:

EXECUTE:
R_1 and R_2 in series have an equivalent resistance of
$R_{12} = R_1 + R_2 = 4.00 \text{ } \Omega$

R_3 and R_4 in series have an equivalent resistance of
$R_{34} = R_3 + R_4 = 12.0 \text{ } \Omega$

The circuit is equivalent to

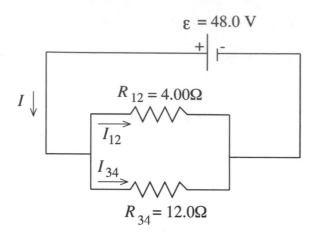

$\varepsilon = 48.0$ V

R_{12} and R_{34} in parallel are equivalent to R_{eq} given by

$$\frac{1}{R_{eq}} = \frac{1}{R_{12}} + \frac{1}{R_{34}} = \frac{R_{12} + R_{34}}{R_{12} R_{34}}$$

$$R_{eq} = \frac{R_{12} R_{34}}{R_{12} + R_{34}}$$

$$R_{eq} = \frac{(4.00\ \Omega)(12.0\ \Omega)}{4.00\ \Omega + 12.0\ \Omega} = 3.00\ \Omega$$

The voltage across each branch of the parallel combination is ε, so $\varepsilon - I_{12} R_{12} = 0$.

$$I_{12} = \frac{\varepsilon}{R_{12}} = \frac{48.0\ \text{V}}{4.00\ \Omega} = 12.0\ \text{A}$$

$$\varepsilon - I_{34} R_{34} = 0 \text{ so } I_{34} = \frac{\varepsilon}{R_{34}} = \frac{48.0\ \text{V}}{12.0\ \Omega} = 4.0\ \text{A}$$

The current is 12.0 Ω through the 1.00 Ω and 3.00 Ω resistors, and it is 4.0 A through the 7.00 Ω and 5.00 Ω resistors.

EVALUATE: The current through the battery is $I = I_{12} + I_{34} = 12.0$ A $+$ 4.0 A $= 16.0$ A, and this is equal to $\varepsilon / R_{eq} = 48.0$ V$/3.00\ \Omega = 16.0$ A.

26.11 IDENTIFY: In both circuits, with and without R_4, replace series and parallel combinations of resistors by their equivalents. Calculate the currents and voltages in the equivalent circuit and infer from this the currents and voltages in the original circuit. Use $P = I^2 R$ to calculate the power dissipated in each bulb.

a) SET UP:

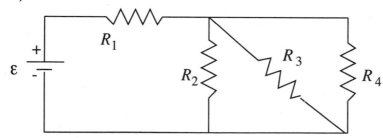

EXECUTE:
R_2, R_3, and R_4 are in parallel, so their equivalent resistance R_{eq} is given by

$$\frac{1}{R_{eq}} = \frac{1}{R_2} + \frac{1}{R_3} + \frac{1}{R_4}$$

$$\frac{1}{R_{eq}} = \frac{3}{4.50\ \Omega} \text{ and } R_{eq} = 1.50\ \Omega.$$

The equivalent circuit is

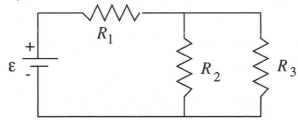

$$\varepsilon - I(R_1 + R_{eq}) = 0$$

$$I = \frac{\varepsilon}{R_1 + R_{eq}}$$

$$I = \frac{9.00 \text{ V}}{4.50 \ \Omega + 1.50 \ \Omega} = 1.50 \text{ A and } I_1 = 1.50 \text{ A}$$

Then $V_1 = I_1 R_1 = (1.50 \text{ A})(4.50 \ \Omega) = 6.75 \text{ V}$

$I_{eq} = 1.50 \text{ A}$, $V_{eq} = I_{eq} R_{eq} = (1.50 \text{ A})(1.50 \ \Omega) - 2.25 \text{ V}$

For resistors in parallel the voltages are equal and are the same as the voltage across the equivalent resistor, so $V_2 = V_3 = V_4 = 2.25 \text{ V}$.

$$I_2 = \frac{V_2}{R_2} = \frac{2.25 \text{ V}}{4.50 \ \Omega} = 0.500 \text{ A}, \ I_3 = \frac{V_3}{R_3} = 0.500 \text{ A}, \ I_4 = \frac{V_4}{R_4} = 0.500 \text{ A}$$

EVALUATE: Note that $I_2 + I_3 + I_4 = 1.50 \text{ A}$, which is I_{eq}. For resistors in parallel the currents add and their sum is the current through the equivalent resistor.

b) SET UP: $P - I^2 R$

EXECUTE: $P_1 = (1.50 \text{ A})^2 (4.50 \ \Omega) = 10.1 \text{ W}$

$P_2 = P_3 = P_4 = (0.500 \text{ A})^2 (4.50 \ \Omega) = 1.125 \text{ W}$, which rounds to 1.12 W.

EVALUATE: Note that $P_2 + P_3 + P_4 = 3.37 \text{ W}$. This equals $P_{eq} = I_{eq}^2 R_{eq} = (1.50 \text{ A})^2 (1.50 \ \Omega) = 3.37 \text{ W}$, the power dissipated in the equivalent resistor.

c) SET UP: With R_4 removed the circuit becomes

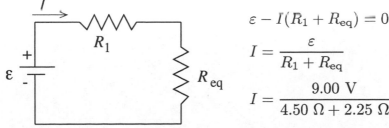

EXECUTE:

R_2 and R_3 are in parallel and their equivalent resistance R_{eq} is given by

$$\frac{1}{R_{eq}} = \frac{1}{R_2} + \frac{1}{R_3} = \frac{2}{4.50 \ \Omega}$$

and $R_{eq} = 2.25 \ \Omega$

The equivalent circuit is

$$\varepsilon - I(R_1 + R_{eq}) = 0$$

$$I = \frac{\varepsilon}{R_1 + R_{eq}}$$

$$I = \frac{9.00 \text{ V}}{4.50 \ \Omega + 2.25 \ \Omega} = 1.333 \text{ A}$$

$I_1 = 1.33$ A, $V_1 = I_1 R_1 = (1.333$ A$)(4.50 \ \Omega) = 6.00$ V

$I_{eq} = 1.33$ A, $V_{eq} = I_{eq} R_{eq} = (1.333$ A$)(2.25 \ \Omega) = 3.00$ V and $V_2 = V_3 = 3.00$ V.

$$I_2 = \frac{V_2}{R_2} = \frac{3.00 \text{ V}}{4.50 \ \Omega} = 0.667 \text{ A}, \quad I_3 = \frac{V_3}{R_3} = 0.667 \text{ A}$$

d) **SET UP:** $P = I^2 R$

EXECUTE: $P_1 = (1.333$ A$)^2(4.50 \ \Omega) = 8.00$ W

$P_2 = P_3 = (0.667$ A$)^2(4.50 \ \Omega) = 2.00$ W.

e) **EVALUATE:** When R_4 is removed, P_1 decreases and P_2 and P_3 increase. Bulb R_1 glows less brightly and bulbs R_2 and R_3 glow more brightly. When R_4 is removed the equivalent resistance of the circuit increases and the current through R_1 decreases. But in the parallel combination this current divides into two equal currents rather than three, so the currents through R_2 and R_3 increase. Can also see this by noting that with R_4 removed and less current through R_1 the voltage drop across R_1 is less so the voltage drop across R_2 and across R_3 must become larger.

26.15 IDENTIFY: For resistors in series, the voltages add and the current is the same. For resistors in parallel, the voltages are the same and the currents add. $P = I^2 R$.

a) **SET UP:**

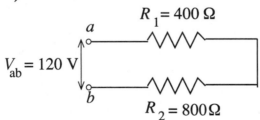

For resistors in series the current is the same through each.

EXECUTE: $R_{eq} = R_1 + R_2 = 1200 \ \Omega$.

$I = \dfrac{V}{R_{eq}} = \dfrac{120 \text{ V}}{1200 \ \Omega} = 0.100$ A. This is the current drawn from the line.

b) $P_1 = I_1^2 R_1 = (0.100$ A$)^2(400 \ \Omega) = 4.0$ W

$P_2 = I_2^2 R_2 = (0.100$ A$)^2(800 \ \Omega) = 8.0$ W

$P_{out} = P_1 + P_2 = 12.0$ W, the total power dissipated in both bulbs.

Note that $P_{in} = V_{ab} I = (120$ V$)(0.100$ A$) = 12.0$ W, the power delivered by the potential source, equals P_{out}.

c) **SET UP:**

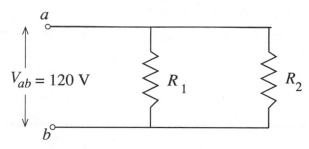

For resistors in parallel the voltage across each resistor is the same.

EXECUTE: $I_1 = \dfrac{V_1}{R_1} = \dfrac{120 \text{ V}}{400 \ \Omega} = 0.300 \text{ A}, \quad I_2 = \dfrac{V_2}{R_2} = \dfrac{120 \text{ V}}{800 \ \Omega} = 0.150 \text{ A}$

EVALUATE: Note that each current is larger than the current when the resistors are connected in series.

d) EXECUTE: $P_1 = I_1^2 R_1 = (0.300 \text{ A})^2 (400 \ \Omega) = 36.0 \text{ W}$

$P_2 = I_2^2 R_2 = (0.150 \text{ A})^2 (800 \ \Omega) = 18.0 \text{ W}$

$P_{\text{out}} = P_1 + P_2 = 54.0 \text{ W}$

EVALUATE: Note that the total current drawn from the line is $I = I_1 + I_2 = 0.450$ A. The power input from the line is $P_{\text{in}} = V_{ab}I = (120 \text{ V})(0.450 \text{ A}) = 54.0$ W, which equals the total power dissipated by the bulbs.

e) The bulb that is dissipating the most power glows most brightly. For the series connection the currents are the same and by $P = I^2 R$ the bulb with the larger R has the larger P; the 800 Ω bulb glows more brightly.

For the parallel combination the voltages are the same and by $P = V^2/R$ the bulb with the smaller R has the larger P; the 400 Ω bulb glows more brightly.

The total power output P_{out} equals $P_{\text{in}} = V_{ab}I$, so P_{out} is larger for the parallel connection where the current drawn from the line is larger (because the equivalent resistance is smaller).

26.17 IDENTIFY and **SET UP:** Replace series and parallel combinations of resistors by their equivalents until the circuit is reduced to a single loop. Use the loop equation to find the current through the 20.0 Ω resistor. Set $P = I^2 R$ for the 20.0 Ω resistor equal to the rate Q/t at which heat goes into the water and set $Q = mc\,\Delta T$.

EXECUTE: Replace the network by the equivalent resistor.

$30.0 \text{ V} - I(20.0 \ \Omega + 5.0 \ \Omega + 5.0 \ \Omega) = 0; \qquad I = 1.00 \text{ A}$

For the 20.0-Ω resistor thermal energy is generated at the rate $P = I^2 R = 20.0$ W.

$Q = Pt$ and $Q = mc \, \Delta T$ gives

$$t = \frac{mc \, \Delta T}{P} = \frac{(0.100 \text{ kg})(4190 \text{ J/kg} \cdot \text{K})(48.0 \text{ C}^\circ)}{20.0 \text{ W}} = 1.01 \times 10^3 \text{ s}$$

EVALUATE: The battery is supplying heat at the rate $P = \varepsilon I = 30.0$ W. In the series circuit, more energy is dissipated in the larger resistor (20.0 Ω) than in the smaller ones (5.00 Ω).

26.19 IDENTIFY: Apply Kirchhoff's point rule at point a to find the current through R. Apply Kirchhoff's loop rule to loops (1) and (2) shown in the sketch to calculate R and ε. Travel around each loop in the direction shown.

a) SET UP:

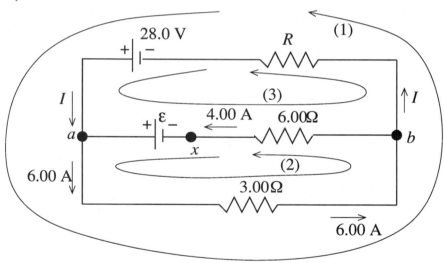

EXECUTE: Apply Kirchhoff's point rule to point a:

$\sum I = 0$ so $I + 4.00 \text{ A} - 6.00 \text{ A} = 0$

$I = 2.00$ A (in the direction shown in the diagram).

b) Apply Kirchhoff's loop rule to loop (1):

$-(6.00 \text{ A})(3.00 \ \Omega) - (2.00 \text{ A})R + 28.0 \text{ V} = 0$

$-18.0 \text{ V} - (2.00 \ \Omega)R + 28.0 \text{ V} = 0$

$$R = \frac{28.0 \text{ V} - 18.0 \text{ V}}{2.00 \text{ A}} = 5.00 \ \Omega$$

c) Apply Kirchhoff's loop rule to loop (2):

$-(6.00 \text{ A})(3.00 \ \Omega) - (4.00 \text{ A})(6.00 \ \Omega) + \varepsilon = 0$

$\varepsilon = 18.0 \text{ V} + 24.0 \text{ V} = 42.0 \text{ V}$

EVALUATE: Can check that the loop rule is satisfied for loop (3), as a check of our work:

$28.0 \text{ V} - \varepsilon + (4.00 \text{ A})(6.00 \text{ }\Omega) - (2.00 \text{ A})R = 0$

$28.0 \text{ V} - 42.0 \text{ V} + 24.0 \text{ V} - (2.00 \text{ A})(5.00 \text{ }\Omega) = 0$

$52.0 \text{ V} = 42.0 \text{ V} + 10.0 \text{ V}$

$52.0 \text{ V} = 52.0 \text{ V}$, so the loop rule is satisfied for this loop.

d) IDENTIFY: If the circuit is broken at point x there can be no current in the 6.00 Ω resistor. There is now only a single current path and we can apply the loop rule to this path.

SET UP:

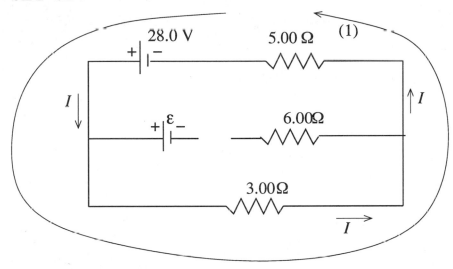

EXECUTE: $+28.0 \text{ V} - (3.00 \text{ }\Omega)I - (5.00 \text{ }\Omega)I = 0$

$I = \dfrac{28.0 \text{ V}}{8.00 \text{ }\Omega} = 3.50 \text{ A}$

EVALUATE: Breaking the circuit at x removes the 42.0 V emf from the circuit and the current through the 3.00 Ω resistor is reduced.

26.21 **IDENTIFY:** Apply the junction rule at points a, b, c and d to calculate the unknown currents. Then apply the loop rule to three loops to calculate ε_1, ε_2 and R.

a) SET UP:

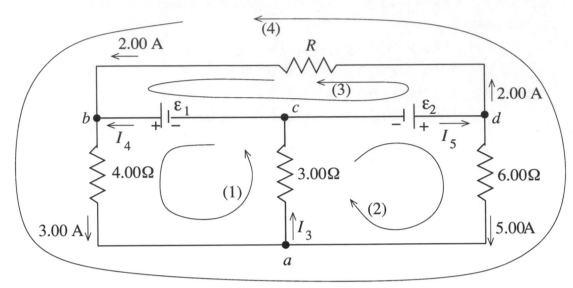

EXECUTE: Apply the junction rule to point a.

$3.00 \text{ A} + 5.00 \text{ A} - I_3 = 0$

$I_3 = 8.00 \text{ A}$

Apply the junction rule to point b.

$2.00 \text{ A} + I_4 - 3.00 \text{ A} = 0$

$I_4 = 1.00 \text{ A}$

Apply the junction rule to point c:

$I_3 - I_4 - I_5 = 0$

$I_5 = I_3 - I_4 = 8.00 \text{ A} - 1.00 \text{ A} = 7.00 \text{ A}$

EVALUATE: As a check, apply the junction rule to point d.

$I_5 - 2.00 \text{ A} - 5.00 \text{ A} = 0$

$I_5 = 7.00 \text{ A}$

b) EXECUTE: Apply the loop rule to loop (1):

$\varepsilon_1 - (3.00 \text{ A})(4.00 \text{ } \Omega) - I_3(3.00 \text{ } \Omega) = 0$

$\varepsilon_1 = 12.0 \text{ V} + (8.00 \text{ A})(3.00 \text{ } \Omega) = 36.0 \text{ V}$

Apply the loop rule to loop (2):

$\varepsilon_2 - (5.00 \text{ A})(6.00 \text{ } \Omega) - I_3(3.00 \text{ } \Omega) = 0$

$\varepsilon_2 = 30.0 \text{ V} + (8.00 \text{ A})(3.00 \text{ } \Omega) = 54.0 \text{ V}$

c) Apply the loop rule to loop (3):

$-(2.00 \text{ A})R - \varepsilon_1 + \varepsilon_2 = 0$

$$R = \frac{\varepsilon_2 - \varepsilon_1}{2.00 \text{ A}} = \frac{54.0 \text{ V} - 36.0 \text{ V}}{2.00 \text{ A}} = 9.00 \ \Omega$$

EVALUATE: Apply the loop rule to loop (4) as a check of our calculations:

$-(2.00 \text{ A})R - (3.00 \text{ A})(4.00 \ \Omega) + (5.00 \text{ A})(6.00 \ \Omega) = 0$

$-(2.00 \text{ A})(9.00 \ \Omega) - 12.0 \text{ V} + 30.0 \text{ V} = 0$

$-18.0 \text{ V} + 18.0 \text{ V} = 0$

26.23 **IDENTIFY:** Apply the junction rule to reduce the number of unknown currents. Apply the loop rule to two loops to obtain two equations for the unknown currents I_1 and I_2

a) SET UP:

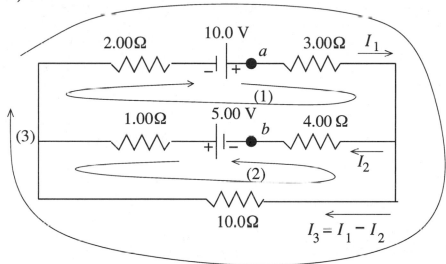

Let I_1 be the current in the 3.00 Ω resistor and I_2 be the current in the 4.00 Ω resistor and assume that these currents are in the directions shown. Then the current in the 10.0 Ω resistor is $I_3 = I_1 - I_2$, in the direction shown, where we have used Kirchhoff's point rule to relate I_3 to I_1 and I_2. If we get a negative answer for any of these currents we know the current is actually in the opposite direction to what we have assumed.

Three loops and directions to travel around the loops are shown in the circuit diagram. Apply Kirchhoff's loop rule to each loop.

EXECUTE:

loop (1)

$+10.0 \text{ V} - I_1(3.00 \ \Omega) - I_2(4.00 \ \Omega) + 5.00 \text{ V} - I_2(1.00 \ \Omega) - I_1(2.00 \ \Omega) = 0$

$15.00 \text{ V} - (5.00 \ \Omega)I_1 - (5.00 \ \Omega)I_2 = 0$

$3.00 \text{ A} - I_1 - I_2 = 0$

loop (2)

$+5.00 \text{ V} - I_2(1.00 \ \Omega) + (I_1 - I_2)10.0 \ \Omega - I_2(4.00 \ \Omega) = 0$

$5.00 \text{ V} + (10.0 \text{ } \Omega)I_1 - (15.0 \text{ } \Omega)I_2 = 0$

$1.00 \text{ A} + 2.00I_1 - 3.00I_2 = 0$

The first equation says $I_2 = 3.00 \text{ A} - I_1$.

Use this in the second equation: $1.00 \text{ A} + 2.00I_1 - 9.00 \text{ A} + 3.00I_1 = 0$

$5.00I_1 = 8.00 \text{ A}, \quad I_1 = 1.60 \text{ A}$

Then $I_2 = 3.00 \text{ A} - I_1 = 3.00 \text{ A} - 1.60 \text{ A} = 1.40 \text{ A}$.

$I_3 = I_1 - I_2 = 1.60 \text{ A} - 1.40 \text{ A} = 0.20 \text{ A}$

EVALUATE: Loop (3) can be used as a check.

$+10.0 \text{ V} - (1.60 \text{ A})(3.00 \text{ } \Omega) - (0.20 \text{ A})(10.00 \text{ } \Omega) - (1.60 \text{ A})(2.00 \text{ } \Omega) = 0$

$10.0 \text{ V} = 4.8 \text{ V} + 2.0 \text{ V} + 3.2 \text{ V}$

$10.0 \text{ V} = 10.0 \text{ V}$

We find that with our calculated currents the loop rule is satisfied for loop (3).

Also, all the currents came out to be positive, so the current directions in the circuit diagram are correct.

b) IDENTIFY and **SET UP:** To find $V_{ab} = V_a - V_b$ start at point b and travel to point a. Many different routes can be taken from b to a and all must yield the same result for V_{ab}.

EXECUTE: Travel through the 4.00 Ω resistor and then through the 3.00 Ω resistor: $V_b + I_2(4.00 \text{ } \Omega) + I_1(3.00 \text{ } \Omega) = V_a$

$V_a - V_b = (1.40 \text{ A})(4.00 \text{ } \Omega) + (1.60 \text{ A})(3.00 \text{ } \Omega) = 5.60 \text{ V} + 4.80 \text{ V} = 10.4 \text{ V}$ (point a is at higher potential than point b)

EVALUATE: Alternatively, travel through the 5.00 V emf, the 1.00 Ω resistor, the 2.00 Ω resistor, and the 10.0 V emf.

$V_b + 5.00 \text{ V} - I_2(1.00 \text{ } \Omega) - I_1(2.00 \text{ } \Omega) + 10.0 \text{ V} = V_a$

$V_a - V_b = 15.0 \text{ V} - (1.40 \text{ A})(1.00 \text{ } \Omega) - (1.60 \text{ A})(2.00 \text{ } \Omega) = 15.0 \text{ V} - 1.40 \text{ V} - 3.20 \text{ V} = 10.4 \text{ V}$, the same as before.

26.29 IDENTIFY: The galvanometer is represented in the circuit as a resistance R_c. Use the junction rule to relate the current through the galvanometer and the current through the shunt resistor. The voltage drop across each parallel path is the same; use this to write an equation for the resistance R.

SET UP:

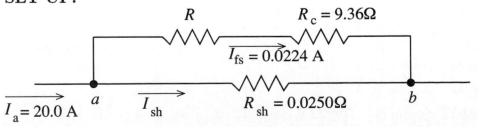

We want that $I_a = 20.0$ A in the external circuit to produce $I_{fs} = 0.0224$ A through the galvanometer coil.

EXECUTE: Applying the junction rule to point a gives

$I_a - I_{fs} - I_{sh} = 0$

$I_{sh} = I_a - I_{fs} = 20.0$ A $- 0.0224$ A $= 19.98$ A

The potential difference V_{ab} between points a and b must be the same for both paths between these two points:

$I_{fs}(R + R_c) = I_{sh}R_{sh}$

$R = \dfrac{I_{sh}R_{sh}}{I_{fs}} - R_c = \dfrac{(19.98 \text{ A})(0.0250 \text{ }\Omega)}{0.0224 \text{ A}} - 9.36 \text{ }\Omega = 22.30 \text{ }\Omega - 9.36 \text{ }\Omega = 12.9 \text{ }\Omega$

EVALUATE: $R_{sh} << R + R_c$; most of the current goes through the shunt. Adding R decreases the fraction of the current that goes through R_c.

26.37 IDENTIFY: Apply the loop rule to obtain a relation between i and q.

The time constant τ is given by Eq.(26.14).

a) SET UP:

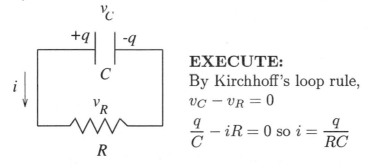

EXECUTE:
By Kirchhoff's loop rule,
$v_C - v_R = 0$
$\dfrac{q}{C} - iR = 0$ so $i = \dfrac{q}{RC}$

Just after the connection is made the charge q on the capacitor hasn't had any time to decrease from its initial value of 6.55×10^{-8} C, so

$i = \dfrac{q}{RC} = \dfrac{6.55 \times 10^{-8} \text{ C}}{(1.28 \times 10^6 \text{ }\Omega)(4.55 \times 10^{-10} \text{ F})} - 1.12 \times 10^{-4} \text{ A}$

b) Eq.(26.14): $\tau = RC = (1.28 \times 10^6 \text{ }\Omega)(4.55 \times 10^{-10} \text{ F}) = 5.82 \times 10^{-4}$ s

EVALUATE: Just after the connection is made the voltage across the capacitor is $v_C = q/C = 143$ V and the voltage across the resistor is $v_R = iR = 143$ V. The time constant is small and the capactior discharges quickly.

26.41 IDENTIFY and **SET UP:** Apply the loop rule. The voltage across the resistor depends on the current through it and the voltage across the capacitor depends on the charge on its plates.

EXECUTE: $\varepsilon - V_R - V_C = 0$

$\varepsilon = 120$ V, $V_R = IR = (0.900 \text{ A})(80.0 \text{ }\Omega) = 72$ V, so $V_C = 48$ V

$Q = CV = (4.00 \times 10^{-6} \text{ F})(48 \text{ V}) = 192 \ \mu\text{C}$

EVALUATE: The initial charge is zero and the final charge is $C\varepsilon = 480 \ \mu\text{C}$. Since current is flowing at the instant considered in the problem the capacitor is still being charged and its charge has not reached its final value.

26.43 IDENTIFY: For each circuit apply the loop rule to relate the voltages across the circuit elements.

a) SET UP: With the switch in position 2 the circuit is the charging circuit.

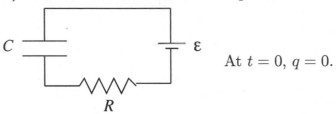

At $t = 0$, $q = 0$.

EXECUTE: The charge q on the capacitor is given as a function of time by Eq.(26.12):

$q = C\varepsilon(1 - e^{-t/RC})$

$Q_f = C\varepsilon = (1.50 \times 10^{-5} \text{ F})(18.0 \text{ V}) = 2.70 \times 10^{-4}$ C.

$RC = (980 \ \Omega)(1.50 \times 10^{-5} \text{ F}) = 0.0147$ s

Thus, at $t = 0.0100$ s, $q = (2.70 \times 10^{-4} \text{ C})(1 - e^{-(0.0100 \text{ s})/(0.0147 \text{ s})}) = 133 \ \mu\text{C}$.

b) $v_C = \dfrac{q}{C} = \dfrac{133 \ \mu\text{C}}{1.50 \times 10^{-5} \text{ F}} = 8.87$ V

The loop rule says $\varepsilon - v_C - v_R = 0$

$v_R = \varepsilon - v_C = 18.0 \text{ V} - 8.87 \text{ V} = 9.13$ V

c) SET UP: Throwing the switch back to position 1 produces the discharging circuit.

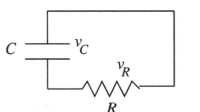

The initial charge Q_0 is the charge calculated in part (b), $Q_0 = 133 \ \mu\text{C}$.

EXECUTE: $v_C = \dfrac{q}{C} = \dfrac{133 \ \mu\text{C}}{1.50 \times 10^{-5} \text{ F}} = 8.87$ V, the same as just before the switch is thrown. But now $v_C - v_R = 0$, so $v_R = v_C = 8.87$ V.

d) SET UP: In the discharging circuit the charge on the capacitor as a function of time is given by Eq.(26.16): $q = Q_0 e^{-t/RC}$.

EXECUTE: $RC = 0.0147$ s, the same as in part (a). Thus at $t = 0.0100$ s,

$q = (133 \ \mu\text{C})e^{-((0.0100 \text{ s})/(0.0147 \text{ s}))} = 67.4 \ \mu\text{C}$.

EVALUATE: $t = 10.0$ ms is less than one time constant, so at the instant described in part (a) the capacitor is not fully charged; its voltage (8.87 V) is less than the emf. There is a charging current and a voltage drop across the resistor. In the discharging circuit the voltage across the capacitor starts at 8.87 V and decreases. After $t = 10.0$ ms it has decreased to $v_C = q/C = 4.49$ V.

26.45 IDENTIFY and **SET UP:** The heater and hair dryer are in parallel so the voltage across each is 120 V and the current through the fuse is the sum of the currents through each appliance. As the power consumed by the dryer increases the current through it increases. The maximum power setting is the highest one for which the current through the fuse is less than 20 A.

EXECUTE: Find the current through the heater.

$P = VI$ so $I = P/V = 1500$ W$/120$ V $= 12.5$ A.

The maximum total current allowed is 20 A, so the current through the dryer must be less than 20 A $-$ 12.5 A $= 7.5$ A. The power dissipated by the dryer if the current has this value is $P = VI = (120$ V$)(7.5$ A$) = 900$ W. For P at this value or larger the circuit breaker trips.

EVALUATE: $P = V^2/R$ and for the dryer V is a constant 120 V. The higher power settings correspond to a smaller resistance R and larger current through the device.

26.47 IDENTIFY and **SET UP:** Ohm's law and Eq.(25.18) can be used to calculate I and P given V and R. Use Eq.(25.12) to calculate the resistance at the higher temperature.

a) EXECUTE: When the heater element is first turned on it is at room temperature and has resistance $R = 20$ Ω.

$$I = \frac{V}{R} = \frac{120 \text{ V}}{20 \text{ }\Omega} = 6.0 \text{ A}$$

$$P = \frac{V^2}{R} = \frac{(120 \text{ V})^2}{20 \text{ }\Omega} = 720 \text{ W}$$

b) Find the resistance $R(T)$ of the element at the operating temperature of 280°C. Take $T_0 = 23.0°$C and $R_0 = 20$ Ω. Eq.(25.12) gives $R(T) = R_0(1 + \alpha(T - T_0)) = 20$ $\Omega(1 + (2.8 \times 10^{-3}(\text{C}°)^{-1})(280°$C $- 23.0°$C$)) = 34.4$ Ω.

$$I = \frac{V}{R} = \frac{120 \text{ V}}{34.4 \text{ }\Omega} = 3.5 \text{ A}$$

$$P = \frac{V^2}{R} = \frac{(120 \text{ V})^2}{34.4 \text{ }\Omega} = 420 \text{ W}$$

EVALUATE: When the temperature increases, R increases and I and P decrease. The changes are substantial.

Problems

26.49 a) IDENTIFY: Two of the resistors in series would each dissipate one-half the total, or 1.2 W, which is ok. But the series combination would have an equivalent resistance of 800 Ω, not the 400 Ω that is required. Resistors in parallel have an equivalent resistance that is less than that of the individual resistors, so a solution is two in series in parallel with another two in series.

SET UP:

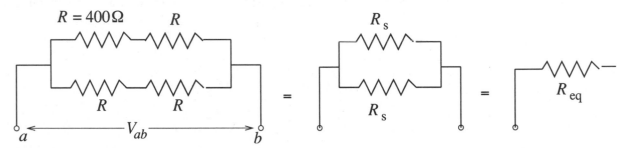

EXECUTE: R_s is the resistance equivalent to two of the 400 Ω resistors in series. $R_s = R + R = 800\ \Omega$.

R_{eq} is the resistance equivalent to the two $R_s = 800\ \Omega$ resistors in parallel:

$$\frac{1}{R_{eq}} = \frac{1}{R_s} + \frac{1}{R_s} = \frac{2}{R_s};\ R_{eq} = \frac{800\ \Omega}{2} = 400\ \Omega.$$

EVALUATE: This combination does have the required 400 Ω equivalent resistance. It will be shown in part (b) that a total of 2.4 W can be dissipated without exceeding the power rating of each individual resistor.

IDENTIFY: Another solution is two resistors in parallel in series with two more in parallel.

SET UP:

EXECUTE: $\dfrac{1}{R_p} = \dfrac{1}{R} + \dfrac{1}{R} = \dfrac{2}{400\ \Omega};\quad R_p = 200\ \Omega$

$R_{eq} = R_p + R_p = 400\ \Omega$

EVALUATE: This combination has the required 400 Ω equivalent resistance. It will be shown in part (b) that a total of 2.4 W can be dissipated without exceeding the power rating of each individual resistor.

b) IDENTIFY and **SET UP:** Find the applied voltage V_{ab} such that a total of 2.4 W is dissipated and then for this V_{ab} find the power dissipated by each resistor.

EXECUTE: For a combination with equivalent resistance $R_{eq} = 400\ \Omega$ to dissipate 2.4 W the voltage V_{ab} applied to the network must be given by

$P = V_{ab}^2/R_{eq}$ so $V_{ab} = \sqrt{PR_{eq}} = \sqrt{(2.4\text{ W})(400\ \Omega)} = 31.0$ V and the current through the equivalent resistance is $I = V_{ab}/R = 31.0\text{ V}/400\ \Omega = 0.0775$ A.

For the first combination this means 31.0 V across each parallel branch and $\frac{1}{2}(31.0\text{ V}) = 15.5$ V across each 400 Ω resistor. The power dissipated by each individual resistor is then $P = V^2/R = (15.5\text{ V})^2/400\ \Omega = 0.60$ W, which is less than the maximum allowed value of 1.20 W.

For the second combination this means a voltage of $IR_p = (0.0775\text{ A})(200\ \Omega) = 15.5$ V across each parallel combination and hence across each separate resistor. The power dissipated by each resistor is again $P = V^2/R - (15.5\text{ V})^2/400\ \Omega = 0.60$ W, which is less than the maximum allowed value of 1.20 W.

EVALUATE: The symmetry of each network says that each resistor in the network dissipates the same power. So, for a total of 2.4 W dissipated by the network, each resistor dissipates $(2.4\text{ W})/4 = 0.60$ W, which agrees with the above analysis.

26.51 IDENTIFY and **SET UP:** Let $R = 1.00\ \Omega$, the resistance of one wire. Each half of the wire has $R_h = R/2 = 0.500\ \Omega$. The combined wires are the same as a resistor network. Use the rules for equivalent resistance for resistors in series and parallel to find the resistance of the network.

EXECUTE:

The equivalent resistance is $R_h + R_h/2 + R_h = 5R_h/2 = \frac{5}{2}(0.500\ \Omega) = 1.25\ \Omega$

EVALUATE: If the two wires were connected end-to-end, the total resistance would be 2.00 Ω. If they were joined side-by-side, the total resistance would be 0.500 Ω. Our answer is between these two limiting values.

26.57 IDENTIFY: Apply the junction rule to express the currents through the 5.00 Ω and 8.00 Ω resistors in terms of I_1, I_2 and I_3. Apply the loop rule to three loops to get three equations in the three unknown currents.

SET UP:

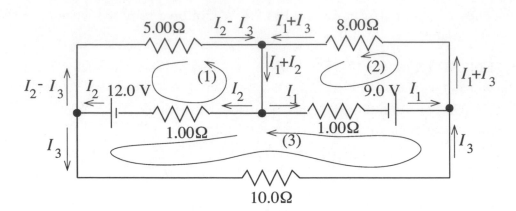

The current in each branch has been written in terms of I_1, I_2 and I_3 such that the junction rule is satisfied at each junction point.

EXECUTE: Apply the loop rule to loop (1).

$-12.0 \text{ V} + I_2(1.00 \text{ }\Omega) + (I_2 - I_3)(5.00 \text{ }\Omega) = 0$

$I_2(6.00 \text{ }\Omega) - I_3(5.00 \text{ }\Omega) = 12.0 \text{ V} \qquad \text{eq.(1)}$

Apply the loop rule to loop (2):

$-I_1(1.00 \text{ }\Omega) + 9.00 \text{ V} - (I_1 + I_3)(8.00 \text{ }\Omega) = 0$

$I_1(9.00 \text{ }\Omega) + I_3(8.00 \text{ }\Omega) = 9.00 \text{ V} \qquad \text{eq.(2)}$

Apply the loop rule to loop (3):

$-I_3(10.0 \text{ }\Omega) - 9.00 \text{ V} + I_1(1.00 \text{ }\Omega) - I_2(1.00 \text{ }\Omega) + 12.0 \text{ V} = 0$

$-I_1(1.00 \text{ }\Omega) + I_2(1.00 \text{ }\Omega) + I_3(10.0 \text{ }\Omega) = 3.00 \text{ V} \qquad \text{eq.(3)}$

Eq.(1) gives $I_2 = 2.00 \text{ A} + \frac{5}{6}I_3$;   eq.(2) gives $I_1 = 1.00 \text{ A} - \frac{8}{9}I_3$

Using these results in eq.(3) gives $-(1.00 \text{ A} - \frac{8}{9}I_3)(1.00 \text{ }\Omega) + (2.00 \text{ A} + \frac{5}{6}I_3)(1.00 \text{ }\Omega) + I_3(10.0 \text{ }\Omega) = 3.00 \text{ V}$

$(\frac{16+15+180}{18})I_3 = 2.00 \text{ A};$ $I_3 = \frac{18}{211}(2.00 \text{ A}) = 0.171 \text{ A}$

Then $I_2 = 2.00 \text{ A} + \frac{5}{6}I_3 = 2.00 \text{ A} + \frac{5}{6}(0.171 \text{ A}) = 2.14 \text{ A}$

and $I_1 = 1.00 \text{ A} - \frac{8}{9}I_3 = 1.00 \text{ A} - \frac{8}{9}(0.171 \text{ A}) = 0.848 \text{ A}.$

EVALUATE: We could check that the loop rule is satisfied for a loop that goes through the 5.00 Ω, 8.00 Ω and 10.0 Ω resistors. Going around the loop clockwise: $-(I_2 - I_3)(5.00 \text{ }\Omega) + (I_1 + I_3)(8.00 \text{ }\Omega) + I_3(10.0 \text{ }\Omega) = -9.85 \text{ V} + 8.15 \text{ V} + 1.71 \text{ V}$, which does equal zero, apart from rounding.

26.59 IDENTIFY and **SET UP:**

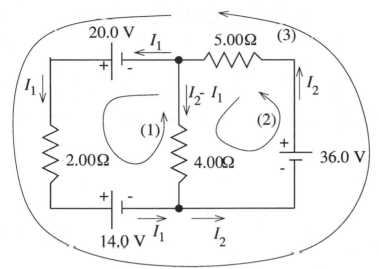

Two unknown currents I_1 (through the 2.00 Ω resistor) and I_2 (through the 5.00 Ω resistor) are labeled on the circuit diagram. The current through the 4.00 Ω resistor has been written as $I_2 - I_1$ using the junction rule.

Apply the loop rule to loops (1) and (2) to get two equations for the unknown currents I_1 and I_2. Loop (3) can then be used to check the results.

EXECUTE:

loop (1):

$+20.0 \text{ V} - I_1(2.00 \text{ } \Omega) - 14.0 \text{ V} + (I_2 - I_1)(4.00 \text{ } \Omega) = 0$

$6.00 I_1 - 4.00 I_2 = 6.00 \text{ A}$

$3.00 I_1 - 2.00 I_2 = 3.00 \text{ A}$ eq.(1)

loop (2):

$+36.0 \text{ V} - I_2(5.00 \text{ } \Omega) - (I_2 - I_1)(4.00 \text{ } \Omega) = 0$

$-4.00 I_1 + 9.00 I_2 = 36.0 \text{ A}$ eq.(2)

Solving eq.(1) for I_1 gives $I_1 = 1.00 \text{ A} + \frac{2}{3} I_2$

Using this in eq.(2) gives $-4.00(1.00 \text{ A} + \frac{2}{3} I_2) + 9.00 I_2 = 36.0 \text{ A}$

$(-\frac{8}{3} + 9.00) I_2 = 40.0 \text{ A}$ and $I_2 = 6.32 \text{ A}$.

Then $I_1 = 1.00 \text{ A} + \frac{2}{3} I_2 = 1.00 \text{ A} + \frac{2}{3}(6.32 \text{ A}) = 5.21 \text{ A}$.

In summary then

Current through the 2.00 Ω resistor: $I_1 = 5.21 \text{ A}$.

Current through the 5.00 Ω resistor: $I_2 = 6.32 \text{ A}$.

Current through the 4.00 Ω resistor: $I_2 - I_1 = 6.32 \text{ A} - 5.21 \text{ A} = 1.11 \text{ A}$.

EVALUATE: Use loop (3) to check.

$+20.0 \text{ V} - I_1(2.00 \text{ } \Omega) - 14.0 \text{ V} + 36.0 \text{ V} - I_2(5.00 \text{ } \Omega) = 0$

$(5.21 \text{ A})(2.00 \text{ } \Omega) + (6.32 \text{ A})(5.00 \text{ } \Omega) = 42.0 \text{ V}$

$10.4 \text{ V} + 31.6 \text{ V} = 42.0 \text{ V}$, so the loop rule is satisfied for this loop.

26.61 **a) IDENTIFY:** Break the circuit between points a and b means no current in the middle branch that contains the 3.00 Ω resistor and the 10.0 V battery. The circuit therefore has a single current path. Find the current, so that potential drops across the resistors can be calculated. Calculate V_{ab} by traveling from a to b, keeping track of the potential changes along the path taken.

SET UP:

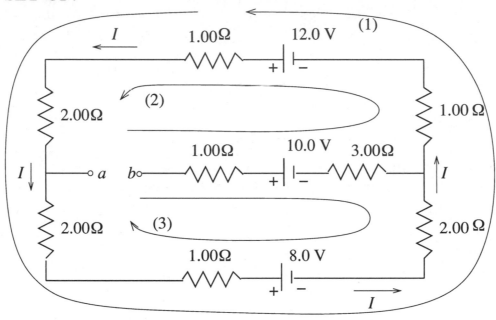

EXECUTE: Apply the loop rule to loop (1).

$+12.0 \text{ V} - I(1.00\ \Omega + 2.00\ \Omega + 2.00\ \Omega + 1.00\ \Omega) - 8.0 \text{ V} - I(2.00\ \Omega + 1.00\ \Omega) = 0$

$I = \dfrac{12.0 \text{ V} - 8.0 \text{ V}}{9.00\ \Omega} = 0.4444 \text{ A}.$

To find V_{ab} start at point b and travel to a, adding up the potential rises and drops. Travel on path (2) shown on the diagram. The 1.00 Ω and 3.00 Ω resistors in the middle branch have no current through them and hence no voltage across them. Therefore,

$V_b - 10.0 \text{ V} + 12.0 \text{ V} - I(1.00\ \Omega + 1.00\ \Omega + 2.00\ \Omega) = V_a;$

thus $V_a - V_b = 2.0 \text{ V} - (0.4444 \text{ A})(4.00\ \Omega) = +0.22 \text{ V}$

(point a is at higher potential)

EVALUATE: As a check on this calculation we also compute V_{ab} by traveling from b to a on path (3).

$V_b - 10.0 \text{ V} + 8.0 \text{ V} + I(2.00\ \Omega + 1.00\ \Omega + 2.00\ \Omega) = V_a$

$V_{ab} = -2.00 \text{ V} + (0.4444 \text{ A})(5.00\ \Omega) = +0.22 \text{ V}$, which checks.

b) IDENTIFY and **SET UP:** With points a and b connected by a wire there are three current branches:

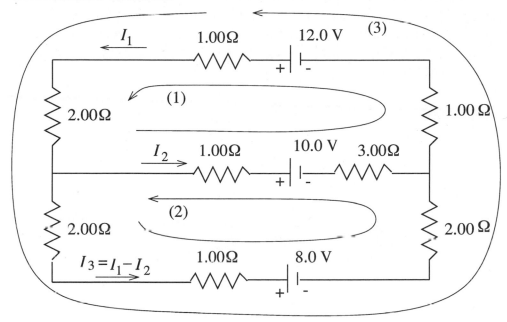

The junction rule has been used to write the third current (in the 8.0 V battery) in terms of the other currents. Apply the loop rule to loops (1) and (2) to obtain two equations for the two unknowns I_1 and I_2.

EXECUTE: Apply the loop rule to loop (1).

$12.0 \text{ V} - I_1(1.00 \ \Omega) - I_1(2.00 \ \Omega) - I_2(1.00 \ \Omega) - 10.0 \text{ V} - I_2(3.00 \ \Omega) - I_1(1.00 \ \Omega) = 0$

$2.0 \text{ V} - I_1(4.00 \ \Omega) - I_2(4.00 \ \Omega) = 0$

$(2.00 \ \Omega)I_1 + (2.00 \ \Omega)I_2 = 1.0 \text{ V} \qquad \text{eq.(1)}$

Apply the loop rule to loop (2):

$-(I_1 - I_2)(2.00 \ \Omega) - (I_1 - I_2)(1.00 \ \Omega) - 8.0 \text{ V} - (I_1 - I_2)(2.00 \ \Omega) + I_2(3.00 \ \Omega) + 10.0 \text{ V} + I_2(1.00 \ \Omega) = 0$

$2.0 \text{ V} - (5.00 \ \Omega)I_1 + (9.00 \ \Omega)I_2 = 0 \qquad \text{eq.(2)}$

Solve eq.(1) for I_2 and use this to replace I_2 in eq.(2):

$I_2 = 0.50 \text{ A} - I_1$

$2.0 \text{ V} - (5.00 \ \Omega)I_1 + (9.00 \ \Omega)(0.50 \text{ A} - I_1) = 0$

$(14.0 \ \Omega)I_1 = 6.50 \text{ V}$ so $I_1 = (6.50 \text{ V})/(14.0 \ \Omega) = 0.464 \text{ A}$

$I_2 = 0.500 \text{ A} - 0.464 \text{ A} = 0.036 \text{ A}.$

The current in the 12.0 V battery is $I_1 = 0.464 \text{ A}$.

EVALUATE: We can apply the loop rule to loop (3) as a check:

$+12.0 \text{ V} - I_1(1.00 \ \Omega + 2.00 \ \Omega + 1.00 \ \Omega) - (I_1 - I_2)(2.00 \ \Omega + 1.00 \ \Omega + 2.00 \ \Omega) - 8.0 \text{ V} = 4.0 \text{ V} - 1.86 \text{ V} - 2.14 \text{ V} = 0$, as it should.

26.63 IDENTIFY: In the following sketch, points a and c are at the same potential and points d and b are at the same potential, so we can calculate V_{ab} by calculating V_{cd}. We know the current through the resistor that is between points c and d. We thus can calculate the teminal voltage of the 24.0 V battery without calculating the current through it.

SET UP:

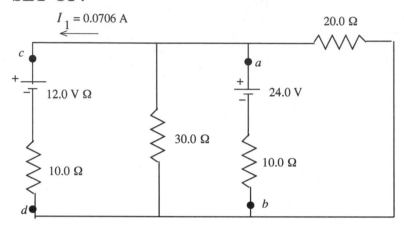

EXECUTE: $V_d + I_1(10.0 \ \Omega) + 12.0 \ V = V_c$

$V_c - V_d = 12.706 \ V; \qquad V_a - V_b = V_c - V_d = 12.7 \ V$

EVALUATE: The voltage across each parallel branch must be the same. The current through the 24.0 V battery must be $(24.0 \ V - 12.7 \ V)/(10.0 \ \Omega) = 1.13 \ A$ in the direction b to a.

26.65 IDENTIFY and **SET UP:** Simplify the circuit by replacing parallel networks of resistors by their equivalents. In this simplified circuit apply the loop and junction rules to find the current in each branch.

EXECUTE: The 20.0-Ω and 30.0-Ω resistors are in parallel and have equivalent resistance 12.0 Ω. The two resistors R are in parallel and have equivalent resistance $R/2$. The circuit is equivalent to

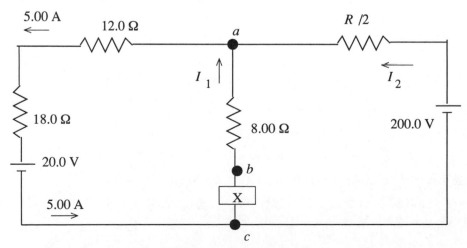

a) Calculate V_{ca} by traveling along the branch that contains the 20.0 V battery, since we know the current in that branch.

$V_a - (5.00\text{ A})(12.0\ \Omega) - (5.00\text{ A})(18.0\ \Omega) - 20.0\text{ V} = V_c$

$V_a - V_c = 20.0\text{ V} + 90.0\text{ V} + 60.0\text{ V} = 170.0\text{ V}$

$V_b - V_a = V_{ba} = 16.0\text{ V}$

$X - V_{ba} = 170.0\text{ V}$ so $X = 186.0\text{ V}$, with the upper terminal $+$

b) $I_1 = (16.0\text{ V})/(8.00\ \Omega) = 2.00\text{ A}$

The junction rule applied to point a gives $I_2 + I_1 = 5.00$ A, so $I_2 = 3.00$ A. The current through the 200.0 V battery is in the direction from the $-$ to the $+$ terminal, as shown in the diagram.

c) $200.0\text{ V} - I_2(R/2) - 170.0\text{ V}$

$(3.00\text{ A})(R/2) = 30.0\text{ V}$ so $R = 20.0\ \Omega$

EVALUATE: We can check the loop rule by going clockwise around the outer circuit loop. This gives

$+20.0\text{ V} + (5.00\text{ A})(18.0\ \Omega + 12.0\ \Omega) + (3.00\text{ A})(10.0\ \Omega) - 200.0\text{ V} = 20.0\text{ V} +$ $150.0\text{ V} + 30.0\text{ V} - 200.0\text{ V}$, which does equal zero.

26.67 **IDENTIFY** and **SET UP:** For part (a) use that the full emf is across each resistor. In part (b), calculate the power dissipated by the equivalent resistance, and in this expression express R_1 and R_2 in terms of P_1, P_2 and ε.

EXECUTE: $P_1 = \varepsilon^2/R_1$ so $R_1 = \varepsilon^2/P_1$

$P_2 = \varepsilon^2/R_2$ so $R_2 = \varepsilon^2/P_2$

a) When the resistors are connected in parallel to the emf, the voltage across each resistor is ε and the power dissipated by each resistor is the same as if only the one resistor were connected. $P_{\text{tot}} = P_1 + P_2$

b) When the resistors are connected in series the equivalent resistance is $R_{\text{eq}} = R_1 + R_2$

$$P_{\text{tot}} = \frac{\varepsilon^2}{R_1 + R_2} = \frac{\varepsilon^2}{\varepsilon^2/P_1 + \varepsilon^2/P_2} = \frac{P_1 P_2}{P_1 + P_2}$$

EVALUATE: The result in part (b) can be written as $\dfrac{1}{P_{\text{tot}}} = \dfrac{1}{P_1} + \dfrac{1}{P_2}$. Our results are that for parallel the powers add and that for series the reciprocals of the powers add. This is opposite the result for combining resistance. Since $P = \varepsilon^2/R$ tells us that P is proportional to $1/R$, this makes sense.

26.69 a) IDENTIFY and **SET UP:**

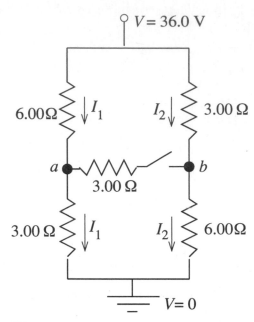

With the switch open there is no current through it and there are only the two currents I_1 and I_2 indicated in the sketch.

The potential drop across each parallel branch is 36.0 V. Use this fact to calculate I_1 and I_2. Then travel from point a to point b and keep track of the potential rises and drops in order to calculate V_{ab}.

EXECUTE:

$-I_1(6.00\ \Omega + 3.00\ \Omega) + 36.0\ \text{V} = 0$

$I_1 = \dfrac{36.0\ \text{V}}{6.00\ \Omega + 3.00\ \Omega} = 4.00\ \text{A}$

$-I_2(3.00\ \Omega + 6.00\ \Omega) + 36.0\ \text{V} = 0$

$I_2 = \dfrac{36.0\ \text{V}}{3.00\ \Omega + 6.00\ \Omega} = 4.00\ \text{A}$

To calculate $V_{ab} = V_a - V_b$ start at point b and travel to point a, adding up all the potential rises and drops along the way. We can do this by going from b up through the 3.00 Ω resistor:

$V_b + I_2(3.00\ \Omega) - I_1(6.00\ \Omega) = V_a$

$V_a - V_b = (4.00\ \text{A})(3.00\ \Omega) - (4.00\ \text{A})(6.00\ \Omega) = 12.0\ \text{V} - 24.0\ \text{V} = -12.0\ \text{V}$

$V_{ab} = -12.0\ \text{V}$ (point a is 12.0 V lower in potential than point b)

EVALUATE: Alternatively, we can go from point b down through the 6.00 Ω resistor.

$V_b - I_2(6.00\ \Omega) + I_1(3.00\ \Omega) = V_a$

$V_a - V_b = -(4.00\ \text{A})(6.00\ \Omega) + (4.00\ \text{A})(3.00\ \Omega) = -24.0\ \text{V} + 12.0\ \text{V} = -12.0\ \text{V}$, which checks.

b) IDENTIFY: Now there are multiple current paths. Use the junction rule to write the current in each branch in terms of three unknown currents I_1, I_2, and I_3. Apply the loop rule to three loops to get three equations for the three unknowns. The target variable is I_3, the current through the switch. R_{eq} is calculated from $V = IR_{eq}$, where I is the total current that passes through the network.

SET UP:

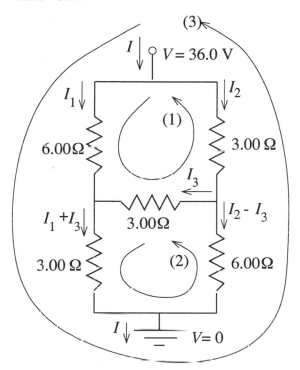

The three unknown currents I_1, I_2, and I_3 are labeled on the sketch.

EXECUTE: Apply the loop rule to loops (1), (2), and (3).

<u>loop (1)</u>: $-I_1(6.00 \ \Omega) + I_3(3.00 \ \Omega) + I_2(3.00 \ \Omega) = 0$

$I_2 = 2I_1 - I_3$ eq.(1)

<u>loop (2)</u>: $-(I_1 + I_3)(3.00 \ \Omega) + (I_2 - I_3)(6.00 \ \Omega) - I_3(3.00 \ \Omega) = 0$

$6I_2 - 12I_3 - 3I_1 = 0$ so $2I_2 - 4I_3 - I_1 = 0$

Use eq.(1) to replace I_2:

$4I_1 - 2I_3 - 4I_3 - I_1 = 0$

$3I_1 = 6I_3$ and $I_1 = 2I_3$ eq.(2)

<u>loop (3)</u> (This loop is completed through the battery [not shown], in the direction from the $-$ to the $+$ terminal.):

$-I_1(6.00 \ \Omega) \quad (I_1 + I_3)(3.00 \ \Omega) + 36.0 \ V = 0$

$9I_1 + 3I_3 = 36.0 \ A$ and $3I_1 + I_3 = 12.0 \ A$ eq.(3)

Use eq.(2) in eq.(3) to replace I_1:

$3(2I_3) + I_3 = 12.0 \ A$

$I_3 = 12.0 \ A/7 = 1.71 \ A$

$I_1 = 2I_3 = 3.42 \ A$

$$I_2 = 2I_1 - I_3 = 2(3.42 \text{ A}) - 1.71 \text{ A} = 5.13 \text{ A}$$

The current through the switch is $I_3 = 1.71$ A.

c) From the results in part (a) the current through the battery is $I = I_1 + I_2 = 3.42$ A $+ 5.13$ A $= 8.55$ A. The equivalent circuit is a single resitor that produces the same current through the 36.0 V battery.

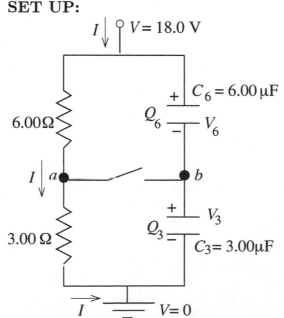

$$-IR + 36.0 \text{ V} = 0$$

$$R = \frac{36.0 \text{ V}}{I} = \frac{36.0 \text{ V}}{8.55 \text{ A}} = 4.21 \ \Omega$$

EVALUATE: With the switch open (part a), point b is at higher potential than point a, so when the switch is closed the current flows in the direction from b to a. With the switch closed the circuit cannot be simplified using series and parallel combinations but there is still an equivalent resistance that represents the network.

26.71 a) IDENTIFY: With the switch open the circuit has two resistors in series that are in parallel with two capacitors in series. Apply the loop rule to each parallel branch, find the current through each resistor and the charge on each capacitor, and from the currents and charges find the voltage across each circuit element. Calculate V_{ab} by traveling from point b to point a, keeping track of the potential rises and drops.

SET UP:

After the capacitors have been charged to their final charge there is no current through them. There is only one current path.

EXECUTE:

$$-I(6.00 \ \Omega + 3.00 \ \Omega) + 18.0 \text{ V} = 0$$

$$I = \frac{18.0 \text{ V}}{9.00 \ \Omega} = 2.00 \text{ A}$$

There is also a potential difference of 18.0 V applied across the two capacitors in series. The capacitors have the same charge: $Q_3 = Q_6 = Q$.

$V_6 + V_3 = 18.0$ V and $V = Q/C$ so

$$Q\left(\frac{1}{C_6} + \frac{1}{C_3}\right) = 18.0 \text{ V so } Q\left(\frac{C_3 + C_6}{C_3 C_6}\right) = 18.0 \text{ V}$$

$$Q = \left(\frac{C_3 C_6}{C_3 + C_6}\right)(18.0 \text{ V}) = \left[\frac{(3.00 \times 10^{-6} \text{ F})(6.00 \times 10^{-6} \text{ F})}{3.00 \times 10^{-6} \text{ F} + 6.00 \times 10^{-6} \text{ F}}\right] 18.0 \text{ V} = 36.0 \text{ } \mu\text{C}$$

And then $V_6 = \dfrac{Q}{C_6} = \dfrac{36.0 \text{ } \mu\text{C}}{6.00 \text{ } \mu\text{C}} = 6.00$ V, $V_3 = \dfrac{Q}{C_3} = \dfrac{36.0 \text{ } \mu\text{C}}{3.00 \text{ } \mu\text{C}} = 12.0$ V

Travel from point b counterclockwise through the network to point a:

$V_b + V_6 - I(6.00 \text{ } \Omega) = V_a$

$V_a - V_b = 6.00 \text{ V} - (2.00 \text{ A})(6.00 \text{ } \Omega) = -6.00$ V

EVALUATE: Could also travel clockwise from b to a: $V_b - V_3 + I(3.00 \text{ } \Omega) = V_a$

$V_a - V_b = (2.00 \text{ A})(3.00 \text{ } \Omega) - 12.0 \text{ V} = -6.00$ V, which checks

b) $V_{ab} < 0$; point b is at higher potential

c) IDENTIFY and **SET UP:**

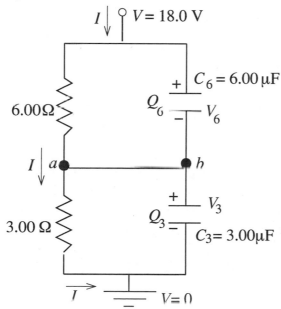

The only current path is still the one through both resistors, so $I = 2.00$ A as calculated in part (a).

The effect of closing the switch is to put points a and b at the same potential.
EXECUTE:
$I(6.00 \text{ } \Omega) = 12.0$ V is the potential V_6 across the 6.00 μF capacitor and $I(3.00 \text{ } \Omega) = 6.00$ V is the potential V_3 across the 3.00 μF capacitor.

The potential of point b above ground is $V_b = I(3.00 \text{ } \Omega) = V_3 = 6.00$ V.

d) IDENTIFY and **SET UP:** Find the charges on the capacitors after the switch is closed and compare those to the charges on the capacitors before the switch was closed.

EXECUTE: The charges on the capacitors after the switch is closed are

$Q_6 = C_6 V_6 = (6.00 \ \mu\text{F})(12.0 \ \text{V}) = 72.0 \ \mu\text{C}$

$Q_3 = C_3 V_3 = (3.00 \ \mu\text{F})(6.00 \ \text{V}) = 18.0 \ \mu\text{C}$

From part (a), with the switch open the charge on each capacitor was 36.0 μC.

switch open

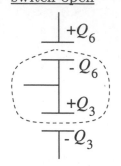

The net charge on the conductor enclosed by the dashed line is zero.

switch closed

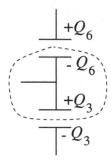

The net charge on the conductor enclosed by the dashed line is now $-Q_6 + Q_3 = -72.0 \ \mu\text{C} + 18.0 \ \mu\text{C} = -54.0 \ \mu\text{C}$

The charge $-54.0 \ \mu$C must have flowed through the switch when it was closed.

EVALUATE: If charge $-54.0 \ \mu$C flowed through the switch to the capacitors this is equivalent to $+54.0 \ \mu$C flowing from b to a. With the switch open, point b is at higher potential so it is expected that positive charge would flow from b to a when the switch is closed.

26.73 **IDENTIFY:** In each case the sum of the voltage drops across the resistors in the circuit must equal the full-scale voltage reading. The resistors are in series so the total resistance is the sum of the resistances in the circuit.

SET UP: For each range setting the circuit has the form

$I_{\text{fs}} = 1.00 \times 10^{-3} \text{A}$

$R_G = 40.0 \Omega$ R

V

EXECUTE: 3.00 V

For $V = 3.00$ V, $R = R_1$ and the total meter resistance R_m is $R_m = R_G + R_1$.

$$V = I_{fs}R_m \text{ so } R_m = \frac{V}{I_{fs}} = \frac{3.00 \text{ V}}{1.00 \times 10^{-3} \text{ A}} = 3.00 \times 10^3 \text{ } \Omega.$$

$$R_m = R_G + R_1 \text{ so } R_1 = R_m - R_G = 3.00 \times 10^3 \text{ } \Omega - 40.0 \text{ } \Omega = 2960 \text{ } \Omega$$

15.0 V

For $V = 15.0$ V, $R = R_1 + R_2$ and the total meter resistance is $R_m = R_G + R_1 + R_2$.

$$V = I_{fs}R_m \text{ so } R_m = \frac{V}{I_{fs}} = \frac{15.0 \text{ V}}{1.00 \times 10^{-3} \text{ A}} = 1.50 \times 10^4 \text{ } \Omega.$$

$$R_2 = R_m - R_G - R_1 = 1.50 \times 10^4 \text{ } \Omega - 40.0 \text{ } \Omega - 2960 \text{ } \Omega = 1.20 \times 10^4 \text{ } \Omega$$

150 V

For $V = 150$ V, $R = R_1 + R_2 + R_3$ and the total meter resistance is $R_m = R_G + R_1 + R_2 + R_3$.

$$V = I_{fs}R_m \text{ so } R_m = \frac{V}{I_{fs}} = \frac{150 \text{ V}}{1.00 \times 10^{-3} \text{ A}} = 1.50 \times 10^5 \text{ } \Omega.$$

$$R_3 = R_m - R_G - R_1 - R_2 = 1.50 \times 10^5 \text{ } \Omega - 40.0 \text{ } \Omega - 2960 \text{ } \Omega - 1.20 \times 10^4 \text{ } \Omega = 1.35 \times 10^5 \text{ } \Omega.$$

EVALUATE: The greater the total resistance in series inside the meter the greater the potential difference between the two connections to the meter when the same 1.00 mA current flows through it.

26.79 IDENTIFY and **SET UP:** Without the meter, the circuit consists of the two resistors in series. When the meter is connected, its resistance is added to the circuit in parallel with the resistor it is connected across.

a) EXECUTE: $I = I_1 = I_2$

$$I = \frac{90.0 \text{ V}}{R_1 + R_2} = \frac{90.0 \text{ V}}{224 \text{ } \Omega + 589 \text{ } \Omega} = 0.1107 \text{ A}$$

$V_1 = I_1 R_1 = (0.1107 \text{ A})(224 \text{ } \Omega) = 24.8 \text{ V}$; $V_2 = I_2 R_2 = (0.1107 \text{ A})(589 \text{ } \Omega) = 65.2 \text{ V}$

b) SET UP:

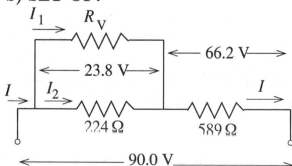

The voltmeter reads the potential difference across its terminals, which is 23.8 V. If we can find the current I_1 through the voltmeter then we can use Ohm's law to find its resistance.

EXECUTE: The voltage drop across the 589 Ω resistor is 90.0 V − 23.8 V = 66.2 V, so $I = \frac{V}{R} = \frac{66.2 \text{ V}}{589 \text{ } \Omega} = 0.1124 \text{ A}.$

The voltage drop across the 224 Ω resistor is 23.8 V, so $I_2 = \dfrac{V}{R} = \dfrac{23.8 \text{ V}}{224 \text{ }\Omega} = 0.1062$ A.

Then $I = I_1 + I_2$ gives $I_1 = I - I_2 = 0.1124$ A $- 0.1062$ A $= 0.0062$ A.

$$R_V = \frac{V}{I_1} = \frac{23.8 \text{ V}}{0.0062 \text{ A}} = 3840 \text{ }\Omega$$

c) SET UP:

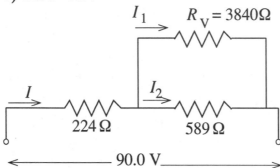

EXECUTE: Replace the two resistors in parallel by their equivalent.

$$\frac{1}{R_{eq}} = \frac{1}{3840 \text{ }\Omega} + \frac{1}{589 \text{ }\Omega};$$

$$R_{eq} = \frac{(3840 \text{ }\Omega)(589 \text{ }\Omega)}{3840 \text{ }\Omega + 589 \text{ }\Omega} = 510.7 \text{ }\Omega$$

$$I = \frac{90.0 \text{ V}}{224 \text{ }\Omega + 510.7 \text{ }\Omega} = 0.1225 \text{ A}$$

The potential drop across the 224 Ω resistor then is $IR = (0.1225 \text{ A})(224 \text{ }\Omega) = 27.4$ V, so the potential drop across the 589 Ω resistor and across the voltmeter (what the voltmeter reads) is 90.0 V $- 27.4$ V $= 62.6$ V.

d) EVALUATE: No, any real voltmeter will draw some current and thereby reduce the current through the resistance whose voltage is being measured. Thus the presence of the voltmeter connected in parallel with the resistance lowers the voltage drop across that resistance.

The resistance of the voltmeter is only about a factor of ten larger than the resistances in the circuit, so the voltmeter has a noticeable effect on the circuit.

26.81 **IDENTIFY:** Apply the loop rule to the circuit. The voltage across the resistor depends on the current through it and the voltage across the capacitor depends on the charge on it.

a) SET UP:

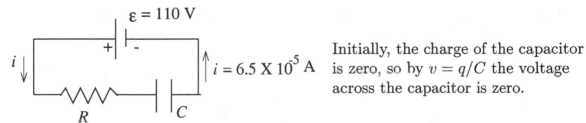

EXECUTE:

$$v_C = \frac{q}{C}$$

$$v_C = \frac{815 \times 10^{-6} \text{ C}}{3.40 \times 10^{-6} \text{ F}} = 239.7 \text{ V}$$

$$+v_C - iR - \varepsilon = 0$$

$$iR = v_C - \varepsilon = 239.7 \text{ V} - 180 \text{ V} = 59.7 \text{ V}$$

$$i = \frac{59.7 \text{ V}}{7.25 \times 10^3 \ \Omega} = 8.24 \times 10^{-3} \text{ A} = 8.24 \text{ mA, toward the negative plate.}$$

b) After a long time $i = 0$ so $v_C = \varepsilon$.

$q = \varepsilon C = (180 \text{ V})(3.40 \times 10^{-6} \text{ F}) = 6.12 \times 10^{-4} \text{ C} = 612 \ \mu\text{C}.$

EVALUATE: At any time the sum of the voltage across the resistor and the emf of the battery equals the capacitor voltage. Just after the circuit is completed the capacitor voltage exceeds the battery emf and the capacitor starts to discharge. After a long time the capacitor is fully charged, the current is zero, and the voltage across the capacitor equals the emf.

26.83 IDENTIFY: Apply the loop rule to the circuit. The initial current determines R. We can then use the time constant to calculate C.

SET UP:

$\varepsilon = 110$ V

$i = 6.5 \times 10^5$ A

Initially, the charge of the capacitor is zero, so by $v = q/C$ the voltage across the capacitor is zero.

EXECUTE: The loop rule therefore gives $\varepsilon - iR = 0$ and

$$R = \frac{\varepsilon}{i} = \frac{110 \text{ V}}{6.5 \times 10^{-5} \text{ A}} = 1.7 \times 10^6 \ \Omega$$

The time constant is given by $\tau = RC$ (Eq.26.14), so

$$C = \frac{\tau}{R} = \frac{6.2 \text{ s}}{1.7 \times 10^6 \ \Omega} = 3.6 \ \mu\text{F}.$$

EVALUATE: The resistance is large so the initial current is small and the time constant is large.

26.87 IDENTIFY and **SET UP:** For parts (a) and (b) evaluate the integrals as specified in the problem. The current as a function of time is gvien by Eq.(26.13) $i = \dfrac{\varepsilon}{R}e^{-t/RC}$. The enegy stored in the capacitor is given by $Q^2/2C$.

EXECUTE:

a) $P = \varepsilon i$

The total energy supplied by the battery is

$\int_0^\infty P\,dt = \int_0^\infty \varepsilon i\,dt = (\varepsilon^2/R)\int_0^\infty e^{-t/RC}\,dt = (\varepsilon^2/R)\left[-RCe^{-t/RC}\right]_0^\infty = C\varepsilon^2.$

b) $P = i^2 R$

The total energy dissipated in the resistor is

$\int_0^\infty P\,dt = \int_0^\infty i^2 R\,dt = (\varepsilon^2/R)\int_0^\infty e^{-2t/RC}\,dt = (\varepsilon^2/R)\left[-(RC/2)e^{-2t/RC}\right]_0^\infty = \frac{1}{2}C\varepsilon^2.$

c) The final charge on the capacitor is $Q = C\varepsilon$. The energy stored is
$U = Q^2/(2C) = \frac{1}{2}C\varepsilon^2.$

The final energy stored in the capacitor ($\frac{1}{2}C\varepsilon^2$) = total energy supplied by the battery ($C\varepsilon^2$) - energy dissipated in the resistor ($\frac{1}{2}C\varepsilon^2$)

d) EVALUATE: $\frac{1}{2}$ of the energy supplied by the battery is stored in the capacitor. This fraction is independent of R. The other $\frac{1}{2}$ of the energy supplied by the battery is dissipated in the resistor. When R is small the current initially is large but dies away quickly. When R is large the current initially is small but lasts longer.

CHAPTER 27

MAGNETIC FIELD AND MAGNETIC FORCES

Exercises

27.1 **IDENTIFY** and **SET UP:** Apply Eq.(27.2) to calculate $\vec{F}$. Use the cross products of unit vectors from Section 1.10.

EXECUTE: $\vec{v} = (+4.19 \times 10^4 \text{ m/s})\hat{i} + (-3.85 \times 10^4 \text{ m/s})\hat{j}$

a) $\vec{B} = (1.40 \text{ T})\hat{i}$

$\vec{F} = q\vec{v} \times \vec{B} = (-1.24 \times 10^{-8} \text{ C})(1.40 \text{ T})[(+4.19 \times 10^4 \text{ m/s})\hat{i} \times \hat{i} - (3.85 \times 10^4 \text{ m/s})\hat{j} \times \hat{i}]$

$\hat{i} \times \hat{i} = 0, \quad \hat{j} \times \hat{i} = -\hat{k}$

$\vec{F} = (-1.24 \times 10^{-8} \text{ C})(1.40 \text{ T})(-3.85 \times 10^4 \text{ m/s})(-\hat{k}) = (-6.68 \times 10^{-4} \text{ N})\hat{k}$

EVALUATE:

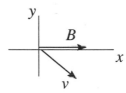

The right-hand rule gives that $\vec{v} \times \vec{B}$ is directed out of the paper ($+z$-direction). The charge is negative so $\vec{F}$ is opposite to $\vec{v} \times \vec{B}$;

$\vec{F}$ is in the $-z$-direction. This agrees with the direction calculated with unit vectors.

b) **EXECUTE:** $\vec{B} = (1.40 \text{ T})\hat{k}$

$\vec{F} = q\vec{v} \times \vec{B} = (-1.24 \times 10^{-8} \text{ C})(1.40 \text{ T})[(+4.19 \times 10^4 \text{ m/s})\hat{i} \times \hat{k} - (3.85 \times 10^4 \text{ m/s})\hat{j} \times \hat{k}]$

$\hat{i} \times \hat{k} = -\hat{j}, \quad \hat{j} \times \hat{k} = \hat{i}$

$\vec{F} = (-7.27 \times 10^{-4} \text{ N})(-\hat{j}) + (6.68 \times 10^{-4} \text{ N})\hat{i} = (6.68 \times 10^{-4} \text{ N})\hat{i} + (7.27 \times 10^{-4} \text{ N})\hat{j}]$

EVALUATE:

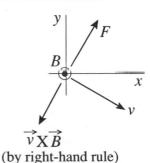

$\vec{v} \times \vec{B}$
(by right-hand rule)

The direction of $\vec{F}$ is opposite to $\vec{v} \times \vec{B}$ since q is negative. The direction of $\vec{F}$ computed from the right-hand rule agrees qualitatively with the direction calculated with unit vectors.

27.3   IDENTIFY and SET UP: The force must be in the direction the particle is deflected.

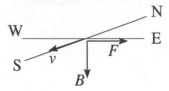

Or, if view from above,

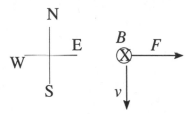

Use the right-hand rule to determine the direction of $\vec{v} \mathbf{X} \vec{B}$. $\vec{F}$ is in this direction if $q > 0$ and opposite this direction if $q < 0$.

EXECUTE: $\vec{F}$ is in the direction of $\vec{v} \mathbf{X} \vec{B}$ as given by the right-hand rule, so q is positive.

EVALUATE: Note that $\vec{F}$ is perpendicular to both $\vec{v}$ and $\vec{B}$.

27.11   IDENTIFY and SET UP: $\Phi_B = \int \vec{B} \cdot d\vec{A}$

Circular area in the xy-plane, so $A = \pi r^2 = \pi(0.0650 \text{ m})^2 = 0.01327 \text{ m}^2$ and $d\vec{A}$ is in the z-direction. Use Eq.(1.18) to calculate the scalar product.

EXECUTE:

a) $\vec{B} = (0.230 \text{ T})\hat{k}$; $\vec{B}$ and $d\vec{A}$ are parallel ($\phi = 0°$) so $\vec{B} \cdot d\vec{A} = B \, dA$.

B is constant over the circular area so

$\Phi_B = \int \vec{B} \cdot d\vec{A} = \int B \, dA = B \int dA = BA = (0.230 \text{ T})(0.01327 \text{ m}^2) =$
3.05×10^{-3} Wb

b)

$$\vec{B} \cdot d\vec{A} = B \cos\phi \, dA$$
with $\phi = 53.1°$

B and ϕ are constant over the circular area so

$\Phi_B = \int \vec{B} \cdot d\vec{A} = \int B \cos\phi \, dA = B \cos\phi \int dA = B \cos\phi A$

$\Phi_B = (0.230 \text{ T}) \cos 53.1°(0.01327 \text{ m}^2) = 1.83 \times 10^{-3}$ Wb

c)

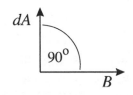

$\vec{B} \cdot d\vec{A} = 0$ since $d\vec{A}$
and $\vec{B}$ are perpendicular ($\phi = 90°$)
$\Phi_B = \int \vec{B} \cdot d\vec{A} = 0.$

EVALUATE: Magnetic flux is a measure of how many magnetic field lines pass through the surface. It is maximum when $\vec{B}$ is perpendicular to the plane of the loop (part a) and is zero when $\vec{B}$ is parallel to the plane of the loop (part c).

27.13 **IDENTIFY** and **SET UP:** Use Eq.(27.6) to calculate the flux through each surface. For each surface $d\vec{A}$ is normal to the surface. Eq.(27.8) says that the total flux through the surface surrounding the shaded volume must be zero.

EXECUTE:

a) $\vec{B} = (\beta - \gamma y^2)\hat{j}$ with $\beta = 0.300$ T and $\gamma = 2.00$ T/m^2

surface *abcd*

$d\vec{A} = dA(-\hat{i})$ $\vec{B} \cdot d\vec{A} = -(\beta - \gamma y^2)dA(\hat{j} \cdot \hat{i}) = 0$, so $\Phi_B = 0.$

surface *befc*

$d\vec{A} = dA(-\hat{k})$ $\vec{B} \cdot d\vec{A} = -(\beta - \gamma y^2)dA(\hat{j} \cdot \hat{k}) = 0$, so $\Phi_B = 0.$

surface *aefd*

$d\vec{A} = dA(\hat{i} + \hat{k})/\sqrt{2}$ $\vec{B} \cdot d\vec{A} = (\beta - \gamma y^2)dA(1/\sqrt{2})(\hat{i} + \hat{k}) \cdot \hat{j} = 0$, so $\Phi_B = 0.$

surface *abe*

$d\vec{A} = dA\hat{j}$ $\vec{B} \cdot d\vec{A} = (\beta - \gamma y^2)dA\hat{j} \cdot \hat{j} = (\beta - \gamma y^2)dA$

$\Phi_B = \int \vec{B} \cdot d\vec{A} = \int (\beta - \gamma y^2)\, dA = (\beta - \gamma y^2)\int dA = (\beta - \gamma y^2)A$ (since y is constant on the surface)

$y = 0.300$ m, $A = \frac{1}{2}(0.400$ m$)(0.300$ m$) = 0.0600$ m^2

$\Phi_B = (0.300$ T $- (2.00$ T/m$^2)(0.300$ m$)^2)(0.0600$ m$^2) = 0.00720$ Wb

surface *cfd*

On this surface $y = 0$ so $\vec{B} = \beta\hat{j}$. $d\vec{A} = -dA\hat{j}$, so $\vec{B} \cdot d\vec{A} = -\beta\, dA$. Then $\Phi_B = -\beta A = -(0.300$ T$)(0.0600$ m$^2) = -0.0180$ Wb.

The net flux is the sum of the fluxes through each surface. Only for surfaces *abe* and *cfd* is the flux nonzero, so the net flux is $\Phi_B = +0.00720$ Wb $- 0.0180$ Wb $= -0.0108$ Wb.

b) Gauss's law for magnetism (Eq.(27.8)) says $\oint \vec{B} \cdot d\vec{A} = 0$. But in part (a) we found $\oint \vec{B} \cdot d\vec{A} =$ net $\Phi_B = -0.0108$ Wb. The magnetic field produces a flux that violates Gauss's law for magnetism so is not possible.

EVALUATE: All the surfaces except for *cdf* and *abe* are parallel to the field direction so have zero flux. The magnetic field is in the $+y$-direction at surfaces *cdf* and *abe* but has a larger magnitude at surface *cdf*. More magnetic field lines enter the volume at surface *cdf* than leave at surface *abe* and this causes the violation of Eq.(27.8).

27.15 a) IDENTIFY: Apply Eq.(27.2) to relate the magnetic force $\vec{F}$ to the directions of $\vec{v}$ and $\vec{B}$. The electron has negative charge so $\vec{F}$ is opposite to the direction of $\vec{v} \times \vec{B}$. For motion in an arc of a circle the acceleration is toward the center of the arc so $\vec{F}$ must be in this direction. $a = v^2/R$.

SET UP:

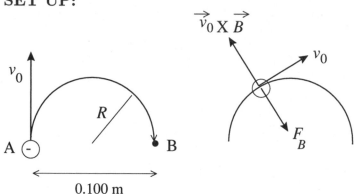

As the electron moves in the semicircle, its velocity is tangent to the circular path.

EXECUTE: For circular motion the acceleration of the electron $\vec{a}_{\rm rad}$ is directed in toward the center of the circle. Thus the force $\vec{F}_B$ exerted by the magnetic field, since it is the only force on the electron, must be radially inward. Since q is negative, $\vec{F}_B$ is opposite to the direction given by the right-hand rule for $\vec{v}_0 \times \vec{B}$. Thus $\vec{B}$ is directed into the page.

Apply Newton's 2nd law to calculate the magnitude of $\vec{B}$:

$\sum \vec{F} = m\vec{a}$ gives $\sum F_{\rm rad} = ma$

$F_B = m(v^2/R)$

$F_B = |q|vB \sin\phi = |q|vB$, so $|q|vB = m(v^2/R)$

$$B = \frac{mv}{|q|R} = \frac{(9.109 \times 10^{-31} \text{ kg})(1.41 \times 10^6 \text{ m/s})}{(1.602 \times 10^{-19} \text{ C})(0.050 \text{ m})} = 1.60 \times 10^{-4} \text{ T}$$

b) IDENTIFY and **SET UP:** The speed of the electron as it moves along the path is constant. ($\vec{F}_B$ changes the direction of $\vec{v}$ but not its magnitude.) The time is given by the distance divided by v_0.

EXECUTE: The distance along the semicircular path is πR, so

$$t = \frac{\pi R}{v_0} = \frac{\pi(0.050 \text{ m})}{1.41 \times 10^6 \text{ m/s}} = 1.11 \times 10^{-7} \text{ s}$$

EVALUATE: The magnetic field required increases when v increases or R decreases and also depends on the mass to charge ratio of the particle.

27.19 IDENTIFY and **SET UP:** Use conservation of energy to find the speed of the ball when it reaches the bottom of the shaft. The right-hand rule gives the direction of $\vec{F}$ and Eq.(27.1) gives its magnitude. The number of excess electrons determines the charge of the ball.

EXECUTE: $q = (4.00 \times 10^8)(-1.602 \times 10^{-19} \text{ C}) = -6.408 \times 10^{-11} \text{ C}$

speed at bottom of shaft: $\frac{1}{2}mv^2 = mgy$; $v = \sqrt{2gy} = 49.5$ m/s

$\vec{v}$ is downward and $\vec{B}$ is west, so $\vec{v} \times \vec{B}$ is north. Since $q < 0$, $\vec{F}$ is south.

$F = |q|vB \sin\theta = (6.408 \times 10^{-11} \text{ C})(49.5 \text{ m/s})(0.250 \text{ T})\sin 90° = 7.93 \times 10^{-10}$ N

EVALUATE: Both the charge and speed of the ball are relatively small so the magnetic force is small, much less than the gravity force of 1.5 N.

27.21 a) IDENTIFY and **SET UP:** Apply Newton's 2nd law, with $a = v^2/R$ since the path of the particle is circular.

EXECUTE: $\sum \vec{F} = m\vec{a}$ says $|q|vB = m(v^2/R)$

$v = \dfrac{|q|BR}{m} = \dfrac{(1.602 \times 10^{-19} \text{ C})(2.50 \text{ T})(6.96 \times 10^{-3} \text{ m})}{3.34 \times 10^{-27} \text{ kg}} = 8.35 \times 10^5$ m/s

b) IDENTIFY and **SET UP:** The speed is constant so $t = \text{distance}/v$.

EXECUTE: $t = \dfrac{\pi R}{v} = \dfrac{\pi(6.96 \times 10^{-3} \text{ m})}{8.35 \times 10^5 \text{ m/s}} = 2.62 \times 10^{-8}$ s

c) IDENTIFY and **SET UP:** kinetic energy gained = electric potential energy lost

EXECUTE: $\frac{1}{2}mv^2 = |q|V$

$V = \dfrac{mv^2}{2|q|} = \dfrac{(3.34 \times 10^{-27} \text{ kg})(8.35 \times 10^5 \text{ m/s})^2}{2(1.602 \times 10^{-19} \text{ C})} = 7.27 \times 10^3 \text{ V} = 7.27$ kV

EVALUATE: The deuteron has a much larger mass to charge ratio than an electron so a much larger B is required for the same v and R. The deuteron has positive charge so gains kinetic energy when it goes from high potential to low potential.

27.25 a) IDENTIFY and **SET UP:** Eq.(27.4) gives the total force on the proton.

EXECUTE: In the plane perpendicular to $\vec{B}$ (the yz-plane) the motion is circular. But there is a velocity component in the direction of $\vec{B}$, so the motion is a helix. The electric field in the $+\hat{i}$ direction exerts a force in the $+\hat{i}$ direction. This force produces an acceleration in the $+\hat{i}$ direction and this causes the pitch of the helix to vary. The force does not affect the circular motion in the yz-plane, so the electric field does not affect the radius of the helix.

b) **IDENTIFY** and **SET UP:** Use Eq.(27.12)and $T = 2\pi/\omega$ to calculate the period of the motion. Calculate a_x produced by the electric force and use a constant acceleration equation to calculate the displacement in the x-direction in time $T/2$.

EXECUTE: Calculate the period T:

$\omega = |q|B/m$

$$T = \frac{2\pi}{\omega} = \frac{2\pi m}{|q|B} = \frac{2\pi(1.67 \times 10^{-27} \text{ kg})}{(1.60 \times 10^{-19} \text{ C})(0.500 \text{ T})} = 1.312 \times 10^{-7} \text{ s.}$$

Then $t = T/2 = 6.56 \times 10^{-8}$ s.

$v_{0x} = 1.50 \times 10^5$ m/s

$$a_x = \frac{F_x}{m} = \frac{(1.60 \times 10^{-19} \text{ C})(2.00 \times 10^4 \text{ V/m})}{1.67 \times 10^{-27} \text{ kg}} = +1.916 \times 10^{12} \text{ m/s}^2$$

$x - x_0 = v_{0x}t + \frac{1}{2}a_x t^2$

$x - x_0 = (1.50 \times 10^5 \text{ m/s})(6.56 \times 10^{-8} \text{ s}) + \frac{1}{2}(1.916 \times 10^{12} \text{ m/s}^2)(6.56 \times 10^{-8} \text{ s})^2 = 1.40$ cm

EVALUATE: The electric and magnetic fields are in the same direction but produce forces that are in perpendicular directions to each other.

27.31 IDENTIFY and **SET UP:** Use the fields in the velocity selector to find the speed v of the particles that pass through. Apply Newton's 2nd law with $a = v^2/R$ to the ciruclar motion in the second region of the spectrometer. Solve for the mass m of the ion.

EXECUTE: In the velocity selector $|q|E = |q|vB$.

$$v = \frac{E}{B} = \frac{1.12 \times 10^5 \text{ V/m}}{0.540 \text{ T}} = 2.074 \times 10^5 \text{ m/s}$$

In the region of the circular path $\sum \vec{F} = m\vec{a}$ gives

$|q|vB = m(v^2/R)$ so $m = |q|RB/v$

Singly charged ion, so $|q| = +e = 1.602 \times 10^{-19}$ C

$$m = \frac{(1.602 \times 10^{-19} \text{ C})(0.310 \text{ m})(0.540 \text{ T})}{2.074 \times 10^5 \text{ m/s}} = 1.29 \times 10^{-25} \text{ kg}$$

Mass number = mass in atomic mass units, so is $\dfrac{1.29 \times 10^{-25} \text{ kg}}{1.66 \times 10^{-27} \text{ kg}} = 78.$

EVALUATE: Appendix D gives the average atomic mass of selenium to be 78.96. One of its isotopes has atomic mass 78.

27.33 a) IDENTIFY and **SET UP:** The force $\vec{F}_B$ on the current due to the magnetic field must be upward and and equal in magnitude to the weight mg of the rod. This force has its maximum magnitude $F_B = IlB = ILB$ when the magnetic field is pependicular to the current direction.

EXECUTE: $ILB = mg$ and $B = mg/IL$

b) IDENTIFY and **SET UP:** Use the right-hand rule to relate the direction of the current, the direction of $\vec{B}$ and the direction of the magnetic force $\vec{F}_B$.

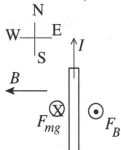

EXECUTE:
To produce a force that opposes gravity the magnetic field must be directed to the west.

EVALUATE: $\vec{B}$ is perpendicular to the current direction and to $\vec{F}_B$, so is either to the left or to the right in the sketch. The right-hand rule tells us which of these possibilities gives $\vec{B}$ in the required direction. A component of $\vec{B}$ along the direction of I exerts no force so B could be larger than calculated in part (a), but the problem asks for the minimum B.

27.37 IDENTIFY and **SET UP:** Use Eq.(27.19) to calculate $\vec{F}$. Use the cross products between unit vectors as discussed in Section 1.10.

$$\vec{F} = I\vec{l}\mathbf{X}\vec{B}$$

$I = 3.50$ A, $\vec{l} = -(0.0100 \text{ m})\hat{\imath}$ (since the current is in the $-x$-direction)

EXECUTE:

a) $\vec{B} = -(0.65 \text{ T})\hat{\jmath}$

$\vec{F} = (3.50 \text{ A})(-0.0100 \text{ m})(-0.65 \text{ T})\hat{\imath}\mathbf{X}\hat{\jmath}$

$\hat{\imath}\mathbf{X}\hat{\jmath} = \hat{k}$, so $\vec{F} = +(0.023 \text{ N})\hat{k}$

b) $\vec{B} = +(0.56 \text{ T})\hat{k}$

$\vec{F} = (3.50 \text{ A})(-0.0100 \text{ m})(0.56 \text{ T})\hat{\imath}\mathbf{X}\hat{k}$

$\hat{\imath}\mathbf{X}\hat{k} = -\hat{\jmath}$, so $\vec{F} = +(0.020 \text{ N})\hat{\jmath}$

c) $\vec{B} = -(0.31 \text{ T})\hat{\imath}$

$\vec{F} = (3.50 \text{ A})(-0.0100 \text{ m})(-0.31 \text{ T})\hat{\imath}\mathbf{X}\hat{\imath}$

$\hat{\imath}\mathbf{X}\hat{\imath} = 0$, so $F = 0$

d) $\vec{B} = (0.33 \text{ T})\hat{\imath} - (0.28 \text{ T})\hat{k}$

$\vec{F} = (3.50 \text{ A})(-0.0100 \text{ m})[(0.33 \text{ T})\hat{\imath}\mathbf{X}\hat{\imath} - (0.28 \text{ T})\hat{\imath}\mathbf{X}\hat{k}]$

$\hat{\imath}\mathbf{X}\hat{\imath} = 0$, $\hat{\imath}\mathbf{X}\hat{k} = -\hat{\jmath}$ so $\vec{F} = (3.50 \text{ A})(-0.0100 \text{ m})(-0.28 \text{ T})(-\hat{\jmath}) = -(0.0098 \text{ N})\hat{\jmath}$

e) $\vec{B} = (0.74 \text{ T})\hat{j} - (0.36 \text{ T})\hat{k}$

$\vec{F} = (3.50 \text{ A})(-0.0100 \text{ m})[(0.74 \text{ T})\hat{i} \times \hat{j} - (0.36 \text{ T})\hat{i} \times \hat{k}]$

$\hat{i} \times \hat{j} = \hat{k}, \hat{i} \times \hat{k} = -\hat{j}$ so

$\vec{F} = -(0.026 \text{ N})\hat{k} + (0.013 \text{ N})(-\hat{j}) = -(0.013 \text{ N})\hat{j} - (0.026 \text{ N})\hat{k}$

EVALUATE: Components of $\vec{B}$ along the direction of the current produce no force. In each case $\vec{F}$ is perpendicular to both $\vec{B}$ and the direction of I.

27.39 IDENTIFY and **SET UP:** The magnetic force is given by Eq.(27.19). $F_I = mg$ when the bar is just ready to levitate. When I becomes larger, $F_I > mg$ and $F_I - mg$ is the net force that accelerates the bar upward. Use Newton's 2nd law to find the acceleration.

a) EXECUTE: $IlB = mg$, $I = \dfrac{mg}{lB} = \dfrac{(0.750 \text{ kg})(9.80 \text{ m/s}^2)}{(0.500 \text{ m})(0.450 \text{ T})} = 32.67 \text{ A}$

$\varepsilon = IR = (32.67 \text{ A})(25.0 \ \Omega) = 817 \text{ V}$

b) $R = 2.0 \ \Omega$, $I = \varepsilon/R = (816.7 \text{ V})/(2.0 \ \Omega) = 408 \text{ A}$

$F_I = IlB = 92 \text{ N}$

$a = (F_I - mg)/m = 113 \text{ m/s}^2$

EVALUATE: I increases by over an order of magnitude when R changes so $F_I \gg mg$ and a is an order of magnitude larger than g.

27.47 IDENTIFY and **SET UP:** The potential energy is given by Eq.(27.27): $U = -\vec{\mu} \cdot \vec{B}$. The scalar product depends on the angle between $\vec{\mu}$ and $\vec{B}$.

EXECUTE:

For $\vec{\mu}$ and $\vec{B}$ parallel, $\phi = 0°$ and $\vec{\mu} \cdot \vec{B} = \mu B \cos\phi = \mu B$.

For $\vec{\mu}$ and $\vec{B}$ antiparallel, $\phi = 180°$ and $\vec{\mu} \cdot \vec{B} = \mu B \cos\phi = -\mu B$.

$U_1 = +\mu B$, $U_2 = -\mu B$

$\Delta U = U_2 - U_1 = -2\mu B = -2(1.45 \text{ A} \cdot \text{m}^2)(0.835 \text{ T}) = -2.42 \text{ J}$

EVALUATE: U is maximum when $\vec{\mu}$ and $\vec{B}$ are antiparallel and minimum when they are parallel. When the coil is rotated as specified its magnetic potential energy decreases.

27.49 IDENTIFY: The circuit consists of two parallel branches with the potential difference of 120 V applied across each. One branch is the rotor, represented by a resistance R_r and an induced emf that opposes the applied potential. Apply the loop rule to each parallel branch and use the junction rule to relate the currents through the field coil and through the rotor to the 4.82 A supplied to the motor.

SET UP:

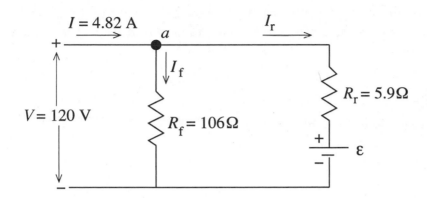

EXECUTE:

a) The field coils and the rotor are in parallel with the applied potential difference V, so $V = I_f R_f$.

$$I_f = \frac{V}{R_f} = \frac{120 \text{ V}}{106 \text{ } \Omega} = 1.13 \text{ A.}$$

b) Applying the junction rule to point a in the circuit diagram gives $I - I_f - I_r = 0$. $I_r = I - I_f = 4.82 \text{ A} - 1.13 \text{ A} = 3.69 \text{ A.}$

c) The potential drop across the rotor, $I_r R_r + \varepsilon$, must equal the applied potential difference V: $V = I_r R_r + \varepsilon$

$\varepsilon = V - I_r R_r = 120 \text{ V} - (3.69 \text{ A})(5.9 \text{ } \Omega) = 98.2 \text{ V}$

d) The mechanical power output is the electrical power input minus the rate of dissipation of electrical energy in the resistance of the motor:

electrical power input to the motor
$P_{in} = IV = (4.82 \text{ A})(120 \text{ V}) = 578 \text{ W}$

electrical power loss in the two resistances
$P_{loss} = I_f^2 R_f + I_r^2 R = (1.13 \text{ A})^2 (106 \text{ } \Omega) + (3.69 \text{ A})^2 (5.9 \text{ } \Omega) = 216 \text{ W}$

mechanical power output
$P_{out} = P_{in} - P_{loss} = 578 \text{ W} - 216 \text{ W} = 362 \text{ W}$

The mechanical power output is the power associated with the induced emf ε $P_{out} = P_\varepsilon = \varepsilon I_r = (98.2 \text{ V})(3.69 \text{ A}) = 362 \text{ W}$, which agrees with the above calculation.

EVALUATE: The induced emf reduces the amount of current that flows through the rotor. This motor differs from the one described in Example 27.12. In that example the rotor and field coils are connected in series and in this problem they are in parallel.

27.51 IDENTIFY: The drift velocity is related to the current density by Eq.(25.4). The electric field is determined by the requirement that the electric and magnetic forces on the current-carrying charges are equal in magnitude and opposite in direction.

a) SET UP:

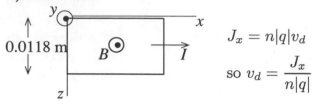

$$J_x = n|q|v_d$$

$$\text{so } v_d = \frac{J_x}{n|q|}$$

EXECUTE: $J_x = \dfrac{I}{A} = \dfrac{I}{y_1 z_1} = \dfrac{120 \text{ A}}{(0.23 \times 10^{-3} \text{ m})(0.0118 \text{ m})} = 4.42 \times 10^7 \text{ A/m}^2$

$v_d = \dfrac{J_x}{n|q|} = \dfrac{4.42 \times 10^7 \text{ A/m}^2}{(5.85 \times 10^{28}/\text{ m}^3)(1.602 \times 10^{-19} \text{ C})} = 4.7 \times 10^{-3} \text{ m/s} = 4.7 \text{ mm/s}$

b) <u>magnitude of $\vec{E}$</u>

$|q|E_z = |q|v_d B_y$

$E_z = v_d B_y = (4.7 \times 10^{-3} \text{ m/s})(0.95 \text{ T}) = 4.5 \times 10^{-3} \text{ V/m}$

<u>direction of $\vec{E}$</u>

The drift velocity of the electrons is in the opposite direction to the current.

$$\vec{v} \mathbf{X} \vec{B} \uparrow$$

$$\vec{F}_B = q\vec{v}\mathbf{X}\vec{B} = -e\vec{v}\mathbf{X}\vec{B} \downarrow$$

$\vec{F}_E$ must oppose $\vec{F}_B$
so $\vec{F}_E$ is in the $-z$-direction

$\vec{F}_E = q\vec{E} = -e\vec{E}$ so $\vec{E}$ is opposite to the direction of $\vec{F}_E$ and thus $\vec{E}$ is in the $+z$-direction.

c) The Hall emf is the potential difference between the two edges of the strip (at $z = 0$ and $z = z_1$) that results from the electric field calculated in part (b).

$\varepsilon_{\text{Hall}} = Ez_1 = (4.5 \times 10^{-3} \text{ V/m})(0.0118 \text{ m}) = 53 \ \mu\text{V}$

EVALUATE: Even though the current is quite large the Hall emf is very small. Our calculated Hall emf is more than an order of magnitude larger than in Example 27.13. In this problem the magnetic field and current density are larger than in the example, and this leads to a larger Hall emf.

Problems

27.53 a) IDENTIFY: Use Eq.(27.2) to relate $\vec{v}$, $\vec{B}$, and $\vec{F}$.
SET UP:

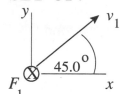

$\vec{F} = q\vec{v}\textbf{X}\vec{B}$ says
that $\vec{F}$ is perpendicular to $\vec{v}$ and $\vec{B}$.

The information given here means that
$\vec{B}$ can have no z-component.

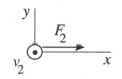

$\vec{F}$ is perpendicular to $\vec{v}$ and $\vec{B}$, so
$\vec{B}$ can have no x component.

Both pieces of information taken together say that $\vec{B}$ is in the y-direction; $\vec{B} = B_y\hat{j}$.

EXECUTE: Use the information given about $\vec{F}_2$ to calculate F_y: $\vec{F}_2 = F_2\hat{i}$, $\vec{v}_2 = v_2\hat{k}$, $\vec{B} = B_y\hat{j}$.

$\vec{F}_2 = q\vec{v}_2\textbf{X}\vec{B}$ says $F_2\hat{i} = qv_2B_y\hat{k}\textbf{X}\hat{j} = qv_2B_y(-\hat{i})$ and $F_2 = -qv_2B_y$

$B_y = -F_2/(qv_2) = -F_2/(qv_1)$

$\vec{B}$ has magnitude $F_2/(qv_1)$ and is in the $-y$-direction.

b) $F_1 = qvB\sin\phi = qv_1|B_y|/\sqrt{2} = F_2/\sqrt{2}$

EVALUATE: $v_1 = v_2$. $\vec{v}_2$ is perpendicular to $\vec{B}$ whereas only the component of $\vec{v}_1$ perpendicular to $\vec{B}$ contributes to the force, so it is expected that $F_2 > F_1$, as we found.

27.55 IDENTIFY: The magnetic force $\vec{F}_B$ is given by Eq.(27.2) and the electric force $\vec{F}_E$ is given by Eq.(21.3). The problem calls for zero deflection of the particle and this occurs when $\vec{F}_B$ and $\vec{F}_E$ are equal in magnitude and opposite in direction. The direction of $\vec{F}_E$ is the direction of $\vec{E}$ and the direction of $\vec{F}_B$ is given by the right-hand rule.

SET UP: The direction of $\vec{E}$ is horizontal and perpendicular to $\vec{v}$, as shown in the sketch:

EXECUTE: $F_B = qvB$, $F_E = qE$

$F_B = F_E$ for no deflection, so $qvB = qE$

$E = vB = (14.0 \text{ m/s})(0.500 \text{ T}) = 7.00 \text{ V/m}$

EVALUATE: We ignored the gravity force. If the target is 5.0 m from the rifle, it takes the bullet 0.36 s to reach the target and during this time the bullet moves downward $y - y_0 = \frac{1}{2}a_y t^2 = 0.62$ m. The magnetic and electric forces we considered are horizontal. A vertical electric field of $E = mg/q = 0.038$ V/m would be required to cancel the gravity force. Air resistance has also been neglected.

27.57 a) IDENTIFY and **SET UP:** The maximum radius of the orbit determines the maximum speed v of the protons. Use Newton's 2nd law and $a_c = v^2/R$ for circular motion to relate the variables. The energy of the particle is the kinetic energy $K = \frac{1}{2}mv^2$.

EXECUTE: $\sum \vec{F} = m\vec{a}$ gives $|q|vB = m(v^2/R)$

$$v = \frac{|q|BR}{m} = \frac{(1.60 \times 10^{-19} \text{ C})(0.85 \text{ T})(0.40 \text{ m})}{1.67 \times 10^{-27} \text{ kg}} = 3.257 \times 10^7 \text{ m/s.}$$

The kinetic energy of a proton moving with this speed is

$K = \frac{1}{2}mv^2 = \frac{1}{2}(1.67 \times 10^{-27} \text{ kg})(3.257 \times 10^7 \text{ m/s})^2 = 8.9 \times 10^{-13} \text{ J} = 5.6 \text{ MeV}$

b) The time for one revolution is the period

$$T = \frac{2\pi R}{v} = \frac{2\pi (0.40 \text{ m})}{3.257 \times 10^7 \text{ m/s}} = 7.7 \times 10^{-8} \text{ s}$$

c) $K = \frac{1}{2}mv^2 = \frac{1}{2}m\left(\frac{|q|BR}{m}\right)^2 = \frac{1}{2}\frac{|q|^2 B^2 R^2}{m}$. Or, $B = \frac{\sqrt{2Km}}{|q|R}$.

B is proportional to $\sqrt{K}$, so if K is increased by a factor of 2 then B must be increased by a factor of $\sqrt{2}$.

$B = \sqrt{2}(0.85 \text{ T}) = 1.2 \text{ T}$.

d) $v = \frac{|q|BR}{m} = \frac{(3.20 \times 10^{-19} \text{ C})(0.85 \text{ T})(0.40 \text{ m})}{6.65 \times 10^{-27} \text{ kg}} = 1.636 \times 10^7 \text{ m/s}$

$K = \frac{1}{2}mv^2 = \frac{1}{2}(6.65 \times 10^{-27} \text{ kg})(1.636 \times 10^7 \text{ m/s})^2 = 8.9 \times 10^{-13} \text{ J} = 5.5 \text{ MeV}$, the same as the maximum energy for protons.

EVALUATE: We can see that the maximum energy must be approximately the same as follows:

From part (c), $K = \frac{1}{2}m\left(\frac{|q|BR}{m}\right)^2$. For alpha particles $|q|$ is larger by a factor of 2 and m is larger by a factor of 4 (approximately). Thus $|q|^2/m$ is unchanged and K is the same.

27.61 IDENTIFY and **SET UP:** Use Eq.(27.2) to relate q, $\vec{v}$, $\vec{B}$ and $\vec{F}$.

The force $\vec{F}$ and $\vec{a}$ are related by Newton's 2nd law.

$\vec{B} = -(0.120 \text{ T})\hat{k}$, $\vec{v} = (1.05 \times 10^6 \text{ m/s})(-3\hat{i} + 4\hat{j} + 12\hat{k})$, $F = 1.25 \text{ N}$

a) **EXECUTE:** $\vec{F} = q\vec{v}\mathbf{X}\vec{B}$

$\vec{F} = q(-0.120 \text{ T})(1.05 \times 10^6 \text{ m/s})(-3\hat{i}\mathbf{X}\hat{k} + 4\hat{j}\mathbf{X}\hat{k} + 12\hat{k}\mathbf{X}\hat{k})$

$\hat{i}\mathbf{X}\hat{k} = -\hat{j}, \hat{j}\mathbf{X}\hat{k} = \hat{i}, \hat{k}\mathbf{X}\hat{k} = 0$

$\vec{F} = -q(1.26 \times 10^5 \text{ N/C})(+3\hat{j} + 4\hat{i}) = -q(1.26 \times 10^5 \text{ N/C})(+4\hat{i} + 3\hat{j})$

The magnitude of the vector $+4\hat{i} + 3\hat{j}$ is $\sqrt{3^2 + 4^2} = 5$.

Thus $F = -q(1.26 \times 10^5 \text{ N/C})(5)$.

$$q = -\frac{F}{5(1.26 \times 10^5 \text{ N/C})} = -\frac{1.25 \text{ N}}{5(1.26 \times 10^5 \text{ N/C})} = -1.98 \times 10^{-6} \text{ C}$$

b) $\sum \vec{F} = m\vec{a}$ so $\vec{a} = \vec{F}/m$

$\vec{F} = -q(1.26\times10^5 \text{ N/C})(+4\hat{i} +3\hat{j}) = -(-1.98\times10^{-6} \text{ C})(1.26\times10^5 \text{ N/C})(+4\hat{i} + 3\hat{j}) = +0.250 \text{ N}(+4\hat{i} + 3\hat{j})$

Then $\vec{a} = \vec{F}/m = \left(\dfrac{0.250 \text{ N}}{2.58 \times 10^{-15} \text{ kg}}\right)(+4\hat{i} + 3\hat{j}) =$

$(9.69 \times 10^{13} \text{ m/s}^2)(+4\hat{i} + 3\hat{j})$

c) **IDENTIFY** and **SET UP:** $\vec{F}$ is in the xy-plane, so in the z-direction the particle moves with constant speed 12.6×10^6 m/s.

In the xy-plane the force $\vec{F}$ causes the particle to move in a circle, with $\vec{F}$ directed in towards the center of the circle.

EXECUTE: $\sum \vec{F} = m\vec{a}$ gives $F = m(v^2/R)$ and $R = mv^2/F$

$v^2 = v_x^2 + v_y^2 = (-3.15 \times 10^6 \text{ m/s})^2 + (+4.20 \times 10^6 \text{ m/s})^2 = 2.756 \times 10^{13} \text{ m}^2/\text{s}^2$

$F = \sqrt{F_x^2 + F_y^2} = (0.250 \text{ N})\sqrt{4^2 + 3^2} = 1.25 \text{ N}$

$$R = \frac{mv^2}{F} = \frac{(2.58 \times 10^{-15} \text{ kg})(2.756 \times 10^{13} \text{ m}^2/\text{s}^2)}{1.25 \text{ N}} = 0.0569 \text{ m} = 5.69 \text{ cm}$$

d) **IDENTIFY** and **SET UP:** By Eq.(27.12) the cyclotron frequency is $f = \omega/2\pi = v/2\pi R$.

EXECUTE: The circular motion is in the xy-plane, so $v = \sqrt{v_x^2 + v_y^2} = 5.25 \times 10^6$ m/s.

$$f = \frac{v}{2\pi R} = \frac{5.25 \times 10^6 \text{ m/s}}{2\pi(0.0569 \text{ m})} = 1.47 \times 10^7 \text{ Hz, and } \omega = 2\pi f = 9.23 \times 10^7 \text{ rad/s}$$

e) **IDENTIFY** and **SET UP:** Compare t to the period T of the circular motion in the xy-plane to find the x and y coordinates at this t. In the z-direction the particle moves with constant speed, so $z = z_0 + z_z t$.

EXECUTE: The period of the motion in the xy-plane is given by

$$T = \frac{1}{f} = \frac{1}{1.47 \times 10^7 \text{ Hz}} = 6.80 \times 10^{-8} \text{ s}$$

In $t = 2T$ the particle has returned to the same x and y coordinates. The z-component of the motion is motion with a constant velocity of $v_z = +12.6 \times 10^6$ m/s. Thus $z = z_0 + v_z t = 0 + (12.6 \times 10^6 \text{ m/s})(2)(6.80 \times 10^{-8} \text{ s}) = +1.71$ m.

The coordinates at $t = 2T$ are $x = R$, $y = 0$, $z = +1.71$ m.

EVALUATE: The circular motion is in the plane perpendicular to $\vec{B}$. The radius of this motion gets smaller when B increases and it gets larger when v increases. There is no magnetic force in the direction of $\vec{B}$ so the particle moves with constant velocity in that direction. The superposition of circular motion in the xy-plane and constant speed motion in the z-direction is a helical path.

27.65 IDENTIFY and **SET UP:** Use Eq.(27.19) to calculate the force on each segment.

EXECUTE: $\vec{F} = I\vec{l} \times \vec{B}$, $\vec{B} = (0.860 \text{ T})\hat{i}$, $I = 6.58$ A

a) segment ab

$\vec{l} = (0.750 \text{ m})\hat{j}$

$\vec{F}_{ab} = I\vec{l} \times \vec{B} = (6.58 \text{ A})(0.750 \text{ m})(0.860 \text{ T})\hat{j} \times \hat{i} = (4.24 \text{ N})(-\hat{k}) = -(4.24 \text{ N})\hat{k}$.

The force has magnitude 4.24 N and is in the $-z$-direction.

segment bc

$\vec{l} = (0.750 \text{ m})(\hat{i} - \hat{k})$

$\vec{F}_{bc} = I\vec{l} \times \vec{B} = (6.58 \text{ A})(0.750 \text{ m})(0.860 \text{ T})(\hat{i} \times \hat{i} - \hat{k} \times \hat{i})$

$\hat{i} \times \hat{i} = 0$, $\hat{k} \times \hat{i} = \hat{j}$

$\vec{F}_{bc} = -(4.24 \text{ N})\hat{j}$.

The force has magnitdue 4.24 N and is in the $-y$-direction.

segment cd

$\vec{l} = (0.750 \text{ m})(-\hat{j} + \hat{k})$

$\vec{F}_{cd} = I\vec{l} \times \vec{B} = (6.58 \text{ A})(0.750 \text{ m})(0.860 \text{ T})(-\hat{j} \times \hat{i} + \hat{k} \times \hat{i})$

$\hat{j} \times \hat{i} = -\hat{k}$, $\hat{k} \times \hat{i} = \hat{j}$

$\vec{F}_{cd} = (4.24 \text{ N})(\hat{j} + \hat{k})$, so $F_{cd} = 4.24 \text{ N}\sqrt{1^2 + 1^2} = 6.00$ N.

The force has magnitude 6.00 N and is directed midway between the $+y$-axis and the $+z$-axis.

segment de

$$\vec{l} = -(0.750 \text{ m})\hat{k}$$

$$\vec{F}_{de} = I\vec{l}\mathbf{X}\vec{B} = -(6.58 \text{ A})(0.750 \text{ m})(0.860 \text{ T})\hat{k}\mathbf{X}\hat{i} = -(4.24 \text{ N})\hat{j}$$

The force has magnitude 4.24 N and is in the $-y$-direction.

segment ef

$$\vec{l} = -(0.750 \text{ m})\hat{i}$$

$$\vec{F}_{ef} = I\vec{l}\mathbf{X}\vec{B} = -(6.58 \text{ A})(0.750 \text{ m})(0.860 \text{ T})\hat{i}\mathbf{X}\hat{i} = 0.$$

b) $\vec{F}_{\text{tot}} = \vec{F}_{ab} + \vec{F}_{bc} + \vec{F}_{cd} + \vec{F}_{de} + \vec{F}_{ef}$

$$\vec{F}_{\text{tot}} = (4.24 \text{ N})(-\hat{k} \ -\hat{j} \ +\hat{j} \ +\hat{k} \ -\hat{j}) = -(4.24 \text{ N})\hat{j}$$

The total force has magnitude 4.24 N and is in the $-y$-direction.

EVALUATE: The wire connects point a to point f. A straight wire segment from a to f has length $l = 0.750$ m and makes an angle of $\phi = 90°$ with $\vec{B}$. The force on it would be in the $-y$-direction and would have magnitude $F = IlB \sin \phi = 4.24$ N. The force on the wire $abcdef$ is thus the same as on a straight wire from a to f that carries the same current. This is a general result.

27.67 IDENTIFY: The force exerted by the magnetic field is given by Eq.(27.19). The net force on the wire must be zero.

SET UP: For the wire to remain at rest the force exerted on it by the magnetic field must have a component directed up the incline. To produce a force in this direction, the current in the wire must be directed from right to left in Fig.27.55.

Or, viewing the wire from its left-hand end:

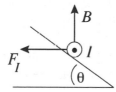

Free-body diagram for the wire:

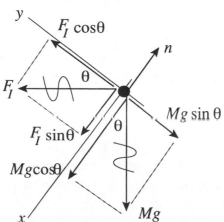

EXECUTE:

$$\sum F_y = 0$$

$$F_I \cos \theta - Mg \sin \theta = 0$$

$$F_I = ILB \sin \phi$$

$\phi = 90°$ since $\vec{B}$ is perpendicular to the current direction.

Thus $(ILB) \cos\theta - Mg \sin\theta = 0$ and

$$I = \frac{Mg \tan\theta}{LB}$$

EVALUATE: The magnetic and gravitational forces are in perpendicular directions so their components parallel to the incline involve different trig functions. As the tilt angle θ increases there is a larger component of Mg down the incline and the component of F_I up the incline is smaller; I must increase with θ to compensate. As $\theta \to 0$, $I \to 0$ and as $\theta \to 90°$, $I \to \infty$.

27.71 IDENTIFY: Use Eq.(27.20) to calculate the force and then the torque on each small section of the rod and integrate to find the total magnetic torque. At equilibrium the torques from the spring force and from the magnetic force cancel. The spring force depends on the amount x the spring is stretched and then $U = \frac{1}{2}kx^2$ gives the energy stored in the spring.

a) SET UP:

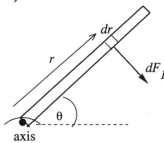

Divide the rod into infinitesimal sections

of length dr.

EXECUTE: The magnetic force on this section is $dF_I = IB\,dr$ and is perpendicular to the rod. The torque $d\tau$ due to the force on this section is $d\tau = r\,dF_I = IBr\,dr$. The total torque is $\int d\tau = IB \int_0^l r\,dr = \frac{1}{2}Il^2B = 0.0442$ N·m, clockwise.

b) SET UP: F_I produces a clockwise torque so the spring force must produce a counterclockwise torque. The spring force must be to the left; the spring is stretched.

EXECUTE: Find x, the amount the spring is stretched:

$\sum \tau = 0$, axis at hinge, counterclockwise torques positive

$(kx)l \sin 53° - \frac{1}{2}Il^2B = 0$

$$x = \frac{IlB}{2k \sin 53.0°} = \frac{(6.50 \text{ A})(0.200 \text{ m})(0.340 \text{ T})}{2(4.80 \text{ N/m}) \sin 53.0°} = 0.05765 \text{ m}$$

$U = \frac{1}{2}kx^2 = 7.98 \times 10^{-3}$ J

EVALUATE: The magnetic torque calculated in part (a) is the same torque calculated from a force diagram in which the total magnetic force $F_I = IlB$ acts at the center of the rod. We didn't include a gravity torque since the problem said the rod had negligible mass.

27.75 IDENTIFY: For the loop to be in equilibrium the net torque on it must be zero. Use Eq.(27.26) to calculate the torque due to the magnetic field and use Eq.(10.3) for the torque due to the gravity force.

SET UP:

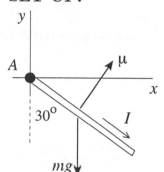

Use $\sum \tau_A = 0$, where point A is at the origin.

EXECUTE:

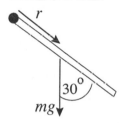

$\tau_{mg} = mgr\sin\phi = mg(0.0400 \text{ m})\sin 30.0°$
The torque is clockwise; $\vec{\tau}_{mg}$ is directed into the paper.

For the loop to be in equilibrium the torque due to $\vec{B}$ must be counterclockwise (opposite to $\vec{\tau}_{mg}$) and it must be that $\tau_B = \tau_{mg}$.

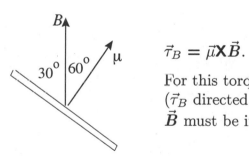

$\vec{\tau}_B = \vec{\mu} \mathbf{X} \vec{B}.$

For this torque to be counterclockwise ($\vec{\tau}_B$ directed out of the paper), $\vec{B}$ must be in the $+y$-direction.

$\tau_B = \mu B \sin\phi = IAB\sin 60.0°$

$\tau_B = \tau_{mg}$ gives $IAB\sin 60.0° = mg(0.0400 \text{ m})\sin 30.0°$

$m = (0.15 \text{ g/cm})2(8.00 \text{ cm} + 6.00 \text{ cm}) = 4.2 \text{ g} = 4.2 \times 10^{-3} \text{ kg}$

$A = (0.0800 \text{ m})(0.0600 \text{ m}) = 4.80 \times 10^{-3} \text{ m}^2$

$B = \dfrac{mg(0.0400 \text{ m})(\sin 30.0°)}{IA\sin 60.0°}$

$B = \dfrac{(4.2 \times 10^{-3} \text{ kg})(9.80 \text{ m/s}^2)(0.0400 \text{ m})\sin 30.0°}{(8.2 \text{ A})(4.80 \times 10^{-3} \text{ m}^2)\sin 60.0°} = 0.024 \text{ T}$

EVALUATE: As the loop swings up the torque due to $\vec{B}$ decreases to zero and the torque due to mg increases from zero, so there must be an orientation of the loop where the net torque is zero.

27.77 IDENTIFY and **SET UP:** The magnitude τ of the restoring torque due to the magnetic field is given by Eq.(27.23). Use this torque in Eq.(10.6) and for small angles compare the result to Eq.(13.37) to find the quantity analogous to k/m for a spring-mass system and then use Eq.(13.12) for the period.

EXECUTE: The restoring torque applied by the magnetic field is given by $\tau = -NIAB \sin \phi$. The minus sign indicates that τ is directed opposite to the angular displacement; it is a restoring torque.

For small angles, $\sin \phi \approx \phi$, when ϕ is measured in radians.

Thus $\tau = -NIAB\phi$.

Use this in $\tau = I\alpha$, and write $\alpha = \dfrac{d^2\phi}{dt^2}$: $-(NIAB)\phi = I_S \dfrac{d^2\phi}{dt^2}$

$\dfrac{d^2\phi}{dt^2} = -\left(\dfrac{NIAB}{I_S}\right)\phi = -\omega^2\phi$, where ω is the angular frequency of the oscillations and we have used the results of Section 13.6.

Thus $\omega = \sqrt{\dfrac{NIAB}{I_S}}$ and $T = \dfrac{2\pi}{\omega} = 2\pi\sqrt{\dfrac{I_S}{NIAB}}$.

EVALUATE: When N, I, A, or B are larger the restoring torque is larger and the period is smaller. For larger I_S the period is smaller.

27.79 IDENTIFY: Use Eq.(27.20) to calculate the force on a short segment of the coil and integrate over the entire coil to find the total force.

SET UP:

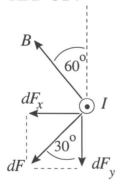

Consider the force $d\vec{F}$ on a short segment dl at the left-hand side of the coil, as viewed in Fig.27.61. The current at this point is directed out of the page. $d\vec{F}$ is perpendicular both to $\vec{B}$ and to the direction of I.

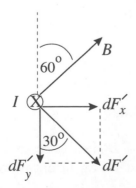

Consider also the force $d\vec{F}'$ on a short segment on the opposite side of the coil, at the right-hand side of the coil in Fig.27.61. The current at this point is directed into the page.

The two sketches show that the x-components cancel and that the y-components add. This is true for all pairs of short segments on opposite sides of the coil. The net magnetic force on the coil is in the y-direction and its magnitude is given by $F = \int dF_y$.

EXECUTE:

$dF = I\,dl\,B\sin\phi$. But $\vec{B}$ is perpendicular to the current direction so $\phi = 90°$.

$dF_y = dF\cos 30.0° = IB\cos 30.0°\,dl$

$F = \int dF_y = IB\cos 30.0° \int dl$

But $\int dl = N(2\pi r)$, the total length of wire in the coil.

$F = IB\cos 30.0° N(2\pi r) = (0.950\text{ A})(0.220\text{ T})(\cos 30.0°)(50)2\pi(0.0078\text{ m}) =$

0.444 N and $\vec{F} = -(0.444\text{ N})\hat{j}$

EVALUATE: The magnetic field makes a constant angle with the plane of the coil but has a different direction at different points around the circumference of the coil so is not uniform. The net force is proportional to the magnitude of the current and reverses direction when the current reverses direction.

27.83 **IDENTIFY:** While the ends of the wire are in contact with the mercury and current flows in the wire, the magnetic field exerts an upward force and the wire has an upward acceleration. After the ends leave the mercury the electrical connection is broken and the wire is in free-fall.

a) SET UP: After the wire leaves the mercury its acceleration is g, downward. The wire travels upward a total distance of 0.350 m from its initial position. Its ends lose contact with the mercury after the wire has traveled 0.025 m, so the wire travels upward 0.325 m after it leaves the mercury. Consider the motion of the wire after it leaves the mercury. Take $+y$ to be upward and take the origin at the position of the wire as it leaves the mercury.

$a_y = -9.80\text{ m/s}^2$, $\quad y - y_0 = +0.325\text{ m}$, $\quad v_y = 0$ (at maximum height), $\quad v_{0y} = ?$

$v_y^2 = v_{0y}^2 + 2a_y(y - y_0)$

EXECUTE: $v_{0y} = \sqrt{-2a_y(y - y_0)} = \sqrt{-2(-9.80\text{ m/s}^2)(0.325\text{ m})} = 2.52\text{ m/s}$

b) SET UP: Now consider the motion of the wire while it is in contact with the mercury. Take $+y$ to be upward and the origin at the initial position of the wire.

Calculate the acceleration:

$y - y_0 = +0.025\text{ m}$, $\quad v_{0y} = 0$ (starts from rest), $\quad v_y = +2.52\text{ m/s}$ (from part (a)),

$a_y = ?$

$v_y^2 = v_{0y}^2 + 2a_y(y - y_0)$

EXECUTE: $a_y = \dfrac{v_y^2}{2(y - y_0)} = \dfrac{(2.52\text{ m/s})^2}{2(0.025\text{ m})} = 127\text{ m/s}^2$

SET UP: Free-body diagram for the wire

EXECUTE:

$$\sum F_y = ma_y$$

$$F_B - mg = ma_y$$

$$IlB = m(g + a_y)$$

$$I = \frac{m(g + a_y)}{lB}$$

l is the length of the horizontal section of the wire; $l = 0.150$ m

$$I = \frac{(5.40 \times 10^{-5} \text{ kg})(9.80 \text{ m/s}^2 + 127 \text{ m/s}^2)}{(0.150 \text{ m})(0.00650 \text{ T})} = 7.58 \text{ A}$$

c) IDENTIFY and **SET UP:** Use Ohm's law.

EXECUTE: $V = IR$ so $R = \dfrac{V}{I} = \dfrac{1.50 \text{ V}}{7.58 \text{ A}} = 0.198 \ \Omega$

EVALUATE: The current is large and the magnetic force provides a large upward aceleration. During this upward acceleration the wire moves a much shorter distance as it gains speed than the distance it moves while in free-fall with a much smaller acceleration, as it loses the speed it gained. The large current means the resistance of the wire must be small.

27.85 a) IDENTIFY: Use Eq.(27.27) to relate U, μ and $\vec{B}$ and use Eq.(27.26) to relate $\vec{\tau}$, $\vec{\mu}$ and $\vec{B}$. We also know that $B_0^2 = B_x^2 + B_y^2 + B_z^2$. This gives three equations for the three components of $\vec{B}$.

SET UP:

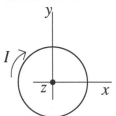

$\vec{\mu}$ is into the plane of the paper, in the $-z$-direction

$$\vec{\mu} = -\mu\hat{k} = -IA\hat{k}$$

b) EXECUTE: $\vec{\tau} = D(+4\hat{i} - 3\hat{j})$, where $D > 0$.

$\vec{\mu} = -IA\hat{k}$, $\vec{B} = B_x\hat{i} + B_y\hat{j} + B_z\hat{k}$

$\vec{\tau} = \vec{\mu} \times \vec{B} = (-IA)(B_x\hat{k}\times\hat{i} + B_y\hat{k}\times\hat{j} + B_z\hat{k}\times\hat{k}) = IAB_y\hat{i} - IAB_x\hat{j}$

Compare this to the expression given for $\vec{\tau}$:

$IAB_y = 4D$ so $B_y = 4D/IA$ and $-IAB_x = -3D$ so $B_x = 3D/IA$

B_z doesn't contribute to the torque since $\vec{\mu}$ is along the z-direction.

But $B = B_0$ and $B_x^2 + B_y^2 + B_z^2 = B_0^2$; with $B_0 = 13D/IA$.

Thus $B_z = \pm\sqrt{B_0^2 - B_x^2 - B_y^2} = \pm(D/IA)\sqrt{169 - 9 - 16} = \pm12(D/IA)$

That $U = -\vec{\mu} \cdot \vec{B}$ is negative determines the sign of B_z:

$U = -\vec{\mu} \cdot \vec{B} = -(-IA\hat{k}) \cdot (B_x\hat{i} + B_y\hat{j} + B_z\hat{k}) = +IAB_z$

So U negative says that B_z is negative, and thus $B_z = -12D/IA$.

EVALUATE: $\vec{\mu}$ is along the z-axis so only B_x and B_y contribute to the torque. B_x produces a y-component of $\vec{\tau}$ and B_y produces an x-component of $\vec{\tau}$. Only B_z affects U, and U is negative when $\vec{\mu}$ and $\vec{B}_z$ are parallel.

CHAPTER 28
SOURCES OF MAGNETIC FIELD

Exercises

28.1 **IDENTIFY** and **SET UP:** Use Eq.(28.2) to calculate $\vec{B}$ at each point.

$$\vec{B} = \frac{\mu_0}{4\pi} \frac{q\vec{v} \times \hat{r}}{r^2} = \frac{\mu_0}{4\pi} \frac{q\vec{v} \times \vec{r}}{r^3}, \text{ since } \hat{r} = \frac{\vec{r}}{r}.$$

$\vec{v} = (8.00 \times 10^6 \text{ m/s})\hat{j}$ and $\vec{r}$ is the vector from the charge to the point where the field is calculated.

EXECUTE:

a) $\vec{r} = (0.500 \text{ m})\hat{i}$, $r = 0.500$ m

$\vec{v} \times \vec{r} = vr\hat{j} \times \hat{i} = -vr\hat{k}$

$$\vec{B} = -\frac{\mu_0}{4\pi} \frac{qv}{r^2}\hat{k} = -(1 \times 10^{-7} \text{ T} \cdot \text{m/A})\frac{(6.00 \times 10^{-6} \text{ C})(8.00 \times 10^6 \text{ m/s})}{(0.500 \text{ m})^2}\hat{k}$$

$\vec{B} = -(1.92 \times 10^{-5} \text{ T})\hat{k}$

b) $\vec{r} = -(0.500 \text{ m})\hat{j}$, $r = 0.500$ m

$\vec{v} \times \vec{r} = -vr\hat{j} \times \hat{j} = 0$ and $\vec{B} = 0$.

c) $\vec{r} = (0.500 \text{ m})\hat{k}$, $r = 0.500$ m

$\vec{v} \times \vec{r} = vr\hat{j} \times \hat{k} = vr\hat{i}$

$$\vec{B} = (1 \times 10^{-7} \text{ T} \cdot \text{m/A})\frac{(6.00 \times 10^{-6} \text{ C})(8.00 \times 10^6 \text{ m/s})}{(0.500 \text{ m})^2}\hat{i} = +(1.92 \times 10^{-5} \text{ T})\hat{i}$$

d) $\vec{r} = -(0.500 \text{ m})\hat{j} + (0.500 \text{ m})\hat{k}$, $r = \sqrt{(0.500 \text{ m})^2 + (0.500 \text{ m})^2} = 0.7071$ m

$\vec{v} \times \vec{r} = v(0.500 \text{ m})(-\hat{j} \times \hat{j} + \hat{j} \times \hat{k}) = (4.00 \times 10^6 \text{ m}^2/\text{s})\hat{i}$

$$\vec{B} = (1 \times 10^{-7} \text{ T} \cdot \text{m/A})\frac{(6.00 \times 10^{-6} \text{ C})(4.00 \times 10^6 \text{ m}^2/\text{s})}{(0.7071 \text{ m})^3}\hat{i} = +(6.79 \times 10^{-6} \text{ T})\hat{i}$$

EVALUATE: At each point $\vec{B}$ is perpendicular to both $\vec{v}$ and $\vec{r}$. $B = 0$ along the direction of $\vec{v}$.

28.5 **IDENTIFY:** Use Eq.(28.2) to calculate $\vec{B}$ produced by each moving charge. Add the two field vectors to get the total field.

SET UP:

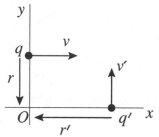

$$\vec{B}_{\text{tot}} = \vec{B}_q + \vec{B}_{q'}$$

$v = 2.00 \times 10^5$ m/s, $v' = 8.00 \times 10^5$ m/s
$q = +4.00 \times 10^{-6}$ C, $q' = -1.50 \times 10^{-6}$ C

EXECUTE: $\vec{B} = \dfrac{\mu_0}{4\pi}\dfrac{q\vec{v}\times\vec{r}}{r^3}$

field $\vec{B}_q$ due to q:

$\vec{v} = (2.00\times 10^5 \text{ m/s})\hat{i}, \quad \vec{r} = -(0.300 \text{ m})\hat{j}$

$\vec{v}\times\vec{r} = -(2.00\times 10^5 \text{ m/s})(0.300 \text{ m})(\hat{i}\times\hat{j}) = -(6.00\times 10^4 \text{ m}^2/\text{s})\hat{k}$

$\vec{B}_q = -(1\times 10^{-7} \text{ T·m/A})\dfrac{(4.00\times 10^{-6}\text{ C})(6.00\times 10^4\text{m}^2/\text{s})}{(0.300 \text{ m})^3}\hat{k} = -(8.889\times 10^{-7}\text{ T})\hat{k}$

field $\vec{B}_{q'}$ due to q':

$\vec{v}' = (8.00\times 10^5 \text{ m/s})\hat{j}, \quad \vec{r} = -(0.400 \text{ m})\hat{i}$

$\vec{v}'\times\vec{r} = -(8.00\times 10^5 \text{ m/s})(0.400 \text{ m})(\hat{j}\times\hat{i}) = +(3.20\times 10^5 \text{ m}^2/\text{s})\hat{k}$

$\vec{B}_{q'} = (1\times 10^{-7} \text{ T·m/A})\dfrac{(-1.50\times 10^{-6}\text{ C})(3.20\times 10^5\text{ m}^2/\text{s})}{(0.400 \text{ m})^3}\hat{k} = -(7.50\times 10^{-7}\text{ T})\hat{k}$

$\vec{B}_{\text{tot}} = \vec{B}_q + \vec{B}_{q'} = (-8.889\times 10^{-7}\text{ T} - 7.50\times 10^{-7}\text{ T})\hat{k} = -(1.64\times 10^{-6})\hat{k}$

The resultant field at the origin has magnitude 1.64×10^{-6} T and is in the $-z$-direction.

EVALUATE: Each field is perpendicular to both $\vec{v}$ and $\vec{r}$. The direction of $B_{q'}$ is opposite to $\vec{v}'\times\vec{r}$ since q' is negative. The two fields are in the same direction so their magnitudes add when calculating the total field.

28.9 IDENTIFY and **SET UP:** The magnetic field produced by an infinitesimal current element is given by Eq.(28.6).

$d\vec{B} = \dfrac{\mu_0}{4\pi}\dfrac{I\vec{l}\times\hat{r}}{r^2}$ As in Example 28.2 use this equation for the finite 0.500-mm segment of wire since the $\Delta l = 0.500$ mm length is much smaller than the distances to the field points.

$\vec{B} = \dfrac{\mu_0}{4\pi}\dfrac{I\,\Delta\vec{l}\times\hat{r}}{r^2} = \dfrac{\mu_0}{4\pi}\dfrac{I\Delta\vec{l}\times\vec{r}}{r^3}$

I is in the $+z$-direction, so $\Delta\vec{l} = (0.500\times 10^{-3}\text{ m})\hat{k}$

EXECUTE:

a) Field point is at $x = 2.00$ m, $y = 0$, $z = 0$ so the vector $\vec{r}$ from the source point (at the origin) to the field point is $\vec{r} = (2.00$ m$)\hat{i}$.

$\Delta\vec{l} \times \vec{r} = (0.500 \times 10^{-3}$ m$)(2.00$ m$)\hat{k} \times \hat{i} = +(1.00 \times 10^{-3}$ m$^2)\hat{j}$

$$\vec{B} = \frac{(1 \times 10^{-7}\text{ T} \cdot \text{m/A})(4.00\text{ A})(1.00 \times 10^{-3}\text{ m}^2)}{(2.00\text{ m})^3}\hat{j} = (5.00 \times 10^{-11}\text{ T})\hat{j}$$

b) $\vec{r} = (2.00$ m$)\hat{j}$, $r = 2.00$ m.

$\Delta\vec{l} \times \vec{r} = (0.500 \times 10^{-3}$ m$)(2.00$ m$)\hat{k} \times \hat{j} = -(1.00 \times 10^{-3}$ m$^2)\hat{i}$

$$\vec{B} = -\frac{(1 \times 10^{-7}\text{ T} \cdot \text{m/A})(4.00\text{ A})(1.00 \times 10^{-3}\text{ m}^2)}{(2.00\text{ m})^3}\hat{i} = -(5.00 \times 10^{-11}\text{ T})\hat{i}$$

c) $\vec{r} = (2.00$ m$)(\hat{i} + \hat{j})$, $r = \sqrt{2}(2.00$ m$)$.

$\Delta\vec{l} \times \vec{r} = (0.500 \times 10^{-3}$ m$)(2.00$ m$)\hat{k} \times (\hat{i} + \hat{j}) = (1.00 \times 10^{-3}$ m$^2)(\hat{j} - \hat{i})$

$$\vec{B} = \frac{(1 \times 10^{-7}\text{ T} \cdot \text{m/A})(4.00\text{ A})(1.00 \times 10^{-3}\text{ m}^2)}{[\sqrt{2}(2.00\text{ m})]^3}(\hat{j} - \hat{i}) =$$

$(-1.77 \times 10^{-11}\text{ T})(\hat{i} - \hat{j})$

d) $\vec{r} = (2.00$ m$)\hat{k}$, $r = 2.00$ m.

$\Delta\vec{l} \times \vec{r} = (0.500 \times 10^{-3}$ m$)(2.00$ m$)\hat{k} \times \hat{k} = 0$; $\vec{B} = 0$.

EVALUATE: At each point $\vec{B}$ is perpendicular to both $\vec{r}$ and $\Delta\vec{l}$. $B = 0$ along the length of the wire.

28.11 IDENTIFY: For each wire $B = \dfrac{\mu_0 I}{2\pi r}$ (Eq.28.9), and the direction of $\vec{B}$ is given by the right-hand rule (Fig.28.6). Add the field vectors for each wire to calculate the total field.

a) SET UP:

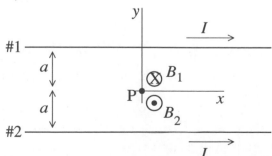

EXECUTE:
At point P midway between the two wires the fields $\vec{B}_1$ and $\vec{B}_2$ due to the two currents are in opposite directions, so $B = B_2 - B_1$.

But $B_1 = B_2 = \frac{\mu_0 I}{2\pi a}$, so $B = 0$.

b) SET UP:

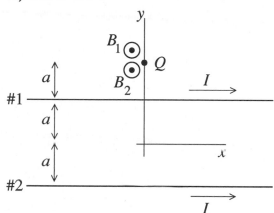

EXECUTE:
At point Q above the upper wire
$\vec{B}_1$ and $\vec{B}_2$ are both directed out
of the page ($+z$-direction),
so $B = B_1 + B_2$

$$B_1 = \frac{\mu_0 I}{2\pi a}, \quad B_2 = \frac{\mu_0 I}{2\pi (3a)}$$

$$B = \frac{\mu_0 I}{2\pi a}\left(1 + \frac{1}{3}\right) = \frac{2\mu_0 I}{3\pi a}; \quad \vec{B} = \frac{2\mu_0 I}{3\pi a}\hat{k}$$

c) SET UP:

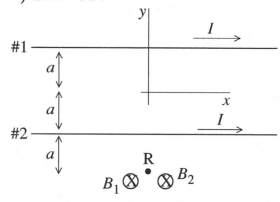

EXECUTE:
At point R below the lower wire
$\vec{B}_1$ and $\vec{B}_2$ are both directed into
the page ($-z$-direction), so $B = B_1 + B_2$.

$$B_1 = \frac{\mu_0 I}{2\pi (3a)}, \quad B_2 = \frac{\mu_0 I}{2\pi a}$$

$$B_1 = \frac{\mu_0 I}{2\pi a}\left(1 + \frac{1}{3}\right) = \frac{2\mu_0 I}{3\pi a}; \quad \vec{B} = -\frac{2\mu_0 I}{3\pi a}\hat{k}$$

EVALUATE: In the figures we have drawn, $\vec{B}$ due to each wire is out of the page at points above the wire and into the page at points below the wire. If the two field vectors are in opposite directions the magnitudes subtract.

28.15 IDENTIFY and **SET UP:** The magnitude of $\vec{B}$ is given by Eq.(28.9) and the direction is given by the right-hand rule.

a) **EXECUTE:** Viewed from above,

N

W ———|——— E   Directly below the wire the direction of
                 the magnetic field due to the current in
I↓ S   the wire is east.

$$B = \frac{\mu_0 I}{2\pi r} = (2 \times 10^{-7} \text{ T} \cdot \text{m/A}) \left(\frac{800 \text{ A}}{5.50 \text{ m}} \right) = 2.91 \times 10^{-5} \text{ T}$$

b) **EVALUATE:** B from the current is nearly equal in magnitude to the earth's field, so, yes, the current really is a problem.

28.17 **IDENTIFY:** Use Eq.(28.9) and the right-hand rule to determine points where the fields of the two wires cancel.

a) **SET UP:** The only place where the magnetic fields of the two wires are in opposite directions is between the wires, in the plane of the wires.

Consider a point a distance x from the wire carrying $I_2 = 75.0$ A. B_{tot} will be zero where $B_1 = B_2$.

EXECUTE: $\dfrac{\mu_0 I_1}{2\pi(0.400 \text{ m} - x)} = \dfrac{\mu_0 I_2}{2\pi x}$

$I_2(0.400 \text{ m} - x) = I_1 x$; $I_1 = 25.0$ A, $I_2 = 75.0$ A

$x = 0.300$ m; $B_{tot} = 0$ along a line 0.300 m from the wire carrying 75.0 A and 0.100 m from the wire carrying current 25.0 A.

b) **SET UP:** Let the wire with $I_1 = 25.0$ A be 0.400 m above the wire with $I_2 = 75.0$ A. The magnetic fields of the two wires are in opposite directions in the plane of the wires and at points above both wires or below both wires. But to have $B_1 = B_2$ must be closer to wire #1 since $I_1 < I_2$, so can have $B_{tot} = 0$ only at points above both wires.

Consider a point a distance x from the wire carrying $I_1 = 25.0$ A. B_{tot} will be zero where $B_1 = B_2$.

EXECUTE: $\dfrac{\mu_0 I_1}{2\pi x} = \dfrac{\mu_0 I_2}{2\pi(0.400 \text{ m} + x)}$

$I_2 x = I_1(0.400 \text{ m} + x)$; $x = 0.200$ m

$B_{tot} = 0$ along a line 0.200 m from the wire carrying current 25.0 A and 0.600 m from the wire carrying current $I_2 = 75.0$ A.

EVALUATE: For parts (a) and (b) the locations of zero field are in different regions. In each case the points of zero field are closer to the wire that has the smaller current.

28.19 **IDENTIFY:** Use Eq.(28.9) and the right-hand rule to determine the field due to each wire. Set the sum of the four fields equal to zero and use that equation to solve for the field and the current of the fourth wire.

SET UP:

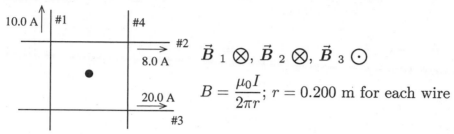

$\vec{B}_1 \otimes, \vec{B}_2 \otimes, \vec{B}_3 \odot$

$B = \dfrac{\mu_0 I}{2\pi r}$; $r = 0.200$ m for each wire

EXECUTE: Let $\odot$ be the positive z-direction. $I_1 = 10.0$ A, $I_2 = 8.0$ A, $I_3 = 20.0$ A. Then $B_1 = 1.00 \times 10^{-5}$ T, $B_2 = 0.80 \times 10^{-5}$ T, and $B_3 = 2.00 \times 10^{-5}$ T.

$B_{1z} = -1.00 \times 10^{-5}$ T, $B_{2z} = -0.80 \times 10^{-5}$ T, $B_{3z} = +2.00 \times 10^{-5}$ T

$B_{1z} + B_{2z} + B_{3z} + B_{4z} = 0$

$B_{4z} = -(B_{1z} + B_{2z} + B_{3z}) = -2.0 \times 10^{-6}$ T

To give $\vec{B}_4$ in the $\otimes$ direction the current in wire 4 must be toward the bottom of the page.

$B_4 = \dfrac{\mu_0 I}{2\pi r}$ so $I_4 = \dfrac{rB_4}{(\mu_0/2\pi)} = \dfrac{(0.200 \text{ m})(2.0 \times 10^{-6} \text{ T})}{(2 \times 10^{-7} \text{ T} \cdot \text{m/A})} = 2.0$ A

EVALUATE: The fields of wires #2 and #3 are in opposite directions and their net field is the same as due to a current 20.0 A $- 8.0$ A $= 12.0$ A in one wire. The field of wire #4 must be in the same direction as that of wire #1, and 10.0 A $+ I_4 = 12.0$ A.

28.21 IDENTIFY: The wire CD rises until the upward force F_I due to the currents balances the downward force of gravity.

SET UP:

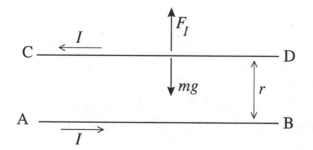

Currents in opposite directions so the force is repulsive and F_I is upward, as shown.

Eq.(28.11) says $F_I = \dfrac{\mu_0 I^2 L}{2\pi h}$ where L is the length of wire CD and h is the distance between the wires.

EXECUTE: $mg = \lambda L g$

Thus $F_I - mg = 0$ says $\dfrac{\mu_0 I^2 L}{2\pi h} = \lambda L g$ and $h = \dfrac{\mu_0 I^2}{2\pi g \lambda}$.

EVALUATE: The larger I is or the smaller λ is, the larger h will be.

28.25 **IDENTIFY:** Calculate the magnetic field vector produced by each wire and add these fields to get the total field.

SET UP: First consider the field at P produced by the current I_1 in the upper semicircle of wire.

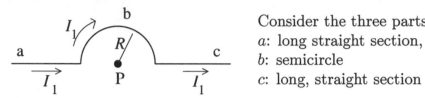

Consider the three parts of this wire
a: long straight section,
b: semicircle
c: long, straight section

Apply the Biot-Savart law $d\vec{B} = \dfrac{\mu_0}{4\pi} \dfrac{I \, d\vec{l} \times \hat{r}}{r^2} = \dfrac{\mu_0}{4\pi} \dfrac{I \, d\vec{l} \times \vec{r}}{r^3}$ to each piece.

EXECUTE:

part a

$d\vec{l} \times \vec{r} = 0$,
so $dB = 0$

The same is true for all the infinitesimal segments that make up this piece of the wire, so $B = 0$ for this piece.

part c

$d\vec{l} \times \vec{r} = 0$,
so $dB = 0$ and $B = 0$ for this piece.

part b

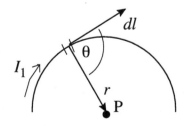

$d\vec{l} \times \vec{r}$ is directed into the paper for all infinitesimal segments that make up this semicircular piece, so $\vec{B}$ is directed into the paper and $B = \int dB$ (the vector sum of the $d\vec{B}$ is obtained by adding their magnitudes since they are in the same direction).

$|d\vec{l} \times \vec{r}| = r \, dl \sin\theta$. The angle θ between $d\vec{l}$ and $\vec{r}$ is $90°$ and $r = R$, the radius of the semicircle. Thus $|d\vec{l} \times \vec{r}| = R \, dl$

$$dB = \frac{\mu_0}{4\pi} \frac{I \, |d\vec{l} \times \vec{r}|}{r^3} = \frac{\mu_0 I_1}{4\pi} \frac{R}{R^3} dl = \left(\frac{\mu_0 I_1}{4\pi R^2} \right) dl$$

$$B = \int dB = \left(\frac{\mu_0 I_1}{4\pi R^2}\right) \int dl = \left(\frac{\mu_0 I_1}{4\pi R^2}\right)(\pi R) = \frac{\mu_0 I_1}{4R}$$

(We used that $\int dl$ is equal to πR, the length of wire in the semicircle.)

We have shown that the two straight sections make zero contribution to $\vec{B}$, so $B_1 = \mu_0 I_1/4R$ and is directed into the page.

For
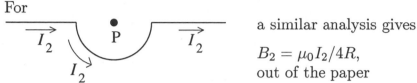
a similar analysis gives

$B_2 = \mu_0 I_2/4R$,
out of the paper

$\vec{B}_1$ and $\vec{B}_2$ are in opposite directions, so the magnitude of the net field at P is
$B = |B_1 - B_2| = \dfrac{\mu_0 |I_1 - I_2|}{4R}$.

EVALUATE: When $I_1 = I_2$, $B = 0$.

28.29 IDENTIFY and **SET UP:** The magnetic field at a point on the axis of N circular loops is given by $B_x = \dfrac{\mu_0 N I a^2}{2(x^2 + a^2)^{3/2}}$. Solve for N and set $x = 0.0600$ m.

EXECUTE: $N = \dfrac{2B_x(x^2 + a^2)^{3/2}}{\mu_0 I a^2} =$

$\dfrac{2(6.39 \times 10^{-4} \text{ T})[(0.0600 \text{ m})^2 + (0.0600 \text{ m})^2]^{3/2}}{(4\pi \times 10^{-7} \text{ T} \cdot \text{m/A})(2.50 \text{ A})(0.0600 \text{ m})^2} = 69.$

EVALUATE: At the center of the coil the field is $B_x = \dfrac{\mu_0 N I}{2a} = 1.8 \times 10^{-3}$ T. The field 6.00 cm from the center is a factor of $1/2^{3/2}$ times smaller.

28.33 IDENTIFY: Apply Ampere's law to calculate $\vec{B}$.

a) SET UP: $\underline{a < r < b}$ end view

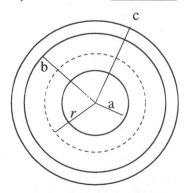

Apply Ampere's law to a circle of radius r, where $a < r < b$. Take currents I_1 and I_2 to be directed into the page. Take this direction to be positive, so go around the integration path in the clockwise direction.

EXECUTE: $\oint \vec{B} \cdot d\vec{l} = \mu_0 I_{encl}$

$$\oint \vec{B} \cdot d\vec{l} = B(2\pi r), \quad I_{encl} = I_1$$

Thus $B(2\pi r) = \mu_0 I_1$ and $B = \dfrac{\mu_0 I_1}{2\pi r}$

b) SET UP: $r > c$

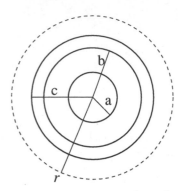

Apply Ampere's law to a circle of radius r, where $r > c$. Both currents are in the positive direction.

EXECUTE: $\oint \vec{B} \cdot d\vec{l} = \mu_0 I_{encl}$

$\oint \vec{B} \cdot d\vec{l} = B(2\pi r), \quad I_{encl} = I_1 + I_2$

Thus $B(2\pi r) = \mu_0 (I_1 + I_2)$ and $B = \dfrac{\mu_0 (I_1 + I_2)}{2\pi r}$

EVALUATE: For $a < r < b$ the field is due only to the current in the central conductor. For $r > c$ both currents contribute to the total field.

28.35 a) IDENTIFY and **SET UP:** The magnetic field near the center of a long solenoid is given by Eq.(28.23), $B = \mu_0 n I$.

EXECUTE: turns per unit length $n = \dfrac{B}{\mu_0 I} = \dfrac{0.0270 \text{ T}}{(4\pi \times 10^{-7} \text{ T} \cdot \text{m/A})(12.0 \text{ A})} = $ 1790 turns/m

b) $N = nL = (1790 \text{ turns/m})(0.400 \text{ m}) = 716$ turns

Each turn of radius R has a length $2\pi R$ of wire. The total length of wire required is

$N(2\pi R) = (716)(2\pi)(1.40 \times 10^{-2} \text{ m}) = 63.0 \text{ m}.$

EVALUATE: A large length of wire is required. Due to the length of wire the solenoid will have appreciable resistance.

28.41 IDENTIFY and **SET UP:** $B = \dfrac{K_m \mu_0 N I}{2\pi r}$ (Eq.28.24, with μ_0 replaced by $K_m \mu_0$)

EXECUTE:

a) $K_m = 1400$

$$I = \frac{2\pi r B}{\mu_0 K_m N} = \frac{(2.90 \times 10^{-2} \text{ m})(0.350 \text{ T})}{(2 \times 10^{-7} \text{ T} \cdot \text{m/A})(1400)(500)} = 0.0725 \text{ A}$$

b) $K_m = 5200$

$$I = \frac{2\pi r B}{\mu_0 K_m N} = \frac{(2.90 \times 10^{-2} \text{ m})(0.350 \text{ T})}{(2 \times 10^{-7} \text{ T} \cdot \text{m/A})(5200)(500)} = 0.0195 \text{ A}$$

EVALUATE: If the solenoid were air-filled instead, a much larger current would be required to produce the same magnetic field.

Problems

28.47 IDENTIFY and **SET UP:** Use Eq.(28.9) and the right-hand rule to calculate $\vec{B}$ at the location of the electron. Then use Eq.(27.2) to calculate the force this field exerts on the electron.

EXECUTE: At the electron's position the magnetic field $\vec{B}$ due to the current in the wire has magnitude

$$B = \frac{\mu_0 I}{2\pi r} = \frac{(2 \times 10^{-7} \text{ T} \cdot \text{m/A})(2.50 \text{ A})}{0.0450 \text{ m}} = 1.111 \times 10^{-5} \text{ T}$$

By the right hand rule, $\vec{B}$ is out of the page at this point.

But, since the electron has negative charge, $\vec{F} = q\vec{v} \mathbf{X} \vec{B} = -e\vec{v}\mathbf{X}\vec{B}$ has direction ↓ (toward the wire)

$F = |q|vB \sin\phi = evB = (1.602 \times 10^{-19} \text{ C})(6.00 \times 10^{4} \text{ m/s})(1.111 \times 10^{-5} \text{ T}) = 1.07 \times 10^{-19} \text{ N}$

The force has magnitude 1.07×10^{-19} N and is directed toward the wire.

EVALUATE: This force is many orders of magnitude larger than the weight of the electron. Negative charge moving to the left corresponds to current to the right, so the situation corresponds to two currents in the same direction. Our result for the direction of the force agrees therefore with the general result that two currents in the same direction attract each other.

28.49 IDENTIFY: Use Eq.(28.9) and the right-hand rule to calculate the magnetic field due to each wire. Add these field vectors to calculate the net field and then use Eq.(27.2) to calculate the force.

SET UP: Let the wire connected to the 25.0 Ω resistor be #2 and the wire connected to the 10.0 Ω resistor be #1. Both I_1 and I_2 are directed toward the right in the figure, so at the location of the proton B_2 is $\otimes$ and $B_1 = \odot$.

$B_1 = \dfrac{\mu_0 I_1}{2\pi r}$ and $B_2 = \dfrac{\mu_0 I_2}{2\pi r}$, with $r = 0.0250$ m. $I_1 = (100.0\text{ V})/(10.0\ \Omega) = 10.0$ A and $I_2 = (100.0\text{ V})/(25.0\ \Omega) = 4.00$ A

EXECUTE: $B_1 = 8.00 \times 10^{-5}$ T, $B_2 = 3.20 \times 10^{-5}$ T and $B = B_1 - B_2 = 4.80 \times 10^{-5}$ T and in the direction $\odot$.

Force is to the right.

$F = qvB = (1.602 \times 10^{-19}\text{ C})(650 \times 10^3\text{ m/s})(4.80 \times 10^{-5}\text{ T}) = 5.00 \times 10^{-18}$ N

EVALUATE: The force is perpendicular to both $\vec{v}$ and $\vec{B}$. The magnetic force is much larger than the gravity force on the proton.

28.53 IDENTIFY and **SET UP:** $\vec{B} = B_0(x/a)\hat{i}$

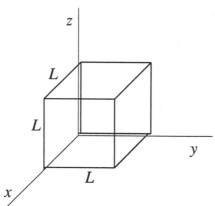

Apply Gauss's law for magnetic fields to a cube with side length L, one corner at the origin, and sides parallel to the x, y and z axes.

EXECUTE: Since $\vec{B}$ is parallel to the x-axis the only sides that have nonzero flux are the front side (parallel to the yz-plane at $x = L$) and the back side (parallel to the yz-plane at $x = 0$.)

front

$\Phi_B = \int \vec{B} \cdot d\vec{A} = B_0(x/a) \int dA(\hat{i}\cdot\hat{i}) = B_0(x/a) \int dA$

$x = L$ on this face so $\vec{B} \cdot d\vec{A} = B_0(L/a)\, dA$

$\Phi_B = B_0(L/a) \int dA = B_0(L/a)L^2 = B_0(L^3/a)$

back

On the back face $x = 0$ so $B = 0$ and $\Phi_B = 0$.

The total flux through the cubical Gaussian surface is $\Phi_B = B_0(L^3/a)$.

EVALUATE: This violates Eq.(27.8), which says that $\Phi_B = 0$ for any closed surface. The claimed $\vec{B}$ is impossible because it has been shown to violate Gauss's law for magnetism.

28.55 **IDENTIFY:** Use Eq.(28.9) and the right-hand rule to calculate the magnitude and direction of the magnetic field at P produced by each wire. Add these two field vectors to find the net field.

a) SET UP:

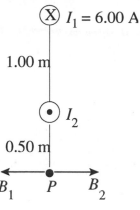

EXECUTE:
$\vec{B}_1$ and $\vec{B}_2$ must be equal and opposite for the resultant field at P to be zero.
$\vec{B}_2$ is to the right so
I_2 is out of the page.

$$B_1 = \frac{\mu_0 I_1}{2\pi r_1} = \frac{\mu_0}{2\pi}\left(\frac{6.00\ \text{A}}{1.50\ \text{m}}\right) \qquad B_2 = \frac{\mu_0 I_2}{2\pi r_2} = \frac{\mu_0}{2\pi}\left(\frac{I_2}{0.50\ \text{m}}\right)$$

$B_1 = B_2$ says $\dfrac{\mu_0}{2\pi}\left(\dfrac{6.00\ \text{A}}{1.50\ \text{m}}\right) = \dfrac{\mu_o}{2\pi}\left(\dfrac{I_2}{0.50\ \text{m}}\right)$

$$I_2 = \left(\frac{0.50\ \text{m}}{1.50\ \text{m}}\right)(6.00\ \text{A}) = 2.00\ \text{A}$$

b) SET UP:

EXECUTE:
$$B_1 = \frac{\mu_0 I_1}{2\pi r_1}$$

$$B_1 = (2 \times 10^{-7}\ \text{T}\cdot\text{m/A})\left(\frac{6.00\ \text{A}}{0.50\ \text{m}}\right) = 2.40 \times 10^{-6}\ \text{T}$$

$$B_2 = \frac{\mu_0 I_2}{2\pi r_2}$$

$$B_2 = (2 \times 10^{-7}\ \text{T}\cdot\text{m/A})\left(\frac{2.00\ \text{A}}{1.50\ \text{m}}\right) = 2.67 \times 10^{-7}\ \text{T}$$

$\vec{B}_1$ and $\vec{B}_2$ are in opposite directions and $B_1 > B_2$ so
$B = B_1 - B_2 = 2.40 \times 10^{-6}\ \text{T} - 2.67 \times 10^{-7}\ \text{T} = 2.13 \times 10^{-6}\ \text{T}$, and $\vec{B}$ is to the right.

c) SET UP:

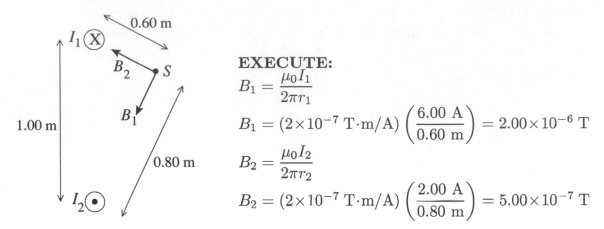

EXECUTE:

$$B_1 = \frac{\mu_0 I_1}{2\pi r_1}$$

$$B_1 = (2 \times 10^{-7} \text{ T·m/A}) \left(\frac{6.00 \text{ A}}{0.60 \text{ m}} \right) = 2.00 \times 10^{-6} \text{ T}$$

$$B_2 = \frac{\mu_0 I_2}{2\pi r_2}$$

$$B_2 = (2 \times 10^{-7} \text{ T·m/A}) \left(\frac{2.00 \text{ A}}{0.80 \text{ m}} \right) = 5.00 \times 10^{-7} \text{ T}$$

$\vec{B}_1$ and $\vec{B}_2$ are at right angles to each other, so the magnitude of their resultant is given by

$$B = \sqrt{B_1^2 + B_2^2} = \sqrt{(2.00 \times 10^{-6} \text{ T})^2 + (5.00 \times 10^{-7} \text{ T})^2} = 2.06 \times 10^{-6} \text{ T}$$

EVALUATE: The magnetic field lines for a long, straight wire are concentric circles with the wire at the center. The magnetic field at each point is tangent to the field line, so $\vec{B}$ is perpendicular to the line from the wire to the point where the field is calculated.

28.59 IDENTIFY and **SET UP:** The currents in the wires are in opposite directions, so the wires repel. Set the force one wire exerts on the other equal to the total force the springs exert on that wire. $F = kx$ relates the force to the force constant of the spring.

EXECUTE: The current in the wires is $I = \varepsilon/R = (45.0 \text{ V})/(0.500 \text{ }\Omega) = 90.0$ A. The force each wire exerts on the other is

$$F = \frac{\mu_0 I I' L}{2\pi r} = \frac{(2 \times 10^{-7} \text{ N/A}^2)(90.0 \text{ A})^2(3.50 \text{ m})}{(0.0150 \text{ m})} = 0.378 \text{ N}$$

To hold the wires at rest, each spring exerts a force of 0.189 N on each wire.

$F = kx$ so $k = F/x = (0.189 \text{ N})/(0.0050 \text{ m}) = 37.8$ N/m

EVALUATE: The magnetic force decreases as the separation between the wires increases and the spring force increases, so there is a separation where these two forces balance.

28.61 IDENTIFY: Apply $\sum \vec{F} = 0$ to one of the wires. The force one wire exerts on the other depends on I so $\sum \vec{F} = 0$ gives two equations for the two unknowns T and I.

SET UP: The force diagram for one of the wires is

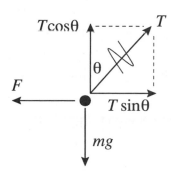

The force one wire exerts on the other is

$$F = \left(\frac{\mu_0 I^2}{2\pi r}\right) L,$$

where $r = 2(0.040 \text{ m}) \sin \theta = 8.362 \times 10^{-3}$ m is the distance between the two wires.

EXECUTE:

$\sum F_y = 0$ gives $T \cos \theta = mg$ and $T = mg/\cos \theta$

$\sum F_x = 0$ gives $F = T \sin \theta - (mg/\cos \theta) \sin \theta = mg \tan \theta$

And $m = \lambda L$, so $F = \lambda L g \tan \theta$

$$\left(\frac{\mu_0 I^2}{2\pi r}\right) L = \lambda L g \tan \theta$$

$$I = \sqrt{\frac{\lambda g r \tan \theta}{(\mu_0/2\pi)}}$$

$$I = \sqrt{\frac{(0.0125 \text{ kg/m})(9.80 \text{ m/s}^2)(\tan 6.00^\circ)(8.362 \times 10^{-3} \text{ m})}{2 \times 10^{-7} \text{ T} \cdot \text{m/A}}} = 23.2 \text{ A}$$

EVALUATE: Since the currents are in opposite directions the wires repel. When I is increased, the angle θ from the vertical increases; a large current is required even for the small displacement specified in this problem.

28.69 a) IDENTIFY: Consider current density J for a small concentric ring and integrate to find the total current in terms of α and R.

SET UP: We can't say $I = JA = J\pi R^2$, since J varies across the cross section.

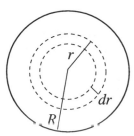

To integrate J over the cross section of the wire divide the wire cross section up into thin concentric rings of radius r and width dr.

EXECUTE: The area of such a ring is dA, and the current through it is $dI = J \, dA$; $dA = 2\pi r \, dr$ and $dI = J \, dA = \alpha r (2\pi r \, dr) = 2\pi \alpha r^2 \, dr$

$$I = \int dI = 2\pi \alpha \int_0^R r^2 \, dr = 2\pi \alpha (R^3/3) \text{ so } \alpha = \frac{3I}{2\pi R^3}$$

b) IDENTIFY: and **SET UP:** (i)$r \leq R$

Apply Ampere's law to a circle of radius $r < R$. Use the method of part (a) to find the current enclosed by the Ampere's law path.

EXECUTE: $\oint \vec{B} \cdot d\vec{l} = \oint B \, dl = B \oint dl = B(2\pi r)$, by the symmetry and direction of $\vec{B}$.

The current pasing through the path is $I_{\text{encl}} = \int dI$, where the integration is from 0 to r.

$$I_{\text{encl}} = 2\pi\alpha \int_0^r r^2 \, dr = \frac{2\pi\alpha r^3}{3} = \frac{2\pi}{3}\left(\frac{3I}{2\pi R^3}\right)r^3 = \frac{Ir^3}{R^3}.$$

Thus $\oint \vec{B} \cdot d\vec{l} = \mu_0 I_{\text{encl}}$ gives $B(2\pi r) = \mu_0\left(\dfrac{Ir^3}{R^3}\right)$ and $B = \dfrac{\mu_0 I r^2}{2\pi R^3}$

(ii) **IDENTIFY** and **SET UP:** $r \geq R$

Apply Ampere's law to a circle of radius $r > R$.

EXECUTE: $\oint \vec{B} \cdot d\vec{l} = \oint B \, dl = B \oint dl = B(2\pi r)$

$I_{\text{encl}} = I$; all the current in the wire passes through this path.

Thus $\oint \vec{B} \cdot d\vec{l} = \mu_0 I_{\text{encl}}$ gives $B(2\pi r) = \mu_0 I$ and $B = \dfrac{\mu_0 I}{2\pi r}$

EVALUATE: Note that at $r = R$ the expression in (i) (for $r \leq R$) gives $B = \dfrac{\mu_0 I}{2\pi R}$.

At $r = R$ the expression in (ii) (for $r \geq R$) gives $B = \dfrac{\mu_0 I}{2\pi R}$, which is the same.

28.73 IDENTIFY: Use Ampere's law to find the magnetic field at $r = 2a$ from the axis. The analysis of Example 28.9 shows that the field outside the cylinder is the same as for a long, straight wire along the axis of the cylinder.

SET UP:

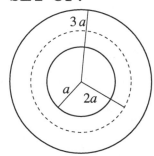

EXECUTE:

Apply Ampere's law to a circular path of radius $2a$.

$B(2\pi r) = \mu_0 I_{\text{encl}}$

$I_{\text{encl}} = I\left(\dfrac{(2a)^2 - a^2}{(3a)^2 - a^2}\right) = 3I/8$

$B = \dfrac{3}{16}\dfrac{\mu_0 I}{2\pi a}$; this is the magnetic field inside the metal at a distance of $2a$ from the cylinder axis.

Outside the cylinder, $B = \dfrac{\mu_0 I}{2\pi r}$. The value of r where these two fields are equal is given by $1/r = 3/(16a)$ and $r = 16a/3$.

EVALUATE: For $r < 3a$, as r increases the magnetic field increases from zero at $r = 0$ to $\mu_0 I/(2\pi(3a))$ at $r = 3a$. For $r > 3a$ the field decreases as r increases, so it is reasonable for there to be a $r > 3a$ where the field is the same as at $r = 2a$.

28.75 IDENTIFY: Use the current density J to find dI through a concentric ring and integrate over the appropriate cross section to find the current through that cross section. Then use Ampere's law to find $\vec{B}$ at the specified distance from the center of the wire.

a) SET UP:

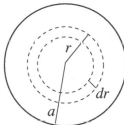

Divide the cross section of the cylinder into thin concentric rings of radius r and width dr. The current through each ring is
$dI = J\,dA = J2\pi r\,dr$.

EXECUTE: $dI = \dfrac{2I_0}{\pi a^2}\left[1 - (r/a)^2\right]2\pi r\,dr = \dfrac{4I_0}{a^2}\left[1 - (r/a)^2\right]r\,dr.$

The total current I is obtained by integrating dI over the cross section

$I = \displaystyle\int_0^a dI = \left(\dfrac{4I_0}{a^2}\right)\int_0^a (1 - r^2/a^2)r\,dr = \left(\dfrac{4I_0}{a^2}\right)\left[\dfrac{1}{2}r^2 - \dfrac{1}{4}r^4/a^2\right]_0^a = I_0$, as was to be shown.

b) SET UP: Apply Ampere's law to a path that is a circle of radius $r > a$.

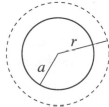

$$\oint \vec{B}\cdot d\vec{l} = B(2\pi r)$$

$I_{\text{encl}} = I_0$ (the path encloses the entire cylinder)

EXECUTE: $\oint \vec{B}\cdot d\vec{l} = \mu_0 I_{\text{encl}}$ says $B(2\pi r) = \mu_0 I_0$ and $B = \dfrac{\mu_0 I_0}{2\pi r}.$

c) SET UP:

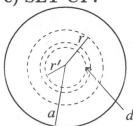

Divide the cross section of the cylinder into concentric rings of radius r' and width dr', as was done in part (a). The current dI through each ring is

$dI = \dfrac{4I_0}{a^2}\left[1 - \left(\dfrac{r'}{a}\right)^2\right]r'\,dr'$

EXECUTE: The current I is obtained by integrating dI from $r' = 0$ to $r' = r$:

$$I = \int dI = \frac{4I_0}{a^2} \int_0^r \left[1 - \left(\frac{r'}{a}\right)^2\right] r'\, dr' = \frac{4I_0}{a^2}\left[\frac{1}{2}(r')^2 - \frac{1}{4}(r')^4/a^2\right]_0^r$$

$$I = \frac{4I_0}{a^2}(r^2/2 - r^4/4a^2) = \frac{I_0 r^2}{a^2}\left(2 - \frac{r^2}{a^2}\right)$$

d) SET UP: Apply Ampere's law to a path that is a circle of radius $r < a$.

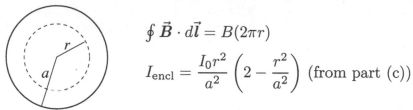

$$\oint \vec{B} \cdot d\vec{l} = B(2\pi r)$$

$$I_{\text{encl}} = \frac{I_0 r^2}{a^2}\left(2 - \frac{r^2}{a^2}\right) \text{ (from part (c))}$$

EXECUTE: $\oint \vec{B} \cdot d\vec{l} = \mu_0 I_{\text{encl}}$ says $B(2\pi r) = \mu_0 \dfrac{I_0 r^2}{a^2}(2 - r^2/a^2)$

and $B = \dfrac{\mu_0 I_0}{2\pi}\dfrac{r}{a^2}(2 - r^2/a^2)$

EVALUATE: Result in part (b) evaluated at $r = a$: $B = \dfrac{\mu_0 I_0}{2\pi a}$.

Result in part (d) evaluated at $r = a$: $B = \dfrac{\mu_0 I_0}{2\pi}\dfrac{a}{a^2}(2 - a^2/a^2) = \dfrac{\mu_0 I_0}{2\pi a}$.

The two results, one for $r > a$ and the other for $r < a$, agree at $r = a$.

28.79 IDENTIFY: Use what we know about the magnetic field of a long, straight conductor to deduce the symmetry of the magnetic field. Then apply Ampere's law to calculate the magnetic field at a distance a above and below the current sheet.

SET UP: Do parts (a) and (b) together.

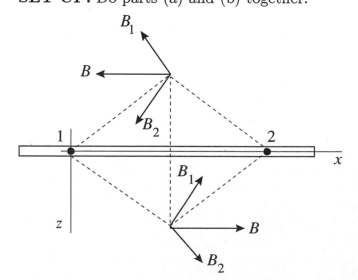

Consider the individual currents in pairs, where the currents in each pair are equidistant on either side of the point where $\vec{B}$ is being calculated.

The sketch shows that for each pair the z-components cancel, and that above the sheet the field is in the $-x$-direction and that below the sheet it is in the $+x$-direction.

Also, by symmetry the magnitude of $\vec{B}$ a distance a above the sheet must equal the magnitude of $\vec{B}$ a distance a below the sheet.

Now that we have deduced the symmetry of $\vec{B}$, apply Ampere's law. Use a path that is a rectangle:

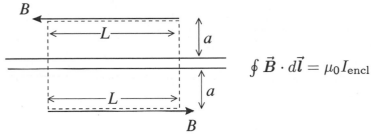

$$\oint \vec{B} \cdot d\vec{l} = \mu_0 I_{encl}$$

I is directed out of the page, so for I to be positive the integral around the path is taken in the counterclockwise direction.

EXECUTE: Since $\vec{B}$ is parallel to the sheet, on the sides of the rectangle that have length $2a$, $\oint \vec{B} \cdot d\vec{l} = 0$. On the long sides of length L, $\vec{B}$ is parallel to the side, in the direction we are integrating around the path, and has the same magnitude, B, on each side. Thus $\oint \vec{B} \cdot d\vec{l} = 2BL$.

n conductors per unit length and current I out of the page in each conductor gives $I_{encl} = InL$.

Ampere's law then gives $2BL = \mu_0 InL$ and $B = \frac{1}{2}\mu_0 In$.

EVALUATE: Note that B is independent of the distance a from the sheet. Compare this result to the electric field due to an infinite sheet of charge (Example 22.7).

28.81   IDENTIFY and **SET UP:** Use Eq.(28.28) to calculate the total magnetic moment of a volume V of the iron. Use the density and atomic mass of iron to find the number of atoms in this volume and use that to find the magnetic dipole moment per atom.

EXECUTE: $M = \dfrac{\mu_{total}}{V}$, so $\mu_{total} = MV$ The average magnetic moment per atom is $\mu_{atom} = \mu_{total}/N = MV/N$, where N is the number of atoms in volume V. The mass of volume V is $m = \rho V$, where ρ is the density. ($\rho_{iron} = 7.8 \times 10^3 \text{ kg/m}^3$).

The number of moles of iron in volume V is

$$n = \frac{m}{55.847 \times 10^{-3} \text{ kg/mol}} = \frac{\rho V}{55.847 \times 10^{-3} \text{ kg/mol}}, \text{ where } 55.847 \times 10^{-3} \text{ kg/mol}$$

is the atomic mass of iron from appendix D.

$N = nN_A$, where $N_A = 6.022 \times 10^{23}$ atoms/mol is Avogadro's number.

Thus $N = nN_A = \dfrac{\rho V N_A}{55.847 \times 10^{-3} \text{ kg/mol}}$.

$$\mu_{\text{atom}} = \frac{MV}{N} = MV \left(\frac{55.847 \times 10^{-3} \text{ kg/mol}}{\rho V N_{\text{A}}} \right) = \frac{M(55.847 \times 10^{-3} \text{ kg/mol})}{\rho N_{\text{A}}}.$$

$$\mu_{\text{atom}} = \frac{(6.50 \times 10^4 \text{ A/m})(55.847 \times 10^{-3} \text{ kg/mol})}{(7.8 \times 10^3 \text{ kg/m}^3)(6.022 \times 10^{23} \text{ atoms/mol})}$$

$$\mu_{\text{atom}} = 7.73 \times 10^{-25} \text{ A·m}^2 = 7.73 \times 10^{-25} \text{ J/T}$$

$$\mu_{\text{B}} = 9.274 \times 10^{-24} \text{ A·m}^2, \text{ so } \mu_{\text{atom}} = 0.0834 \mu_{\text{B}}.$$

EVALUATE: The magnetic moment per atom is much less than one Bohr magneton. The magnetic moments of each electron in the iron must be in different directions and mostly cancel each other.

CHAPTER 29
ELECTROMAGNETIC INDUCTION

Exercises 1, 3, 5, 9, 17, 19, 23, 25, 27, 29, 35, 37, 39
Problems 43, 45, 49, 55, 61, 63, 65, 67, 69, 71

Exercises

29.1 **IDENTIFY** and **SET UP:** The magnitude of the average induced emf is
$|\varepsilon_{av}| = N|\frac{\Delta\Phi_B}{\Delta t}|$. Use Eq.(27.6) to calculate the magnetic flux before and after the coil is rotated.

EXECUTE: $\Delta\Phi_B = \Phi_{Bf} - \Phi_{Bi}$

initial

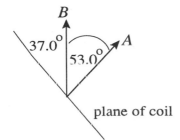

$\Phi_{Bi} = BA\cos\phi$
$\Phi_{Bi} - (1.10 \text{ T})(0.250 \text{ m})(0.400 \text{ m})\cos 53.0°$
$\Phi_{Bi} = 0.0662 \text{ Wb}$

final

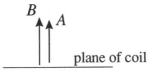

$\Phi_{Bf} = BA\cos\phi$
$\Phi_{Bf} - (1.10 \text{ T})(0.250 \text{ m})(0.400 \text{ m})\cos 0° = 0.1100 \text{ Wb}$

Then $|\varepsilon_{av}| = N|\frac{\Delta\Phi_B}{\Delta t}| = 80\left(\frac{0.1100 \text{ Wb} - 0.0662 \text{ Wb}}{0.0600 \text{ s}}\right) - 58.4 \text{ V}.$

EVALUATE: The flux is zero when the plane of the coil is parallel to the magnetic field and maximum when it is perpendicular, so when the coil is rotated the flux increases. The faster the coil is rotated (shorter t) the greater the induced emf.

29.3 **IDENTIFY** and **SET UP:** Use Faraday's law to calculate the average induced emf and apply Ohm's law to the coil to calculate the average induced current and charge that flows.

a) EXECUTE: The magnitude of the average emf induced in the coil is
$|\varepsilon_{av}| = N|\frac{\Delta\Phi_B}{\Delta t}|.$

Initially, $\Phi_{Bi} = BA\cos\phi = BA.$

The final flux is zero, so $|\varepsilon_{av}| = N\dfrac{|\Phi_{Bf} - \Phi_{Bi}|}{\Delta t} = \dfrac{NBA}{\Delta t}$.

The average induced current is $I = \dfrac{|\varepsilon_{av}|}{R} = \dfrac{NBA}{R\,\Delta t}$.

The total charge that flows through the coil is $Q = I\,\Delta t = \left(\dfrac{NBA}{R\,\Delta t}\right)\Delta t = \dfrac{NBA}{R}$.

EVALUATE: The charge that flows is proportional to the magnetic field but does not depend on the time Δt.

b) The magnetic stripe consists of a pattern of magnetic fields. The pattern of charges that flow in the reader coil tell the card reader the magnetic field pattern and hence the digital information coded onto the card.

c) According to the result in part (a) the charge that flows depends only on the change in the magnetic flux and it does not depend on the rate at which this flux changes.

29.5   IDENTIFY and **SET UP:** Apply the result derived in Exercise 29.3: $Q = NBA/R$. In the present exercise the flux changes from its maximum value of $\Phi_B = BA$ to zero, so this equation applies. R is the total resistance so here $R = 60.0\ \Omega + 45.0\ \Omega = 105.0\ \Omega$.

EXECUTE: $Q = \dfrac{NBA}{R}$ says $B = \dfrac{QR}{NA} = \dfrac{(3.56\times 10^{-5}\ \text{C})(105.0\ \Omega)}{120(3.20\times 10^{-4}\ \text{m}^2)} = 0.0973\ \text{T}$.

EVALUATE: A field of this magnitude is easily produced.

29.9   IDENTIFY and **SET UP:** Use Faraday's law to calculate the emf (magnitude and direction). The direction of the induced current is the same as the direction of the emf. The flux changes becasue the area of the loop is changing; relate dA/dt to dc/dt, where c is the circumference of the loop.

a) EXECUTE: $c = 2\pi r$ and $A = \pi r^2$ so $A = c^2/4\pi$

$\Phi_B = BA = (B/4\pi)c^2$

$|\varepsilon| = \left|\dfrac{d\Phi_B}{dt}\right| = \left(\dfrac{B}{2\pi}\right)c\left|\dfrac{dc}{dt}\right|$

At $t = 9.0$ s, $c = 1.650\ \text{m} - (9.0\ \text{s})(0.120\ \text{s}) = 0.570\ \text{m}$

$|\varepsilon| = (0.500\ \text{T})(1/2\pi)(0.570\ \text{m})(0.120\ \text{m/s}) = 5.44\ \text{mV}$

b) SET UP:

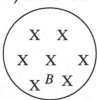

Take into the page to be the positive direction for $\vec{A}$.
Then the magnetic flux is positive.

EXECUTE: The positive flux is decreasing in magnitude; $d\Phi_B/dt$ is negative and ε is positive. By the right-hand rule, for $\vec{A}$ into the page, positive ε is clockwise.

EVALUATE: Even though the circumference is changing at a constant rate, dA/dt is not constant and $|\varepsilon|$ is not constant. Flux $\otimes$ is decreasing so the flux of the induced current is $\otimes$ and this means that I is clockwise, which checks.

29.17 IDENTIFY and **SET UP:** Apply Lenz's law, in the form that states that the flux of the induced current tends to oppose the change in flux.

EXECUTE:

a) With the switch closed the magnetic field of coil A is to the right at the location of coil B. When the switch is opened the magnetic field of coil A goes away. Hence by Lenz's law the field of the current induced in coil B is to the right, to oppose the decrease in the flux in this direction. To produce magnetic field that is to the right the current in the circuit with coil B must flow through the resistor in the direction a to b.

b) With the switch closed the magnetic field of coil A is to the right at the location of coil B. This field is stronger at points closer to coil A so when coil B is brought closer the flux through coil B increases. By Lenz's law the field of the induced current in coil B is to the left, to oppose the increase in flux to the right. To produce magnetic field that is to the left the current in the circuit with coil B must flow through the resistor in the direction b to a.

c) With the switch closed the magnetic field of coil A is to the right at the location of coil B. The current in the circuit that includes coil A increases when R is decreased and the magnetic field of coil A increases when the current through the coil increases. By Lenz's law the field of the induced current in coil B is to the left, to oppose the increase in flux to the right. To produce magnetic field that is to the left the current in the circuit with coil B must flow through the resistor in the direction b to a.

EVALUATE: In parts (b) and (c) the change in the circuit causes the flux through circuit B to increase and in part (a) it causes the flux to decrease. Therefore, the direction of the induced current is the same in parts (b) and (c) and opposite in part (a).

29.19 IDENTIFY and **SET UP:** Lenz's law requires that the flux of the induced current opposes the change in flux.

EXECUTE:

a) Φ_B is $\odot$ and increasing so the flux Φ_{ind} of the induced current is $\otimes$ and the induced current is clockwise.

b) The current reaches a constant value so Φ_B is constant. $d\Phi_B/dt = 0$ and there is no induced current.

c) Φ_B is $\odot$ and decreasing, so Φ_{ind} is $\odot$ and current is counterclockwise.

EVALUATE: Only a change in flux produces an induced current. The induced current is in one direction when the current in the outer ring is increasing and is in the opposite direction when that current is decreasing.

29.23 IDENTIFY and **SET UP:** Use Eq.(29.6) to calculate the speed of the rod, use the sign rule associated with Faraday's law to determine the direction of the induced emf, use Ohm's law for I and then use Eq.(27.19) to calculate the force on the current in the rod. We need the direction of ε and I in order to determine the direction of the force $\vec{F}$.

EXECUTE:

a)

The magnitude of the induced emf is given by $|\varepsilon| = vLB$.

Thus $v = \dfrac{|\varepsilon|}{LB} = \dfrac{0.620 \text{ V}}{(0.850 \text{ m})(0.850 \text{ T})} = 0.858 \text{ m/s}.$

b) $I = \dfrac{|\varepsilon|}{R} = \dfrac{0.620 \text{ V}}{0.750 \text{ }\Omega} = 0.827 \text{ A}$

c) The direction of the induced emf and induced current can be determined as discussed in Sect.29.2:

Let positive $\vec{A}$ be into the page (in the same direction as $\vec{B}$).

$\vec{B}$ is in the positive direction (the direction of $\vec{A}$) so Φ_B is positive. The magnitude of the flux through the circuit is increasing as the area of the circuit is getting larger, so $d\Phi_B/dt$ is positive. Then by $\varepsilon = -d\Phi_B/dt$, ε is negative. With our chosen direction of $\vec{A}$, clockwise is positive so a negative ε is counterclockwise and I is counterclockwise.

Force on the current in the rod: $\vec{F} = I\vec{l} \times \vec{B}.$

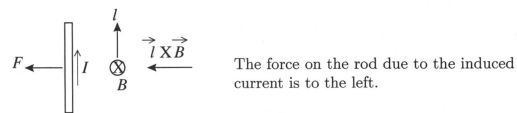

The force on the rod due to the induced current is to the left.

$F = IlB \sin\phi = IlB = (0.827 \text{ A})(0.850 \text{ m})(0.850 \text{ T}) = 0.598 \text{ N}.$

EVALUATE: The direction of the force opposes the motion of the rod, in agreement with Lenz's law.

29.25 IDENTIFY: Use Faraday's law to calculate the induced emf. Ohm's law applied to the loop gives I. Use Eq.(27.19) to calculate the force exerted on each side of the loop.

SET UP:

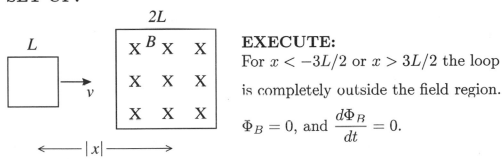

EXECUTE:
For $x < -3L/2$ or $x > 3L/2$ the loop is completely outside the field region.
$\Phi_B = 0$, and $\dfrac{d\Phi_B}{dt} = 0.$

Thus $\varepsilon = 0$ and $I = 0$, so there is no force from the magnetic field and the external force F necessary to maintain constant velocity is zero.

SET UP:

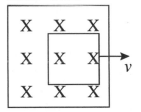

EXECUTE:
For $-L/2 < x < L/2$ the loop is completely inside the field region and $\Phi_B = BL^2$.

But $\dfrac{d\Phi_B}{dt} = 0$ so $\varepsilon = 0$ and $I = 0$. There is no force $\vec{F} = I\vec{l}\times\vec{B}$ from the magnetic field and the external force F necessary to maintian constant velocity is zero.

SET UP:

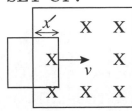

EXECUTE:
For $-3L/2 < x < -L/2$ the loop is entering the field region. Let x' be the length of the loop that is within the field.

Then $|\Phi_B| = BLx'$ and $|\frac{d\Phi_B}{dt}| = Blv$.

The magnitude of the induced emf is $|\varepsilon| = |\frac{d\Phi_B}{dt}| = BLv$ and the induced current is

$$I = \frac{|\varepsilon|}{R} = \frac{BLv}{R}.$$

Direction of I: Let $\vec{A}$ be directed into the plane of the figure. Then Φ_B is positive. The flux is positive and increasing in magnitude, so $\frac{d\Phi_B}{dt}$ is positive. Then by Faraday's law ε is negative, and with our choice for direction of $\vec{A}$ a negative ε is counterclockwise. The current induced in the loop is counterclockwise.

SET UP:

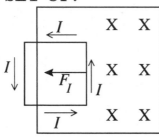

EXECUTE:
$\vec{F}_I = I\vec{l} \mathbf{X} \vec{B}$ gives that the force $\vec{F}_I$ exerted on the loop by the magnetic field is to the left and has magnitude

$$F_I = ILB = \left(\frac{BLv}{R}\right)LB = \frac{B^2L^2v}{R}.$$

The external force $\vec{F}$ needed to move the loop at constant speed is equal in magnitude and opposite in direction to $\vec{F}_I$ so is to the right and has this same magnitude.

SET UP:

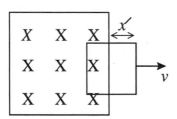

EXECUTE:
For $L/2 < x < 3L/2$ the loop is leaving the field region. Let x' be the length of the loop that is outside the field.

Then $|\Phi_B| = BL(L - x')$ and $|\frac{d\Phi_B}{dt}| = BLv$.

The magnitude of the induced emf is $|\varepsilon| = |\frac{d\Phi_B}{dt}| = BLv$ and the induced current is

$$I = \frac{|\varepsilon|}{R} = \frac{BLv}{R}.$$

Direction of I: Again let $\vec{A}$ be directed into the plane of the figure. Then Φ_B is positive and decreasing in magnitude, so $\frac{d\Phi_B}{dt}$ is negative. Then by Faraday's law

ε is positive, and with our choice for direction of $\vec{A}$ a positive ε is clockwise. The current induced in the loop is clockwise.

SET UP:

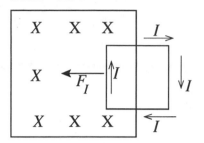

EXECUTE:
$\vec{F}_I = I\vec{l} \mathbf{X} \vec{B}$ gives that the force $\vec{F}_I$ exerted on the loop by the magnetic field is to the left and has magnitude

$$F_I = ILB = \left(\frac{BLv}{R}\right)LB = \frac{B^2L^2v}{R}.$$

The external force $\vec{F}$ needed to move the loop at constant speed is equal in magnitude and opposite in direction to $\vec{F}_I$ so is to the right and has this same magnitude.

a)

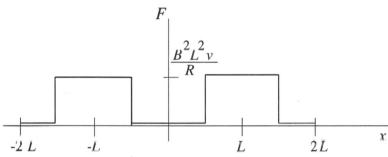

b)

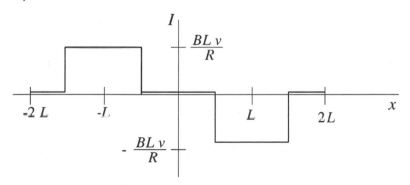

EVALUATE: When the loop is either totally outside or totally inside the magnetic field region the flux isn't changing, there is no induced current, and no external force is needed for the loop to maintain constant speed. When the loop is entering the field the external force required is directed so as to pull the loop in and when the loop is leaving the field the external force required is directed so as to pull the loop out of the field. These directions agree with Lenz's law: the force on the induced current (opposite in direction to the required external force) is directed so as to oppose the loop entering or leaving the field.

29.27 IDENTIFY: Use Eq.(29.10) to calculate the induced electric field E at a distance r from the center of the solenoid. Away from the ends of the solenoid, $B = \mu_0 nI$ inside and $B = 0$ outside.

a) SET UP: end view

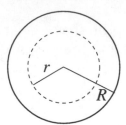

Let R be the radius of the solenoid.

Apply $\oint \vec{E} \cdot d\vec{l} = -\dfrac{d\Phi_B}{dt}$ to an integration path that is a circle of radius r, where $r < R$. We need to calculate just the magnitude of E so we can take absolute values.

EXECUTE: $\left| \oint \vec{E} \cdot d\vec{l} \right| = E(2\pi r)$

$$\Phi_B = B\pi r^2, \quad \left| -\frac{d\Phi_B}{dt} \right| = \pi r^2 \left| \frac{dB}{dt} \right|$$

$$\left| \oint \vec{E} \cdot d\vec{l} \right| = \left| -\frac{d\Phi_B}{dt} \right| \text{ implies } E(2\pi r) = \pi r^2 \left| \frac{dB}{dt} \right|$$

$$E = \tfrac{1}{2} r \left| \frac{dB}{dt} \right|$$

$$B = \mu_0 nI, \text{ so } \frac{dB}{dt} = \mu_0 n \frac{dI}{dt}$$

Thus $E = \tfrac{1}{2} r \mu_0 n \dfrac{dI}{dt} = \dfrac{1}{2}(0.00500 \text{ m})(4\pi \times 10^{-7} \text{ T} \cdot \text{m/A})(900 \text{ m}^{-1})(60.0 \text{ A/s}) = 1.70 \times 10^{-4} \text{ V/m}$

b) $r = 0.0100$ cm is still inside the solenoid so the expression in part (a) applies.

$E = \tfrac{1}{2} r \mu_0 n \dfrac{dI}{dt} = \dfrac{1}{2}(0.0100 \text{ m})(4\pi \times 10^{-7} \text{ T} \cdot \text{m/A})(900 \text{ m}^{-1})(60.0 \text{ A/s}) = 3.39 \times 10^{-4} \text{ V/m}$

EVALUATE: Inside the solenoid E is proportional to r, so E doubles when r doubles.

29.29 IDENTIFY: Use Eq.(29.10) to calculate the induced electric field E and use this E in Eq.(29.9) to calculate ε between two points.

a) SET UP: Because of the axial symmetry and the absence of any electric charge, the field lines are concentric circles.

b)

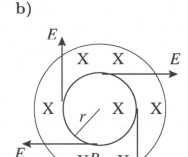

$\vec{E}$ is tangent to the ring. The direction of $\vec{E}$ (clockwise or counterclockwise) is the direction in which current will be induced in the ring.

EXECUTE: Use the sign convention for Faraday's law to deduce this direction. Let $\vec{A}$ be into the paper. Then Φ_B is positive. B decreasing then means $\dfrac{d\Phi_B}{dt}$ is negative, so by $\varepsilon = -\dfrac{d\Phi_D}{dt}$, ε is positive and therefore clockwise. Thus $\vec{E}$ is clockwise around the ring.

To calculate E apply $\oint \vec{E} \cdot d\vec{l} = -\dfrac{d\Phi_B}{dt}$ to a circular path that coincides with the ring.

$$\oint \vec{E} \cdot d\vec{l} = E(2\pi r)$$

$$\Phi_D = B\pi r^2; \quad \left|\frac{d\Phi_B}{dt}\right| = \pi r^2 \left|\frac{dB}{dt}\right|$$

$$E(2\pi r) = \pi r^2\left|\frac{dB}{dt}\right| \text{ and } E = \tfrac{1}{2}r\left|\frac{dB}{dt}\right| = \frac{1}{2}(0.100 \text{ m})(0.0350 \text{ T/s}) = 1.75 \times 10^{-3} \text{ V/m}$$

c) The induced emf has magnitude

$$\varepsilon = \oint \vec{E} \cdot d\vec{l} = E(2\pi r) = (1.75 \times 10^{-3} \text{ V/m})(2\pi)(0.100 \text{ m}) = 1.100 \times 10^{-3} \text{ V}.$$

Then $I = \dfrac{\varepsilon}{R} = \dfrac{1.100 \times 10^{-3} \text{ V}}{4.00 \text{ } \Omega} = 2.75 \times 10^{-4} \text{ A}.$

d) Points a and b are separated by a distance around the ring of πr so

$$\varepsilon = E(\pi r) = (1.75 \times 10^{-3} \text{ V/m})(\pi)(0.100 \text{ m}) = 5.50 \times 10^{-4} \text{ V}$$

e) The ends are separated by a distance around the ring of $2\pi r$ so

$$\varepsilon = 1.10 \times 10^{-3} \text{ V as calculated in part (c).}$$

EVALUATE: The induced emf, calculated from Faraday's law and used to calculate the induced current, is associated with the induced electric field integrated around the total circumference of the ring.

29.35 IDENTIFY and **SET UP:** Eqs.(29.13)and (29.14) show that $i_C = i_D$ and also relate i_D to the rate of change of the electric field flux between the plates. Use this to calculate dE/dt and apply the generalized form of Ampere's law (Eq.29.15) to calculate B.

a) **EXECUTE:** $i_C = i_D$, so $j_D = \dfrac{i_D}{A} = \dfrac{i_C}{A} = \dfrac{0.280\ \text{A}}{\pi r^2} = \dfrac{0.280\ \text{A}}{\pi(0.0400\ \text{m})^2} = 55.7$ A/m^2

b) $j_D = \epsilon_0 \dfrac{dE}{dt}$ so $\dfrac{dE}{dt} = \dfrac{j_D}{\epsilon_0} = \dfrac{55.7\ \text{A/m}^2}{8.854 \times 10^{-12}\ \text{C}^2/\text{N} \cdot \text{m}^2} = 6.29 \times 10^{12}$ V/m·s

c) **SET UP:** Apply Ampere's law $\oint \vec{B} \cdot d\vec{l} = \mu_0 (i_C + i_D)_{\text{encl}}$ (Eq.(28.20)) to a circular path with radius $r = 0.0200$ m.

end view

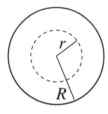

By symmetry the magnetic field is tangent to the path and constant around it.

EXECUTE: Thus $\oint \vec{B} \cdot d\vec{l} = \oint B\,dl = B \int dl = B(2\pi r)$.

$i_C = 0$ (no conduction current flows through the air space between the plates)

The displacement current enclosed by the path is $j_D \pi r^2$.

Thus $B(2\pi r) = \mu_0 (j_D \pi r^2)$ and

$B = \tfrac{1}{2}\mu_0 j_D r = \tfrac{1}{2}(4\pi \times 10^{-7}\ \text{T} \cdot \text{m/A})(55.7\ \text{A/m}^2)(0.0200\ \text{m}) = 7.00 \times 10^{-7}$ T

d) $B = \tfrac{1}{2}\mu_0 j_D r$. Now r is $\tfrac{1}{2}$ the value in (c), so B is $\tfrac{1}{2}$ also:

$B = \tfrac{1}{2}(7.00 \times 10^{-7}\ \text{T}) = 3.50 \times 10^{-7}$ T

EVALUATE: The definition of displacement current allows the current to be continuous at the capacitor. The magnetic field between the plates is zero on the axis ($r = 0$) and increases as r increases.

29.37 **IDENTIFY** and **SET UP:** Use $i_C = q/t$ to calculate the charge q that the current has carried to the plates in time t. The two equations preceeding Eq.(24.2) relate q to the electric field E and the potential difference between the plates. The displacement current density is defined by Eq.(29.16).

EXECUTE:

a) $i_C = 1.80 \times 10^{-3}$ A

$q = 0$ at $t = 0$

The amount of charge brought to the plates by the charging current in time t is

$q = i_C t = (1.80 \times 10^{-3}\ \text{A})(0.500 \times 10^{-6}\ \text{s}) = 9.00 \times 10^{-10}$ C

$E = \dfrac{\sigma}{\epsilon_0} = \dfrac{q}{\epsilon_0 A} = \dfrac{9.00 \times 10^{-10}\ \text{C}}{(8.854 \times 10^{-12}\ \text{C}^2/\text{N} \cdot \text{m}^2)(5.00 \times 10^{-4}\ \text{m}^2)} = 2.03 \times 10^5$ V/m

$$V = Ed = (2.03 \times 10^5 \text{ V/m})(2.00 \times 10^{-3} \text{ m}) = 406 \text{ V}$$

b) $E = q/\epsilon_0 A$

$$\frac{dE}{dt} = \frac{dq/dt}{\epsilon_0 A} = \frac{i_C}{\epsilon_0 A} =$$

$$\frac{1.80 \times 10^{-3} \text{ A}}{(8.854 \times 10^{-12} \text{ C}^2/\text{N} \cdot \text{m}^2)(5.00 \times 10^{-4} \text{ m}^2)} = 4.07 \times 10^{11} \text{ V/m·s}$$

Since i_C is constant dE/dt does not vary in time.

c) $j_D = \epsilon_0 \dfrac{dE}{dt}$ (Eq.(29.16), with ϵ replaced by ϵ_0 since there is vacuum between the plates.)

$$j_D = (8.854 \times 10^{-12} \text{ C}^2/\text{N} \cdot \text{m}^2)(4.07 \times 10^{11} \text{ V/m} \cdot \text{s}) = 3.60 \text{ A/m}^2$$

$$i_D = j_D A = (3.60 \text{ A/m}^2)(5.00 \times 10^{-4} \text{ m}^2) = 1.80 \times 10^{-3} \text{ A}; \quad i_D = i_C$$

EVALUATE: $i_C = i_D$. The constant conduction current means the charge q on the plates and the electric field between them both increase linearly with time and i_D is constant.

29.39 IDENTIFY: Apply Ampere's law to a circular path of radius $r < R$, where R is the radius of the wire.

SET UP:

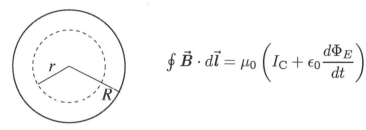

$$\oint \vec{B} \cdot d\vec{l} = \mu_0 \left(I_C + \epsilon_0 \frac{d\Phi_E}{dt} \right)$$

EXECUTE: There is no displacement current, so $\oint \vec{B} \cdot d\vec{l} = \mu_0 I_C$

The magnetic field inside the superconducting material is zero, so $\oint \vec{B} \cdot d\vec{l} = 0$. But then Ampere's law says that $I_C = 0$; there can be no conduction current through the path. This same argument applies to any circular path with $r < R$, so all the current must be at the surface of the wire.

EVALUATE: If the current were uniformly spread over the wire's cross section, the magnetic field would be like that calculated in Example 28.9.

Problems

29.43 IDENTIFY and SET UP: Use Faraday's law to calculate the magnitude of the induced emf and Lenz's law to determine its direction. Apply Ohm's law to calculate I. Use Eq.(25.10) to calculate the resistance of the coil.

a) EXECUTE: The angle ϕ between the normal to the coil and the direction of $\vec{B}$ is 30.0°.

$$|\varepsilon| = \left|\frac{d\Phi_B}{dt}\right| = (N\pi r^2)(dB/dt) \text{ and } I = |\varepsilon|/R.$$

For $t < 0$ and $t > 1.00$ s, $dB/dt = 0$, $|\varepsilon| = 0$ and $I = 0$.

For $0 \le t \le 1.00$ s, $dB/dt = (0.120 \text{ T})\pi \sin \pi t$

$|\varepsilon| = (N\pi r^2)\pi(0.120 \text{ T}) \sin \pi t = (0.9475 \text{ V}) \sin \pi t$

R for wire: $R_{\mathrm{w}} = \dfrac{\rho L}{A} = \dfrac{\rho L}{\pi r^2}$; $\rho = 1.72 \times 10^{-8} \ \Omega \cdot \text{m}$, $r = 0.0150 \times 10^{-3}$ m

$L = Nc = N2\pi r = (500)(2\pi)(0.0400 \text{ m}) = 125.7$ m

$R_{\mathrm{w}} = 3058 \ \Omega$ and the total resistance of the circuit is $R = 3058 \ \Omega + 600 \ \Omega = 3658 \ \Omega$

$I = |\varepsilon|/R = (0.259 \text{ mA}) \sin \pi t$

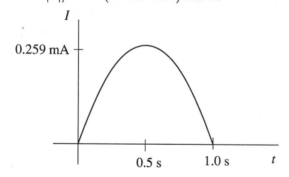

b)

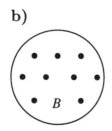

B increasing so Φ_B is $\odot$ and increasing

Φ_{ind} is $\otimes$ so I is clockwise

EVALUATE: The long length of small diameter wire used to make the coil has a rather large resistance, larger than the resistance of the 600-Ω resistor connected to it in the circuit. The flux has a cosine time dependence so the rate of change of flux and the current have a sine time dependence. There is no induced current for $t < 0$ or $t > 1.00$ s.

29.45 IDENTIFY and SET UP: Use Faraday's law to calculate the emf induced in the coil and then apply Ohm's law to the coil to calculate the current. Eq.(29.9) relates the emf induced in one turn of the coil to the induced electric field.

a) EXECUTE:

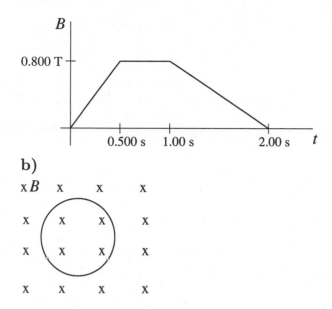

b)

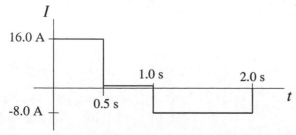

When $\vec{B}$ is increasing in magnitude ($t = 0$ to $t = 0.500$ s), by Lenz's law $\vec{B}_{\text{induced}}$ is directed out of the page inside the coil and the induced current I is counterclockwise.

When $\vec{B}$ is decreasing in magnitude ($t = 1.00$ s to $t = 2.00$ s), by Lenz's law $\vec{B}_{\text{induced}}$ is directed into the page inside the coil and the induced current I is clockwise.

When $\vec{B}$ is constant ($t = 0.500$ s to $t = 1.00$ s), the induced current is zero.

<u>Magnitude of I</u>

$$|\varepsilon| = N\left|\frac{d\Phi_B}{dt}\right| = N\pi r^2\left|\frac{dB}{dt}\right|, \ I = \frac{|\varepsilon|}{R}$$

$t = 0$ to $t = 0.500$ s: $\left|\frac{dB}{dt}\right| = \dfrac{0.800 \text{ T}}{0.500 \text{ s}} = 1.60 \text{ T/s}$

$|\varepsilon| = 20\pi(0.500 \text{ m})^2(1.60 \text{ T/s}) = 25.13 \text{ V}$

$I = \dfrac{|\varepsilon|}{R} = \dfrac{25.13 \text{ V}}{1.57 \ \Omega} = 16.0 \text{ A}$

$t = 1.00$ to $t = 2.00$ s: $\left|\frac{dB}{dt}\right| = \dfrac{0.800 \text{ T}}{1.00 \text{ s}} = 0.800 \text{ T/s}$

$|\varepsilon| = 20\pi(0.500 \text{ m})^2(0.800 \text{ T/s}) = 12.57 \text{ V}; \ I = \dfrac{|\varepsilon|}{R} = \dfrac{12.57 \text{ V}}{1.57 \ \Omega} = 8.0 \text{ A}$

c) $N \oint \vec{E} \cdot d\vec{l} = \varepsilon$ ($\oint \vec{E} \cdot d\vec{l} = \varepsilon/N$ is the emf in one turn of the coil)

$NE(2\pi r) = \varepsilon$ and $E = \dfrac{\varepsilon}{N2\pi r}$

E is maximum when ε is maximum. From part (b) we have that $\varepsilon_{max} = 25.13$ V.

$E_{max} = \dfrac{\varepsilon_{max}}{N2\pi r} = \dfrac{25.13 \text{ V}}{20(2\pi)(0.500 \text{ m})} = 0.400 \text{ V/m}$

EVALUATE: When B is increasing the induced current is in one direction and when B is decreasing the induced current is in the opposite direction. When B is constant the flux isn't changing and the induced current is zero.

29.49 a) IDENTIFY: (i) $|\varepsilon| = \left| \dfrac{d\Phi_B}{dt} \right|$. The flux is changing because the magnitude of the magnetic field of the wire decreases with distance from the wire. Find the flux through a narrow strip of area and integrate over the loop to find the total flux.

SET UP:

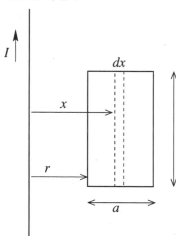

Consider a narrow strip of width dx and a distance x from the long wire.

The magnetic field of the wire at the strip is $B = \mu_0 I/2\pi x$.

The flux through the strip is
$d\Phi_B = B b\, dx = (\mu_0 I b/2\pi)(dx/x)$

EXECUTE: The total flux through the loop is $\Phi_B = \int d\Phi_B = \left(\dfrac{\mu_0 I b}{2\pi} \right) \displaystyle\int_r^{r+a} \dfrac{dx}{x}$

$\Phi_B = \left(\dfrac{\mu_0 I b}{2\pi} \right) \ln \left(\dfrac{r+a}{r} \right)$

$\dfrac{d\Phi_B}{dt} = \dfrac{d\Phi_B}{dt} \dfrac{dr}{dt} = \dfrac{\mu_0 I b}{2\pi} \left(-\dfrac{a}{r(r+a)} \right) v$

$|\varepsilon| = \dfrac{\mu_0 I a b v}{2\pi r(r+a)}$

(ii) **IDENTIFY:** $\varepsilon = Bvl$ for a bar of length l moving at speed v perpendicular to a magnetic field B. Calculate the induced emf in each side of the loop, and combine the emfs according to their polarity.

SET UP:

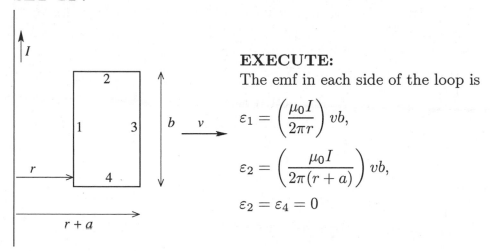

EXECUTE:
The emf in each side of the loop is

$$\varepsilon_1 = \left(\frac{\mu_0 I}{2\pi r}\right) vb,$$

$$\varepsilon_2 = \left(\frac{\mu_0 I}{2\pi (r + a)}\right) vb,$$

$$\varepsilon_2 = \varepsilon_4 = 0$$

Both emfs ε_1 and ε_2 are directed toward the top of the loop so oppose each other. The net emf is

$$\varepsilon = \varepsilon_1 - \varepsilon_2 = \frac{\mu_0 I vb}{2\pi}\left(\frac{1}{r} - \frac{1}{r + a}\right) = \frac{\mu_0 I abv}{2\pi r(r + a)}$$

This expression agrees with what was obtained in (i) using Faraday's law.

b) (i) IDENTIFY and **SET UP:** The flux of the induced current opposes the change in flux.

EXECUTE: $\vec{B}$ is $\otimes$. Φ_B is $\otimes$ and decreasing, so the flux Φ_{ind} of the induced current is $\otimes$ and the current is clockwise.

(ii) IDENTIFY and **SET UP:** Use the right-hand rule to find the force on the positive charges in each side of the loop.

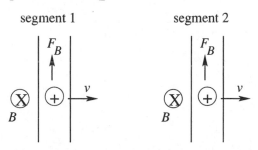

EXECUTE: B is larger at segment 1 since it is closer to the long wire, so F_B is larger in segment 1 and the induced current in the loop is clockwise. This agrees with the direction deduced in (i) using Lenz's law.

c) EVALUATE: When $v = 0$ the induced emf should be zero; the expression in part (a) gives this. When $a \to 0$ the flux goes to zero and the emf should approach zero; the expression in part (a) gives this. When $r \to \infty$ the magnetic field through the loop goes to zero and the emf should go to zero; the expression in part (a) gives this.

29.55 IDENTIFY: Use Faraday's law to calculate the induced emf and Ohm's law to find the induced current. Use Eq.(27.19) to calculate the magnetic force F_I on the induced current. Use the net force $F - F_I$ in Newton's 2nd law to calculate the acceleration of the rod and use that to describe its motion.

a) SET UP:

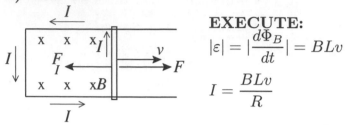

EXECUTE:

$$|\varepsilon| = \left|\frac{d\Phi_B}{dt}\right| = BLv$$

$$I = \frac{BLv}{R}$$

Use $\varepsilon = -\dfrac{d\Phi_B}{dt}$ to find the direction of I:

Let $\vec{A}$ be into the page. Then $\Phi_B > 0$. The area of the circuit is increasing, so $\dfrac{d\Phi_B}{dt} > 0$. Then $\varepsilon < 0$ and with our direction for $\vec{A}$ this means that ε and I are counterclockwise, as shown in the sketch. The force F_I on the rod due to the induced current is given by $\vec{F_I} = I\vec{l}\times\vec{B}$. This gives $\vec{F_I}$ to the left with magnitude $F_I = ILB = (BLv/R)LB = B^2L^2v/R$. Note that $\vec{F_I}$ is directed to oppose the motion of the rod, as required by Lenz's law.

EVALUATE: The net force on the rod is $F - F_I$, so its acceleration is $a = (F - F_I)/m = (F - B^2L^2v/R)/m$. The rod starts with $v = 0$ and $a = F/m$. As the speed v increases the acceleration a decreases. When $a = 0$ the rod has reached its terminal speed v_t.

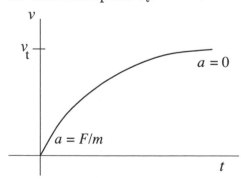

(Recall that a is the slope of the tangent to the v versus t curve.)

b) EXECUTE: $v = v_t$ when $a = 0$ so $\dfrac{F - B^2L^2v_t/R}{m} = 0$ and $v_t = \dfrac{RF}{B^2L^2}$.

EVALUATE: A large F produces a large v_t. If B is larger, or R is smaller, the induced current is larger at a given v so F_I is larger and the terminal speed is less.

29.61 a) and b) IDENTIFY and SET UP:

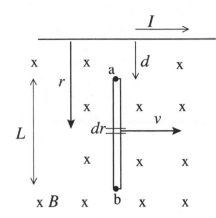

The magnetic field of the wire is given by $B = \dfrac{\mu_0 I}{2\pi r}$ and varies along the length of the bar. At every point along the bar $\vec{B}$ has direction into the page. Divide the bar up into thin slices.

EXECUTE: The emf $d\varepsilon$ induced in each slice is given by $d\varepsilon = \vec{v} \mathbf{X} \vec{B} \cdot d\vec{l}$. $\vec{v} \mathbf{X} \vec{B}$ is directed toward the wire, so

$$d\varepsilon = -vB\,dr = -v\left(\frac{\mu_0 I}{2\pi r}\right)dr.$$

The total emf induced in the bar is

$$V_{ba} = \int_a^b d\varepsilon = -\int_d^{d+L}\left(\frac{\mu_0 I v}{2\pi r}\right)dr = -\frac{\mu_0 I v}{2\pi}\int_d^{d+L}\frac{dr}{r} = -\frac{\mu_0 I v}{2\pi}\left[\ln(r)\right]_d^{d+L}$$

$$V_{ba} = -\frac{\mu_0 I v}{2\pi}\left(\ln(d+L) - \ln(d)\right) = -\frac{\mu_0 I v}{2\pi}\ln(1 + L/d)$$

EVALUATE: The minus sign means that V_{ba} is negative; point a is at higher potential than point b. (The force $\vec{F} = q\vec{v}\mathbf{X}\vec{B}$ on positive charge carriers in the bar is towards a, so a is at higher potential.) The potential difference increases when I or v increase, or d decreases.

c) IDENTIFY: Use Faraday's law to calculate the induced emf.

SET UP:

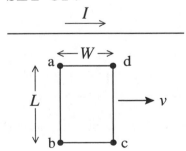

EXECUTE:
As the loop moves to the right the magnetic flux through it doesn't change.

Thus $\varepsilon = -\dfrac{d\Phi_B}{dt} = 0$

and $I = 0$.

EVALUATE: This result can also be understood as follows. The induced emf in section ab puts point a at higher potential; the induced emf in section dc puts point d at higher potential. If you travel around the loop then these two induced emf's sum to zero. There is no emf in the loop and hence no current.

29.63 a) IDENTIFY: Use the expression for motional emf to calculate the emf induced in the rod.

SET UP:

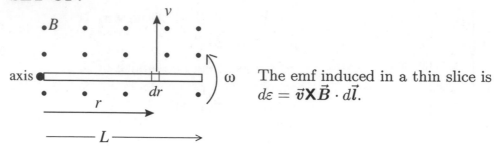

The emf induced in a thin slice is
$d\varepsilon = \vec{v} \mathbf{X} \vec{B} \cdot d\vec{l}.$

EXECUTE: Assume that $\vec{B}$ is directed out of the page. Then $\vec{v} \mathbf{X} \vec{B}$ is directed radially outward and $dl = dr$, so $\vec{v} \mathbf{X} \vec{B} \cdot d\vec{l} = vB\,dr$

$v = r\omega$ so $d\varepsilon = \omega B r\,dr.$

The $d\varepsilon$ for all the thin slices that make up the rod are in series so they add:

$$\varepsilon = \int d\varepsilon = \int_0^L \omega B r\,dr = \frac{1}{2}\omega BL^2 = \frac{1}{2}(8.80 \text{ rad/s})(0.650 \text{ T})(0.240 \text{ m})^2 = 0.165 \text{ V}$$

EVALUATE: ε increases with ω, B or L^2.

b) No current flows so there is no IR drop in potential. Thus the potential difference between the ends equals the emf of 0.165 V calculated in part (a).

c) SET UP:

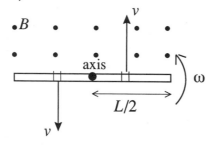

EXECUTE: The emf between the center of the rod and each end is

$\varepsilon = \frac{1}{2}\omega B(L/2)^2 = \frac{1}{4}(0.165 \text{ V}) = 0.0412 \text{ V}$, with the direction of the emf from the center of the rod toward each end. The emfs in each half of the rod thus oppose each other and there is no net emf between the ends of the rod.

EVALUATE: ω and B are the same as in part (a) but L of each half is $\frac{1}{2}L$ for the whole rod. ε is proportional to L^2, so is smaller by a factor of $\frac{1}{4}$.

29.65 a) IDENTIFY: Use Faraday's law to calculate the induced emf, Ohm's law to calculate I, and Eq.(27.19) to calculate the force on the rod due to the induced current.

SET UP:

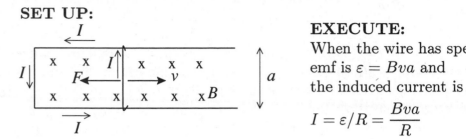

EXECUTE:
When the wire has speed v the induced emf is $\varepsilon = Bva$ and the induced current is

$$I = \varepsilon/R = \frac{Bva}{R}$$

The induced current flows upward in the wire as shown, so the force $\vec{F} = I\vec{l}\times\vec{B}$ exerted by the magnetic field on the induced current is to the left. $\vec{F}$ opposes the motion of the wire, as it must by Lenz's law. The magnitude of the force is $F = IaB = B^2a^2v/R$.

b) Apply $\sum \vec{F} = m\vec{a}$ to the wire. Take $+x$ to be toward the right and let the origin be at the location of the wire at $t = 0$, so $x_0 = 0$.

$\sum F_x = ma_x$ says $-F = ma_x$

$$a_x = -\frac{F}{m} = -\frac{B^2a^2v}{mR}$$

Use this expression to solve for $v(t)$:

$$a_x - \frac{dv}{dt} = -\frac{B^2a^2v}{mR} \text{ and } \frac{dv}{v} = -\frac{B^2a^2}{mR}dt$$

$$\int_{v_0}^{v} \frac{dv'}{v'} = -\frac{B^2a^2}{mR} \int_0^t dt'$$

$$\ln(v) - \ln(v_0) = -\frac{B^2a^2t}{mR}$$

$$\ln\left(\frac{v}{v_0}\right) = -\frac{B^2a^2t}{mR} \text{ and } v = v_0e^{-B^2a^2t/mR}$$

Note: At $t = 0$, $v = v_0$ and $v \to 0$ when $t \to \infty$

Now solve for $x(t)$:

$$v = \frac{dx}{dt} = v_0e^{-B^2a^2t/mR} \text{ so } dx = v_0e^{-B^2a^2t/mR} dt$$

$$\int_0^x dx' = \int_0^t v_0e^{-B^2a^2t/mR}dt'$$

$$x = v_0\left(-\frac{mR}{B^2a^2}\right)\left[e^{-B^2a^2t'/mR}\right]_0^t = \frac{mRv_0}{B^2a^2}\left(1 - e^{-B^2a^2t/mR}\right)$$

Comes to rest implies $v = 0$. This happens when $t \to \infty$.

$t \to \infty$ gives $x = \dfrac{mRv_0}{B^2a^2}$. Thus this is the distance the wire travels before coming to rest.

EVALUATE: The motion of the slide wire causes an induced emf and current. The magnetic force on the induced current opposes the motion of the wire and eventually brings it to rest. The force and acceleration depend on v and are constant. If the acceleration were constant, not changing from its initial value of $a_x = -B^2a^2v_0/mR$, then the stopping distance would be $x = -v_0^2/2a_x = mRv_0/2B^2a^2$. The actual stopping distance is twice this.

29.67 IDENTIFY: Use Eq.(29.10) to calculate the induced electric field at each point and then use $\vec{F} = q\vec{E}$.

SET UP:

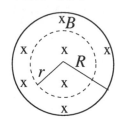

Apply $\oint \vec{E} \cdot d\vec{l} = -\dfrac{d\Phi_B}{dt}$

to a concentric circle of radius r.
Take $\vec{A}$ to be into the
page, in the direction of $\vec{B}$.

EXECUTE: B increasing then gives $\dfrac{d\Phi_B}{dt} > 0$, so $\oint \vec{E} \cdot d\vec{l}$ is negative. This means that E is tangent to the circle in the counterclockwise direction.

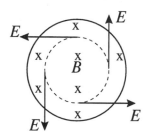

$$\oint \vec{E} \cdot d\vec{l} = -E(2\pi r)$$

$$\frac{d\Phi_B}{dt} = \pi r^2 \frac{dB}{dt}$$

$-E(2\pi r) = -\pi r^2 \dfrac{dB}{dt}$ so $E = \frac{1}{2}r\dfrac{dB}{dt}$

<u>point a</u>

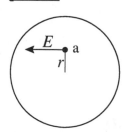

$$F = qE = \frac{1}{2}qr\frac{dB}{dt}$$

$\vec{F}$ is to the left
($\vec{F}$ is in the same direction as $\vec{E}$ since
q is positive.)

point b

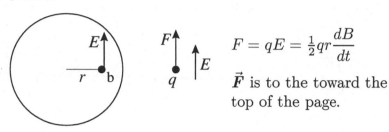

$$F = qE = \tfrac{1}{2}qr\frac{dB}{dt}$$

$\vec{F}$ is to the toward the
top of the page.

point c $r = 0$ here, so $E = 0$ and $F = 0$.

EVALUATE: If there were a concentric conducting ring of radius r in the magnetic field region, Lenz's law tells us that the increasing mangetic field would induce a counterclockwise current in the ring. This agrees with the direction of the force we calculated for the individual positive point charges.

29.69 IDENTIFY and SET UP: At the terminal speed v_t, the upward force F_I exerted on the loop due to the induced current equals the downward force of gravity: $F_I = mg$. Use Eq.(29.6) to find the induced emf in the side of the loop that is totally within the magnetic field. There is no induced emf in the other sides of the loop.

EXECUTE: $\varepsilon = Bvs$, $I = Bvs/R$ and $F_I = IsB = B^2s^2v/R$

$$\frac{B^2s^2v_T}{R} = mg \text{ and } v_t = \frac{mgR}{B^2s^2}$$

$$m = \rho_m V = \rho_m(4s)\pi(d/2)^2 = \rho_m\pi s d^2$$

$$R = \frac{\rho L}{A} = \frac{\rho_R 4s}{\tfrac{1}{4}\pi d^2} = \frac{16\rho_R s}{\pi d^2}$$

Using these expressions for m and R gives $v_t = 16\rho_m\rho_R g/B^2$

EVALUATE: We know $\rho_m = 8900$ kg/m^3 (Table 14.1) and $\rho_R = 1.72 \times 10^{-8}$ Ω·m (Table 25.1). Taking $B = 0.5$ T gives $v_t = 9.6$ cm/s.

29.71 IDENTIFY and SET UP: Apply Ohm's law to the dielectric to relate the current in the dielectric to the charge on the plates. Use Eq.(25.1) for the current and obtain a differential equation for $q(t)$. Integrate this equation to obtain $q(t)$ and $i(t)$. Use $E = q/\epsilon A$ and Eq.(29.16) to calculate j_D.

EXECUTE:

a) Apply Ohm's law to the dielectric:

$$i(t) = \frac{v(t)}{R}$$

$$v(t) = \frac{q(t)}{C} \text{ and } C = K\frac{\epsilon_0 A}{d}$$

$$v(t) = \left(\frac{d}{K\epsilon_0 A}\right) q(t)$$

The resistance R of the dielectric slab is $R = \rho d/A$.

Thus $i(t) = \dfrac{v(t)}{R} = \left(\dfrac{q(t)d}{K\epsilon_0 A}\right)\left(\dfrac{A}{\rho d}\right) = \dfrac{q(t)}{K\epsilon_0 \rho}$.

But the current $i(t)$ in the dielectric is related to the rate of change dq/dt of the charge $q(t)$ on the plates by $i(t) = -dq/dt$ (a positive i in the direction from the $+$ to the $-$ plate of the capacitor corresponds to a decrease in the charge).

Using this in the above gives $-\dfrac{dq}{dt} = \left(\dfrac{1}{K\rho\epsilon_0}\right) q(t)$.

$$\frac{dq}{q} = -\frac{dt}{K\rho\epsilon_0}$$

Integrate both sides of this equation from $t = 0$, where $q = Q_0$, to a later time t when the charge is $q(t)$

$$\int_{Q_0}^{q} \frac{dq}{q} = -\left(\frac{1}{K\rho\epsilon_0}\right)\int_{0}^{t} dt$$

$$\ln\left(\frac{q}{Q_0}\right) = -\frac{t}{K\rho\epsilon_0} \quad \text{and} \quad q(t) = Q_0 e^{-t/K\rho\epsilon_0}.$$

Then $i(t) = -\dfrac{dq}{dt} = \left(\dfrac{Q_0}{K\rho\epsilon_0}\right) e^{-t/K\rho\epsilon_0}$

and $j_C = \dfrac{i(t)}{A} = \left(\dfrac{Q_0}{AK\rho\epsilon_0}\right) e^{-t/K\rho\epsilon_0}$

The conduction current flows from the positive to the negative plate of the capacitor.

b) $E(t) = \dfrac{q(t)}{\epsilon A} = \dfrac{q(t)}{K\epsilon_0 A}$

$$j_D(t) = \epsilon\frac{dE}{dt} = K\epsilon_0\frac{dE}{dt} = K\epsilon_0\frac{dq(t)/dt}{K\epsilon_0 A} = -\frac{i_C(t)}{A} = -j_C(t)$$

The minus sign means that $j_D(t)$ is directed from the negative to the positive plate. $\vec{E}$ is from $+$ to $-$ but dE/dt is negative (E decreases) so $j_D(t)$ is from $-$ to $+$.

EVALUATE: There is no conduction current to and from the plates so the concept of dispalcement current, with $\vec{j}_D = -\vec{j}_C$ in the dielectric, allows the current to be continuous at the capacitor.

CHAPTER 30
INDUCTANCE

Exercises

30.1 **IDENTIFY** and **SET UP:** Apply Eq.(30.4).

EXECUTE:

a) $|\varepsilon_2| = M|\frac{di_1}{dt}| - (3.25 \times 10^{-4} \text{ H})(830 \text{ A/s}) - 0.270 \text{ V}$; yes, it is constant.

b) $|\varepsilon_1| = M|\frac{di_2}{dt}|$; M is a property of the pair of coils so is the same as in part (a). Thus $|\varepsilon_1| = 0.270 \text{ V}$.

EVALUATE: The induced emf is the same in either case. A constant di/dt produces a constant emf.

30.3 **IDENTIFY** and **SET UP:** Apply Eq.(30.5).

EXECUTE:

a) $M = \frac{N_2 \Phi_{B2}}{i_1} = \frac{400(0.0320 \text{ Wb})}{6.52 \text{ A}} = 1.96 \text{ H}$

b) $M = \frac{N_1 \Phi_{B1}}{i_2}$ so $\Phi_{B1} = \frac{Mi_2}{N_1} = \frac{(1.96 \text{ H})(2.54 \text{ A})}{700} = 7.11 \times 10^{-3} \text{ Wb}$

EVALUATE: M relates the current in one coil to the flux through the other coil. Eq.(30.5) shows that M is the same for a pair of coils, no matter which one has the current and which one has the flux.

30.9 **IDENTIFY** and **SET UP:** Use Eq.(30.6) to relate L to the flux through each turn of the solenoid. Use Eq.(28.23) for the magnetic field through the solenoid.

EXECUTE: $L = \frac{N\Phi_B}{i}$ If the magnetic field is uniform inside the solenoid $\Phi_B = BA$.

From Eq.(28.23), $B = \mu_0 ni = \mu_0 \left(\frac{N}{l}\right) i$ so $\Phi_B = \frac{\mu_0 NiA}{l}$.

Then $L = \frac{N}{i}\left(\frac{\mu_0 NiA}{l}\right) = \frac{\mu_0 N^2 A}{l}$.

EVALUATE: Our result is the same as L for a toroidal solenoid calculated in Example 30.3, except that the average circumference $2\pi r$ of the toroid is replaced by the length l of the straight solenoid.

30.13 **IDENTIFY** and **SET UP:** Use Eq.(30.9) to relate the energy stored to the inductance. Example 30.3 gives the inductance of a toroidal solenoid to be $L = \dfrac{\mu_0 N^2 A}{2\pi r}$, so once we know L we can solve for N.

EXECUTE: $U = \frac{1}{2}LI^2$ so $L = \dfrac{2U}{I^2} = \dfrac{2(0.390 \text{ J})}{(12.0 \text{ A})^2} = 5.417 \times 10^{-3} \text{ H}$

$$N = \sqrt{\dfrac{2\pi r L}{\mu_0 A}} = \sqrt{\dfrac{2\pi(0.150 \text{ m})(5.417 \times 10^{-3} \text{ H})}{(4\pi \times 10^{-7} \text{ T} \cdot \text{m/A})(5.00 \times 10^{-4} \text{ m}^2)}} = 2850.$$

EVALUATE: L and hence U increase according to the square of N.

30.17 **IDENTIFY** and **SET UP:** The energy density (energy per unit volume) in a magnetic field (in vacuum) is given by $u = \dfrac{U}{V} = \dfrac{B^2}{2\mu_0}$ (Eq.30.10).

EXECUTE:
a) $V = \dfrac{2\mu_0 U}{B^2} = \dfrac{2(4\pi \times 10^{-7} \text{ T} \cdot \text{m/A})(3.60 \times 10^6 \text{ J})}{(0.600 \text{ T})^2} = 25.1 \text{ m}^3.$

b) $u = \dfrac{U}{V} = \dfrac{B^2}{2\mu_0}$

$$B = \sqrt{\dfrac{2\mu_0 U}{V}} = \sqrt{\dfrac{2(4\pi \times 10^{-7} \text{ T} \cdot \text{m/A})(3.60 \times 10^6 \text{ J})}{(0.400 \text{ m})^3}} = 11.9 \text{ T}$$

EVALUATE: Large-scale energy storage in a magnetic field is not practical. The volume in part (a) is quite large and the field in part (b) would be very difficult to achieve.

30.19 **IDENTIFY:** Apply Kirchhoff's loop rule to the circuit. $i(t)$ is given by Eq.(30.14).
SET UP:

$\dfrac{di}{dt}$ is positive as the current increases from its initial value of zero.

EXECUTE: $\varepsilon - v_R - v_L = 0$

$\varepsilon - iR - L\dfrac{di}{dt} = 0$ so $i = \dfrac{\varepsilon}{R}\left(1 - e^{-(R/L)t}\right)$

a) Initially $(t = 0)$, $i = 0$ so $\varepsilon - L\dfrac{di}{dt} = 0$

$\dfrac{di}{dt} = \dfrac{\varepsilon}{L} = \dfrac{6.00\ \text{V}}{2.50\ \text{H}} = 2.40\ \text{A/s}$

b) $\varepsilon - iR - L\dfrac{di}{dt} = 0$ (Use this equation rather than Eq.(30.15) since i rather than t is given.)

Thus $\dfrac{di}{dt} = \dfrac{\varepsilon - iR}{L} = \dfrac{6.00\ \text{V} - (0.500\ \text{A})(8.00\ \Omega)}{2.50\ \text{H}} = 0.800\ \text{A/s}$

c) $i = \dfrac{\varepsilon}{R}\left(1 - e^{-(R/L)t}\right) = \left(\dfrac{6.00\ \text{V}}{8.00\ \Omega}\right)\left(1 - e^{-(8.00\ \Omega/2.50\ \text{H})(0.250\ \text{s})}\right) =$

$0.750\ \text{A}\left(1 - e^{-0.800}\right) = 0.413\ \text{A}$

d) Final steady state means $t \to \infty$ and $\dfrac{di}{dt} \to 0$, so $\varepsilon - iR = 0$.

$i = \dfrac{\varepsilon}{R} = \dfrac{6.00\ \text{V}}{8.00\ \Omega} = 0.750\ \text{A}$

EVALUATE: Our results agree with Fig.30.12. The current is initially zero and increases to its final value of ε/R. The slope of the current in the figure, which is di/dt, decreases with t.

30.23 IDENTIFY: Apply the concepts of current decay in an *R-L* circuit. Apply the loop rule to the circuit. $i(t)$ is given by Eq.(30.18). The voltage across the resistor depends on i and the voltage across the inductor depends on di/dt.

SET UP:

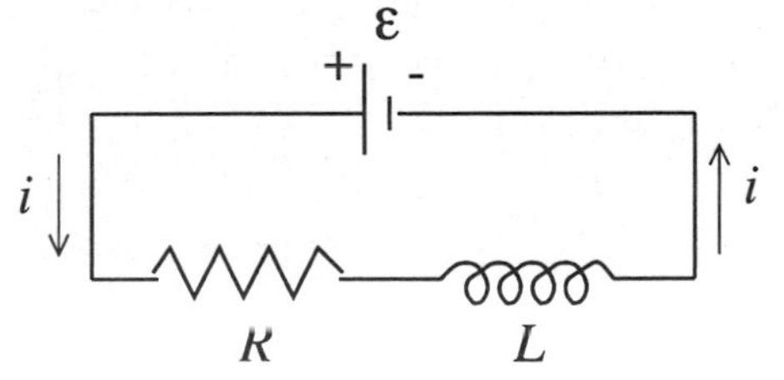

$\varepsilon - iR - L\dfrac{di}{dt} = 0$

Constant current established means $\dfrac{di}{dt} = 0$.

EXECUTE: $i = \dfrac{\varepsilon}{R} = \dfrac{60.0\ \text{V}}{240\ \Omega} = 0.250\ \text{A}$

a) SET UP:

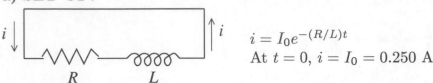

$i = I_0 e^{-(R/L)t}$

At $t = 0$, $i = I_0 = 0.250$ A

The inductor prevents an instantaneous change in the current; the current in the inductor just after S_2 is closed and S_1 is opened equals the current in the inductor just before this is done.

b) EXECUTE: $i = I_0 e^{-(R/L)t} = (0.250 \text{ A})e^{-(240 \text{ }\Omega/0.160 \text{ H})(4.00 \times 10^{-4} \text{ s})}$
$= (0.250 \text{ A})e^{-0.600} = 0.137$ A

c) SET UP:

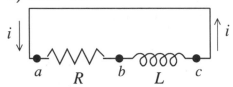

EXECUTE: If we trace around the loop in the direction of the current the potential falls as we travel through the resistor so it must rise as we pass through the inductor: $v_{ab} > 0$ and $v_{bc} < 0$. So point c is at higher potential than point b.

$v_{ab} + v_{bc} = 0$ and $v_{bc} = -v_{ab}$

Or, $v_{cb} = v_{ab} = iR = (0.137 \text{ A})(240 \text{ }\Omega) = 32.9$ V

d) $i = I_0 e^{-(R/L)t}$

$i = \frac{1}{2}I_0$ says $\frac{1}{2}I_0 = I_0 e^{-(R/L)t}$ and $\frac{1}{2} = e^{-(R/L)t}$

Taking natural logs of both sides of this equation gives $\ln(\frac{1}{2}) = -Rt/L$

$$t = \left(\frac{0.160 \text{ H}}{240 \text{ }\Omega}\right) \ln 2 = 4.62 \times 10^{-4} \text{ s}$$

EVALUATE: The current decays, as shown in Fig.30.13. The time constant is $\tau = L/R = 6.67 \times 10^{-4}$ s. The values of t in the problem are less than one time constant. At any instant the potential drop across the resistor (in the direction of the current) equals the potential rise across the inductor.

30.29 IDENTIFY and **SET UP:** The angular frequency is given by Eq.(30.22).

$q(t)$ and $i(t)$ are given by Eqs.(30.21) and (30.23). The energy stored in the capacitor is $U_C = \frac{1}{2}CV^2 = q^2/2C$. The energy stored in the inductor is $U_L = \frac{1}{2}Li^2$.

EXECUTE:

a) $\omega = \dfrac{1}{\sqrt{LC}} = \dfrac{1}{\sqrt{(1.50 \text{ H})(6.00 \times 10^{-5} \text{ F})}} = 105.4$ rad/s, which rounds to 105 rad/s.

The period is given by $T = \dfrac{2\pi}{\omega} = \dfrac{2\pi}{105.4 \text{ rad/s}} = 0.0596$ s

b)

$\varepsilon - \dfrac{Q}{C} = 0$

$Q = \varepsilon C = (12.0 \text{ V})(6.00 \times 10^{-5} \text{ F}) = 7.20 \times 10^{-4}$ C

c) $U = \frac{1}{2}CV^2 = \frac{1}{2}(6.00 \times 10^{-5} \text{ F})(12.0 \text{ V})^2 = 4.32 \times 10^{-3}$ J

d) $q = Q\cos(\omega t + \phi)$ (Eq.30.21).

$q = Q$ at $t = 0$ so $\phi = 0$

$q = Q\cos\omega t = (7.20 \times 10^{-4} \text{ C})\cos([105.4 \text{ rad/s}][0.0230 \text{ s}]) = -5.42 \times 10^{-4}$ C

The minus sign means that the capacitor has discharged fully and then partially charged again by the current maintained by the inductor; the plate that initially had positive charge now has negative charge and the plate that initially had negative charge now has positive charge.

e) $i = -\omega Q\sin(\omega t + \phi)$ (Eq.30.23)

$i = -(105 \text{ rad/s})(7.20 \times 10^{-4} \text{ C})\sin([105.4 \text{ rad/s}][0.0230 \text{ s}]) = -0.050$ A

or

$\dfrac{1}{2}Li^2 + \dfrac{q^2}{2C} = \dfrac{Q^2}{2C}$ gives $i = \pm\sqrt{\dfrac{1}{LC}}\sqrt{Q^2 - q^2}$ (Eq.30.26)

$i = \pm(105 \text{ rad/s})\sqrt{(7.20 \times 10^{-4} \text{ C})^2 - (-5.42 \times 10^{-4} \text{ C})^2} = \pm0.050$ A, which checks.

f) $U_C = \dfrac{q^2}{2C} = \dfrac{(-5.42 \times 10^{-4} \text{ C})^2}{2(6.00 \times 10^{-5} \text{ F})} = 2.45 \times 10^{-3}$ J

$U_L = \frac{1}{2}Li^2 = \frac{1}{2}(1.50 \text{ H})(0.050 \text{ A})^2 = 1.87 \times 10^{-3}$ J

EVALUATE: Note that $U_C + U_L = 2.45 \times 10^{-3}$ J $+ 1.87 \times 10^{-3}$ J $= 4.32 \times 10^{-3}$ J. This agrees with the total energy initially stored in the capacitor,

$U = \dfrac{Q^2}{2C} = \dfrac{(7.20 \times 10^{-4} \text{ C})^2}{2(6.00 \times 10^{-5} \text{ F})} = 4.32 \times 10^{-3}$ J.

Energy is conserved. At some times there is energy stored in both the capacitor and the inductor. When $i = 0$ all the energy is stored in the capacitor and when $q = 0$ all the energy is stored in the inductor. But at all times the total energy stored is the same.

30.33 IDENTIFY: Apply the loop rule to the circuit.

a) SET UP:

$$v_L = v_C$$

$$L\frac{di}{dt} = \frac{q}{C}$$

EXECUTE: $q = LC\frac{di}{dt} = (0.640 \text{ H})(3.60 \times 10^{-6} \text{ F})(2.80 \text{ A/s}) = 6.45 \times 10^{-6} \text{ C}$

b) $v_C = \dfrac{q}{C} = \dfrac{8.50 \times 10^{-6} \text{ C}}{3.60 \times 10^{-6} \text{ F}} = 2.36$ V

$v_L = v_C = 2.36$ V

EVALUATE: At any time the voltage across the capacitor equals in magnitude the voltage across the inductor. This relates q and di/dt.

30.41 IDENTIFY and **SET UP:** Use the equation $\omega' = \sqrt{\dfrac{1}{LC} - \dfrac{R^2}{4L^2}}$ and solve for R.

EXECUTE: Squaring both sides gives $\omega'^2 = \dfrac{1}{LC} - \dfrac{R^2}{4L^2}$.

Set $\omega'^2 = 1/6LC$ and solve for R:

$$R = \sqrt{\frac{10L}{3C}} = \sqrt{\frac{10(0.285 \text{ H})}{3(4.60 \times 10^{-4} \text{ F})}} = 45.4 \ \Omega$$

EVALUATE: For $R = 0$, $\omega' = 1/\sqrt{LC}$. As R increases, ω' decreases.

Problems

30.47 IDENTIFY and **SET UP:** Eq.(30.7) relates the rate of change of the current to the induced emf. Eq.(30.6) relates the current in the inductor to the flux through each turn. The rate of energy storage or dissipation is vi.

a) EXECUTE: $|\varepsilon| = L|\dfrac{di}{dt}|$ so $L = \dfrac{|\varepsilon|}{|di/dt|}$.

$\dfrac{di}{dt} = \dfrac{\Delta i}{\Delta t}$ (since the rate of increase is constant), so $\dfrac{di}{dt} = \dfrac{48.0 \text{ A}}{12.0 \text{ s}} = 4.00$ A/s

Then $L = \dfrac{30.0 \text{ V}}{4.00 \text{ A/s}} = 7.50$ H

b) $N\Phi_B = Li = (7.50\ \text{H})(48.0\ \text{A}) = 360\ \text{Wb}$

c) Rate at which electrical energy is being dissipated by the resistance is
$P_R = i^2 R = (48.0\ \text{A})^2 (60.0\ \Omega) = 1.38 \times 10^5\ \text{W}$

Rate at which electrical energy is being stored in the magnetic field of the inductor is

$P_L = |\varepsilon_L|i = Li\left|\dfrac{di}{dt}\right| = (7.50\ \text{H})(48.0\ \text{A})(4.00\ \text{A/s}) = 1.44 \times 10^3\ \text{W}.$

The ratio is $\dfrac{P_L}{P_R} = \dfrac{1.44 \times 10^3\ \text{W}}{1.38 \times 10^5\ \text{W}} = 0.0104.$

EVALUATE: When the current is 48.0 A, the voltage due to the resistance is $iR = 2880$ V and the voltage due to the inductance is $L|di/dt| = 30$ V. Energy is being dissipated in the resistance of the coil at a much greater rate than it is being stored in the magnetic field of the coil.

30.51 a) IDENTIFY and **SET UP:**

end view

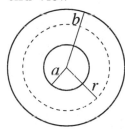

Apply Ampere's law to a circular path of radius r.
$\oint \vec{B} \cdot d\vec{l} = \mu_0 I_{\text{encl}}$

EXECUTE: $\oint \vec{B} \cdot d\vec{l} = B(2\pi r)$

$I_{\text{encl}} = i$, the current in the inner conductor

Thus $B(2\pi r) = \mu_0 i$ and $B = \dfrac{\mu_0 i}{2\pi r}$.

b) IDENTIFY and **SET UP:** Follow the procedure specified in the problem.

EXECUTE: $u = \dfrac{B^2}{2\mu_0}$

$dU = u\,dV$, where $dV = 2\pi r l\,dr$

$dU = \dfrac{1}{2\mu_0}\left(\dfrac{\mu_0 i}{2\pi r}\right)^2 (2\pi r l)\,dr = \dfrac{\mu_0 i^2 l}{4\pi r}\,dr$

c) $U = \int dU = \dfrac{\mu_0 i^2 l}{4\pi} \int_a^b \dfrac{dr}{r} = \dfrac{\mu_0 i^2 l}{4\pi}[\ln r]_a^b$

$U = \dfrac{\mu_0 i^2 l}{4\pi}(\ln b - \ln a) = \dfrac{\mu_0 i^2 l}{4\pi}\ln\left(\dfrac{b}{a}\right)$

d) Eq.(30.9): $U = \frac{1}{2}Li^2$

Part (c): $U = \frac{\mu_0 i^2 l}{4\pi} \ln\left(\frac{b}{a}\right)$

$\frac{1}{2}Li^2 = \frac{\mu_0 i^2 l}{4\pi} \ln\left(\frac{b}{a}\right)$

$L = \frac{\mu_0 l}{2\pi} \ln\left(\frac{b}{a}\right).$

EVALUATE: The value of L we obtain from these energy considerations agrees with L calculated in part (d) of Problem 30.50 by considering flux and Eq.(30.6).

30.53 **IDENTIFY** and **SET UP:** Energy density in the electric field: $u_E = \frac{1}{2}\epsilon_0 E^2$ (Eq.24.11). Energy density in the magnetic field: $u_B = B^2/2\mu_0$ (Eq.30.10). Set u_E equal to u_B and solve for B.

EXECUTE: $u_E = u_B$ so $\frac{1}{2}\epsilon_0 E^2 = B^2/2\mu_0$

$B = (\sqrt{\mu_0 \epsilon_0})E =$

$(\sqrt{(4\pi \times 10^{-7}\ \text{T}\cdot\text{m/A})(8.854 \times 10^{-12}\ \text{C}^2/\text{N}\cdot\text{m}^2)})(650\ \text{V/m}) = 2.17 \times 10^{-6}\ \text{T}$

EVALUATE: This is a very small magnetic field. The energy density of each field is $\frac{1}{2}\epsilon_0 E^2 = 1.9 \times 10^{-6}\ \text{J/m}^3$, also very small.

30.55 **IDENTIFY** and **SET UP:** Follow the procedure specified in the problem.
$L = 2.50$ H, $R = 8.00\ \Omega$, $\varepsilon = 6.00$ V $i = (\varepsilon/R)(1 - e^{-t/\tau})$, $\tau = L/R$

EXECUTE:

a) Eq.(30.9): $U_L = \frac{1}{2}Li^2$
$t = \tau$ so $i = (\varepsilon/R)(1 - e^{-1}) = (6.00\ \text{V}/8.00\ \Omega)(1 - e^{-1}) = 0.474$ A
Then $U_L = \frac{1}{2}Li^2 = \frac{1}{2}(2.50\ \text{H})(0.474\ \text{A})^2 = 0.281$ J

Exercise 30.25(c): $P_L = \dfrac{dU_L}{dt} = Li\dfrac{di}{dt}$

$i = \left(\dfrac{\varepsilon}{R}\right)(1 - e^{-t/\tau}); \quad \dfrac{di}{dt} = \left(\dfrac{\varepsilon}{L}\right)e^{-(R/L)t} = \dfrac{\varepsilon}{L}e^{-t/\tau}$

$P_L = L\left(\dfrac{\varepsilon}{R}(1 - e^{-t/\tau})\right)\left(\dfrac{\varepsilon}{L}e^{-t/\tau}\right) = \dfrac{\varepsilon^2}{R}(e^{-t/\tau} - e^{-2t\tau})$

$U_L = \displaystyle\int_0^\tau P_L\,dt = \dfrac{\varepsilon^2}{R}\int_0^\tau (e^{-t/\tau} - e^{-2t/\tau})\,dt = \dfrac{\varepsilon^2}{R}\left[-\tau e^{-t/\tau} + \dfrac{\tau}{2}e^{-2t/\tau}\right]_0^\tau$

$$U_L = -\frac{\varepsilon^2}{R}\tau \left[e^{-t/\tau} - \frac{1}{2}e^{-2t/\tau} \right]_0^\tau = \frac{\varepsilon^2}{R}\tau \left[1 - \frac{1}{2} - e^{-1} + \frac{1}{2}e^{-2} \right]$$

$$U_L = \left(\frac{\varepsilon^2}{2R} \right) \left(\frac{L}{R} \right) (1 - 2e^{-1} + e^{-2}) = \frac{1}{2} \left(\frac{\varepsilon}{R} \right)^2 L(1 - 2e^{-1} + e^{-2})$$

$$U_L = \frac{1}{2} \left(\frac{6.00\ \mathrm{V}}{8.00\ \Omega} \right)^2 (2.50\ \mathrm{H})(0.3996) = 0.281\ \mathrm{J}, \text{ which checks.}$$

b) Exercise 30.25(a): The rate at which the battery supplies energy is

$$P_\varepsilon = \varepsilon i = \varepsilon \left(\frac{\varepsilon}{R}(1 - e^{-t/\tau}) \right) = \frac{\varepsilon^2}{R}(1 - e^{-t/\tau})$$

$$U_\varepsilon = \int_0^\tau P_\varepsilon\, dt = \frac{\varepsilon^2}{R} \int_0^\tau (1 - e^{-t/\tau})dt = \frac{\varepsilon^2}{R} \left[t + \tau e^{-t/\tau} \right]_0^\tau = \left(\frac{\varepsilon^2}{R} \right)(\tau + \tau e^{-1} - \tau)$$

$$U_\varepsilon = \left(\frac{\varepsilon^2}{R} \right)\tau e^{-1} = \left(\frac{\varepsilon^2}{R} \right)\left(\frac{L}{R} \right)e^{-1} = \left(\frac{\varepsilon}{R} \right)^2 Le^{-1}$$

$$U_\varepsilon = \left(\frac{6.00\ \mathrm{V}}{8.00\ \Omega} \right)^2 (2.50\ \mathrm{H})(0.3679) = 0.517\ \mathrm{J}$$

c) $P_R = i^2 R = \left(\frac{\varepsilon^2}{R} \right)\left(1 - e^{-t/\tau} \right)^2 = \frac{\varepsilon^2}{R}(1 - 2e^{-t/\tau} + e^{-2t/\tau})$

$$U_R = \int_0^\tau P_R\, dt = \frac{\varepsilon^2}{R} \int_0^\tau (1 - 2e^{-t/\tau} + e^{-2t/\tau})dt - \frac{\varepsilon^2}{R} \left[t + 2\tau e^{-t/\tau} - \frac{\tau}{2}e^{-2t/\tau} \right]_0^\tau$$

$$U_R = \frac{\varepsilon^2}{R} \left[\tau + 2\tau e^{-1} - \frac{\tau}{2}e^{-2} - 2\tau + \frac{\tau}{2} \right] = \frac{\varepsilon^2}{R} \left[-\frac{\tau}{2} + 2\tau e^{-1} - \frac{\tau}{2}e^{-2} \right]$$

$$U_R = \left(\frac{\varepsilon^2}{2R} \right) \left(\frac{L}{R} \right) \left[-1 + 4e^{-1} - e^{-2} \right]$$

$$U_R = \left(\frac{\varepsilon}{R} \right)^2 \left(\tfrac{1}{2}L \right) \left[-1 + 4e^{-1} - e^{-2} \right] = \left(\frac{6.00\ \mathrm{V}}{8.00\ \Omega} \right)^2 \tfrac{1}{2}(2.50\ \mathrm{H})(0.3362) = 0.236\ \mathrm{J}$$

d) EVALUATE: $U_\varepsilon = U_R + U_L$. (0.517 J = 0.236 J + 0.281 J)

The energy supplied by the battery equals the sum of the energy stored in the magnetic field of the inductor and the energy dissipated in the resistance of the inductor.

30.57 IDENTIFY and **SET UP:** Follow the procedure specified in the problem. $\frac{1}{2}Li^2$ is the energy stored in the inductor and $q^2/2C$ is the energy stored in the capacitor. The equation is $-iR - L\frac{di}{dt} - \frac{q}{C} = 0$.

EXECUTE: Multiplying by $-i$ gives $i^2 R + Li\frac{di}{dt} + \frac{qi}{C} = 0$.

$$\frac{d}{dt}U_L = \frac{d}{dt}\left(\frac{1}{2}Li^2\right) = \frac{1}{2}L\frac{d}{dt}(i^2) = \frac{1}{2}L\left(2i\frac{di}{dt}\right) = Li\frac{di}{dt}, \text{ the second term}$$

$$\frac{d}{dt}U_C = \frac{d}{dt}\left(\frac{q^2}{2C}\right) = \frac{1}{2C}\frac{d}{dt}(q^2) = \frac{1}{2C}(2q)\frac{dq}{dt} = \frac{qi}{C}, \text{ the third term.}$$

$i^2 R = P_R$, the rate at which electrical energy is dissipated in the resistance.

$\frac{d}{dt}U_L = P_L$, the rate at which the amount of energy stored in the inductor is changing.

$\frac{d}{dt}U_C = P_C$, the rate at which the amount of energy stored in the capacitor is changing.

EVALUATE: The equation says that $P_R + P_L + P_C = 0$; the net rate of change of energy in the circuit is zero. Note that at any given time one of P_C or P_L is negative. If the current and U_L are increasing the charge on the capacitor and U_C are decreasing, and vice versa.

30.59 **IDENTIFY** and **SET UP:** Use $U_C = \frac{1}{2}CV_C^2$ (energy stored in a capacitor) to solve for C. Then use Eq.(30.22) and $\omega = 2\pi f$ to solve for the L that gives the desired current oscillation frequency.

EXECUTE:
$V_C = 12.0$ V; $U_C = \frac{1}{2}CV_C^2$ so $C = 2U_C/V_C^2 = 2(0.0160\text{ J})/(12.0\text{ V})^2 = 222\ \mu\text{F}$

$$f = \frac{1}{2\pi\sqrt{LC}} \text{ so } L = \frac{1}{(2\pi f)^2 C}$$

$f = 3500$ Hz gives $L = 9.31\ \mu\text{H}$

EVALUATE: f is in Hz and ω is in rad/s; we must be careful not to confuse the two.

30.63 **IDENTIFY** and **SET UP:** The current grows in the circuit as given by Eq.(30.14). In an R-L circuit the full emf initially is across the inductance and after a long time is totally across the resistance. A solenoid in a circuit is represented as a resistance in series with an inductance. Apply the loop rule to the circuit; the voltage across a resistance is given by Ohm's law.

EXECUTE:

a) In the R-L circuit the voltage across the resistor starts at zero and increases to the battery voltage. The voltage across the solenoid (inductor) starts at the battery voltage and decreases to zero. In the graph, the voltage drops, so the oscilloscope is across the solenoid.

b) At $t \to \infty$ the current in the circuit approaches its final, constant value. The voltage doesn't go to zero because the solenoid has some resistance R_L. The final voltage across the solenoid is IR_L, where I is the final current in the circuit.

c) The emf of the battery is the initial voltage across the inductor, 50 V. Just after the switch is closed, the current is zero and there is no voltage drop across any of the resistance in the circuit.

d) As $t \to \infty$, $\varepsilon - IR - IR_L = 0$

$\varepsilon = 50$ V and from the graph $IR_L = 15$ V (the final voltage across the inductor), so $IR = 35$ V and $I = (35 \text{ V})/R = 3.5$ A

e) $IR_L = 15$ V, so $R_L = (15 \text{ V})/(3.5 \text{ A}) = 4.3 \; \Omega$

$\varepsilon - V_L - iR = 0$, where V_L includes the voltage across the resistance of the solenoid.

$V_L = \varepsilon - iR$, $i = \dfrac{\varepsilon}{R_{\text{tot}}}(1 - e^{-t/\tau})$, so $V_L = \varepsilon[1 - \dfrac{R}{R_{\text{tot}}}(1 - e^{-t/\tau})]$

$\varepsilon = 50$ V, $R = 10 \; \Omega$, $R_{\text{tot}} = 14.3 \; \Omega$, so when $t = \tau$, $V_L = 27.9$ V

From the graph, V_L has this value when $t = 3.0$ ms (read approximately from the graph), so $\tau = L/R_{\text{tot}} = 3.0$ ms. Then $L = (3.0 \text{ ms})(14.3 \; \Omega) = 43$ mH.

EVALUATE: At $t = 0$ there is no current and the 50 V measured by the oscilloscope is the induced emf due to the inductance of the solenoid. As the current grows, there are voltage drops across the two resistances in the circuit. We derived an equation for V_L, the voltage across the solenoid. At $t = 0$ it gives $V_L = \varepsilon$ and at $t \to \infty$ it gives $V_L = \varepsilon R/R_{\text{tot}} = iR$.

30.65 **IDENTIFY** and **SET UP:** Just after the switch is closed, the current in each branch containing an inductor is zero and the voltage across any capacitor is zero. The inductors can be treated as breaks in the circuit and the capacitors can be replaced by wires. After a long time there is no voltage across each inductor and no current in any branch containing a capacitor. The inductors can be replaced by wires and the capacitors by breaks in the circuit.

EXECUTE:

a) Just after the switch is closed the voltage V_5 across the capacitor is zero and there is also no current through the inductor, so $V_3 = 0$. $V_2 + V_3 = V_4 = V_5$, and since $V_5 = 0$ and $V_3 = 0$, V_4 and V_2 are also zero. $V_4 = 0$ means V_3 reads zero.

V_1 then must equal 40.0 V, and this means the current read by A_1 is $(40.0 \text{ V})/(50.0 \; \Omega) = 0.800$ A.

$A_2 + A_3 + A_4 = A_1$, but $A_2 = A_3 = 0$ so $A_4 = A_1 = 0.800$ A.

$A_1 = A_4 = 0.800$ A; all other ammeters read zero.

$V_1 = 40.0$ V and all other voltmeters read zero.

b) After a long time the capacitor is fully charged so $A_4 = 0$. The current through the inductor isn't changing, so $V_2 = 0$. The currents can be calculated from the equivalent circuit that replaces the inductor by a short-circuit:

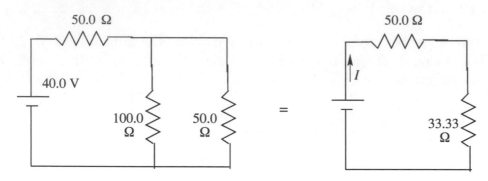

$I = (40.0 \text{ V})/(83.33 \ \Omega) = 0.480 \text{ A}; A_1$ reads 0.480 A

$V_1 = I(50.0 \ \Omega) = 24.0 \text{ V}$

The voltage across each parallel branch is $40.0 \text{ V} - 24.0 \text{ V} = 16.0 \text{ V}$

$V_2 = 0, V_3 = V_4 = V_5 = 16.0 \text{ V}$

$V_3 = 16.0 \text{ V}$ means A_2 reads 0.160 A. $V_4 = 16.0 \text{ V}$ means A_3 reads 0.320 A. A_4 reads zero. Note that $A_2 + A_3 = A_1$.

c) $V_5 = 16.0 \text{ V}$ so $Q = CV = (12.0 \ \mu\text{F})(16.0 \text{ V}) = 192 \ \mu\text{C}$

d) At $t = 0$ and $t \to \infty$, $V_2 = 0$. As the current in this branch increases from zero to 0.160 A the voltage V_2 reflects the rate of change of the current.

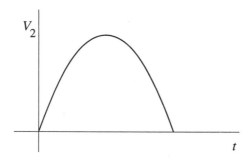

EVALUATE: This reduction of the circuit to resistor networks only apply at $t = 0$ and $t \to \infty$. At intermediate times the analysis is complicated.

30.69 IDENTIFY: Apply the loop rule to each parallel branch. The voltage across a resistor is given by iR and the voltage across an inductor is given by $L|di/dt|$. The rate of change of current through the inductor is limited.

SET UP: With S closed the circuit is

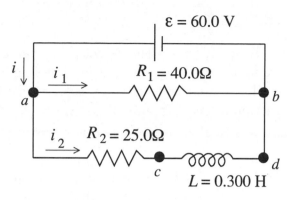

$\varepsilon = 60.0 \text{ V}$

$R_1 = 40.0\Omega$

$R_2 = 25.0\Omega$

$L = 0.300 \text{ H}$

The rate of change of the current through the inductor is limited by the induced emf. Just after the switch is closed the current in the inductor has not had time to increase from zero, so $i_2 = 0$.

EXECUTE:

a) $\varepsilon - v_{ab} = 0$, so $v_{ab} = 60.0$ V

b) The voltage drops across R, as we travel through the resistor in the direction of the current, so point a is at higher potential.

c) $i_2 = 0$ so $v_{R_2} = i_2 R_2 = 0$

$\varepsilon - v_{R_2} - v_L = 0$ so $v_L = \varepsilon = 60.0$ V

d) The voltage rises when we go from b to a through the emf, so it must drop when we go from a to b through the inductor. Point c must be at higher potential than point d.

e) After the switch has been closed a long time, $\dfrac{di_2}{dt} \rightarrow 0$ so $v_L = 0$. Then

$\varepsilon - v_{R_2} = 0$ and $i_2 R_2 = \varepsilon$ so $i_2 = \dfrac{\varepsilon}{R_2} = \dfrac{60.0 \text{ V}}{25.0 \ \Omega} = 2.40$ A.

SET UP: The rate of change of the current through the inductor is limited by the induced emf. Just after the switch is opened again the current through the inductor hasn't had time to change and is still $i_2 = 2.40$ A. The circuit is

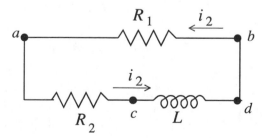

R_1 $\quad i_2$

a $\qquad\qquad b$

i_2

R_2 $\quad c \quad L$ $\qquad d$

EXECUTE:

The current through R_1 is $i_2 = 2.40$ A, in the direction b to a. Thus

$v_{ab} = -i_2 R_1 = -(2.40 \text{ A})(40.0 \ \Omega)$

$v_{ab} = -96.0$ V

f) Point where current enters resistor is at higher potential; point b is at higher potential.

g) $v_L - v_{R_1} - v_{R_2} = 0$

$v_L = v_{R_1} + v_{R_2}$

$v_{R_1} = -v_{ab} = 96.0$ V; $\quad v_{R_2} = i_2 R_2 = (2.40 \text{ A})(25.0 \ \Omega) = 60.0$ V

Then $v_L = v_{R_1} + v_{R_2} = 96.0 \text{ V} + 60.0 \text{ V} = 156 \text{ V}$.

As you travel counterclockwise around the circuit in the direction of the current, the voltage drops across each resistor, so it must rise across the inductor and point d is at higher potential than point c. The current is decreasing, so the induced emf in the inductor is directed in the direction of the current. Thus, $v_{cd} = -156 \text{ V}$.

h) Point d is at higher potential.

EVALUATE: The voltage across R_1 is constant once the switch is closed. In the branch containing R_2, just after S is closed the voltage drop is all across L and after a long time it is all across R_2. Just after S is opened the same current flows in the single loop as had been flowing through the inductor and the sum of the voltage across the resistors equals the voltage across the inductor. This voltage dies away, as the energy stored in the inductor is dissipated in the resistors.

30.71   IDENTIFY and **SET UP:** Apply the loop rule. Just after S_1 is closed, $i = 0$. After a long time i has reached its final value and $di/dt = 0$. The voltage across a resistor depends on i and the voltage across an inductor depends on di/dt.

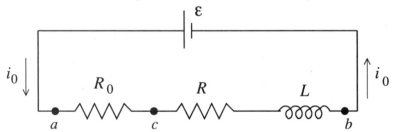

EXECUTE:

a) At time $t = 0$, $i_0 = 0$ so $v_{ac} = i_0 R_0 = 0$. By the loop rule $\varepsilon - v_{ac} - v_{cb} = 0$, so $v_{cb} = \varepsilon - v_{ac} = \varepsilon = 36.0 \text{ V}$. ($i_0 R = 0$ so this potential difference of 36.0 V is across the inductor and is an induced emf produced by the changing current.)

b) After a long time $\dfrac{di_0}{dt} \to 0$ so the potential $-L\dfrac{di_0}{dt}$ across the inductor becomes zero. The loop rule gives $\varepsilon - i_0(R_0 + R) = 0$.

$$i_0 = \frac{\varepsilon}{R_0 + R} = \frac{36.0 \text{ V}}{50.0 \text{ }\Omega + 150 \text{ }\Omega} = 0.180 \text{ A}$$

$$v_{ac} = i_0 R_0 = (0.180 \text{ A})(50.0 \text{ }\Omega) = 9.0 \text{ V}$$

Thus $v_{cb} = i_0 R + L\dfrac{di_0}{dt} = (0.180 \text{ A})(150 \text{ }\Omega) + 0 = 27.0 \text{ V}$ (Note that $v_{ac} + v_{cb} = \varepsilon$.)

c) $\varepsilon - v_{ac} - v_{cb} = 0$

$$\varepsilon - iR_0 - iR - L\frac{di}{dt} = 0$$

$$L\frac{di}{dt} = \varepsilon - i(R_0 + R) \text{ and } \left(\frac{L}{R + R_0}\right)\frac{di}{dt} = -i + \frac{\varepsilon}{R + R_0}$$

$$\frac{di}{-i + \varepsilon/(R + R_0)} = \left(\frac{R + R_0}{L}\right)dt$$

Integrate from $t = 0$, when $i = 0$, to t, when $i = i_0$:

$$\int_0^{i_0} \frac{di}{-i + \varepsilon/(R + R_0)} = \frac{R + R_0}{L}\int_0^t dt = -\ln\left[-i + \frac{\varepsilon}{R + R_0}\right]_0^{i_0} = \left(\frac{R + R_0}{L}\right)t, \text{ so}$$

$$\ln\left(-i_0 + \frac{\varepsilon}{R + R_0}\right) - \ln\left(\frac{\varepsilon}{R + R_0}\right) = -\left(\frac{R + R_0}{L}\right)t$$

$$\ln\left(\frac{-i_0 + \varepsilon/(R + R_0)}{\varepsilon/(R + R_0)}\right) = -\left(\frac{R + R_0}{L}\right)t$$

Taking exponentials of both sides gives $\dfrac{-i_0 + \varepsilon/(R + R_0)}{\varepsilon/(R + R_0)} = e^{-(R+R_0)t/L}$ and

$$i_0 = \frac{\varepsilon}{R + R_0}\left(1 - e^{-(R+R_0)t/L}\right)$$

Substituting in the numerical values gives

$$i_0 = \frac{36.0 \text{ V}}{50 \ \Omega + 150 \ \Omega}\left(1 - e^{-(200 \ \Omega/4.00 \text{ H})t}\right) = (0.180 \text{ A})\left(1 - e^{-t/0.020 \text{ s}}\right)$$

At $t \to 0$, $i_0 = (0.180 \text{ A})(1 - 1) = 0$ (agrees with part (a)).
At $t \to \infty$, $i_0 = (0.180 \text{ A})(1 - 0) = 0.180 \text{ A}$ (agrees with part (b)).

$$v_{ac} = i_0 R_0 = \frac{\varepsilon R_0}{R + R_0}\left(1 - e^{-(R+R_0)t/L}\right) = 9.0 \text{ V}\left(1 - e^{-t/0.020 \text{ s}}\right)$$

$$v_{cb} = \varepsilon - v_{ac} = 36.0 \text{ V} - 9.0 \text{ V}\left(1 - e^{-t/0.020 \text{ s}}\right) = 9.0 \text{ V}\left(3.00 + e^{-t/0.020 \text{ s}}\right)$$

At $t \to 0$, $v_{ac} = 0$, $v_{cb} = 36.0 \text{ V}$ (agrees with part (a)).
At $t \to \infty$, $v_{ac} = 9.0 \text{ V}$, $v_{cb} = 27.0 \text{ V}$ (agrees with part (b)).

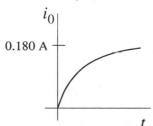

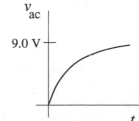

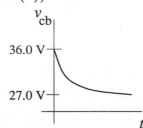

EVALUATE: The expression for $i(t)$ we derived becomes Eq.(30.14) if the two resistors R_0 and R in series are replaced by a single equivalent resistance $R_0 + R$.

30.73 IDENTIFY and **SET UP:** Just after the switch is closed there is no current in the inductors. After a long time the current is steady and there is no voltage across each inductor. For intermediate times, use the results of Problem 30.49 to replace the network of inductors by a single equivalent inductor.

EXECUTE:

a) Just after the switch is closed there is no current in the inductors. There is no current in the resistors so there is no voltage drop across either resistor. A reads zero and V reads 20.0 V.

b) After a long time the currents are no longer changing, there is no voltage across the inductors, and the inductors can be replaced by short-circuits. The circuit becomes equivalent to

$$I = (20.0 \text{ V})/(75.0 \text{ }\Omega) = 0.267 \text{ A}$$

The voltage between points a and b is zero, so the voltmeter reads zero.

c) Use the results of problem 30.49 to combine the inductor network into its equivalent:

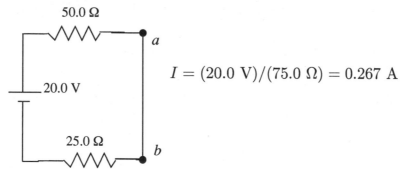

$R = 75.0 \text{ }\Omega$ is the equivalent resistance.

Eq.(30.14) says $i = (\varepsilon/R)(1 - e^{-t/\tau})$, with $\tau = L/R = (10.8 \text{ mH}/(75.0 \text{ }\Omega) = 0.144$ ms

$\varepsilon = 20.0 \text{ V}$, $R = 75.0 \text{ }\Omega$, $t = 0.115 \text{ ms}$, so $i = 0.147 \text{ A}$

$V_R = iR = (0.147 \text{ A})(75.0 \text{ }\Omega) = 11.0 \text{ V}$

$20.0 \text{ V} - V_R - V_L = 0$ so $V_L = 20.0 \text{ V} - V_R = 9.0 \text{ V}$

EVALUATE: With the three inductors replaced by their equivalent, the circuit is an *R-L* circuit like the one analyzed in the first part of Section 30.4. The current through the equivalent inductor has the behavior shown in Fig.30.12. The voltage across the equivalent inductor is intially ε and falls to zero, with a time constant $\tau = L/R$.

30.75 a) IDENTIFY and **SET UP:** With switch S closed the circuit is

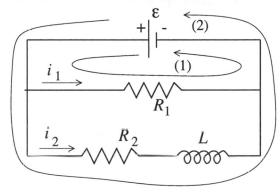

Apply the loop rule to loops 1 and 2.
EXECUTE:

<u>loop 1</u>
$$\varepsilon - i_1 R_1 = 0$$

$$i_1 = \frac{\varepsilon}{R_1} \text{ (independent of } t)$$

<u>loop (2)</u>

$$\varepsilon - i_2 R_2 - L\frac{di_2}{dt} = 0$$

This is in the form of equation (30.12), so the solution is analogous to Eq.(30.14):

$$i_2 = \frac{\varepsilon}{R_2}\left(1 - e^{-R_2 t/L}\right)$$

b) EVALUATE: The expressions derived in part (a) give that as $t \to \infty$, $i_1 = \dfrac{\varepsilon}{R_1}$ and $i_2 = \dfrac{\varepsilon}{R_2}$. Since $\dfrac{di_2}{dt} \to 0$ at steady-state, the inductance then has no effect on the circuit.

The current in R_1 is constant; the current in R_2 starts at zero and rises to ε/R_2.

c) IDENTIFY and **SET UP:** The circuit now becomes

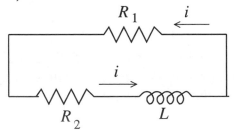

Let $t = 0$ now be when S is opened.

At $t = 0$, $i = \dfrac{\varepsilon}{R_2}$.

Apply the loop rule to the single current loop.

EXECUTE: $-i(R_1 + R_2) - L\dfrac{di}{dt} = 0$. (Now $\dfrac{di}{dt}$ is negative.)

$$L\frac{di}{dt} = -i(R_1 + R_2) \text{ gives } \frac{di}{i} = -\left(\frac{R_1 + R_2}{L}\right) dt$$

Integrate from $t = 0$, when $i = I_0 = \varepsilon/R_2$, to t.

$$\int_{I_0}^{i} \frac{di}{i} = -\left(\frac{R_1 + R_2}{L}\right) \int_0^t dt \text{ and } \ln\left(\frac{i}{I_0}\right) = -\left(\frac{R_1 + R_2}{L}\right) t$$

Taking exponentials of both sides of this equation gives

$$i = I_0 e^{-(R_1 + R_2)t/L} = \frac{\varepsilon}{R_2} e^{-(R_1 + R_2)t/L}$$

d) IDENTIFY and **SET UP:** Use the equation derived in part (c) and solve for R_2 and ε.

EXECUTE: $L = 22.0$ H

$$P_{R_1} = \frac{V^2}{R_1} = 40.0 \text{ W gives } R_1 = \frac{V^2}{P_{R_1}} = \frac{(120 \text{ V})^2}{40.0 \text{ W}} = 360 \ \Omega.$$

We are asked to find R_2 and ε. Use the expression derived in part (c).
$I_0 = 0.600$ A so $\varepsilon/R_2 = 0.600$ A

$i = 0.150$ A when $t = 0.080$ s, so $i = \frac{\varepsilon}{R_2} e^{-(R_1 + R_2)t/L}$ gives

$0.150 \text{ A} = (0.600 \text{ A})e^{-(R_1 + R_2)t/L}$

$\frac{1}{4} = e^{-(R_1 + R_2)t/L}$ so $\ln 4 = (R_1 + R_2)t/L$

$$R_2 = \frac{L \ln 4}{t} - R_1 = \frac{(22.0 \text{ H}) \ln 4}{0.080 \text{ s}} - 360 \ \Omega = 381.2 \ \Omega - 360 \ \Omega = 21.2 \ \Omega$$

Then $\varepsilon = (0.600 \text{ A})R_2 = (0.600 \text{ A})(21.2 \ \Omega) = 12.7$ V.

e) IDENTIFY and **SET UP:** Use the expressions derived in part (a).

EXECUTE: The current through the light bulb before the switch is opened is
$$i_1 = \frac{\varepsilon}{R_1} = \frac{12.7 \text{ V}}{360 \ \Omega} = 0.0353 \text{ A}$$

EVALUATE: When the switch is opened the current through the light bulb jumps from 0.0353 A to 0.600 A. Since the electrical power dissipated in the bulb (brightness) depends on i^2, the bulb suddenly becomes much brighter.

CHAPTER 31
ALTERNATING CURRENT

Exercises 5, 7, 9, 13, 21, 23, 25, 27, 29, 31, 33
Problems 37, 39, 41, 43, 45, 57, 59, 61

Exercises

31.5 **IDENTIFY** and **SET UP:** Use Eqs.(31.12) and (31.18).

EXECUTE:

a) $X_L = \omega L = 2\pi f L = 2\pi(80.0 \text{ Hz})(3.00 \text{ H}) = 1510 \ \Omega$

b) $X_L = 2\pi f L$ gives $L = \dfrac{X_L}{2\pi f} = \dfrac{120 \ \Omega}{2\pi(80.0 \text{ Hz})} = 0.239 \text{ H}$

c) $X_C = \dfrac{1}{\omega C} = \dfrac{1}{2\pi f C} = \dfrac{1}{2\pi(80.0 \text{ Hz})(4.00 \times 10^{-6} \text{ F})} = 497 \ \Omega$

d) $X_C = \dfrac{1}{2\pi f C}$ gives $C = \dfrac{1}{2\pi f X_C} = \dfrac{1}{2\pi(80.0 \text{ Hz})(120 \ \Omega)} = 1.66 \times 10^{-5} \text{ F}$

EVALUATE: X_L increases when L increases; X_C decreases when C increases.

31.7 **IDENTIFY** and **SET UP:** Apply Eqs.(31.18) and (31.19).

EXECUTE: $V = I X_C$ so $X_C = \dfrac{V}{I} = \dfrac{170 \text{ V}}{0.850 \text{ A}} = 200 \ \Omega$

$X_C = \dfrac{1}{\omega C}$ gives $C = \dfrac{1}{2\pi f X_C} = \dfrac{1}{2\pi(60.0 \text{ Hz})(200 \ \Omega)} = 1.33 \times 10^{-5} \text{ F} = 13.3 \ \mu\text{F}$

EVALUATE: The reactance relates the voltage amplitude to the current amplitude and is similar to Ohm's law.

31.9 **IDENTIFY** and **SET UP:** The voltage and current for a resistor are related by $v_R = iR$. Deduce the frequency of the voltage and use this in Eq.(31.12) to calculate the inductive reactance. Eq.(31.10) gives the voltage across the inductor.

EXECUTE:

a) $v_R = (3.80 \text{ V}) \cos[(720 \text{ rad/s})t]$

$v_R = iR$, so $i = \dfrac{v_R}{R} = \left(\dfrac{3.80 \text{ V}}{150 \ \Omega}\right) \cos[(720 \text{ rad/s})t] = (0.0253 \text{ A}) \cos[(720 \text{ rad/s})t]$

b) $X_L = \omega L$

$\omega = 720 \text{ rad/s}$, $L = 0.250 \text{ H}$, so $X_L = \omega L = (720 \text{ rad/s})(0.250 \text{ H}) = 180 \ \Omega$

c) If $i = I \cos \omega t$ then $v_L = V_L \cos(\omega t + 90°)$ (from Eq.31.10).

$V_L = I \omega L = I X_L = (0.02533 \text{ A})(180 \text{ } \Omega) = 4.56 \text{ V}$

$v_L = (4.56 \text{ V}) \cos[(720 \text{ rad/s})t + 90°]$

But $\cos(a + 90°) = -\sin a$ (Appendix B), so $v_L = -(4.56 \text{ V}) \sin[(720 \text{ rad/s})t]$.

EVALUATE: The current is the same in the resistor and inductor and the voltages are 90° out of phase, with the voltage across the inductor leading.

31.13 **IDENTIFY** and **SET UP:** Calculate the impendance of the circuit and use Eq.(31.22) to find the current amplitude. The voltage amplitudes across each circuit element are given by Eqs.(31.7), (31.13), and (31.19). The phase angle is calculated using Eq.(31.24).

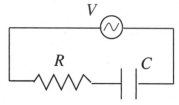

No inductor means $X_L = 0$
$R = 200 \text{ } \Omega$, $C = 6.00 \times 10^{-6} \text{ F}$,
$V = 30.0 \text{ V}$, $\omega = 250 \text{ rad/s}$

EXECUTE:

a) $X_C = \dfrac{1}{\omega C} = \dfrac{1}{(250 \text{ rad/s})(6.00 \times 10^{-6} \text{ F})} = 666.7 \text{ } \Omega$

$Z = \sqrt{R^2 + (X_L - X_C)^2} = \sqrt{(200 \text{ } \Omega)^2 + (666.7 \text{ } \Omega)^2} = 696 \text{ } \Omega$

b) $I = \dfrac{V}{Z} = \dfrac{30.0 \text{ V}}{696 \text{ } \Omega} = 0.0431 \text{ A} = 43.1 \text{ mA}$

c) Voltage amplitude across the resistor: $V_R = IR = (0.0431 \text{ A})(200 \text{ } \Omega) = 8.62 \text{ V}$

Voltage amplitude across the capacito: $V_C = IX_C = (0.0431 \text{ A})(666.7 \text{ } \Omega) = 28.7 \text{ V}$

d) $\tan \phi = \dfrac{X_L - X_C}{R} = \dfrac{0 - 666.7 \text{ } \Omega}{200 \text{ } \Omega} = -3.333$ so $\phi = -73.3°$

The phase angle is negative, so the source voltage lags behind the current.

e) The phasor diagram is qualitatively

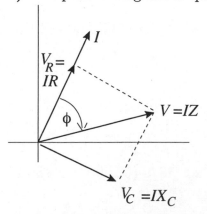

EVALUATE: The voltage across the resistor is in phase with the current and the capacitor voltage lags the current by 90°. The presence of the capacitor causes the source voltage to lag behind the current. Note that $V_R + V_C > V$. The instantaneous voltages in the circuit obey the loop rule at all times but because of the phase differences the voltage amplitudes do not.

31.21 **IDENTIFY** and **SET UP:** Use the equation the preceeds Eq.(31.20):
$V^2 = V_R^2 + (V_L - V_C)^2$
EXECUTE: $V = \sqrt{(30.0 \text{ V})^2 + (50.0 \text{ V} - 90.0 \text{ V})^2} = 50.0 \text{ V}$

EVALUATE: The equation follows directly from the phasor diagrams of Fig.31.9 (b or c). Note that the voltage amplitudes do not simply add to give 170.0 V for the source voltage.

31.23 **IDENTIFY:** The power factor is $\cos\phi$, where ϕ is the phase angle in Fig.31.9. The average power is given by Eq.(31.31). Use the result of part (a) to rewrite this expression.

a) SET UP:

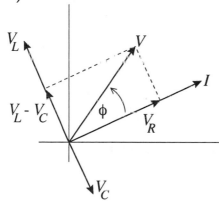

EXECUTE:
From the diagram

$$\cos\phi = \frac{V_R}{V} = \frac{IR}{IZ} = \frac{R}{Z},$$

as was to be shown.

b) $P_{av} = V_{rms}I_{rms}\cos\phi = V_{rms}I_{rms}\left(\frac{R}{Z}\right) = \left(\frac{V_{rms}}{Z}\right)I_{rms}R.$

But $\dfrac{V_{rms}}{Z} = I_{rms}$, so $P_{av} = I_{rms}^2 R.$

EVALUATE: In an L-R-C circuit, electrical energy is stored and released in the inductor and capacitor but none is dissipated in either of these circuit elements. The power delivered by the source equals the power dissipated in the resistor.

31.25 **IDENTIFY** and **SET UP:** Use the equations of Section 31.3 to calculate ϕ, Z and V_{rms}. The average power delivered by the source is given by Eq.(31.31) and the average power dissipated in the resistor is $I_{rms}^2 R$
EXECUTE:
a) $X_L = \omega L = 2\pi f L = 2\pi(400 \text{ Hz})(0.120 \text{ H}) = 301.6 \text{ }\Omega$

$$X_C = \frac{1}{\omega C} = \frac{1}{2\pi f C} = \frac{1}{2\pi (400 \text{ Hz})(7.3 \times 10^{-6} \text{ Hz})} = 54.51 \text{ } \Omega$$

$$\tan \phi = \frac{X_L - X_C}{R} = \frac{301.6 \text{ } \Omega - 54.41 \text{ } \Omega}{240 \text{ } \Omega}, \text{ so } \phi = +45.8°.$$

The power factor is $\cos \phi = +0.697$.

b) $Z = \sqrt{R^2 + (X_L - X_C)^2} = \sqrt{(240 \text{ } \Omega)^2 + (301.6 \text{ } \Omega - 54.51 \text{ } \Omega)^2} = 344 \text{ } \Omega$

c) $V_{\text{rms}} = I_{\text{rms}} Z = (0.450 \text{ A})(344 \text{ } \Omega) = 155 \text{ V}$

d) $P_{\text{av}} = I_{\text{rms}} V_{\text{rms}} \cos \phi = (0.450 \text{ A})(155 \text{ V})(0.697) = 48.6 \text{ W}$

e) $P_{\text{av}} = I_{\text{rms}}^2 R = (0.450 \text{ A})^2 (240 \text{ } \Omega) = 48.6 \text{ W}$

EVALUATE: The average electrical power delivered by the source equals the average electrical power consumed in the resistor.

f) All the energy stored in the capacitor during one cycle of the current is released back to the circuit in another part of the cycle. There is no net dissipation of energy in the capacitor.

g) The answer is the same as for the capacitor. Energy is repeatedly being stored and released in the inductor, but no net energy is dissipated there.

31.27 IDENTIFY and **SET UP:** At the resonance frequency, $Z = R$. Use that $V = IZ$, $V_R = IR$, $V_L = IX_L$ and $V_C = IX_C$. P_{av} is given by Eq.(31.31).

a) EXECUTE: $V = IZ = IR = (0.500 \text{ A})(300 \text{ } \Omega) = 150 \text{ V}$

b) $V_R = IR = 150 \text{ V}$
$X_L = \omega L = L(1/\sqrt{LC}) = \sqrt{L/C} = 2582 \text{ } \Omega;$ $V_L = IX_L = 1290 \text{ V}$
$X_C = 1/(\omega C) = \sqrt{L/C} = 2582 \text{ } \Omega;$ $V_C = IX_C = 1290 \text{ V}$

c) $P_{\text{av}} = \frac{1}{2} VI \cos \phi = \frac{1}{2} I^2 R$, since $V = IR$ and $\cos \phi = 1$ at resonance.
$P_{\text{av}} = \frac{1}{2}(0.500 \text{ A})^2 (300 \text{ } \Omega) = 37.5 \text{ W}$

EVALUATE: At resonance $V_L = V_C$. Note that $V_L + V_C > V$. However, at any instant $v_L + v_C = 0$.

31.29 IDENTIFY and **SET UP:** At resonance $X_L = X_C$, $\phi = 0$ and $Z = R$.
$R = 150 \text{ } \Omega$, $L = 0.750 \text{ H}$, $C = 0.0180 \text{ } \mu\text{F}$, $V = 150 \text{ V}$
EXECUTE:

a) At the resonance frequency $X_L = X_C$ and from $\tan \phi = \dfrac{X_L - X_C}{R}$ we have that
$\phi = 0°$ and the power factor is $\cos \phi = 1.00$.

b) $P_{av} = \frac{1}{2}VI \cos \phi$ (Eq.31.31)

At the resonance frequency $Z = R$, so $I = \dfrac{V}{Z} = \dfrac{V}{R}$

$$P_{av} = \tfrac{1}{2}V\left(\dfrac{V}{R}\right)\cos\phi = \tfrac{1}{2}\dfrac{V^2}{R} = \dfrac{1}{2}\dfrac{(150\text{ V})^2}{150\ \Omega} = 75.0\text{ W}$$

c) EVALUATE: When C and f are changed but the circuit is kept on resonance, nothing changes in $P_{av} = V^2/(2R)$, so the average power is unchanged: $P_{av} = 75.0$ W. The resonance frequency changes but since $Z = R$ at resonance the current doesn't change.

31.31 IDENTIFY and **SET UP:** Calculate the current amplitude and use this to find the voltage amplitude across each circuit element. V_4 measures the voltage across the L-C combination; take account of the relative phases of v_C and v_L when calculating this voltage amplitude.

EXECUTE: $R = 200\ \Omega$, $L = 0.400$ H, $C = 6.00\ \mu$F

a) The resonant angular frequency is given by Eq.(31.32)

$$\omega_0 = \frac{1}{\sqrt{LC}} = \frac{1}{\sqrt{(0.400\text{ H})(6.00\times 10^{-6}\text{ F})}} = 645\text{ rad/s}; \quad f = \frac{\omega}{2\pi} = 103\text{ Hz}$$

b) At resonance $X_L = X_C$, so $\tan\phi = \dfrac{X_L - X_C}{R} = 0$ and $\phi = 0$. The source voltage and the current in the circuit are in phase.

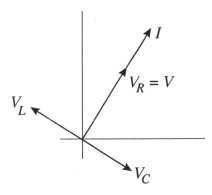

c) $X_L = \omega L = (645\text{ rad/s})(0.400\text{ H}) = 258\ \Omega$

$$X_C = \frac{1}{\omega C} = \frac{1}{(645\text{ rad/s})(6.00\times 10^{-6}\text{ F})} = 258\ \Omega$$

$X_L = X_C$ gives $Z = \sqrt{R^2 + (X_L - X_C)^2} = R = 200\ \Omega$

$$I = \frac{V}{Z} = \frac{30.0\text{ V}}{200\ \Omega} = 0.150\text{ A}; \quad I_{rms} = \frac{I}{\sqrt{2}} = 0.1061\text{ A}$$

V_1 reads $V_{R,\text{rms}} = I_{\text{rms}}R = (0.1061 \text{ A})(200 \text{ }\Omega) = 21.2$ V

V_2 reads $V_{L,\text{rms}} = I_{\text{rms}}X_L = (0.1061 \text{ A})(258 \text{ }\Omega) = 27.4$ V

V_3 reads $V_{C,\text{rms}} = I_{\text{rms}}X_C = (0.1061 \text{ A})(258 \text{ }\Omega) = 27.4$ V

V_4 reads $(V_L - V_C)_{\text{rms}} = I_{\text{rms}}(X_L - X_C) = 0$. At any instant the voltages across the inductor and capacitor are equal and opposite and sum to zero.

V_5 reads $V_{\text{rms}} = 30.0 \text{ V}/\sqrt{2} = 21.2$ V, the same as V_1.

d) $\omega_0 = \dfrac{1}{\sqrt{LC}}$ is independent of R, so $\omega_0 = 645$ rad/s and $f = 103$ Hz, the same as when $R = 200 \text{ }\Omega$.

e) At resonance $X_L = X_C$ and $Z = R$.

$$I_{\text{rms}} = \frac{V_{\text{rms}}}{Z} = \frac{V_{\text{rms}}}{R} = \frac{21.2 \text{ V}}{100 \text{ }\Omega} = 0.212 \text{ A}.$$

The current at resonance is inversely proportional to the resistance so increases by a factor of 2 when the resistance is decreased by a factor of 2.

EVALUATE: At resonance $v_L + v_C = 0$ at all t. Thus $v_R = v$ and $V_R = V$, the source voltage amplitude. Reducing R has no effect on the resonance frequency but decreases Z and increases I.

31.33 **IDENTIFY** and **SET UP:** Eq.(31.35) relates the primary and secondary voltages to the number of turns in each. $I = V/R$ and the power consumed in the resistive load is $I_{\text{rms}}^2 = V_{\text{rms}}^2/R$.

EXECUTE:

a) $\dfrac{V_2}{V_1} = \dfrac{N_2}{N_1}$ so $\dfrac{N_1}{N_2} = \dfrac{V_1}{V_2} = \dfrac{120 \text{ V}}{12.0 \text{ V}} = 10$

b) $I_2 = \dfrac{V_2}{R} = \dfrac{12.0 \text{ V}}{5.00 \text{ }\Omega} = 2.40$ A

c) $P_{\text{av}} = I_2^2 R = (2.40 \text{ A})^2 (5.00 \text{ }\Omega) = 28.8$ W

d) The power drawn from the line by the transformer is the 28.8 W that is delivered by the load.

$$P_{\text{av}} = \frac{V^2}{R} \text{ so } R = \frac{V^2}{P_{\text{av}}} = \frac{(120 \text{ V})^2}{28.8 \text{ W}} = 500 \text{ }\Omega$$

And $\left(\dfrac{N_1}{N_2}\right)^2 (5.00 \text{ }\Omega) = (10)^2 (5.00 \text{ }\Omega) = 500 \text{ }\Omega$, as was to be shown.

EVALUATE: The resistance is "transformed". A load of resistance R connected to the secondary draws the same power as a resistance $(N_1/N_2)^2 R$ connected directly to the supply line, without using the transformer.

Problems

31.37 IDENTIFY and **SET UP:** Use Eq.(31.24) to relate L and R to ϕ.
The voltage across the coil leads the current in it by 52.3°, so $\phi = +52.3°$.

EXECUTE: $\tan \phi = \dfrac{X_L - X_C}{R}$. But there is no capacitance in the circuit so
$X_C = 0$.

Thus $\tan \phi = \dfrac{X_L}{R}$ and $X_L = R \tan \phi = (48.0 \ \Omega) \tan 52.3° = 62.1 \ \Omega$.

$X_L = \omega L = 2\pi f L$ so $L = \dfrac{X_L}{2\pi f} = \dfrac{62.1 \ \Omega}{2\pi (80.0 \ \text{Hz})} = 0.124 \ \text{H}$.

EVALUATE: $\phi > 45°$ when $(X_L - X_C) > R$, which is the case here.

31.39 IDENTIFY and **SET UP:** The rectified current equals the absolute value
of the current i. Evaluate the integral as specified in the problem.

EXECUTE:

a) From Fig.31.2b, the rectified current is zero at the same values of t for which
the sinusoidal current is zero. At these t, $\cos \omega t = 0$ and $\omega t = \pm \pi/2, \pm 3\pi/2, \ldots$.

The two smallest positive times are $t_1 = \pi/2\omega$, $t_2 = 3\pi/2\omega$.

b) $A = \left| \displaystyle\int_{t_1}^{t_2} i \, dt \right| = - \displaystyle\int_{t_1}^{t_2} I \cos \omega t \, dt = -I \left[\dfrac{1}{\omega} \sin \omega t \right]_{t_1}^{t_2} = -\dfrac{I}{\omega} (\sin \omega t_2 - \sin \omega t_1)$

$\sin \omega t_1 = \sin[\omega(\pi/2\omega)] = \sin(\pi/2) = 1$
$\sin \omega t_2 = \sin[\omega(3\pi/2\omega)] = \sin(3\pi/2) = -1$

$A = - \left(\dfrac{I}{\omega} \right)(1 - (-1)) = \dfrac{2I}{\omega}$

c) $I_{\text{rav}}(t_2 - t_1) = 2I/\omega$

$I_{\text{rav}} = \dfrac{2I}{\omega(t_2 - t_1)} = \dfrac{2I}{\omega(3\pi/2\omega - \pi/2\omega)} = \dfrac{2I}{\pi}$, which is Eq.(31.3).

EVALUATE: We have shown that Eq.(31.3) is correct. The average rectified current is less than the current amplitude I, since the rectified current varies between 0 and I. The average of the current is zero, since it has both positive and negative values.

31.41 a) IDENTIFY and **SET UP:** Source voltage lags current so it must
be that $X_C > X_L$ and we must add an inductor in series with the circuit. When

$X_C = X_L$ the power factor has its maximum value of unity, so calculate the additional L needed to raise X_L to equal X_C.

b) EXECUTE: power factor $\cos\phi$ equals 1 so $\phi = 0$ and $X_C = X_L$.

Calculate the present value of $X_C - X_L$ to see how much more X_L is needed:
$R = Z\cos\phi = (60.0\ \Omega)(0.720) = 43.2\ \Omega$

$\tan\phi = \dfrac{X_L - X_C}{R}$ so $X_L - X_C = R\tan\phi$

$\cos\phi = 0.720$ gives $\phi = -43.95°$ (ϕ is negative since the voltage lags the current)
Then $X_L - X_C = R\tan\phi = (43.2\ \Omega)\tan(-43.95°) = -41.64\ \Omega$.

Therefore need to add $41.64\ \Omega$ of X_L.
$X_L = \omega L = 2\pi f L$ and $L = \dfrac{X_L}{2\pi f} = \dfrac{41.64\ \Omega}{2\pi(50.0\ \text{Hz})} = 0.133\ \text{H}$, amount of inductance to add.

EVALUATE: From the information given we can't calculate the original value of L in the circuit, just how much to add. When this L is added the current in the circuit will increase.

31.43 IDENTIFY and **SET UP:** Calculate Z and then I, from Eq.(31.22). Eq.(24.2) allows us to calculate the maximum charge on the capacitor from V_C, the maximum voltage between its plates.

a) EXECUTE: $\omega_0 = 1/\sqrt{LC} = 3162\ \text{rad/s}$; $\omega = 2\omega_0 = 6324\ \text{rad/s}$
$X_L = \omega L = 31.62\ \Omega$; $X_C = 1/(\omega C) = 7.906\ \Omega$
$Z = \sqrt{R^2 + (X_L - X_C)^2} = X_L - X_C = 23.71\ \Omega$
$I = V/Z = (5.00 \times 10^{-3}\ \text{V})/(23.71\ \Omega) = 2.108 \times 10^{-4}\ \text{A}$
$V_C = IX_C = 1.667 \times 10^{-3}\ \text{V}$; this is the maximum voltage across the capacitor.
$Q = CV_C = (20.0 \times 10^{-6}\ \text{F})(1.667 \times 10^{-3}\ \text{V}) = 33.3\ \text{nC}$

b) In part (a) we found $I = 0.211\ \text{mA}$

c) EVALUATE: $X_L > X_C$ and $R = 0$ gives that the source and inductor voltages are in phase; the voltage across the capacitor lags the source and inductor voltages by 180°. It is instructive to draw the phasor diagram.

31.45 IDENTIFY and **SET UP:** Express Z and I in terms of ω, L, C and R.
The voltages across the resistor and the inductor are 90° out of phase, so $V_{out} = \sqrt{V_R^2 + V_L^2}$.

EXECUTE:

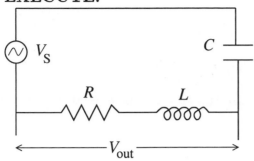

$$X_L = \omega L, \quad X_C = \frac{1}{\omega C}$$

$$Z = \sqrt{R^2 + (\omega L - \frac{1}{\omega C})^2}$$

$$I = \frac{V_s}{Z} = \frac{V_s}{\sqrt{R^2 + (\omega L - \frac{1}{\omega C})^2}}$$

$$V_{out} = I\sqrt{R^2 + X_L^2} = I\sqrt{R^2 + \omega^2 L^2} = V_s\sqrt{\frac{R^2 + \omega^2 L^2}{R^2 + (\omega L - \frac{1}{\omega C})^2}}$$

$$\frac{V_{out}}{V_s} = \sqrt{\frac{R^2 + \omega^2 L^2}{R^2 + (\omega L - \frac{1}{\omega C})^2}}$$

<u>ω small</u>

As ω gets small, $R^2 + (\omega L - \frac{1}{\omega C})^2 \rightarrow \frac{1}{\omega^2 C^2}$, $R^2 + \omega^2 L^2 \rightarrow R^2$

Therefore $\frac{V_{out}}{V_s} \rightarrow \sqrt{\frac{R^2}{(1/\omega^2 C^2)}} = \omega RC$ as ω becomes small.

<u>ω large</u>

As ω gets large, $R^2 + (\omega L - \frac{1}{\omega C})^2 \rightarrow R^2 + \omega^2 L^2 \rightarrow \omega^2 L^2$, $R^2 + \omega^2 L^2 \rightarrow \omega^2 L^2$

Therefore $\frac{V_{out}}{V_s} \rightarrow \sqrt{\frac{\omega^2 L^2}{\omega^2 L^2}} = 1$ as ω becomes large.

EVALUATE: $V_{out}/V_s \rightarrow 0$ as ω becomes small, so there is V_{out} only when the frequency ω of V_s is large. If the source voltage contains a number of frequency components, only the high frequency ones are passed by this filter.

31.57 IDENTIFY: We know R, X_C and ϕ so Eq.(31.24) tells us X_L. Use $P_{av} = I_{rms}^2 R$ from Exercise 31.23 to calculate I_{rms}. Then calculate Z and use Eq.(31.26) to calculate V_{rms} for the source.

SET UP: Source voltage lags current so $\phi = -54.0°$. $X_C = 350 \ \Omega$, $R = 180 \ \Omega$, $P_{av} = 140 \ W$

EXECUTE:

a) $\tan\phi = \dfrac{X_L - X_C}{R}$

$X_L = R\tan\phi + X_C = (180\ \Omega)\tan(-54.0°) + 350\ \Omega = -248\ \Omega + 350\ \Omega = 102\ \Omega$

b) $P_{av} = V_{rms}I_{rms}\cos\phi = I_{rms}^2 R$ (Exercise 31.23).

$I_{rms} = \sqrt{\dfrac{P_{av}}{R}} = \sqrt{\dfrac{140\ \text{W}}{180\ \Omega}} = 0.882\ \text{A}$

c) $Z = \sqrt{R^2 + (X_L - X_C)^2} = \sqrt{(180\ \Omega)^2 + (102\ \Omega - 350\ \Omega)^2} = 306\ \Omega$

$V_{rms} = I_{rms}Z = (0.882\ \text{A})(306\ \Omega) = 270\ \text{V}.$

EVALUATE: We could also use Eq.(31.31): $P_{av} = V_{rms}I_{rms}\cos\phi$

$V_{rms} = \dfrac{P_{av}}{I_{rms}\cos\phi} = \dfrac{140\ \text{W}}{(0.882\ \text{A})\cos(-54.0°)} = 270\ \text{V}$, which agrees. The source voltage lags the current when $X_C > X_L$, and this agrees with what we found.

31.59 **IDENTIFY** and **SET UP:** Eq.(31.19) allows us to calculate I and then Eq.(31.22) gives Z. Solve Eq.(31.21) for L.

EXECUTE:

a) $V_C = IX_C$ so $I = \dfrac{V_C}{X_C} = \dfrac{360\ \text{V}}{480\ \Omega} = 0.750\ \text{A}$

b) $V = IZ$ so $Z = \dfrac{V}{I} = \dfrac{120\ \text{V}}{0.750\ \text{A}} = 160\ \Omega$

c) $Z^2 = R^2 + (X_L - X_C)^2$

$X_L - X_C = \pm\sqrt{Z^2 - R^2}$, so

$X_L = X_C \pm \sqrt{Z^2 - R^2} = 480\ \Omega \pm \sqrt{(160\ \Omega)^2 - (80.0\ \Omega)^2} = 480\ \Omega \pm 139\ \Omega$

$X_L = 619\ \Omega$ or $341\ \Omega$

d) **EVALUATE:** $X_C = \dfrac{1}{\omega C}$ and $X_L = \omega L$. At resonance, $X_C = X_L$. As the frequency is lowered below the resonance frequency X_C increases and X_L decreases. Therefore, for $\omega < \omega_0$, $X_L < X_C$. So for $X_L = 341\ \Omega$ the angular frequency is less than the resonance angular frequency. ω is greater than ω_0 when $X_L = 619\ \Omega$. But at these two values of X_L, the magnitude of $X_L - X_C$ is the same so Z and I are the same. In one case ($X_L = 691\ \Omega$) the source voltage leads the current and in the other ($X_L = 341\ \Omega$) the source voltage lags the current

31.61 **IDENTIFY** and **SET UP:** Consider the cycle of the repeating current that lies between $t_1 = \tau/2$ and $t_2 = 3\tau/2$. In this interval $i = \dfrac{2I_0}{\tau}(t - \tau)$.

$$I_{av} = \frac{1}{t_2 - t_1} \int_{t_1}^{t_2} i \, dt \quad \text{and} \quad I_{rms}^2 = \frac{1}{t_2 - t_1} \int_{t_1}^{t_2} i^2 \, dt$$

EXECUTE:

$$I_{av} = \frac{1}{t_2 - t_1} \int_{t_1}^{t_2} i \, dt = \frac{1}{\tau} \int_{\tau/2}^{3\tau/2} \frac{2I_0}{\tau}(t - \tau) \, dt = \frac{2I_0}{\tau^2}\left[\frac{1}{2}t^2 - \tau t\right]_{\tau/2}^{3\tau/2}$$

$$I_{av} = \left(\frac{2I_0}{\tau^2}\right)\left(\frac{9\tau^2}{8} - \frac{3\tau^2}{2} - \frac{\tau^2}{8} + \frac{\tau^2}{2}\right) = (2I_0)\tfrac{1}{8}(9 - 12 - 1 + 4) = \frac{I_0}{4}(13 - 13) = 0.$$

$$I_{rms}^2 = (I^2)_{av} = \frac{1}{t_2 - t_1} \int_{t_1}^{t_2} i^2 \, dt = \frac{1}{\tau} \int_{\tau/2}^{3\tau/2} \frac{4I_0^2}{\tau^2}(t - \tau)^2 \, dt$$

$$I_{rms}^2 = \frac{4I_0^2}{\tau^3} \int_{\tau/2}^{3\tau/2} (t - \tau)^2 \, dt = \frac{4I_0^2}{\tau^3}\left[\frac{1}{3}(t - \tau)^3\right]_{\tau/2}^{3\tau/2} = \frac{4I_0^2}{3\tau^3}\left[\left(\frac{\tau}{2}\right)^3 - \left(-\frac{\tau}{2}\right)^3\right]$$

$$I_{rms}^2 = \frac{I_0^2}{6}[1 + 1] = \frac{1}{3}I_0^2$$

$$I_{rms} = \sqrt{I_{rms}^2} = \frac{I_0}{\sqrt{3}}.$$

EVALUATE: In each cycle the current has as much negative value as positive value and its average is zero. i^2 is always positive and its average is not zero. The relation between I_{rms} and the current amplitude for this current is different from that for a sinusoidal current (Eq.31.4).

CHAPTER 32
ELECTROMAGNETIC WAVES

Exercises 3, 5, 7, 9, 11, 13, 21, 27, 29
Problems 35, 37, 39, 45, 47, 49, 51

Exercises

32.3 **IDENTIFY** and **SET UP:** The equations are of the form of Eqs.(32.17), with x replaced by z. $\vec{B}$ is along the y-axis; deduce the direction of $\vec{E}$.

EXECUTE: $\omega = 2\pi f = 2\pi(6.10 \times 10^{14} \text{ Hz}) = 3.83 \times 10^{15} \text{ rad/s}$

$k = \dfrac{2\pi}{\lambda} = \dfrac{2\pi f}{c} = \dfrac{\omega}{c} = \dfrac{3.83 \times 10^{15} \text{ rad/s}}{3.00 \times 10^{8} \text{ m/s}} = 1.28 \times 10^{7} \text{ rad/m}$

$B_{max} = 5.80 \times 10^{-4} \text{ T}$

$E_{max} = cB_{max} = (3.00 \times 10^{8} \text{ m/s})(5.80 \times 10^{-4} \text{ T}) = 1.74 \times 10^{5} \text{ V/m}$

$\vec{B}$ is along the y-axis. $\vec{E} \times \vec{B}$ is in the direction of propagation (the $+z$-direction). From this we can deduce the direction of $\vec{E}$.

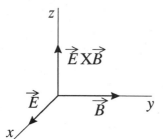

$\vec{E}$ is along the x-axis.

$\vec{E} = E_{max}\hat{i} \cos(kz - \omega t) =$
$(1.74 \times 10^{5} \text{ V/m})\hat{i} \cos[(1.28 \times 10^{7} \text{ rad/m})z - (3.83 \times 10^{15} \text{ rad/s})t]$
$\vec{B} = B_{max}\hat{j} \cos(kz - \omega t) =$
$(5.80 \times 10^{-4} \text{ T})\hat{j} \cos[(1.28 \times 10^{7} \text{ rad/m})z - (3.83 \times 10^{15} \text{ rad/s})t]$

EVALUATE: $\vec{E}$ and $\vec{B}$ are perpendicular and oscillate in phase.

32.5 **IDENTIFY** and **SET UP:** Compare the $\vec{E}(y, t)$ given in the problem to the general form given by Eq.(32.17). Use the direction of propagation and of $\vec{E}$ to find the direction of $\vec{B}$.

a) EXECUTE: The equation for the electric field contains the factor $\sin(ky - \omega t)$ so the wave is traveling in the $+y$-direction. The equation for $\vec{E}(y, t)$ is in terms of $\sin(ky - \omega t)$ rather than $\cos(ky - \omega t)$; the wave is shifted in phase by 90° relative to one with a $\cos(ky - \omega t)$ factor.

b) $\vec{E}(y,t) = -(3.10 \times 10^5 \text{ V/m})\hat{k} \sin[ky - (2.65 \times 10^{12} \text{ rad/s})t]$

Comparing to Eq.(32.17) gives $\omega - 2.65 \times 10^{12}$ rad/s

$$\omega = 2\pi f = \frac{2\pi c}{\lambda} \text{ so } \lambda = \frac{2\pi c}{\omega} = \frac{2\pi(2.998 \times 10^8 \text{ m/s})}{(2.65 \times 10^{12} \text{ rad/s}} = 7.11 \times 10^{-4} \text{ m}$$

c)

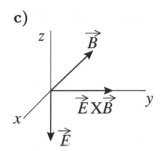

$\vec{E} \times \vec{B}$ must be in the $+y$-direction
(the direction in which the wave is traveling).
When $\vec{E}$ is in the $-z$-direction then
$\vec{B}$ must be in the $-x$-direction.

$$k = \frac{2\pi}{\lambda} = \frac{\omega}{c} = \frac{2.65 \times 10^{12} \text{ rad/s}}{2.998 \times 10^8 \text{ m/s}} = 8.84 \times 10^3 \text{ rad/m}$$

$E_{max} = 3.10 \times 10^5$ V/m

Then $B_{max} = \dfrac{E_{max}}{c} = \dfrac{3.10 \times 10^5 \text{ V/m}}{2.998 \times 10^8 \text{ m/s}} = 1.03 \times 10^{-3}$ T

Using Eq.(32.17) and the fact that $\vec{B}$ is in the $-\hat{i}$ direction when $\vec{E}$ is in the $-\hat{k}$ direction,

$\vec{B} = -(1.03 \times 10^{-3} \text{ T})\hat{i} \sin[(8.84 \times 10^3 \text{ rad/m})y - (2.65 \times 10^{12} \text{ rad/s})t]$

EVALUATE: $\vec{E}$ and $\vec{B}$ are perpendicular and oscillate in phase.

32.7 **IDENTIFY** and **SET UP:** $c = f\lambda$ allows calculation of λ.
$k = 2\pi/\lambda$ and $\omega = 2\pi f$. Eq.(32.18) relates the electric and magnetic field amplitudes.

EXECUTE:

a) $c = f\lambda$ so $\lambda = \dfrac{c}{f} = \dfrac{2.998 \times 10^8 \text{ m/s}}{830 \times 10^3 \text{ Hz}} = 361$ m

b) $k = \dfrac{2\pi}{\lambda} = \dfrac{2\pi \text{ rad}}{361 \text{ m}} = 0.0174$ rad/m

c) $\omega = 2\pi f = (2\pi)(830 \times 10^3 \text{ Hz}) = 5.22 \times 10^6$ rad/s

d) Eq.(32.4): $E = cB = (2.998 \times 10^8 \text{ m/s})(4.82 \times 10^{-11} \text{ T}) = 0.0144$ V/m

EVALUATE: This wave has a very long wavelength; its frequency is in the AM radio broadcast band. The electric and magnetic fields in the wave are very weak.

32.9 **IDENTIFY** and **SET UP:** Use Eq.(32.21) to calculate v and Eq.(32.20) to relate E_{max} and B_{max}.

EXECUTE: $K = 1.74$, $K_m = 1.23$, $B_{max} = 3.80 \times 10^{-9}$ T, $E_{max} = vB_{max}$

By Eq.(32.21) $v = \dfrac{c}{\sqrt{KK_m}}$, so

$$E_{max} = \frac{cB_{max}}{\sqrt{KK_m}} = \frac{(2.998 \times 10^8 \text{ m/s})(3.80 \times 10^{-9} \text{ T})}{\sqrt{(1.74)(1.23)}} = 0.779 \text{ V/m}$$

EVALUATE: The speed of the wave is $v = c/\sqrt{KK_m} = 0.684c$. The wave travels about 32% slower in this material than it would in vaccuum.

32.11 **IDENTIFY** and **SET UP:** $v = f\lambda$ relates frequency and wavelength to the speed of the wave. Use Eq.(32.22) to calculate n and K.

EXECUTE:

a) $\lambda = \dfrac{v}{f} = \dfrac{2.17 \times 10^8 \text{ m/s}}{5.70 \times 10^{14} \text{ Hz}} = 3.81 \times 10^{-7}$ m

b) $\lambda = \dfrac{c}{f} = \dfrac{2.998 \times 10^8 \text{ m/s}}{5.70 \times 10^{14} \text{ Hz}} = 5.26 \times 10^{-7}$ m

c) $n = \dfrac{c}{v} = \dfrac{2.998 \times 10^8 \text{ m/s}}{2.17 \times 10^8 \text{ m/s}} = 1.38$

d) $n = \sqrt{KK_m} \approx \sqrt{K}$ so $K = n^2 = (1.38)^2 = 1.90$

EVALUATE: In the material $v < c$ and f is the same, so λ is less in the material than in air. $v < c$ always, so n is always greater than unity.

32.13 **IDENTIFY** and **SET UP:** Use Eq.(32.29) to calculate I, Eq.(32.18) to calculate B_{max}, and use $I = P_{av}/4\pi r^2$ to calculate P_{av}.

a) **EXECUTE:** $I = \frac{1}{2}\epsilon_0 c E_{max}^2$; $E_{max} = 0.090$ V/m, so $I = 1.1 \times 10^{-5}$ W/m^2

b) $E_{max} = cB_{max}$ so $B_{max} = E_{max}/c = 3.0 \times 10^{-10}$ T

c) $P_{av} = I(4\pi r^2) = (1.075 \times 10^{-5} \text{ W/m}^2)(4\pi)(2.5 \times 10^3 \text{ m})^2 = 840$ W

d) **EVALUATE:** The calculation in part (c) assumes that the transmitter emits uniformly in all directions.

32.21 **IDENTIFY** and **SET UP:** Use Eqs.(32.30) and (32.31).
EXECUTE:

a) By Eq.(32.30) the average momentum density is $\dfrac{dp}{dV} = \dfrac{S_{av}}{c^2} = \dfrac{I}{c^2}$

$$\frac{dp}{dV} = \frac{0.78 \times 10^3 \ \text{W/m}^2}{(2.998 \times 10^8 \ \text{m/s})^2} = 8.7 \times 10^{-15} \ \text{kg/m}^2 \cdot \text{s}$$

b) By Eq.(32.31) the average momentum flow rate per unit area is

$$\frac{S_{av}}{c} = \frac{I}{c} = \frac{0.78 \times 10^3 \ \text{W/m}^2}{2.998 \times 10^8 \ \text{m/s}} = 2.6 \times 10^{-6} \ \text{Pa}$$

EVALUATE: The radiation pressure that the sunlight would exert on an absorbing or reflecting surface is very small.

32.27 a) IDENTIFY and **SET UP:** The distance between adjacent nodal planes of $\vec{B}$ is $\lambda/2$. There is an antinodal plane of $\vec{B}$ midway between any two adjacent nodal planes, so the distance between a nodal plane and an adjacent antinodal plane is $\lambda/4$. Use $v = f\lambda$ to calculate λ.

EXECUTE: $\lambda = \dfrac{v}{f} = \dfrac{2.10 \times 10^8 \ \text{m/s}}{1.20 \times 10^{10} \ \text{Hz}} = 0.0175 \ \text{m}$

$\dfrac{\lambda}{4} = \dfrac{0.0175 \ \text{m}}{4} = 4.38 \times 10^{-3} \ \text{m} = 4.38 \ \text{mm}$

b) IDENTIFY and **SET UP:** The nodal planes of $\vec{E}$ are at $x = 0, \lambda/2, \lambda$. $3\lambda/2, \ldots$, so the antinodal planes of $\vec{E}$ are at $x = \lambda/4, 3\lambda/4, 5\lambda/4, \ldots$. The nodal planes of $\vec{B}$ are at $x = \lambda/4, 3\lambda/4, 5\lambda/4, \ldots$, so the antinodal planes of $\vec{B}$ are at $\lambda/2, \lambda, 3\lambda/2, \ldots$.

EXECUTE: The distance between adjacent antinodal planes of $\vec{E}$ and antinodal planes of $\vec{B}$ is therefore $\lambda/4 = 4.38$ mm.

c) From Eqs.(32.36) and (32.37) the distance between adjacent nodal planes of $\vec{E}$ and $\vec{B}$ is $\lambda/4 = 4.38$ mm.

EVALUATE: The nodes of $\vec{E}$ coincide with the antinodes of $\vec{B}$, and conversely. The nodes of $\vec{B}$ and the nodes of $\vec{E}$ are equally spaced.

32.29 IDENTIFY and **SET UP:** Apply Eqs.(32.36) and (32.37).
EXECUTE:
a) By Eq.(32.37) we see that the nodal planes of the $\vec{B}$ field are a distance $\lambda/2$ apart, so $\lambda/2 = 3.55$ mm and $\lambda = 7.10$ mm.

b) By Eq.(32.36) we see that the nodal planes of the $\vec{E}$ field are also a distance

$\lambda/2 = 3.55$ mm apart.

c) $v = f\lambda = (2.20 \times 10^{10}$ Hz$)(7.10 \times 10^{-3}$ m$) = 1.56 \times 10^{8}$ m/s.

EVALUATE: The spacing between the nodes of $\vec{E}$ is the same as the spacing between the nodes of $\vec{B}$. Note that $v < c$, as it must.

Problems

32.35 **IDENTIFY** and **SET UP:** Take partial derivatives of Eqs.(32.12) and (32.14), as specified in the problem.

EXECUTE:

Eq.(32.12): $\dfrac{\partial E_y}{\partial x} = -\dfrac{\partial B_z}{\partial t}$

Taking $\dfrac{\partial}{\partial t}$ of both sides of this equation gives

$$\frac{\partial^2 E_y}{\partial x \partial t} = -\frac{\partial^2 B_z}{\partial t^2}$$

Eq.(32.14) says $-\dfrac{\partial B_z}{\partial x} = \epsilon_0 \mu_0 \dfrac{\partial E_y}{\partial t}$.

Taking $\dfrac{\partial}{\partial x}$ of both sides of this equation gives

$$-\frac{\partial^2 B_z}{\partial x^2} = \epsilon_0 \mu_0 \frac{\partial^2 E_y}{\partial t \partial x}, \text{ so } \frac{\partial^2 E_y}{\partial t \partial x} = -\frac{1}{\epsilon_0 \mu_0} \frac{\partial^2 B_z}{\partial x^2}$$

But $\dfrac{\partial^2 E_y}{\partial x \partial t} = \dfrac{\partial^2 E_y}{\partial t \partial x}$ (The order in which the partial derivatives are taken doesn't change the result.)

So $-\dfrac{\partial^2 B_z}{\partial t^2} = -\dfrac{1}{\epsilon_0 \mu_0} \dfrac{\partial^2 B_z}{\partial x^2}$

$\dfrac{\partial^2 B_z}{\partial x^2} = \epsilon_0 \mu_0 \dfrac{\partial^2 B_z}{\partial t^2}$, as was to be shown.

EVALUATE: Both fields, electric and magnetic, satisfy the wave equation, Eq.(32.10). We have also shown that both fields propagate with the same speed $v = 1/\sqrt{\epsilon_0 \mu_0}$.

32.37 a) **IDENTIFY** and **SET UP:** I gives the energy flow per unit time per unit area:

$I = \dfrac{1}{A}\dfrac{dU}{dt}$ and thus $\dfrac{dU}{dt} = AI$

EXECUTE:

$$I = \frac{E_{max}^2}{2\mu_0 c} = \frac{(0.0280 \text{ V/m})^2}{2(4\pi \times 10^{-7} \text{ T} \cdot \text{m/A})(2.998 \times 10^8 \text{ m/s})} = 1.04 \times 10^{-6} \text{ W/m}^2$$

Then $\dfrac{dU}{dt} = AI = (5.00 \times 10^{-4} \text{ m}^2)(1.04 \times 10^{-6} \text{ W/m}^2) = 5.20 \times 10^{-10} \text{ W}.$

The energy incident on the mirror in 1.00 s is

$(5.20 \times 10^{-10} \text{ W})(1.00 \text{ s}) = 5.20 \times 10^{-10} \text{ J}.$

b) IDENTIFY and **SET UP:** The light is reflected by the mirror, so the average pressure is given by Eq.(32.33).

EXECUTE: $\dfrac{2I}{c} = \dfrac{2(1.04 \times 10^{-6} \text{ W/m}^2)}{2.998 \times 10^8 \text{ m/s}} = 6.94 \times 10^{-15} \text{ Pa}$

c) IDENTIFY and **SET UP:** Surround the light bulb with a spherical surface of radius $R = 3.20$ m and surface area $A = 4\pi R^2$. All the power radiated by the bulb passes through this surface, so $I = \dfrac{P}{A} = \dfrac{P}{4\pi R^2}.$

EXECUTE: $P = 4\pi R^2 I = 4\pi (3.20 \text{ m})^2 (1.04 \times 10^{-6} \text{ W/m}^2) = 1.34 \times 10^{-4} \text{ W}.$

EVALUATE: The radiation pressure is very small. The expression in part (c) was given in Section 15.5.

32.39 a) IDENTIFY and **SET UP:** Calculate I and then use Eq.(32.29) to calculate E_{max} and Eq.(32.18) to calculate B_{max}.

EXECUTE: The intensity is power per unit area:

$$I = \frac{P}{A} = \frac{3.20 \times 10^{-3} \text{ W}}{\pi (1.25 \times 10^{-3} \text{ m})^2} = 652 \text{ W/m}^2.$$

$I = \dfrac{E_{max}^2}{2\mu_0 c}$, so $E_{max} = \sqrt{2\mu_0 c I}$

$$E_{max} = \sqrt{2(4\pi \times 10^{-7} \text{ T} \cdot \text{m/A})(2.998 \times 10^8 \text{ m/s})(652 \text{ W/m}^2)} = 701 \text{ V/m}$$

$$B_{max} = \frac{E_{max}}{c} = \frac{701 \text{ V/m}}{2.998 \times 10^8 \text{ m/s}} = 2.34 \times 10^{-6} \text{ T}$$

EVALUATE: The magnetic field amplitude is quite small.

b) IDENTIFY and **SET UP:** Eqs.(24.11) and (30.10) give the energy density in terms of the electric and magnetic field values at any time. For sinusoidal fields average over E^2 and B^2 to get the average energy densities.

EXECUTE: The energy density in the electric field is $u_E = \frac{1}{2}\epsilon_0 E^2$.

$E = E_{max}\cos(kx - \omega t)$ and the average value of $\cos^2(kx - \omega t)$ is $\frac{1}{2}$. The average energy density in the electric field then is

$u_{E,av} = \frac{1}{4}\epsilon_0 E_{max}^2 = \frac{1}{4}(8.854 \times 10^{-12} \text{ C}^2/\text{N} \cdot \text{m}^2)(701 \text{ V/m})^2 = 1.09 \times 10^{-6} \text{ J/m}^3.$

The energy density in the magnetic field is $u_B = \dfrac{B^2}{2\mu_0}$.

The average value is $u_{B,av} = \dfrac{B_{max}^2}{4\mu_0} = \dfrac{(2.34 \times 10^{-6} \text{ T})^2}{4(4\pi \times 10^{-7} \text{ T} \cdot \text{m/A})} = 1.09 \times 10^{-6} \text{ J/m}^3.$

EVALUATE: Our result agrees with the statement in Section 32.4 that the average energy density for the electric field is the same as the average energy density for the magnetic field.

c) IDENTIFY and **SET UP:** The total energy in this length of beam is the total energy density $u_{av} = u_{E,av} + u_{B,av} = 2.18 \times 10^{-6} \text{ J/m}^3$ times the volume of this part of the beam.

EXECUTE: $U = u_{av}LA = (2.18 \times 10^{-6} \text{ J/m}^3)(1.00 \text{ m})\pi(1.25 \times 10^{-3} \text{ m})^2 = 1.07 \times 10^{-11} \text{ J.}$

EVALUATE: This quantity can also be calculated as the power output times the time it takes the light to travel $L = 1.00$ m:

$$U = P\left(\frac{L}{c}\right) = (3.20 \times 10^{-3} \text{ W})\left(\frac{1.00 \text{ m}}{2.998 \times 10^8 \text{ m/s}}\right) = 1.07 \times 10^{-11} \text{ J, which checks.}$$

32.45 IDENTIFY and **SET UP:** In the wire the electric field is related to the current density by Eq.(25.7). Use Ampere's law to calculate $\vec{B}$. The Poynting vector is given by Eq.(32.28) and the equation that follows it relates the energy flow through a surface to $\vec{S}$.

EXECUTE:

a) The direction of $\vec{E}$ is parallel to the axis of the cylinder, in the direction of the current. From Eq.(25.7), $E = \rho J = \rho I/\pi a^2$. ($E$ is uniform across the cross section of the conductor.)

b) Cross-sectional view of the conductor; take the current to be coming out of the page.

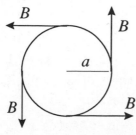

Apply Ampere's law to a circle of radius a.
$\oint \vec{B} \cdot d\vec{l} = B(2\pi a)$
$I_{encl} = I$

32 / ELECTROMAGNETIC WAVES

235

$\oint \vec{B} \cdot d\vec{l} = \mu_0 I_{\text{encl}}$ gives $B(2\pi a) = \mu_0 I$ and

$$B = \frac{\mu_0 I}{2\pi a}$$

The direction of $\vec{B}$ is counterclockwise around the circle.

c)

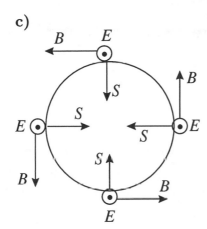

The direction of $\vec{S} = \dfrac{1}{\mu_0}\vec{E}\mathbf{X}\vec{B}$

is radially inward.

$$S = \frac{1}{\mu_0}EB = \frac{1}{\mu_0}\left(\frac{\rho I}{\pi a^2}\right)\left(\frac{\mu_0 I}{2\pi a}\right)$$

$$S = \frac{\rho I^2}{2\pi^2 a^3}$$

d) EVALUATE: Since S is constant over the surface of the conductor, the rate of energy flow P is given by S times the surface area of a length l of the conductor:

$$P = SA = S(2\pi a l) = \frac{\rho I^2}{2\pi^2 a^3}(2\pi a l) = \frac{\rho l I^2}{\pi a^2}.$$

But $R = \dfrac{\rho l}{\pi a^2}$, so the result from the Poynting vector is $P = RI^2$. This agrees with $P_R = I^2 R$, the rate at which electrical energy is being dissipated by the resistance of the wire.

Since $\vec{S}$ is radially inward at the surface of the wire and has magnitude equal to the rate at which electrical energy is being dissipated in the wire, this energy can be thought of as entering through the cylindrical sides of the conductor.

32.47 IDENTIFY and SET UP: The magnitude of the induced emf is given by Faraday's law: $|\varepsilon| = |\dfrac{d\Phi_B}{dt}|$. To calculate $d\Phi_B/dt$ we need dB/dt at the antenna. Use the total power output to calculate I and then combine Eq.(32.29) and (32.18) to calculate $B_{\max}$. The time dependence of B is given by Eq.(32.17).

EXECUTE: $\Phi_B = B\pi R^2$, where $R = 0.0900$ m is the radius of the loop. (This assumes that the magnetic field is uniform across the loop, an excellent approximation.)

$$|\varepsilon| = \pi R^2 |\frac{dB}{dt}|$$

$$B = B_{\max}\cos(kx - \omega t) \text{ so } |\frac{dB}{dt}| = B_{\max}\omega \sin(kx - \omega t)$$

The maximum value of $|\frac{dB}{dt}|$ is $B_{max}\omega$, so $|\varepsilon|_{max} = \pi R^2 B_{max}\omega$.

$R = 0.0900$ m, $\omega = 2\pi f = 2\pi(95.0 \times 10^6$ Hz$) = 5.97 \times 10^8$ rad/s

Calculate the intensity I at this distance from the source, and from that the magnetic field amplitude B_{max}:

$$I = \frac{P}{4\pi r^2} = \frac{55.0 \times 10^3 \text{ W}}{4\pi(2.50 \times 10^3 \text{ m})^2} = 7.00 \times 10^{-4} \text{ W/m}^2.$$

$$I = \frac{E_{max}^2}{2\mu_0 c} = \frac{(cB_{max})^2}{2\mu_0 c} = \frac{c}{2\mu_0}B_{max}^2$$

Thus $B_{max} = \sqrt{\frac{2\mu_0 I}{c}} =$

$$\sqrt{\frac{2(4\pi \times 10^{-7} \text{ T} \cdot \text{m/A})(7.00 \times 10^{-4} \text{ W/m}^2)}{2.998 \times 10^8 \text{ m/s}}} = 2.42 \times 10^{-9} \text{ T}.$$

Then $|\varepsilon|_{max} = \pi R^2 B_{max}\omega = \pi(0.0900$ m$)^2(2.42 \times 10^{-9}$ T$)(5.97 \times 10^8$ rad/s$) = 0.0368$ V.

EVALUATE: An induced emf of this magnitude is easily detected.

32.49 **IDENTIFY** and **SET UP:** Find the force on you due to the momentum carried off by the light. Express this force in terms of the radiated power of the flashlight. Use this force to calculate your acceleration and use a constant acceleration equation to find the time.

a) EXECUTE:

$p_{rad} = I/c$ and $F = p_{rad}A$ gives $F = IA/c = P_{av}/c$

$a_x = F/m = P_{av}/(mc) = (200 \text{ W})/[(150 \text{ kg})(3.00 \times 10^8 \text{ m/s})] = 4.44 \times 10^{-9}$ m/s^2

Then $x - x_0 = v_{0x}t + \frac{1}{2}a_x t^2$ gives

$$t = \sqrt{2(x - x_0)/a_x} = \sqrt{2(16.0 \text{ m})/(4.44 \times 10^{-9} \text{ m/s}^2)} = 8.49 \times 10^4 \text{ s} = 23.6 \text{ h}$$

EVALUATE: The radiation force is very small. In the calculation we have ignored any other forces on you.

b) You could throw the flashlight in the direction away from the ship. By conservation of linear momentum you would move toward the ship with the same magntiude of momentum as you gave the flashlight.

32.51 **IDENTIFY** and **SET UP:** The gravitational force is given by Eq.(12.2). Express the mass of the particle in terms of its density and volume. The radiation pressure is given by Eq.(32.32); relate the power output L of the sun to the intensity at a distance r. The radiation force is the pressure times the cross sectional area of the particle.

EXECUTE:

a) The gravitational force is $F_g = G\dfrac{mM}{r^2}$. The mass of the dust particle

is $m = \rho V = \rho \frac{4}{3}\pi R^3$. Thus $F_g = \dfrac{4\rho G\pi M R^3}{3r^2}$.

b) For a totally absorbing surface $p_{rad} = \dfrac{I}{c}$.

If L is the power output of the sun, the intensity of the solar radiation a distance
r from the sun is $I = \dfrac{L}{4\pi r^2}$.

Thus $p_{rad} = \dfrac{L}{4\pi c r^2}$.

The force F_{rad} that corresponds to p_{rad} is in the direction of propagation of the
radiation, so $F_{rad} = p_{rad}A_\perp$, where $A_\perp = \pi R^2$ is the component of area of the
particle perpendicular to the radiation propagation direction. Thus

$$F_{rad} = \left(\frac{L}{4\pi c r^2}\right)(\pi R^2) - \frac{LR^2}{4cr^2}.$$

c) $F_g = F_{rad}$

$$\frac{4\rho G\pi M R^3}{3r^2} = \frac{LR^2}{4cr^2}$$

$$\left(\frac{4\rho G\pi M}{3}\right)R = \frac{L}{4c} \text{ and } R = \frac{3L}{16c\rho G\pi M}$$

$$R = \frac{3(3.9 \times 10^{26}\ \text{W})}{16(2.998 \times 10^8\ \text{m/s})(3000\ \text{kg/m}^3)(6.673 \times 10^{-11}\ \text{N} \cdot \text{m}^2/\text{kg}^2)\pi(1.99 \times 10^{30}\ \text{kg})}$$

$R = 1.9 \times 10^{-7}\ \text{m} = 0.19\ \mu\text{m}.$

EVALUATE: The gravitation force and the radiation force both have a r^{-2} dependence on the distance from the sun, so this distance divides out in the calculation
of R.

d) $\dfrac{F_{rad}}{F_g} = \left(\dfrac{LR^2}{4cr^2}\right)\left(\dfrac{3r^2}{4\rho G\pi m R^3}\right) = \dfrac{3L}{16c\rho G\pi M R}$. F_{rad} is proportional to R^2 and
F_g is proportional to R^3, so this ratio is proportional to $1/R$.

If $R < 0.20\ \mu\text{m}$ then $F_{rad} > F_g$ and the radiation force will drive the particles out
of the solar system.

CHAPTER 33

THE NATURE AND PROPAGATION OF LIGHT

Exercises 1, 5, 7, 11, 15, 17, 19, 21, 29
Problems 39, 41, 43, 45, 47, 49, 51, 53, 59

Exercises

33.1 **IDENTIFY** and **SET UP:** Use Eqs.(33.1) and (33.5) to calculate v and λ.
EXECUTE:

a) $n = \dfrac{c}{v}$ so $v = \dfrac{c}{n} = \dfrac{2.998 \times 10^8 \text{ m/s}}{1.47} = 2.04 \times 10^8 \text{ m/s}$

b) $\lambda = \dfrac{\lambda_0}{n} = \dfrac{650 \text{ nm}}{1.47} = 442 \text{ nm}$

EVALUATE: Light is slower in the liquid than in vacuum. By $v = f\lambda$, when v is smaller, λ is smaller.

33.5 **IDENTIFY:** Apply Eqs.(33.2) and (33.4) to calculate θ_r and θ_b. The angles in these equations are measured with respect to the normal, not the surface.

a) **SET UP:**

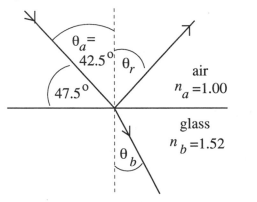

EXECUTE:
$\theta_r = \theta_a = 42.5°$
The reflected ray makes an angle of
$90.0° - \theta_r = 47.5°$ with the
surface of the glass.

b) $n_a \sin \theta_a = n_b \sin \theta_b$, where the angles are measured from the normal to the interface.

$$\sin \theta_b = \frac{n_a \sin \theta_a}{n_b} = \frac{(1.00)(\sin 42.5°)}{1.66} = 0.4070$$

$\theta_b = 24.0°$

The refracted ray makes an angle of $90.0° - \theta_b = 66.0°$ with the surface of the glass.

EVALUATE: The light is bent toward the normal when the light enters the material of larger refractive index.

33.7 **IDENTIFY** and **SET UP:** Use Snell's law to find the index of refraction of the plastic and then use Eq.(33.1) to calculate the speed v of light in the plastic.

EXECUTE: $n_a \sin \theta_a = n_b \sin \theta_b$

$$n_b = n_a \left(\frac{\sin \theta_a}{\sin \theta_b} \right) = 1.00 \left(\frac{\sin 62.7°}{\sin 48.1°} \right) = 1.194$$

$n = c/v$ so $v = c/n = (3.00 \times 10^8 \text{ m/s})/1.194 = 2.51 \times 10^8 \text{ m/s}$

EVALUATE: Light is slower in plastic than in air. When the light goes from air into the plastic it is bent toward the normal.

33.11 **IDENTIFY:** Apply the law of reflection (Eq.33.2).
SET UP:

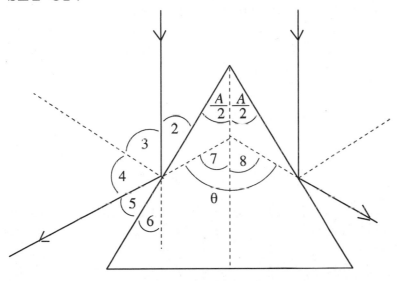

EXECUTE: Angle θ is angle 7 + angle 8. We are asked to show that $\theta = 2A$. By symmetry angle 7 = angle 8, so we need to show that angle 7 = A.

From the sketch we see that angle 5 + angle 6 = angle 7 and that angle 2 = $A/2$. But angle 2 = angle 6, so angle 6 = $A/2$.

The law of reflection $\theta_a = \theta_r$ says that angle 3 = angle 4. But then angle 2 = angle 5. Thus angle 5 = $A/2$.

Then angle 7 = angle 5 + angle 6 = $A/2 + A/2 = A$, which completes the proof.

EVALUATE: If $A = 180°$ then the surface and the reflected rays are in the same direction and the angle between them is $0° = 360°$, so the result holds in this special case.

33.15 **IDENTIFY:** Use the critical angle to find the index of refraction of the liquid.
SET UP: Total internal reflection requires that the light be incident on the

material with the larger n, in this case the liquid. Apply $n_a \sin \theta_a = n_b \sin \theta_b$ with a = liquid and b = air, so $n_a = n_{\text{liq}}$ and $n_b = 1.0$.

EXECUTE: $\theta_a = \theta_{\text{crit}}$ when $\theta_b = 90°$, so $n_{\text{liq}} \sin \theta_{\text{crit}} = (1.0) \sin 90°$

$$n_{\text{liq}} = \frac{1}{\sin \theta_{\text{crit}}} = \frac{1}{\sin 42.5°} = 1.48.$$

a) $n_a \sin \theta_a = n_b \sin \theta_b$ (a = liquid, b = air)

$$\sin \theta_b = \frac{n_a \sin \theta_a}{n_b} = \frac{(1.48) \sin 35.0°}{1.0} = 0.8489 \text{ and } \theta_b = 58.1°$$

b) Now $n_a \sin \theta_a = n_b \sin \theta_b$ with a = air, b = liquid

$$\sin \theta_b = \frac{n_a \sin \theta_a}{n_b} = \frac{(1.0) \sin 35.0°}{1.48} = 0.3876 \text{ and } \theta_b = 22.8°$$

EVALUATE: For light traveling liquid $\rightarrow$ air the light is bent away from the normal. For light traveling air $\rightarrow$ liquid the light is bent toward the normal.

33.17 **IDENTIFY** and **SET UP:** For glass $\rightarrow$ water, $\theta_{\text{crit}} = 48.7°$. Apply Snell's law with $\theta_a = \theta_{\text{crit}}$ to calculate the index of refraction n_a of the glass.

EXECUTE: $n_a \sin \theta_{\text{crit}} = n_b \sin 90°$, so $n_a = \dfrac{n_b}{\sin \theta_{\text{crit}}} = \dfrac{1.333}{\sin 48.7°} = 1.77$

EVALUATE: For total internal reflection to occur the light must be incident in the material of larger refractive index. Our results give $n_{\text{glass}} > n_{\text{water}}$, in agreement with this.

33.19 **IDENTIFY** and **SET UP:** Define the index of refraction n_{air} of air for sound waves to be 1.00. Calculate n_{water} and then use Snell's law to calculate the critical angle.

EXECUTE:

a) $n_{\text{water}} = \dfrac{v_{\text{air}}}{v_{\text{water}}}$ (Eq.33.1), so $n_{\text{water}} = \dfrac{344 \text{ m/s}}{1320 \text{ m/s}} = 0.2606.$

$n_{\text{water}} < n_{\text{air}}$; air has the larger index of refraction for sound waves since sound travels slower in air than it does in water.

b) $n_a \sin \theta_a = n_b \sin \theta_b$

$\theta_a = \theta_{\text{crit}}$ when $\sin \theta_b = 1$

so $\sin \theta_{\text{crit}} = \dfrac{n_b \sin 90°}{n_a} = \dfrac{n_{\text{water}}}{n_{\text{air}}} = \dfrac{0.2606}{1.00} = 0.2606.$

$\theta_{\text{crit}} = 15.1°$

c) **EVALUATE:** For total internal reflection the wave must be traveling in the material with the larger index of refraction, so the sound wave must be traveling in air.

33.21 IDENTIFY and **SET UP:** Reflected beam completely linearly polarized implies that the angle of incidence equals the polarizing angle, so $\theta_p = 54.5°$. Use Eq.(33.8) to calculate the refractive index of the glass. Then use Snell's law to calculate the angle of refraction.

EXECUTE:

a) $\tan \theta_p = \dfrac{n_b}{n_a}$ gives $n_{\text{glass}} = n_{\text{air}} \tan \theta_p = (1.00) \tan 54.5° = 1.40$.

b) $n_a \sin \theta_a = n_b \sin \theta_b$

$\sin \theta_b = \dfrac{n_a \sin \theta_a}{n_b} = \dfrac{(1.00) \sin 54.5°}{1.40} = 0.5815$ and $\theta_b = 35.5°$

EVALUATE:

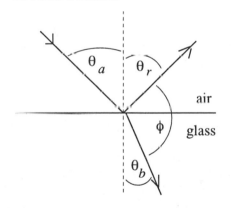

Note: $\phi = 180.0° - \theta_r - \theta_b$ and $\theta_r = \theta_a$. Thus $\phi = 180.0° - 54.5° - 35.5° = 90.0°$; the reflected ray and the refracted ray are perpendicular to each other. This agrees with Fig.33.25.

33.29 IDENTIFY and **SET UP:** Apply Eq.(33.7) to polarizers #2 and #3. The light incident on the first polarizer is unpolarized, so the transmitted light has half the intensity of the incident light, and the transmitted light is polarized.

a) **EXECUTE:**

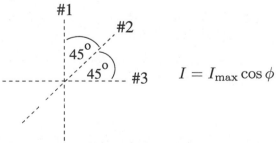

$I = I_{\text{max}} \cos \phi$

After the first filter the intensity is $I_1 = \frac{1}{2} I_0$ and the light is linearly polarized along the axis of the first polarizer.

After the second filter the intensity is

$I_2 = I_1 \cos^2 \phi = (\frac{1}{2} I_0)(\cos 45.0°)^2 = 0.250 I_0$

and the light is linearly polarized along the axis of the second polarizer.

After the third filter the intensity is

$I_3 = I_2 \cos^2 \phi = 0.250 I_0 (\cos 45.0°)^2 = 0.125 I_0$

and the light is linearly polarized along the axis of the third polarizer.

b)

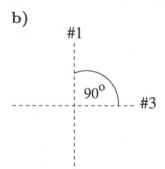

After the first filter the intensity is $I_1 = \frac{1}{2} I_0$ and the light is linearly polarized along the axis of the first polarizer.

After the next filter the intensity is $I_3 = I_1 \cos^2 \phi = (\frac{1}{2} I_0)(\cos 90.0°)^2 = 0$. No light is passed.

EVALUATE: Light is transmitted through all three filters, but no light is transmitted if the middle polarizer is removed.

Problems

33.39 IDENTIFY: Find the critical angle for glass → air. Light incident at this critical angle is reflected back to the edge of the halo.

SET UP:

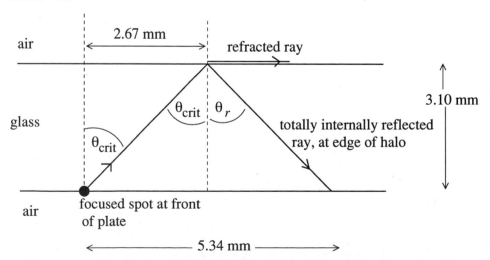

EXECUTE: From the distances given in the sketch, $\tan \theta_{\text{crit}} = \dfrac{2.67 \text{ mm}}{3.10 \text{ mm}} = 0.8613$; $\theta_{\text{crit}} = 40.7°$.

Apply Snell's law to the total internal reflection to find the refractive index of the glass:

$n_a \sin \theta_a = n_b \sin \theta_b$

$n_{\text{glass}} \sin \theta_{\text{crit}} = 1.00 \sin 90°$

$n_{\text{glass}} = \dfrac{1}{\sin \theta_{\text{crit}}} = \dfrac{1}{\sin 40.7°} = 1.53$

EVALUATE: Light incident on the back surface is also totally reflected if it is incident at angles greater than θ_{crit}. If it is incident at less than θ_{crit} it refracts into the air and does not reflect back to the emulsion.

33.41 **IDENTIFY:** Use Snell's law to determine the effect of the liquid on the direction of travel of the light as it enters the liquid.

SET UP: Use geometry to find the angles of incidence and refraction.

Before the liquid is poured in

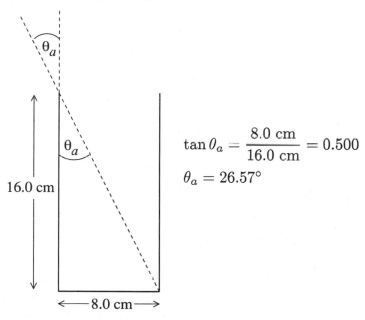

$\tan \theta_a = \dfrac{8.0 \text{ cm}}{16.0 \text{ cm}} = 0.500$

$\theta_a = 26.57°$

After the liquid is poured in, θ_a is the same and the refracted ray passes through the center of the bottom of the glass:

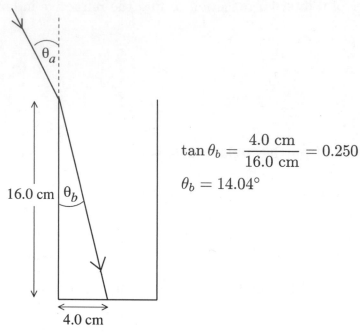

$$\tan \theta_b = \frac{4.0 \text{ cm}}{16.0 \text{ cm}} = 0.250$$

$$\theta_b = 14.04°$$

EXECUTE: Use Snell's law to find n_b, the refractive index of the liquid:

$$n_a \sin \theta_a = n_b \sin \theta_b$$

$$n_b = \frac{n_a \sin \theta_a}{\sin \theta_b} = \frac{(1.00)(\sin 26.57°)}{\sin 14.04°} = 1.84$$

EVALUATE: When the light goes from air to liquid (larger refractive index) it is bent toward the normal.

33.43 IDENTIFY: Apply Snell's law to the water → ice and ice→ air interfaces.

a) SET UP:

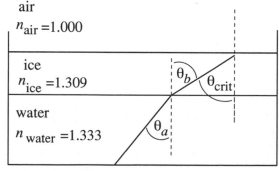

We want to find the incident angle θ_a at the water-ice interface that causes the incident angle at the ice-air interface to be the critical angle.

EXECUTE:

ice-air interface:

$$n_{\text{ice}} \sin \theta_{\text{crit}} = 1.0 \sin 90°$$

$$n_{\text{ice}} \sin \theta_{\text{crit}} = 1.0 \text{ so } \sin \theta_{\text{crit}} = \frac{1}{n_{\text{ice}}}$$

But from the diagram we see that $\theta_b \doteq \theta_{\text{crit}}$, so $\sin \theta_b = \dfrac{1}{n_{\text{ice}}}$.

water-ice interface:

$n_w \sin \theta_a = n_{\text{ice}} \sin \theta_b$

But $\sin \theta_b = \dfrac{1}{n_{\text{ice}}}$ so $n_w \sin \theta_a = 1.0$.

$\sin \theta_a = \dfrac{1}{n_w} = \dfrac{1}{1.333} = 0.7502$ and $\theta_a = 48.6°$.

b) EVALUATE: The angle calculated in part (a) is the critical angle for a water-air interface; the answer would be the same if the ice layer wasn't there!

33.45 IDENTIFY: Apply Snell's law to the refraction of each ray as it emerges from the glass. The angle of incidence equals the angle $A - 25.0°$.

SET UP:

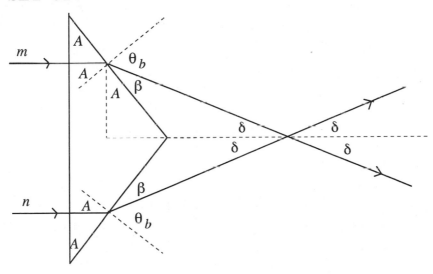

EXECUTE: $n_a \sin \theta_a = n_b \sin \theta_b$

$n_{\text{glass}} \sin 25.0° = 1.00 \sin \theta_b$

$\sin \theta_b = n_{\text{glass}} \sin 25.0°$

$\sin \theta_b = 1.66 \sin 25.0° = 0.7015$

$\theta_b = 44.55°$

$\beta = 90.0° - \theta_b = 45.45°$

Then $\delta - 90.0° - A - \beta - 90.0°$ $25.0° - 45.45° - 19.55°$

The angle between the two rays is $2\delta = 39.1°$.

EVALUATE: The light is incident normally on the front face of the prism so the light is not bent as it enters the prism.

33.47 IDENTIFY: Apply $n_a \sin \theta_a = n_b \sin \theta_b$ to the glass $\rightarrow$ oil interface.
If $\theta_a = 57.2°$ is the critical angle then $\theta_b = 90.0°$.

SET UP:

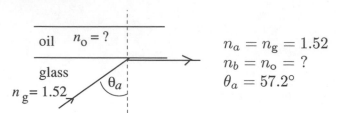

$n_a = n_g = 1.52$
$n_b = n_o = ?$
$\theta_a = 57.2°$

EXECUTE: $(1.52) \sin 57.2° = n_o \sin 90°$

$n_o = (1.52) \sin 57.2° = 1.28$

EVALUATE: If n_o is larger than 1.28, then the critical angle is larger than $57.2°$ and $\theta_a = 57.2°$ would be less than the critical angle. Then at $\theta_a = 57.2°$ the light wouldn't be totally reflected. But n_o could be less than this. If it is less, then the critical angle is less than $57.2°$. A ray with $\theta_a = 57.2°$ is incident at greater than the critical angle and would still be totally reflected. The calculation gives then maximum possible index of refraction.

33.49 a) IDENTIFY: Apply Snell's law to the refraction of the light as it enters the atmosphere.

SET UP:

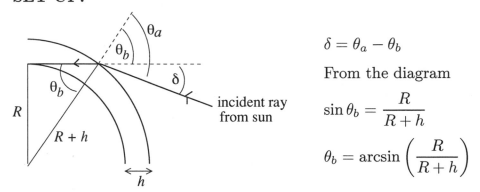

$\delta = \theta_a - \theta_b$

From the diagram

$\sin \theta_b = \dfrac{R}{R+h}$

$\theta_b = \arcsin \left(\dfrac{R}{R+h} \right)$

EXECUTE: Apply Snell's law to the refraction that occurs at the top of the atmosphere:

$n_a \sin \theta_a = n_b \sin \theta_b$

(a = vacuum of space, refractive index 1.0; b = atmosphere, refractive index n)

$\sin \theta_a = n \sin \theta_b = n \left(\dfrac{R}{R+h} \right)$ so $\theta_a = \arcsin \left(\dfrac{nR}{R+h} \right)$

$\delta = \theta_a - \theta_b = \arcsin \left(\dfrac{nR}{R+h} \right) - \arcsin \left(\dfrac{R}{R+h} \right)$

b) $\dfrac{R}{R+h} = \dfrac{6.38 \times 10^6 \text{ m}}{6.38 \times 10^6 \text{ m} + 20 \times 10^3 \text{ m}} = 0.99688$

$\dfrac{nR}{R+h} = 1.0003(0.99688) = 0.99718$

$\theta_b = \arcsin\left(\dfrac{R}{R+h}\right) = 85.47°$

$\theta_b = \arcsin\left(\dfrac{nR}{R+h}\right) = 85.70°$

$\delta = \theta_a - \theta_b = 85.70° - 85.47° = 0.23°$

EVALUATE: The calculated δ is about the same as the angular radius of the sun.

33.51 **IDENTIFY:** The first filter passes half the intensity and the transmitted light is polarized. Apply Eq.(33.7) to filters #2 and #3,

a) SET UP:

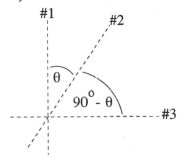

1st filter: $I_1 = \frac{1}{2}I_0$
2nd filter: $I_2 = I_1(\cos\theta)^2$
           $= \frac{1}{2}I_0\cos^2\theta$
3rd filter: $I_3 = I_2(\cos(90° - \theta))^2$
           $= \frac{1}{2}I_0\cos^2\theta\cos^2(90° - \theta)$

EXECUTE: $\cos(90° - \theta) = \cos(\theta - 90°) = \sin\theta$ (Using the trig identities in Appendix B.)

Therefore, $I_3 = \frac{1}{2}I_0\cos^2\theta\sin^2\theta$.

But $\cos\theta\sin\theta = \frac{1}{2}\sin 2\theta$ (Appendix B again), so $I_3 = \frac{1}{8}I_0(\sin 2\theta)^2$

b) I_3 maximum implies $\sin 2\theta = 1$ and $\theta = 45°$.

EVALUATE: If $\theta = 0°$ or $\theta = 90.0°$ then the result from part (a) gives $I_3 = 0$, as it should.

33.53 **IDENTIFY** and **SET UP:** Find the distance that the ray travels in each medium. The travel time in each medium is the distance divided by the speed in that medium.

a) EXECUTE: The light travels a distance $\sqrt{h_1^2 + x^2}$ in traveling from point A to the interface. Along this path the speed of the light is v_1, so the time it takes to travel this distance is $t_1 = \dfrac{\sqrt{h_1^2 + x^2}}{v_1}$.

The light travels a distance $\sqrt{h_2^2 + (l - x)^2}$ in traveling from the interface to point B. Along this path the speed of the light is v_2, so the time it takes to travel this distance is $t_2 = \dfrac{\sqrt{h_2^2 + (l - x)^2}}{v_2}$.

The total time to go from A to B is $t = t_1 + t_2 = \dfrac{\sqrt{h_1^2 + x^2}}{v_1} + \dfrac{\sqrt{h_2^2 + (l - x)^2}}{v_2}$.

b) $\dfrac{dt}{dx} = \dfrac{1}{v_1}(\dfrac{1}{2})(h_1^2 + x^2)^{-1/2}(2x) + \dfrac{1}{v_2}(\dfrac{1}{2})(h_2^2 + (l - x)^2)^{-1/2}2(l - x)(-1) = 0$

$\dfrac{x}{v_1\sqrt{h_1^2 + x^2}} = \dfrac{l - x}{v_2\sqrt{h_2^2 + (l - x)^2}}$

Multiplying both sides by c gives $\dfrac{c}{v_1}\dfrac{x}{\sqrt{h_1^2 + x^2}} = \dfrac{c}{v_2}\dfrac{l - x}{\sqrt{h_2^2 + (l - x)^2}}$

$\dfrac{c}{v_1} = n_1$ and $\dfrac{c}{v_2} = n_2$ (Eq.33.1)

From Fig.33.46, $\sin\theta_1 = \dfrac{x}{\sqrt{h_1^2 + x^2}}$ and $\sin\theta_2 = \dfrac{l - x}{\sqrt{h_2^2 + (l - x)^2}}$.

So $n_1\sin\theta_1 = n_2\sin\theta_2$, which is Snell's law.

EVALUATE: Snell's law is a result of a change in speed when light goes from one material to another.

33.59 IDENTIFY and **SET UP:** The polarizer passes $\frac{1}{2}$ of the intensity of the unpolarized component, independent of ϕ. Out of the intensity I_p of the polarized component the polarizer passes intensity $I_p\cos^2(\phi - \theta)$, where $\phi - \theta$ is the angle between the plane of polarization and the axis of the polarizer.

a) Use the angle where the transmitted intensity is maximum or minimum to find θ.

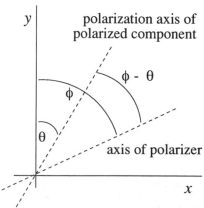

EXECUTE: The total transmitted intensity is $I = \frac{1}{2}I_0 + I_p\cos^2(\phi - \theta)$. This is maximum when $\theta = \phi$ and from the table of data this occurs for ϕ between $30°$ and $40°$, say at $35°$ and $\theta = 35°$.

Alternatively, the total transmitted intensity is minimum when $\phi - \theta = 90°$ and from the data this occurs for $\phi = 125°$. Thus $\theta = \phi - 90° = 125° - 90° = 35°$, in agreement with the above.

b) IDENTIFY and **SET UP:** $I = \frac{1}{2}I_0 + I_p \cos^2(\phi - \theta)$

Use data at two values of ϕ to determine the two constants I_0 and I_p. Use data where the I_p term is large ($\phi = 30°$) and where it is small ($\phi = 130°$) to have the greatest sensitivity to both I_0 and I_p:

EXECUTE: $\phi = 30°$ gives $24.8 \text{ W/m}^2 = \frac{1}{2}I_0 + I_p \cos^2(30° - 35°)$

$24.8 \text{ W/m}^2 = 0.500I_0 + 0.9924I_p$

$\phi = 130°$ gives $5.2 \text{ W/m}^2 = \frac{1}{2}I_0 + I_p \cos^2(130° - 35°)$

$5.2 \text{ W/m}^2 = 0.500I_0 + 0.0076I_p$

Subtracting the second equation from the first gives $19.6 \text{ W/m}^2 = 0.9848I_p$ and

$I_p = 19.9 \text{ W/m}^2$.

And then $I_0 = 2(5.2 \text{ W/m}^2 - 0.0076(19.9 \text{ W/m}^2)) = 10.1 \text{ W/m}^2$.

EVALUATE: Now that we have I_0, I_p and θ we can verify that $I = \frac{1}{2}I_0 + I_p \cos^2(\phi - \theta)$ describes that data in the table.

CHAPTER 34

GEOMETRIC OPTICS

Exercises

34.3 **IDENTIFY** and **SET UP:** Plane mirror: $s = -s'$ (Eq.34.1) and $m = y'/y = -s'/s$ = +1 (Eq.34.2). We are given s and y and are asked to find s' and y'.

EXECUTE:

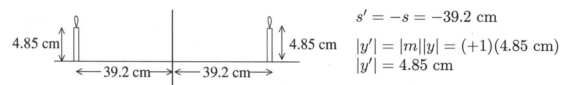

$$s' = -s = -39.2 \text{ cm}$$
$$|y'| = |m||y| = (+1)(4.85 \text{ cm})$$
$$|y'| = 4.85 \text{ cm}$$

The image is 39.2 cm to the right of the mirror and is 4.85 cm tall.

EVALUATE: For a plane mirror the image is always the same distance behind the mirror as the object is in front of the mirror. The image always has the same height as the object.

34.5 **IDENTIFY** and **SET UP:** Use Eq.(34.6) to calculate s' and use Eq.(34.7) to calculate y'. The image is real if s' is positive and is erect if $m > 0$. Concave means R and f are positive; $R = +22.0$ cm; $f = R/2 = +11.0$ cm.

EXECUTE:

a)

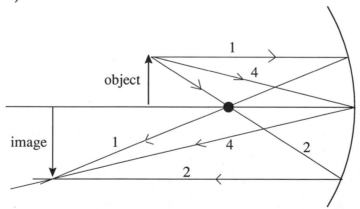

Three principal rays, numbered as in Sect.34.2 are shown.

The principal ray diagram shows that the image is real, inverted, and enlarged.

b) $\dfrac{1}{s} + \dfrac{1}{s'} = \dfrac{1}{f}$

$$\frac{1}{s'} = \frac{1}{f} - \frac{1}{s} = \frac{s-f}{sf} \text{ so } s' = \frac{sf}{s-f} = \frac{(16.5 \text{ cm})(11.0 \text{ cm})}{16.5 \text{ cm} - 11.0 \text{ cm}} = +33.0 \text{ cm}$$

$s' > 0$ so real image, 33.0 cm to left of mirror vertex

$$m = -\frac{s'}{s} = -\frac{33.0 \text{ cm}}{16.5 \text{ cm}} = -2.00 \ (m < 0 \text{ means inverted image})$$

$$|y'| = |m||y| = 2.00(0.600 \text{ cm}) = 1.20 \text{ cm}$$

EVALUATE: The image is 33.0 cm to the left of the mirror vertex. It is real, inverted, and is 1.20 cm tall (enlarged). The calculation agrees with the image characterization from the principal ray diagram.

A concave mirror used alone always forms a real, inverted image if $s > f$ and the image is enlarged if $f < s < 2f$.

34.13 **IDENTIFY** and **SET UP:** Use Eq.(34.6) to calculate s' and use Eq.(34.7) to calculate y'. The image is real if s' is positive and is erect if $m > 0$. Convex means R and f are negative; $R = -20.0$ cm; $f = R/2 = -10.0$ cm.

EXECUTE:

a) $s = 9.00$ cm, so $|s| < |f|$

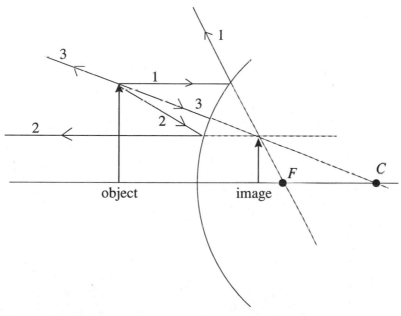

object   image

Three principal rays, numbered as in Sect.34.2, are shown.

The principal ray diagram shows that the image is virtual, erect, reduced in size, and located closer to the mirror than the focal point.

b) $\frac{1}{s} + \frac{1}{s'} = \frac{1}{f}$

$$\frac{1}{s'} = \frac{1}{f} - \frac{1}{s} = \frac{s-f}{sf} \text{ so } s' = \frac{sf}{s-f} = \frac{(12.0 \text{ cm})(-10.0 \text{ cm})}{12.0 \text{ cm} - (-10.0 \text{ cm})} = -5.45 \text{ cm}$$

$s' < 0$ so virtual image, 5.45 cm to right of mirror vertex

$$m = -\frac{s'}{s} = -\frac{-5.45 \text{ cm}}{12.0 \text{ cm}} = +0.454 \ (m > 0 \text{ means erect image})$$

$$|y'| = |m||y| = (+0.454)(9.00 \text{ mm}) = 4.09 \text{ mm}$$

EVALUATE: The image is 5.45 cm to the right of the mirror vertex, closer to the mirror than the focal point. It is 4.09 mm tall (reduced), erect, and virtual. The calculation agrees with the image characterization from the principal ray diagram.

A convex mirror used alone always forms a virtual, erect and reduced image.

34.15 **IDENTIFY:** Apply Eq.(34.11), with $R \to \infty$. $|s'|$ is the apparent depth.

SET UP:

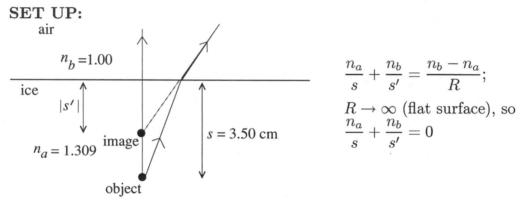

$$\frac{n_a}{s} + \frac{n_b}{s'} = \frac{n_b - n_a}{R};$$

$R \to \infty$ (flat surface), so

$$\frac{n_a}{s} + \frac{n_b}{s'} = 0$$

EXECUTE: $s' = -\dfrac{n_b s}{n_a} = -\dfrac{(1.00)(3.50 \text{ cm})}{1.309} = -2.67 \text{ cm}$

The apparent depth is 2.67 cm.

EVALUATE: When the light goes from ice to air (larger to smaller n), it is bent away from the normal and the virtual image is closer to the surface than the object is.

34.19 **IDENTIFY:** Apply Eq.(34.11). The image and object distances are given; calculate the refractive index of the liquid.

SET UP:

$R = +3.00$ cm

$n_a = n_l$

$n_b = n_g = 1.60$

object   image

$s = +90$ cm $s' = +160$ cm

Let n_l be the refractive index of the liquid.

s, s', and R are all positive.

EXECUTE: $\dfrac{n_a}{s} + \dfrac{n_b}{s'} = \dfrac{n_b - n_a}{R}$

$$\frac{n_l}{90.0 \text{ cm}} + \frac{1.60}{160 \text{ cm}} = \frac{1.60 - n_l}{3.00 \text{ cm}}$$

Multiplying the equation by 1440 cm gives $16.0 n_l + 14.4 = 768 - 480 n_l$

$496n_l = 753.6$ and $n_l = 1.52$.

EVALUATE: Both the center of curvature of the surface and the image are on the outgoing side so R and s' are positive. Note that material a is on the incoming side and material b is on the outgoing side.

34.21 IDENTIFY: Apply Eqs.(34.11) and (34.12). Calculate s' and y'. The image is erect if $m > 0$.

SET UP:

EXECUTE: $\dfrac{n_a}{s} + \dfrac{n_b}{s'} = \dfrac{n_b - n_a}{R}$

$\dfrac{1.00}{24.0 \text{ cm}} + \dfrac{1.60}{s'} = \dfrac{1.60 - 1.00}{-4.00 \text{ cm}}$

Multiplying by 24.0 cm gives $1.00 + \dfrac{38.4}{s'} = -3.60$

$\dfrac{38.4 \text{ cm}}{s'} = -4.60$ and $s' = -\dfrac{38.4 \text{ cm}}{4.60} = -8.35 \text{ cm}$

Eq.(34.12): $m - -\dfrac{n_a s'}{n_b s} = -\dfrac{(1.00)(-8.35 \text{ cm})}{(1.60)(+24.0 \text{ cm})} = +0.217$

$|y'| = |m||y| = (0.217)(1.50 \text{ mm}) = 0.326 \text{ mm}$

EVALUATE: The image is virtual ($s' < 0$) and is 8.35 cm to the left of the vertex. The image is erect ($m > 0$) and is 0.326 mm tall. R is negative since the center of curvature of the surface is on the incoming side.

34.25 IDENTIFY and SET UP: $f = +7.00$ cm ($f > 0$ since the lens is converging).

$m = -\dfrac{s'}{s}$; image is erect implies $m > 0$ so must have $s' < 0$ (image is virtual). Use this equation to relate s and s'. Combine this relation with Eq.(34.16) and calculate s and s'.

EXECUTE: $m = \dfrac{y'}{y} = \dfrac{+1.30 \text{ cm}}{0.400 \text{ cm}} = +3.25$

$s' = -ms = -(3.25)s$

Using this in $\dfrac{1}{s} + \dfrac{1}{s'} = \dfrac{1}{f}$ gives

$\dfrac{1}{s} + \dfrac{1}{(-3.25 \text{ cm})s} = \dfrac{1}{7.00 \text{ cm}}$

$s = +4.85$ cm

$s' = -(3.25)s = -(3.25)(4.85 \text{ cm}) = -15.8$ cm

EVALUATE: The object is 4.85 cm to the left of the lens. $s' < 0$ so the image is 15.8 cm to the left of the lens and is virtual. For a single lens all erect images are virtual. Virtual images are on the same side of the lens as the object.

34.27 IDENTIFY: Use Eq.(34.19) to calculate f and then use Eq.(34.16) to calculate s'.

SET UP:

$R_1 = +5.00$ cm
$R_2 = +3.50$ cm
$n = 1.48$

EXECUTE: $\dfrac{1}{f} = (n-1)\left(\dfrac{1}{R_1} - \dfrac{1}{R_2}\right) = (0.48)\left(\dfrac{1}{5.00 \text{ cm}} - \dfrac{1}{3.50 \text{ cm}}\right);\ f = -24.31$ cm

$s = 18.0$ cm

$\dfrac{1}{s} + \dfrac{1}{s'} = \dfrac{1}{f}$, so $\dfrac{1}{s'} = \dfrac{1}{f} - \dfrac{1}{s} = \dfrac{s-f}{sf}$

$s' = \dfrac{sf}{s-f} = \dfrac{(18.0 \text{ cm})(-24.31 \text{ cm})}{18.0 \text{ cm} - (-24.31 \text{ cm})} = -10.3$ cm

EVALUATE: $s' < 0$ means that the image is virtual and is 10.3 cm to the left of the lens, on the same side of the lens as the object. The lens is diverging and a single diverging lens always forms a virtual image.

34.33 IDENTIFY: Use Eq.(34.16) to calculate the object distance s. m calculated from Eq.(34.17) determines the size and orientation of the image.

SET UP: $f = -48.0$ cm

virtual image 17.0 cm from lens so $s' = -17.0$ cm

EXECUTE: $\dfrac{1}{s} + \dfrac{1}{s'} = \dfrac{1}{f}$, so $\dfrac{1}{s'} = \dfrac{1}{f} - \dfrac{1}{s} = \dfrac{s-f}{sf}$

$s = \dfrac{s'f}{s'-f} = \dfrac{(-17.0 \text{ cm})(-48.0 \text{ cm})}{-17.0 \text{ cm} - (-48.0 \text{ cm})} = +26.3$ cm

$m = -\dfrac{s'}{s} = -\dfrac{-17.0 \text{ cm}}{+26.3 \text{ cm}} = +0.646$

$m = \dfrac{y'}{y}$ so $|y| = \dfrac{|y'|}{|m|} = \dfrac{8.00 \text{ mm}}{0.646} = 12.4$ mm

EVALUATE: Virtual image, real object ($s > 0$) so image and object are on same side of lens.

$m > 0$ so image is erect with respect to the object. The height of the object is 12.4 mm.

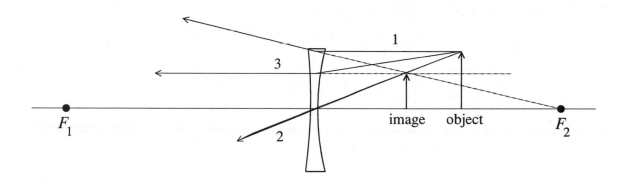

34.35 **IDENTIFY** and **SET UP:** Find the lateral magnification that results in this desired image size. Use Eq.(34.17) to relate m and s' and Eq.(34.16) to relate s and s' to f.

EXECUTE:

a) We need $m = -\dfrac{24 \times 10^{-3} \text{ m}}{160 \text{ m}} = -1.5 \times 10^{-4}$.

Alternatively, $m = -\dfrac{36 \times 10^{-3} \text{ m}}{240 \text{ m}} = -1.5 \times 10^{-4}$.

$s \gg f$ so $s' \approx f$

Then $m = -\dfrac{s'}{s} = -\dfrac{f}{s} = -1.5 \times 10^{-4}$ and

$f = (1.5 \times 10^{-4})(600 \text{ m}) = 0.090 \text{ m} = 90 \text{ mm}$.

A smaller f means a smaller s' and a smaller m, so with $f = 85$ mm the object's image nearly fills the picture area.

b) We need $m = -\dfrac{36 \times 10^{-3} \text{ m}}{9.6 \text{ m}} = -3.75 \times 10^{-3}$.

Then, as in part (a), $\dfrac{f}{s} = 3.75 \times 10^{-3}$ and

$f = (40.0 \text{ m})(3.75 \times 10^{-3}) = 0.15 \text{ m} = 150 \text{ mm}$.

Therefore use the 135 mm lens.

EVALUATE: When $s \gg f$ and $s' \approx f$, $y' = -f(y/s)$. For the mobile home y/s is smaller so a larger f is needed. Note that m is very small; the image is much smaller than the object.

34.41 **IDENTIFY** and **SET UP:** Eq.(34.20) relates the f-number, focal length and lens diameter. The light energy that passes through the lens aperture in time t is proportional to the aperture area. To achieve the correct exposure the light energy incident on the film must be kept constant.

EXECUTE:

a) $f/4$ lens means f-number $= 4$

f-number $= \dfrac{f}{D}$ (Eq.34.20) so $D = \dfrac{f}{f-\text{number}} = \dfrac{300 \text{ m}}{4} = 75$ mm

b) $f/8$ lens means f-number $= 8$; $D = \dfrac{f}{f-\text{number}} = \dfrac{300 \text{ m}}{8} = 37.5$ mm

D is smaller by a factor of 2. The aperture area is smaller by a factor of $2^2 = 4$. So need an exposure time larger by a factor of 4; $4(1/250)$ s $= (1/62.5)$ s.

EVALUATE: A larger f-number corresponds to a smaller aperture and area, so at a larger f-number a longer exposure time is required.

34.45 **a)** **IDENTIFY:** The purpose of the corrective lens is to take an object 25 cm from the eye and form a virtual image at the eye's near point. Use Eq.(34.16) to solve for the image distance when the object distance is 25 cm.

SET UP: $\dfrac{1}{f} = +2.75$ diopters means $f = +\dfrac{1}{2.75}$ m $= +0.3636$ m (converging lens)

$f = 36.36$ cm; $s = 25$ cm; $s' =?$

EXECUTE: $\dfrac{1}{s} + \dfrac{1}{s'} = \dfrac{1}{f}$ so

$s' = \dfrac{sf}{s - f} = \dfrac{(25 \text{ cm})(36.36 \text{ cm})}{25 \text{ cm} - 36.36 \text{ cm}} = -80.0$ cm

The eye's near point is 80.0 cm from the eye.

b) **IDENTIFY:** The purpose of the corrective lens is to take an object at infinity and form a virtual image of it at the eye's far point. Use Eq.(34.16) to solve for the image distance when the object is at infinity.

SET UP: $\dfrac{1}{f} = -1.30$ diopters means $f = -\dfrac{1}{1.30}$ m $= -0.7692$ m (diverging lens)

$f = -76.92$ cm; $s = \infty$; $s' =?$

EXECUTE: $\dfrac{1}{s} + \dfrac{1}{s'} = \dfrac{1}{f}$ and $s = \infty$ says $\dfrac{1}{s'} = \dfrac{1}{f}$ and $s' = f = -76.9$ cm

The eye's far point is 76.9 cm from the eye.

EVALUATE: In each case a virtual image is formed by the lens. The eye views this virtual image instead of the object. The object is at a distance where the eye can't focus on it, but the virtual image is at a distance where the eye can focus.

34.49 **IDENTIFY:** Use Eqs.(34.16) and (34.17) to calculate s and y'.

a) SET UP: $f = 8.00$ cm; $s' = -25.0$ cm; $s =?$

$\dfrac{1}{s} + \dfrac{1}{s'} = \dfrac{1}{f}$, so $\dfrac{1}{s} = \dfrac{1}{f} - \dfrac{1}{s'} = \dfrac{s' - f}{s'f}$

EXECUTE: $s = \dfrac{s'f}{s'-f} = \dfrac{(-25.0 \text{ cm})(+8.00 \text{ cm})}{-25.0 \text{ cm} - 8.00 \text{ cm}} = +6.06 \text{ cm}$

b) $m = -\dfrac{s'}{s} = -\dfrac{-25.0 \text{ cm}}{6.06 \text{ cm}} = +4.125$

$|m| = \dfrac{|y'|}{|y|}$ so $|y'| = |m||y| = (4.125)(1.00 \text{ mm}) = 4.12 \text{ mm}$

EVALUATE: The lens allows the object to be much closer to the eye than the near point. The lens allows the eye to view an image at the near point rather than the object.

34.51 IDENTIFY and **SET UP:** Combine Eqs.(34.16) and (34.17); solve for s and s'. The image formed by a simple magnifier is virtual and $m = \dfrac{s'}{s}$ is positive.

EXECUTE: Thus $m = +6.50$. $m = -\dfrac{s'}{s}$ gives that $s' = -6.50s$.

Use this in $\dfrac{1}{s} + \dfrac{1}{s'} = \dfrac{1}{f}$: $\qquad \dfrac{1}{s} + \dfrac{1}{-6.50s} = \dfrac{1}{4.00 \text{ cm}}$

$s = 3.38 \text{ cm}$ and $s' = -22.0 \text{ cm}$

The flea is 3.38 cm from the lens and the image is 22.0 cm from the lens, on the same side of the lens as the flea.

EVALUATE: The object and image have the same angular size, $1/3.38 = 6.5/22$, but the image is far enough from the eye for the eye to focus on it.

34.53 a) IDENTIFY and **SET UP:**

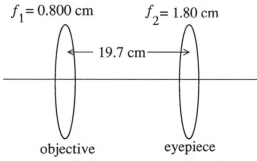

$f_1 = 0.800 \text{ cm}$ $f_2 = 1.80 \text{ cm}$
← 19.7 cm →
objective   eyepiece

Final image is at ∞ so the object for the eyepiece is at its focal point. But the object for the eyepiece is the image of the objective so the image formed by the objective is 10.7 cm   1.80 cm − 17.9 cm to the right of the lens.

Apply Eq.(34.16) to the image formation by the objective; solve for the object distance s.

$f = 0.800 \text{ cm}$; $s' = 17.9 \text{ cm}$; $s = ?$

$$\frac{1}{s} + \frac{1}{s'} = \frac{1}{f}, \text{ so } \frac{1}{s} = \frac{1}{f} - \frac{1}{s'} = \frac{s' - f}{s'f}$$

EXECUTE: $s = \dfrac{s'f}{s' - f} = \dfrac{(17.9 \text{ cm})(+0.800 \text{ cm})}{17.9 \text{ cm} - 0.800 \text{ cm}} = +8.37 \text{ mm}$

b) SET UP: Use Eq.(34.17).

EXECUTE: $m_1 = -\dfrac{s'}{s} = -\dfrac{17.9 \text{ cm}}{0.837 \text{ cm}} = -21.4$

The magnification of the linear magnification of the objective is 21.4.

c) SET UP: Use Eq.(34.23): $M = m_1 M_2$

EXECUTE: $M_2 = \dfrac{25 \text{ cm}}{f_2} = \dfrac{25 \text{ cm}}{1.80 \text{ cm}} = 13.9$

$M = m_1 M_2 = (-21.4)(13.9) = -297$

EVALUATE: M is not accurately given by $(25 \text{ cm})s_1'/f_1 f_2 = 311$, because the object is not quite at the focal point of the objective ($s_1 = 0.837$ cm and $f_1 = 0.800$ cm).

34.55 a) IDENTIFY and **SET UP:** Use Eq.(34.24), with $f_1 = 95.0$ cm (objective) and $f_2 = 15.0$ cm (eyepiece).

EXECUTE: $M = -\dfrac{f_1}{f_2} = -\dfrac{95.0 \text{ cm}}{15.0 \text{ cm}} = -6.33$

b) IDENTIFY: Use Eq.(34.17) to calculate y'.

SET UP: $s = 3.00 \times 10^3$ m

$s' = f_1 = 95.0$ cm (since s is very large, $s' \approx f$)

EXECUTE: $m = -\dfrac{s'}{s} = -\dfrac{0.950 \text{ m}}{3.00 \times 10^3 \text{ m}} = -3.167 \times 10^{-4}$

$|y'| = |m||y| = (3.167 \times 10^{-4})(60.0 \text{ m}) = 0.0190 \text{ m} = 1.90 \text{ cm}$

c) IDENTIFY and **SET UP:** Use Eq.(34.21) and the angular magnification M obtained in part (a) to calculate θ'. The angular size θ of the image formed by the objective (object for the eyepiece) is its height divided by its distance from the objective.

EXECUTE: The angular size of the object for the eyepiece is

$\theta = \dfrac{0.0190 \text{ m}}{0.950 \text{ m}} = 0.0200$ rad.

(Note that this is also the angular size of the object for the objective: $\theta = \dfrac{60.0 \text{ m}}{3.00 \times 10^3 \text{ m}} = 0.0200$ rad. For a thin lens the object and image have the same angular size and the image of the objective is the object for the eyepiece.)

$M = \dfrac{\theta'}{\theta}$ (Eq.34.21) so the angular size of the image is

$\theta' = M\theta = -(6.33)(0.0200 \text{ rad}) = -0.127 \text{ rad}$

(The minus sign shows that the final image is inverted.)

EVALUATE: The lateral magnification of the objective is small; the image it forms is much smaller than the object. But the total angular magnification is larger than 1.00; the angular size of the final image viewed by the eye is 6.33 times larger than the angular size of the original object, as viewed by the unaided eye.

Problems

34.61 IDENTIFY and **SET UP:** For a plane mirror $s' = -s$. $v = \dfrac{ds}{dt}$ and

$v' = \dfrac{ds'}{dt}$, so $v' = -v$.

EXECUTE: The velocities of the object and image relative to the mirror are equal in magnitude and opposite in direction. Thus both you and your image are receding from the mirror surface at 2.40 m/s, in opposite directions. Your image is therefore moving at 4.80 m/s relative to you.

EVALUATE: The result derives from the fact that for a plane mirror the image is the same distance behind the mirror as the object is in front of the mirror.

34.65 IDENTIFY: We are given the image distance, the image height and the object height. Use Eq.(34.7) to calculate the object distance s. Then use Eq.(34.4) to calculate R.

a) SET UP: Image is to be formed on screen so is real image; $s' > 0$. Mirror to screen distance is 8.00 m, so $s' = +800$ cm.

$m = -\dfrac{s'}{s} < 0$ since both s and s' are positive.

EXECUTE: $|m| = \dfrac{|y'|}{|y|} = \dfrac{36.0 \text{ cm}}{0.600 \text{ cm}} = 60.0$ and $m = -60.0$.

Then $m = -\dfrac{s'}{s}$ gives $s = -\dfrac{s'}{m} = -\dfrac{800 \text{ cm}}{-60.0} = +13.3$ cm.

b) $\dfrac{1}{s} + \dfrac{1}{s'} = \dfrac{2}{R}$, so $\dfrac{2}{R} = \dfrac{s + s'}{ss'}$

$R = 2\left(\dfrac{ss'}{s + s'}\right) = 2\left(\dfrac{(13.3 \text{ cm})(800 \text{ cm})}{800 \text{ cm} + 13.3 \text{ cm}}\right) = 26.2$ cm.

EVALUATE: R is calculated to be positive, which is correct for a concave mirror. Also, in part (a) s is calculated to be positive, as it should be for a real object.

34.67 **IDENTIFY** and **SET UP:** Apply Eqs.(34.6) and (34.7). For a virtual object $s < 0$. The image is real if $s' > 0$.

EXECUTE:

a) convex implies $R < 0$; $R = -24.0$ cm; $f = R/2 = -12.0$ cm

$$\frac{1}{s} + \frac{1}{s'} = \frac{1}{f}, \text{ so } \frac{1}{s'} = \frac{1}{f} - \frac{1}{s} = \frac{s - f}{sf}$$

$$s' = \frac{sf}{s - f} = \frac{(-12.0 \text{ cm})s}{s + 12.0 \text{ cm}}$$

s is negative, so write as $s = -|s|$; $s' = +\dfrac{(12.0 \text{ cm})|s|}{12.0 \text{ cm} - |s|}$.

Thus $s' > 0$ (real image) for $|s| < 12.0$ cm. Since s is negative this means $-12.0 \text{ cm} < s < 0$. A real image is formed if the virtual object is closer to the mirror than the focus.

b) $m = -\dfrac{s'}{s}$; real image implies $s' > 0$; virtual object implies $s < 0$. Thus $m > 0$ and the image is erect.

c)

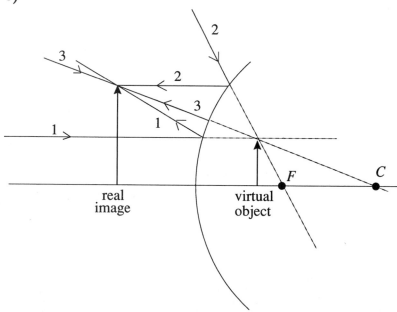

EVALUATE: For a real object, only virtual images are formed by a convex mirror. The virtual object considered in this problem must have been produced by some other optical element, another lens or mirror in addition to the convex one we considered.

34.73 **IDENTIFY** and **SET UP:** Eq.(34.4) relates s and s'. Use this equation to obtain a relation between $v' = ds'/dt$ and $v = ds/dt$, the speeds of the image and object.

convex mirror means $R < 0$ so $R = -1.25$ m; $f = R/2 = -0.625$ m

EXECUTE: Find the relation between s and s':

$$\frac{1}{s} + \frac{1}{s'} = \frac{1}{f}, \text{ so } \frac{1}{s'} = \frac{1}{f} - \frac{1}{s} = \frac{s-f}{sf} \text{ and } s' = \frac{sf}{s-f}$$

The speed of the image is $v' = \frac{ds'}{dt} = \frac{ds'}{ds}\frac{ds}{dt}$. Note that $v' > 0$ if the virtual image ($s' < 0$) is moving toward the mirror.

$$\frac{ds'}{ds} = \frac{f}{s-f} - \frac{sf}{(s-f)^2} = \frac{(s-f)f - sf}{(s-f)^2} = -\frac{f^2}{(s-f)^2} = -\left(\frac{f}{s-f}\right)^2$$

$\frac{ds}{dt} = v$, the speed of the object. Note that $v > 0$ if the object is moving away from the mirror.

Thus $v' = -\left(\frac{f}{s-f}\right)^2 v$.

a) $s = 10.0$ m

$$v' = -\left(\frac{-0.625 \text{ m}}{10.0 \text{ m} - (-0.625 \text{ m})}\right)^2 (-2.50 \text{ m/s}) = 0.00865 \text{ m/s} = 8.65 \text{ mm/s}$$

b) $s = 2.0$ m

$$v' = -\left(\frac{-0.625 \text{ m}}{2.0 \text{ m} - (-0.625 \text{ m})}\right)^2 (-2.50 \text{ m/s}) = 0.142 \text{ m/s} = 14.2 \text{ cm/s}$$

EVALUATE: The speed of the object is constant but the speed of the image is not. Compare to Problem 34.61.

34.77 IDENTIFY: Apply Eqs.(34.11) and (34.12) to the refraction as the light enters the rod and as it leaves the rod. The image formed by the first surface serves as the object for the second surface. The total magnification is $m_{tot} = m_1 m_2$, where m_1 and m_2 are the magnifications for each surface.

SET UP:

a) image formed by refraction at first surface (left end of rod):

$s = +23.0$ cm; $n_a = 1.00$; $n_b = 1.60$; $R = +6.00$ cm

$$\frac{n_a}{s} + \frac{n_b}{s'} = \frac{n_b - n_a}{R}$$

EXECUTE: $\dfrac{1}{23.0 \text{ cm}} + \dfrac{1.60}{s'} = \dfrac{1.60 - 1.00}{6.00 \text{ cm}}$

$\dfrac{1.60}{s'} = \dfrac{1}{10.0 \text{ cm}} - \dfrac{1}{23.0 \text{ cm}} = \dfrac{23 - 10}{230 \text{ cm}} = \dfrac{13}{230 \text{ cm}}$

$s' = 1.60 \left(\dfrac{230 \text{ cm}}{13} \right) = +28.3 \text{ cm}$; image is 28.3 cm to right of first vertex.

This image serves as the object for the refraction at the second surface (right end of rod). It is 28.3 cm − 25.0 cm = 3.3 cm to the right of the second vertex. For the second surface $s = -3.3$ cm (virtual object).

b) EVALUATE: Object is on side of outgoing light, so is a virtual object.

c) SET UP: Image formed by refraction at second surface (right end of rod):

$s = -3.3$ cm; $n_a = 1.60$; $n_b = 1.00$; $R = -12.0$ cm

$\dfrac{n_a}{s} + \dfrac{n_b}{s'} = \dfrac{n_b - n_a}{R}$

EXECUTE: $\dfrac{1.60}{-3.3 \text{ cm}} + \dfrac{1.00}{s'} = \dfrac{1.00 - 1.60}{-12.0 \text{ cm}}$

$s' = +1.9$ cm; $s' > 0$ so image is 1.9 cm to right of vertex at right-hand end of rod.

d) $s' > 0$ so final image is real.

magnification for first surface:

$m = -\dfrac{n_a s'}{n_b s} = -\dfrac{(1.00)(+28.3 \text{ cm})}{(1.60)(+23.0 \text{ cm})} = -0.769$

magnification for second surface:

$m = -\dfrac{n_a s'}{n_b s} = -\dfrac{(1.60)(+1.9 \text{ cm})}{(1.00)(-3.3 \text{ cm})} = +0.92$

The overall magnification is $m_{\text{tot}} = m_1 m_2 = (-0.769)(+0.92) = -0.71$

$m_{\text{tot}} < 0$ so final image is inverted with respect to the original object.

e) $y' = m_{\text{tot}} y = (-0.71)(1.50 \text{ mm}) = -1.06 \text{ mm}$

The final image has a height of 1.06 mm.

EVALUATE: The two refracting surfaces are not close together and Eq.(34.18) does not apply.

34.79 IDENTIFY: Apply Eq.(34.11) to the image formed by refraction at the front surface of the sphere.

SET UP: Let n_g be the index of refraction of the glass.

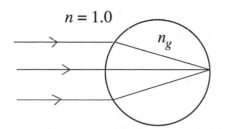

$s = \infty$

$s' = +2r$, where r is
the radius of the sphere

$n_a = 1.00$, $n_b = n_g$, $R = +r$

$$\frac{n_a}{s} + \frac{n_b}{s'} = \frac{n_b - n_a}{R}$$

EXECUTE: $\dfrac{1}{\infty} + \dfrac{n_g}{2r} = \dfrac{n_g - 1.00}{r}$

$\dfrac{n_g}{2r} = \dfrac{n_g}{r} - \dfrac{1}{r}; \dfrac{n_g}{2r} - \dfrac{1}{r}$ and $n_g = 2.00$

EVALUATE: The required refractive index of the glass does not depend on the radius of the sphere.

34.81 **IDENTIFY** and **SET UP:** Apply Eq.(34.11) to the refraction as the light enters the glass and as it exits the glass. The image formed by the first refraction serves as the object for the second refraction.

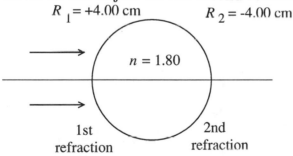

The two vertexes are a distance $2R = 8.00$ cm apart.

EXECUTE:

<u>1st refraction</u>

$n_a = 1.00$; $n_b = 1.80$; $R = +4.00$ cm; $s = \infty$ (parallel rays)

$$\frac{n_a}{s} + \frac{n_b}{s'} = \frac{n_b - n_a}{R}$$

$$\frac{1.00}{\infty} + \frac{1.80}{s'} = \frac{1.80 - 1.00}{+4.00 \text{ cm}}$$

$\dfrac{1.80}{s'} = \dfrac{0.8}{4.00 \text{ cm}}$ and $s' = (1.80)\left(\dfrac{4.00 \text{ cm}}{0.80}\right) = 9.00$ cm

$s' > 0$ means the first image is 9.00 cm to the right of the first vertex, so is 1.00 cm to the right of the second vertex. This image serves as a virtual object for the second refraction, with $s = -1.00$ cm.

2nd refraction

$n_a = 1.80$; $n_b = 1.00$; $R = -4.00$ cm; $s = -1.00$ cm

$$\frac{n_a}{s} + \frac{n_b}{s'} = \frac{n_b - n_a}{R}$$

$$\frac{1.80}{-1.00 \text{ cm}} + \frac{1.00}{s'} = \frac{1.00 - 1.80}{-4.00 \text{ cm}}$$

$$\frac{1.00}{s'} = \frac{0.8}{4.00 \text{ cm}} + \frac{1.80}{1.00 \text{ cm}} \text{ and } s' = 0.50 \text{ cm}$$

$s' > 0$ so this the final image is 0.50 cm to the right of the second vertex, or 4.50 cm from the center of the sphere.

EVALUATE: When applying Eq.(34.11), n_a is the refractive index of the material in which the light is incident on the interface. For the 1st refraction $R > 0$ because the center of curvature of the surface is on the outgoing side of the interface and for the 2nd refraction $R < 0$ because the center of curvature is on the incoming side.

34.83 a) IDENTIFY: Apply Snell's law to the refraction of a ray at each side of the beam to find where these rays strike the table.

SET UP:

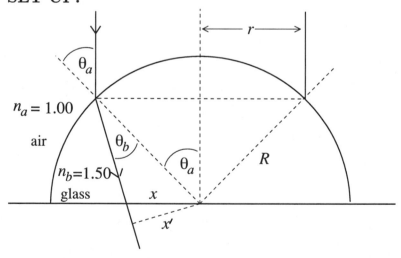

The width of the incident beam is exaggerated in the sketch, to make it easier to draw. Since the diameter of the beam is much less than the radius of the hemisphere, angles θ_a and θ_b are small.

The diameter of the circle of light formed on the table is $2x$. Note the two right triangles containing the angles θ_a and θ_b.

$r = 0.190$ cm is the radius of the incident beam.

$R = 12.0$ cm is the radius of the glass hemisphere.

EXECUTE: θ_a and θ_b small imply $x \approx x'$; $\sin \theta_a = \frac{r}{R}$, $\sin \theta_b = \frac{x'}{R} \approx \frac{x}{R}$

Snell's law: $n_a \sin\theta_a = n_b \sin\theta_b$

Using the above expressions for $\sin\theta_a$ and $\sin\theta_b$ gives $n_a \dfrac{r}{R} = n_b \dfrac{x}{R}$

$n_a r = n_b x$ so $x = \dfrac{n_a r}{n_b} = \dfrac{1.00(0.190 \text{ cm})}{1.50} = 0.1267 \text{ cm}$

The diameter of the circle on the table is $2x = 2(0.1267 \text{ cm}) = 0.253 \text{ cm}$.

b) EVALUATE: R divides out of the expression; the result for the diameter of the spot is independent of the radius R of the hemisphere. It depends only on the diameter of the incident beam and the index of refraction of the glass.

34.85 IDENTIFY: Thin-walled glass means the glass has no effect on the light rays. The problem is that of refraction by a sphere of water surrounded by air. Apply Eq.(34.11) to the refraction of the light as it enters and exits the water. The image formed by the first refraction serves as the object for the second refraction.

SET UP:

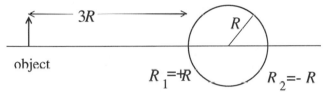

EXECUTE:

First refraction (air→water):

$n_a = 1.00$ (air); $n_b = 4/3$ (water); $s_1 = 3R$; $R_1 = +R$

$\dfrac{n_a}{s_1} + \dfrac{n_b}{s_1'} = \dfrac{n_b - n_a}{R_1}$

$\dfrac{1}{3R} + \dfrac{4/3}{s_1'} = \dfrac{4/3 - 1.00}{R}$, $\dfrac{4}{3s_1'} = \dfrac{1}{3R} - \dfrac{1}{3R} = 0$ and $s_1' = \infty$ (parallel rays)

Second refraction (water→air):

$n_a = 4/3$ (water); $n_b = 1.00$ (air); $s_2 = -\infty$; $R_2 = -R$

$\dfrac{n_a}{s_2} + \dfrac{n_b}{s_2'} = \dfrac{n_b - n_a}{R_2}$

$\dfrac{4/3}{-\infty} + \dfrac{1.00}{s_2'} = \dfrac{1.00 - 4/3}{-R}$

$\dfrac{1.00}{s_2'} = \dfrac{1.00}{3R}$ and $s_2' = +3R$

The final image is $3R$ to the right of the second surface so is $4R$ from the center of the sphere, on the opposite side from the object.

EVALUATE: The image is the same distance to the right of the center of the sphere as the object is to the left of the center of the sphere. This is not a general result and holds only for this particular object distance.

34.87 IDENTIFY and **SET UP:** Apply Eq.(34.16) for each lens position. The lens to screen distance in each case is the image distance. There are two unknowns, the original object distance x and the focal length f of the lens. But each lens position gives an equation, so there are two equations for these two unknowns.

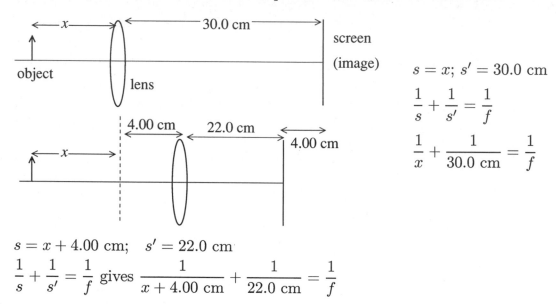

$$s = x; \quad s' = 30.0 \text{ cm}$$

$$\frac{1}{s} + \frac{1}{s'} = \frac{1}{f}$$

$$\frac{1}{x} + \frac{1}{30.0 \text{ cm}} = \frac{1}{f}$$

$$s = x + 4.00 \text{ cm}; \quad s' = 22.0 \text{ cm}$$

$$\frac{1}{s} + \frac{1}{s'} = \frac{1}{f} \text{ gives } \frac{1}{x + 4.00 \text{ cm}} + \frac{1}{22.0 \text{ cm}} = \frac{1}{f}$$

EXECUTE: Equate these two expressions for $1/f$:

$$\frac{1}{x} + \frac{1}{30.0 \text{ cm}} = \frac{1}{x + 4.00 \text{ cm}} + \frac{1}{22.0 \text{ cm}}$$

$$\frac{1}{x} - \frac{1}{x + 4.00 \text{ cm}} = \frac{1}{22.0 \text{ cm}} - \frac{1}{30.0 \text{ cm}}$$

$$\frac{x + 4.00 \text{ cm} - x}{x(x + 4.00 \text{ cm})} = \frac{30.0 - 22.0}{660 \text{ cm}} \text{ and } \frac{4.00 \text{ cm}}{x(x + 4.00 \text{ cm})} = \frac{8}{660 \text{ cm}}$$

$x^2 + (4.00 \text{ cm})x - 330 \text{ cm}^2 = 0$ and $x = \frac{1}{2}(-4.00 \pm \sqrt{16.0 + 4(330)})$ cm

x must be positive so $x = \frac{1}{2}(-4.00 + 36.55)$ cm $= 16.28$ cm

Then $\dfrac{1}{x} + \dfrac{1}{30.0 \text{ cm}} = \dfrac{1}{f}$ and $\dfrac{1}{f} = \dfrac{1}{16.28 \text{ cm}} + \dfrac{1}{30.0 \text{ cm}}$

$f = +10.55$ cm, which rounds to 10.6 cm. $f > 0$; the lens is converging.

EVALUATE: We can check that $s = 16.28$ cm and $f = 10.55$ cm gives $s' = 30.0$ cm and that $s = (16.28 + 4.0)$ cm $= 20.28$ cm and $f = 10.55$ cm gives $s' = 22.0$ cm.

34.89 IDENTIFY: The image formed by the first lens serves as the object for the second lens. The image distance s' for the second lens determines the location of the final image and whether it is real or vitrual. The final image height and orientation is determined by $m_{\text{tot}} = m_1 m_2$, where m_1 and m_2 are the magnifications for lenses 1 and 2.

SET UP:

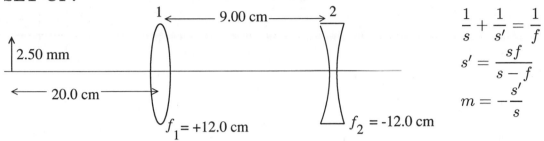

$$\frac{1}{s} + \frac{1}{s'} = \frac{1}{f}$$

$$s' = \frac{sf}{s - f}$$

$$m = -\frac{s'}{s}$$

EXECUTE:

image formed by lens #1

$$s_1' = \frac{s_1 f}{s_1 - f} = \frac{(20.0 \text{ cm})(12.0 \text{ cm})}{20.0 \text{ cm} - 12.0 \text{ cm}} = +30.0 \text{ cm};$$

$$m_1 = -\frac{s_1'}{s_1} = -1.50$$

This image serves as the object for the second lens. The image is 30.0 cm to the right of lens #1 so is 30.0 cm − 9.00 cm = 21.0 cm to the right of lens #2. So for lens #2, $s_2 = -21.0$ cm.

image formed by lens #2

$$s_2' = \frac{s_2 f}{s_2 - f} = \frac{(-21.0 \text{ cm})(-12.0 \text{ cm})}{-21.0 \text{ cm} + 12.0 \text{ cm}} = -28.0 \text{ cm};$$

$$m_2 = -\frac{s_2'}{s_2} = -1.33$$

a) $s_2' = -28.0$ cm so the final image is 28.0 cm to the left of lens #2 and 28.0 cm − 9.00 cm = 19.0 cm to the left of lens #1.

b) $s_2' < 0$ so the final image is virtual.

c) $m_{\text{tot}} = m_1 m_2 = (-1.50)(-1.33) = +2.00$

$y' = m_{\text{tot}} y = (2.00)(2.50 \text{ mm}) = 5.00 \text{ mm}$ (height of final image).

$m_{\text{tot}} > 0$ so final image is erect (with respect to original object)

($m_1 < 0$ so lens #1 inverts the image. But $m_2 < 0$ also, so lens #2 also inverts the image, making it erect.)

EVALUATE: The real image formed by the first lens is to the right of the second lens so serves as a virtual object for the second lens and s_2 is negative.

34.91 IDENTIFY: Apply Eq.(34.16) to calculate the image distance for each lens. The image formed by the 1st lens serves as the object for the 2nd lens, and the image formed by the 2nd lens serves as the object for the 3rd lens.

SET UP:

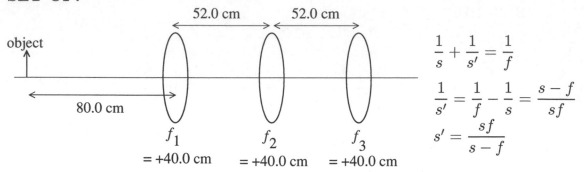

$$\frac{1}{s} + \frac{1}{s'} = \frac{1}{f}$$

$$\frac{1}{s'} = \frac{1}{f} - \frac{1}{s} = \frac{s - f}{sf}$$

$$s' = \frac{sf}{s - f}$$

EXECUTE:

lens #1

$s = +80.0$ cm; $f = +40.0$ cm

$$s' = \frac{sf}{s - f} = \frac{(+80.0 \text{ cm})(+40.0 \text{ cm})}{+80.0 \text{ cm} - 40.0 \text{ cm}} = +80.0 \text{ cm}$$

The image formed by the first lens is 80.0 cm to the right of the first lens, so it is 80.0 cm − 52.0 cm = 28.0 cm to the right of the second lens.

lens #2

$s = -28.0$ cm; $f = +40.0$ cm

$$s' = \frac{sf}{s - f} = \frac{(-28.0 \text{ cm})(+40.0 \text{ cm})}{-28.0 \text{ cm} - 40.0 \text{ cm}} = +16.47 \text{ cm}$$

The image formed by the second lens is 16.47 cm to the right of the second lens, so it is 52.0 cm − 16.47 cm = 35.53 cm to the left of the third lens.

lens #3

$s = +35.53$ cm; $f = +40.0$ cm

$$s' = \frac{sf}{s - f} = \frac{(+35.53 \text{ cm})(+40.0 \text{ cm})}{+35.53 \text{ cm} - 40.0 \text{ cm}} = -318 \text{ cm}$$

The final image is 318 cm to the left of the third lens, so it is 318 cm − 52 cm − 52 cm − 80 cm = 134 cm to the left of the object.

EVALUATE: We used the separation between the lenses and the sign conventions for s and s' to determine the object distances for the 2nd and 3rd lenses. The final image is virtual since the final s' is negative.

34.93 a) IDENTIFY: Use Eq.(34.6) to locate the image formed by each mirror. The image formed by the first mirror serves as the object for the 2nd mirror.

SET UP:

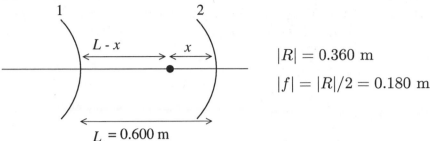

$|R| = 0.360$ m

$|f| = |R|/2 = 0.180$ m

EXECUTE:

Image formed by convex mirror (mirror #1):

convex means $f_1 = -0.180$ m; $s_1 = L - x$

$$s'_1 = \frac{s_1 f_1}{s_1 - f_1} = \frac{(L-x)(-0.180 \text{ m})}{L - x + 0.180 \text{ m}} = -(0.180 \text{ m})\left(\frac{0.600 \text{ m} - x}{0.780 \text{ m} - x}\right) < 0$$

The image is $(0.180 \text{ m})\left(\dfrac{0.600 \text{ m} - x}{0.780 \text{ m} - x}\right)$ to the left of mirror #1 so is

$$0.600 \text{ m} + (0.180 \text{ m})\left(\frac{0.600 \text{ m} - x}{0.780 \text{ m} - x}\right) =$$

$$\frac{0.576 \text{ m}^2 - (0.780 \text{ m})x}{0.780 \text{ m} - x} \text{ to the left of mirror \#2.}$$

Image formed by concave mirror (mirror #2):

concave implies $f_2 = +0.180$ m

$$s_2 = \frac{0.576 \text{ m}^2 - (0.780 \text{ m})x}{0.780 \text{ m} - x}$$

Rays return to the source implies $s'_2 = x$.

Using these expressions in $s_2 = \dfrac{s'_2 f_2}{s'_2 - f_2}$ gives

$$\frac{0.576 \text{ m}^2 - (0.780 \text{ m})x}{0.780 \text{ m} - x} = \frac{(0.180 \text{ m})x}{x - 0.180 \text{ m}}$$

$$0.600x^2 - (0.576 \text{ m})x + 0.10368 \text{ m}^2 = 0$$

$$x = \tfrac{1}{1.20}\left(0.576 \pm \sqrt{(0.576)^2 - 4(0.600)(0.10368)}\right) \text{ m} = \tfrac{1}{1.20}(0.576 \pm 0.288) \text{ m}$$

$x = 0.72$ m (imposible; can't have $x > L = 0.600$ m) or $x = 0.24$ m.

b) SET UP: Which mirror is #1 and which is #2 is now reversed from part (a).

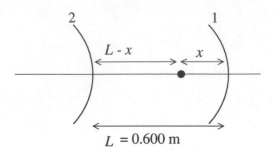

$$L = 0.600 \text{ m}$$

EXECUTE:

Image formed by concave mirror (mirror #1):

concave means $f_1 = +0.180$ m; $s_1 = x$

$$s_1' = \frac{s_1 f_1}{s_1 - f_1} = \frac{(0.180 \text{ m})x}{x - 0.180 \text{ m}}$$

The image is $\dfrac{(0.180 \text{ m})x}{x - 0.180 \text{ m}}$ to the left of mirror #1, so

$$s_2 = 0.600 \text{ m} - \frac{(0.180 \text{ m})x}{x - 0.180 \text{ m}} = \frac{(0.420 \text{ m})x - 0.108 \text{ m}^2}{x - 0.180 \text{ m}}$$

Image formed by convex mirror (mirror #2):

convex means $f_2 = -0.180$ m

rays return to the source means $s_2' = L - x = 0.600 \text{ m} - x$

$\dfrac{1}{s} + \dfrac{1}{s'} = \dfrac{1}{f}$ gives

$$\frac{x - 0.180 \text{ m}}{(0.420 \text{ m})x - 0.108 \text{ m}^2} + \frac{1}{0.600 \text{ m} - x} = -\frac{1}{0.180 \text{ m}}$$

$$\frac{x - 0.180 \text{ m}}{(0.420 \text{ m})x - 0.108 \text{ m}^2} = -\left(\frac{0.780 \text{ m} - x}{0.108 \text{ m}^2 - (0.180 \text{ m})x} \right)$$

$$0.600x^2 - (0.576 \text{ m})x + 0.1036 \text{ m}^2 = 0$$

This is the same quadratic equation as obtained in part (a), so again $x = 0.24$ m.

EVALUATE: For $x = 0.24$ m the image is at the location of the source, both for rays that initially travel from the source toward the left and for rays that travel from the source toward the right.

34.97 IDENTIFY: Apply Eq.(34.11) with $R \to \infty$ to the refraction at each surface. For refraction at the first surface the point P serves as a virtual object. The image formed by the first refraction serves as the object for the second refraction.

SET UP:

$$\xleftarrow{\quad t \quad}$$

$n = 1.60$

$P \quad P'$

$\bullet \quad \bullet$

$\xleftrightarrow{\quad}$

0.30 cm

$\xleftarrow{\quad 14.4 \text{ cm} \quad}$

plane faces means $R \to \infty$ and

$$\frac{n_a}{s} + \frac{n_b}{s'} = 0$$

$$s' = -\frac{n_b}{n_a} s$$

EXECUTE:

refraction at first (left-hand) surface of the piece of glass:

The rays converging toward point P constitute a virtual object for this surface, so $s = -14.4$ cm.

$n_a = 1.00$, $n_b = 1.60$.

$$s' = -\frac{1.60}{1.00}(-14.4 \text{ cm}) = +23.0 \text{ cm}$$

This image is 23.0 cm to the right of the first surface so is a distance 23.0 cm $- t$ to the right of the second surface. This image serves as a virtual object for the second surface.

refraction at the second (right-hand) surface of the piece of glass:

The image is at P' so $s' = 14.4$ cm $+ 0.30$ cm $- t = 14.7$ cm $- t$.

$s = -(23.0 \text{ cm} - t)$; $n_a = 1.60$; $n_b = 1.00$

$s' = -\dfrac{n_b}{n_a} s$ gives 14.7 cm $- t = -\left(\dfrac{1.00}{1.60}\right)(-[23.0 \text{ cm} - t])$

14.7 cm $- t = +14.4$ cm $- 0.625t$

$0.375t = 0.30$ cm and $t = 0.80$ cm

EVALUATE: The overall effect of the piece of glass is to diverge the rays and move their convergence point to the right. For a real object, refraction at a plane surface always produces a virtual image, but with a virtual object the image can be real.

34.101 IDENTIFY: In the sketch the light travels upward from the object.
Apply Eq.(34.11) with $R \to \infty$ to the refraction at each surface. The image formed by the first surface serves as the object for the second surface.
SET UP:

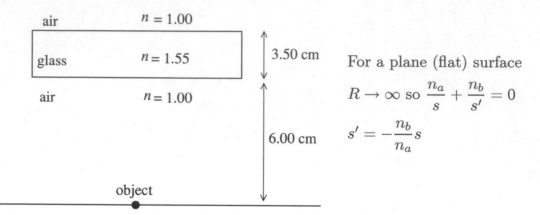

For a plane (flat) surface

$R \to \infty$ so $\dfrac{n_a}{s} + \dfrac{n_b}{s'} = 0$

$s' = -\dfrac{n_b}{n_a}s$

EXECUTE:

First refraction (air→ glass):

$n_a = 1.00$; $n_b = 1.55$; $s = 6.00$ cm

$s' = -\dfrac{n_b}{n_a}s = -\dfrac{1.55}{1.00}(6.00 \text{ cm}) = -9.30$ cm

The image is 9.30 cm below the lower surface of the glass, so is 9.30 cm + 3.50 cm = 12.8 cm below the upper surface.

Second refraction (glass→ air):

$n_a = 1.55$; $n_b = 1.00$; $s = +12.8$ cm

$s' = -\dfrac{n_b}{n_a}s = -\dfrac{1.00}{1.55}(12.8 \text{ cm}) = -8.26$ cm

The image of the page is 8.26 cm below the top surface of the glass plate and therefore 9.50 cm − 8.26 cm = 1.24 cm above the page.

EVALUATE: The image is virtual. If you view the object by looking down from above the plate, the image of the page that you see is closer to your eye than the page is.

34.103 IDENTIFY and **SET UP:** Combine eqs.(34.17) and (34.16) to eliminate s' and solve for s.

EXECUTE:

a) $f = 35.0 \times 10^{-3}$ m

$|m| = \dfrac{|y'|}{|y|} = \dfrac{(3/4)(36.0 \times 10^{-3} \text{ m})}{22.7 \text{ m}} = 1.189 \times 10^{-3}$

Image on film means image is real. $s > 0$, $s' > 0$ and $m = -\dfrac{s'}{s} < 0$, so

$m = -1.189 \times 10^{-3}$

$s' = -ms = -(-1.189 \times 10^{-3})s = +(1.189 \times 10^{-3})s$

Use this in $\dfrac{1}{s} + \dfrac{1}{s'} = \dfrac{1}{f}$, so $\dfrac{1}{s} + \dfrac{1}{(1.189 \times 10^{-3})s} = \dfrac{1}{f}$

$\dfrac{842}{s} = \dfrac{1}{f}$ so $s = 842f = 842(35.0 \times 10^{-3} \text{ m}) = 29.5 \text{ m}$

b) Fill the viewfinder frame means $|m| = \dfrac{36.0 \times 10^{-3} \text{ m}}{22.7 \text{ m}} = 1.586 \times 10^{-3}$.

Thus $s' = (1.586 \times 10^{-3})s$.

$\dfrac{1}{s} + \dfrac{1}{s'} = \dfrac{1}{f}$ gives $\dfrac{1}{s} + \dfrac{1}{(1.586 \times 10^{-3})s} = \dfrac{1}{f}$

$\dfrac{631.5}{s} = \dfrac{1}{f}$ so $s = 631.5f = 631.5(35.0 \times 10^{-3} \text{ m}) = 22.1 \text{ m}$

EVALUATE: When the object is closer to the lens (smaller s), the magnitude of the lateral magnification $|m|$ increases and the image becomes larger.

34.105 IDENTIFY: Use that the angular size of the image equals the angular size of the object.

a) SET UP:

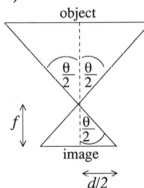

EXECUTE:

From the sketch, $\tan(\theta/2) = \dfrac{d/2}{f} = \dfrac{d}{2f}$

$\dfrac{\theta}{2} = \arctan\left(\dfrac{d}{2f}\right)$

$\theta = 2\arctan\left(\dfrac{d}{2f}\right)$

b) $d = \sqrt{(24 \text{ mm})^2 + (36 \text{ mm})^2} = 43.3 \text{ mm}$

$f = 28 \text{ mm}$ gives $\theta = 2\arctan\left(\dfrac{43.3 \text{ mm}}{2(28 \text{ mm})}\right) = 75°$ (Fig.34.38d says 75°)

$f = 105 \text{ mm}$ gives $\theta = 2\arctan\left(\dfrac{43.3 \text{ mm}}{2(105 \text{ mm})}\right) = 23°$ (Fig.34.38d says 25°)

$f = 300 \text{ mm}$ gives $\theta = 2\arctan\left(\dfrac{43.3 \text{ mm}}{2(300 \text{ mm})}\right) = 8.3°$ (Fig.34.38d says 8°)

EVALUATE: The calculated angles are in close agreement with those given in Fig.34.38. A smaller focal length gives a larger angle of view.

34.107 IDENTIFY and **SET UP:** The generalization of Eq.(34.22) is $M = \dfrac{\text{near point}}{f}$, so $f = \dfrac{\text{near point}}{M}$.

EXECUTE:

a) age 10, near point = 7 cm

$f = \dfrac{7 \text{ cm}}{2.0} = 3.5 \text{ cm}$

b) age 30, near point = 14 cm

$f = \dfrac{14 \text{ cm}}{2.0} = 7.0 \text{ cm}$

c) age 60, near point = 200 cm

$f = \dfrac{200 \text{ cm}}{2.0} = 100 \text{ cm}$

d) $f = 3.5$ cm (from part (a)) and near point = 200 cm (for 60-year-old)

$M = \dfrac{200 \text{ cm}}{3.5 \text{ cm}} = 57$

e) EVALUATE: No. The reason $f = 3.5$ cm gives a larger M for a 60-year-old than for a 10-year-old is that the eye of the older person can't focus on as close of an object as the younger person can. The unaided eye of the 60-year-old must view a much smaller angular size, and that is why the same f gives a much larger M. The angular size of the image depends only on f and is the same for the two ages.

34.111 IDENTIFY: Use similar triangles in Fig.34.56 and Eq.(34.16) to derive the expressions called for in the problem.

a) SET UP:

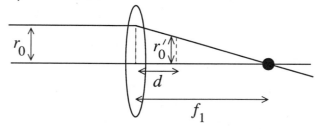

EXECUTE:
From similar triangles
in the sketch,

$\dfrac{r_0}{f_1} = \dfrac{r_0'}{f_1 - d}$

Thus $r_0' = \left(\dfrac{f_1 - d}{f_1}\right) r_0$, as was to be shown.

b) SET UP: The image at the focal point of the first lens, a distance f_1 to the right of the first lens, serves as the object for the second lens. The image is a distance $f_1 - d$ to the right of the second lens, so $s_2 = -(f_1 - d) = d - f_1$.

EXECUTE: $s_2' = \dfrac{s_2 f_2}{s_2 - f_2} = \dfrac{(d - f_1)f_2}{d - f_1 - f_2}$

$f_2 < 0$ so $|f_2| = -f_2$ and $s_2' = \dfrac{(f_1 - d)|f_2|}{|f_2| - f_1 + d}$, as was to be shown.

c) SET UP:

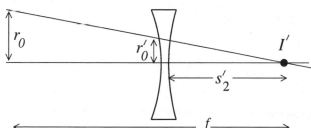

EXECUTE:
From similar triangles in the sketch,

$$\frac{r_0}{f} = \frac{r_0'}{s_2'}$$

Thus $\frac{r_0}{r_0'} = \frac{f}{s_2'}$

From the results of part (a), $\frac{r_0}{r_0'} = \frac{f_1}{f_1 - d}$.

Combining the two results gives $\frac{f_1}{f_1 - d} = \frac{f}{s_2'}$.

$$f = s_2'\left(\frac{f_1}{f_1 - d}\right) = \frac{(f_1 - d)|f_2|f_1}{(|f_2| - f_1 + d)(f_1 - d)} = \frac{f_1|f_2|}{|f_2| - f_1 + d}, \text{ as was to be shown.}$$

d) SET UP: Put the numerical values into the expression derived in part (c).

EXECUTE: $f = \dfrac{f_1|f_2|}{|f_2| - f_1 + d}$

$f_1 = 12.0$ cm, $|f_2| = 18.0$ cm, so $f = \dfrac{216 \text{ cm}^2}{6.0 \text{ cm} + d}$

$d - 0$ gives $f = 36.0$ cm; maximum f

$d = 4.0$ gives $f = 21.6$ cm; minimum f

$f = 30.0$ cm says 30.0 cm $= \dfrac{216 \text{ cm}^2}{6.0 \text{ cm} + d}$

6.0 cm $+ d = 7.2$ cm and $d = 1.2$ cm

EVALUATE: Changing d produces a range of effective focal lengths. The effective focal length can be both smaller and larger than $f_1 + |f_2|$.

34.113 IDENTIFY and **SET UP:** The image formed by the objective is the object for the eyepiece. The total lateral magnification is $m_{\text{tot}} = m_1 m_2$. $f_1 = 8.00$ mm (objective); $f_2 = 7.50$ cm (eyepiece)

a)

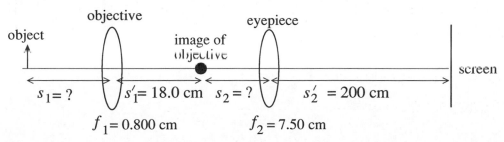

EXECUTE:

Find the object distace s_1 for the objective:

$s_1' = +18.0$ cm, $f_1 = 0.800$ cm, $s_1 = ?$

$$\frac{1}{s_1} + \frac{1}{s_1'} = \frac{1}{f_1}, \text{ so } \frac{1}{s_1} = \frac{1}{f_1} - \frac{1}{s_1'} = \frac{s_1' - f_1}{s_1' f_1}$$

$$s_1 = \frac{s_1' f_1}{s_1' - f_1} = \frac{(18.0 \text{ cm})(0.800 \text{ cm})}{18.0 \text{ cm} - 0.800 \text{ cm}} = 0.8372 \text{ cm}$$

Find the object distance s_2 for the eyepiece:

$s_2' = +200$ cm, $f_2 = 7.50$ cm, $s_2 = ?$

$$\frac{1}{s_2} + \frac{1}{s_2'} = \frac{1}{f_2}$$

$$s_2 = \frac{s_2' f_2}{s_2' - f_2} = \frac{(200 \text{ cm})(7.50 \text{ cm})}{200 \text{ cm} - 7.50 \text{ cm}} = 7.792 \text{ cm}$$

Now we can calculate the magnification for each lens:

$$m_1 = -\frac{s_1'}{s_1} = -\frac{18.0 \text{ cm}}{0.8372 \text{ cm}} = -21.50$$

$$m_2 = -\frac{s_2'}{s_2} = -\frac{200 \text{ cm}}{7.792 \text{ cm}} = -25.67$$

$$m_{\text{tot}} = m_1 m_2 = (-21.50)(-25.67) = 552.$$

b) From the sketch we can see that the distance between the two lenses is

$s_1' + s_2 = 18.0$ cm $+ 7.792$ cm $= 25.8$ cm.

EVALUATE: The microscope is not being used in the conventional way; it merely serves as a two-lens system. In particular, the final image formed by the eyepiece in the problem is real, not virtual as is the case normally for a microscope. Eq.(34.23) does not apply here, and in any event gives the angular not the lateral magnification.

CHAPTER 35
INTERFERENCE

Exercises 5, 7, 9, 11, 13, 15, 19, 23, 25, 29, 31, 35, 37
Problems 39, 41, 43, 49, 53, 55, 57, 59

Exercises

35.5 **IDENTIFY:** Use $c = f\lambda$ to calculate the wavelength of the transmitted waves. Compare the difference in the distance from A to P and from B to P. For constructive interence this path difference is an integer multiple of the wavelength.

SET UP:

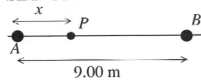

The distance of point P from each coherent source is $r_A = x$ and $r_B = 9.00 \text{ m} - x$.

EXECUTE: The path difference is $r_B - r_A = 9.00 \text{ m} - 2x$.

$r_B - r_A = m\lambda$, $m = 0, \pm 1, \pm 2, \ldots$

$$\lambda = \frac{c}{f} = \frac{2.998 \times 10^8 \text{ m/s}}{120 \times 10^6 \text{ Hz}} = 2.50 \text{ m}$$

Thus $9.00 \text{ m} - 2x = m(2.50 \text{ m})$ and $x = \dfrac{9.00 \text{ m} - m(2.50 \text{ m})}{2} = 4.50 \text{ m} - (1.25 \text{ m})m$.

x must lie in the range 0 to 9.00 m since P is said to be between the two antennas.

$m = 0$ gives $x = 4.50$ m

$m = +1$ gives $x = 4.50 \text{ m} - 1.25 \text{ m} = 3.25$ m

$m = +2$ gives $x = 4.50 \text{ m} - 2.50 \text{ m} = 2.00$ m

$m = +3$ gives $x = 4.50 \text{ m} - 3.75 \text{ m} = 0.75$ m

$m = -1$ gives $x = 4.50 \text{ m} + 1.25 \text{ m} = 5.75$ m

$m = -2$ gives $x = 4.50 \text{ m} + 2.50 \text{ m} = 7.00$ m

$m = -3$ gives $x = 4.50 \text{ m} + 3.75 \text{ m} = 8.25$ m

All other values of m give values of x out of the allowed range.

Constuctive interference will occur for $x = 0.75$ m, 2.00 m, 3.25 m, 4.50 m, 5.75 m, 7.00 m, and 8.25 m.

EVALUATE: Constructive interference occurs at the midpoint between the two sources since that point is the same distance from each source. The other points of constructive interference are symmetrically placed relative to this point.

35.7 **IDENTIFY** and **SET UP:** For destructive interference the path difference $r_2 - r_1$

must equal a half-integer number of wavelengths:
$r_2 - r_1 = (m + \frac{1}{2})\lambda$, $m = 0, 1, 2, \ldots$

EXECUTE: $\lambda = \dfrac{r_2 - r_1}{m + \frac{1}{2}} = \dfrac{2040 \text{ nm}}{m + \frac{1}{2}}$

$m = 0$ gives $\lambda = 4080$ nm; $m = 1$ gives $\lambda = 1360$ nm; $m = 2$ gives $\lambda = 816$ nm; $m = 3$ gives $\lambda = 583$ nm; $m = 4$ gives $\lambda = 453$ nm; $m = 5$ gives $\lambda = 371$ nm; $\ldots$
Of these wavelengths, 583 nm and 453 nm are in the visible region.

EVALUATE: For $\lambda = 4080$ nm the path difference of 2040 nm is $\lambda/2$. For $\lambda = 1360$ nm the path difference is $3\lambda/2$, etc.

35.9 **IDENTIFY** and **SET UP:** The positions of the bright fringes are given by Eq.(35.6): $y_m = R(m\lambda/d)$. For each fringe the adjacent fringe is located at $y_{m+1} = R(m+1)\lambda/d$. Solve for λ.

EXECUTE: The separation between adjacent fringes is $\Delta y = y_{m+1} - y_m = R\lambda/d$.

$\lambda = \dfrac{d\,\Delta y}{R} = \dfrac{(0.460 \times 10^{-3} \text{ m})(2.82 \times 10^{-3} \text{ m})}{2.20 \text{ m}} = 5.90 \times 10^{-7}$ m $= 590$ nm

EVALUATE: Eq.(35.6) requires that the angular position on the screen be small. The angular position of bright fringes is given by $\sin\theta = m\lambda/d$. The slit separation is much larger than the wavelength ($\lambda/d = 1.3 \times 10^{-3}$), so θ is small so long as m is not extremely large.

35.11 **IDENTIFY** and **SET UP:** The dark lines correspond to destructive interference and hence are located by Eq.(35.5):

$d\sin\theta = (m + \frac{1}{2})\lambda$ so $\sin\theta = \dfrac{(m + \frac{1}{2})\lambda}{d}$, $m = 0, \pm 1, \pm 2, \ldots$

Solve for θ that locates the second and third dark lines. Use $y = R\tan\theta$ to find the distance of each of the dark lines from the center of the screen.

EXECUTE:

1st dark line is for $m = 0$

2nd dark line is for $m = 1$ and
$\sin\theta_1 = \dfrac{3\lambda}{2d} = \dfrac{3(500 \times 10^{-9} \text{ m})}{2(0.450 \times 10^{-3} \text{ m})} = 1.667 \times 10^{-3}$ and $\theta_1 = 1.667 \times 10^{-3}$ rad

3rd dark line is for $m = 2$ and
$\sin\theta_2 = \dfrac{5\lambda}{2d} = \dfrac{5(500 \times 10^{-9} \text{ m})}{2(0.450 \times 10^{-3} \text{ m})} = 2.778 \times 10^{-3}$ and $\theta_2 = 2.778 \times 10^{-3}$ rad

(Note that θ_1 and θ_2 are small so that the approximation $\theta \approx \sin\theta \approx \tan\theta$ is valid.)
The distance of each dark line from the center of the central bright band is given by $y_m = R\tan\theta$, where $R = 0.850$ m is the distance to the screen.

$\tan\theta \approx \theta$ so $y_m = R\theta_m$

$y_1 = R\theta_1 = (0.750 \text{ m})((1.667 \times 10^{-3} \text{ rad}) = 1.25 \times 10^{-3} \text{ m}$

$y_2 = R\theta_2 = (0.750 \text{ m})((2.778 \times 10^{-3} \text{ rad}) = 2.08 \times 10^{-3} \text{ m}$

$\Delta y = y_2 - y_1 = 2.08 \times 10^{-3} \text{ m} - 1.25 \times 10^{-3} \text{ m} = 0.83 \text{ mm}$

EVALUATE: Since θ_1 and θ_2 are very small we could have used Eq.(35.6), generalized to destructive interference: $y_m = R(m + \frac{1}{2})\lambda/d$.

35.13 **IDENTIFY** and **SET UP:** Use the information given about the bright fringe to find the distance d between the two slits. Then use Eq.(35.5) and $y = R\tan\theta$ to calculate λ for which there is a first-order dark fringe at this same place on the screen.

EXECUTE: $y_1 = \dfrac{R\lambda_1}{d}$, so $d = \dfrac{R\lambda_1}{y_1} = \dfrac{(3.00 \text{ m})(600 \times 10^{-9} \text{ m})}{4.84 \times 10^{-3} \text{ m}} = 3.72 \times 10^{-4} \text{ m}$.
(R is much greater than d, so Eq.35.6 is valid.)

The dark fringes are located by $d\sin\theta = (m + \frac{1}{2})\lambda$, $m = 0, \pm1, \pm2, \ldots$ The first order dark fringe is located by $\sin\theta = \lambda_2/2d$, where λ_2 is the wavelength we are seeking.

$y = R\tan\theta \approx R\sin\theta = \dfrac{\lambda_2 R}{2d}$

We want λ_2 such that $y = y_1$. This gives $\dfrac{R\lambda_1}{d} = \dfrac{R\lambda_2}{2d}$ and $\lambda_2 = 2\lambda_1 = 1200 \text{ nm}$.

EVALUATE: For $\lambda = 600$ nm the path difference from the two slits to this point on the screen is 600 nm. For this same path difference (point on the screen) the path difference is $\lambda/2$ when $\lambda = 1200$ nm.

35.15 **IDENTIFY** and **SET UP:** The dark lines are located by $d\sin\theta = (m + \frac{1}{2})\lambda$. The distance of each line from the center of the screen is given by $y = R\tan\theta$.

EXECUTE: First dark line is for $m = 0$ and $d\sin\theta_1 = \lambda/2$.

$\sin\theta_1 = \dfrac{\lambda}{2d} = \dfrac{550 \times 10^{-9} \text{ m}}{2(1.80 \times 10^{-6} \text{ m})} = 0.1528$ and $\theta_1 = 8.789°$.

Second dark line is for $m = 1$ and $d\sin\theta_2 = 3\lambda/2$.

$\sin\theta_2 = \dfrac{3\lambda}{2d} = 3\left(\dfrac{550 \times 10^{-9} \text{ m}}{2(1.80 \times 10^{-6} \text{ m})}\right) = 0.4583$ and $\theta_2 = 27.28°$.

$y_1 = R\tan\theta_1 = (0.350 \text{ m})\tan 8.789° = 0.0541 \text{ m}$

$y_2 = R\tan\theta_2 = (0.350 \text{ m})\tan 27.28° = 0.1805 \text{ m}$

The distance between the lines is $\Delta y = y_2 - y_1 = 0.1805 \text{ m} - 0.0541 \text{ m} = 0.126 \text{ m} = 12.6 \text{ cm}$.

EVALUATE: $\sin\theta_1 = 0.1528$ and $\tan\theta_1 = 0.1546$. $\sin\theta_2 = 0.4583$ and $\tan\theta_2 = 0.5157$. As the angle increases, $\sin\theta \approx \tan\theta$ becomes a poorer approximation.

35.19 **IDENTIFY** and **SET UP:** The phase difference ϕ is given by $\phi = (2\pi d/\lambda)\sin\theta$ (Eq.35.13.)

EXECUTE: $\phi = [2\pi(0.340 \times 10^{-3} \text{ m})/(500 \times 10^{-9} \text{ m})]\sin 23.0° = 1670$ rad

EVALUATE: The mth bright fringe occurs when $\phi = 2\pi m$, so there are a large number of bright fringes within $23.0°$ from the centerline. Note that Eq.(35.13) gives ϕ in radians.

35.23 **a) IDENTIFY** and **SET UP:** The minima are located at angles θ given by $d\sin\theta = (m + \frac{1}{2})\lambda$. The first minimum corresponds to $m = 0$. Solve for θ. Then the distance on the screen is $y = R\tan\theta$.

EXECUTE: $\sin\theta = \dfrac{\lambda}{2d} = \dfrac{660 \times 10^{-9} \text{ m}}{2(0.260 \times 10^{-3} \text{ m})} = 1.27 \times 10^{-3}$ and

$\theta = 1.27 \times 10^{-3}$ rad

$y = (0.700 \text{ m})\tan(1.27 \times 10^{-3} \text{ rad}) = 0.889$ mm.

b) IDENTIFY and **SET UP:** Eq.(35.15) given the intensity I as a function of the position y on the screen: $I = I_0\cos^2\left(\dfrac{\pi dy}{\lambda R}\right)$. Set $I = I_0/2$ and solve for y.

EXECUTE: $I = \frac{1}{2}I_0$ says $\cos^2\left(\dfrac{\pi dy}{\lambda R}\right) = \frac{1}{2}$

$\cos\left(\dfrac{\pi dy}{\lambda R}\right) = \dfrac{1}{\sqrt{2}}$ so $\dfrac{\pi dy}{\lambda R} = \dfrac{\pi}{4}$ rad

$y = \dfrac{\lambda R}{4d} = \dfrac{(660 \times 10^{-9} \text{ m})(0.700 \text{ m})}{4((0.260 \times 10^{-3} \text{ m})} = 0.444$ mm

EVALUATE: $I = I_0/2$ at a point on the screen midway between where $I = I_0$ and $I = 0$.

35.25 **a) IDENTIFY** and **SET UP:** The minima are located by $d\sin\theta = (m + \frac{1}{2})\lambda$. Solve for θ for the first minimum and use $y = R\tan\theta$ to find the distance on the screen.

EXECUTE: The first minimum is for $m = 0$ so $\sin\theta = \dfrac{\lambda}{2d} = \dfrac{550 \times 10^{-9} \text{ m}}{2(0.130 \times 10^{-3} \text{ m})} =$ 2.115×10^{-3} and

$\theta = 2.115 \times 10^{-3}$ rad

(θ is small so $\theta \approx \sin\theta \approx \tan\theta$)

The distance on the screen is $y_1 = R\tan\theta \approx R\theta$, where R is the distance to the screen.

$y_1 = R\theta_1 = (0.900 \text{ m})(2.115 \times 10^{-3} \text{ rad}) = 1.90 \times 10^{-3} \text{ m} = 1.90 \text{ mm}$.

b) IDENTIFY and **SET UP:** Since θ is small we can use Eq.(35.15): $I = I_0 \cos^2\left(\dfrac{\pi dy}{\lambda R}\right)$.

Set I for $y = \frac{1}{2}y_1 = 0.950 \times 10^{-3}$ m and solve for I.

EXECUTE: $I = (4.00 \times 10^{-6} \text{ W/m}^2)\left(\cos\left[\dfrac{\pi(0.130 \times 10^{-3} \text{ m})(0.950 \times 10^{-3} \text{ m})}{(550 \times 10^{-9} \text{ m})(0.900 \text{ m})}\right]\right)^2$

$= 2.01 \times 10^{-6} \text{ W/m}^2$.

EVALUATE: The intensity is very close to $I_0/2$ midway between the center of the central maximum and the first minimum. This same result was found in Exercise 35.23.

35.29 IDENTIFY: Consider interference between rays reflected at the upper and lower surfaces of the film. Consider phase difference due to the path difference of $2t$ and any phase differences due to phase changes upon reflection.

SET UP:

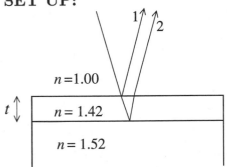

Both rays (1) and (2) undergo a 180° phase change on reflection, so there is no net phase difference introduced and the condition for destructive interference is $2t = (m + \frac{1}{2})\lambda$.

EXECUTE: $t = \dfrac{(m + \frac{1}{2})\lambda}{2}$; thinnest film says $m = 0$ so $t = \dfrac{\lambda}{4}$

$\lambda = \dfrac{\lambda_0}{1.42}$ and $t = \dfrac{\lambda_0}{4(1.42)} = \dfrac{650 \times 10^{-9} \text{ m}}{4(1.42)} = 1.14 \times 10^{-7} \text{ m} = 114 \text{ nm}$

EVALUATE: We compared the path difference to the wavelength in the film, since that is where the path difference occurs.

35.31 IDENTIFY: Consider interference between rays reflected from the top and bottom surfaces of the film. Use the fact that destructive interference occurs for $\lambda_1 = 800$ nm incident light to obtain an expression for the thickness of the film.

SET UP: Let n be the refractive index of the oil. There is a $\lambda/2$ phase shift for the reflection at the air-oil interface but no phase shift for the reflection at the oil-water interface. Therefore, there is a net $\lambda/2$ phase difference due to the reflections, and the condition for destructive interference is $2t = m(\lambda/n)$. Smallest nonzero thickness means $m = 1$, so $2tn = \lambda_1$.

The condition for constructive interference with incident wavelength λ is $2t = (m + \frac{1}{2})(\lambda/n)$ and $2tn = (m + \frac{1}{2})\lambda$.

EXECUTE: $2tn = \lambda_1$, so $\lambda = \lambda_1/(m + \frac{1}{2})$, where $\lambda_1 = 800$ nm.

for $m = 0$, $\lambda = 1600$ nm
for $m = 1$, $\lambda = 533$ nm
for $m = 2$, $\lambda = 320$ nm, and so on

The visible wavelength for which there is constructive interference is 533 nm.

EVALUATE: Our answer does not depend on the refractive index of the oil.

35.35 IDENTIFY: Consider the interference between rays reflected from the two surfaces of the soap film. Strongly reflected means constructive interference. Consider phase difference due to the path difference of $2t$ and any phase difference due to phase changes upon reflection.

a) SET UP:

There is a 180° phase change when the light is reflected from the outside surface of the bubble and no phase change when the light is reflected from the inside surface.

EXECUTE: The reflections produce a net 180° phase difference and for there to be constructive interference the path difference $2t$ must correspond to a half-integer number of wavelengths to compensate for the $\lambda/2$ shift due to the reflections. Hence the condition for constructive interference is

$2t = (m + \frac{1}{2})(\lambda_0/n)$, $m = 0, 1, 2, \ldots$

Here λ_0 is the wavelength in air and (λ_0/n) is the wavelength in the bubble, where the path difference occurs.

$$\lambda_0 = \frac{2tn}{m + \frac{1}{2}} = \frac{2(290 \text{ nm})(1.33)}{m + \frac{1}{2}} = \frac{771.4 \text{ nm}}{m + \frac{1}{2}}$$

for $m = 0$, $\lambda = 1543$ nm;   for $m = 1$, $\lambda = 514$ nm;   for $m = 2$, $\lambda = 308$ nm; $\ldots$

Only 514 nm is in the visible region; the color for this wavelength is green.

b) $\lambda_0 = \dfrac{2tn}{m + \frac{1}{2}} = \dfrac{2(340 \text{ nm})(1.33)}{m + \frac{1}{2}} = \dfrac{904.4 \text{ nm}}{m + \frac{1}{2}}$

for $m = 0$, $\lambda = 1809$ nm;   for $m = 1$, $\lambda = 603$ nm;   for $m = 2$, $\lambda = 362$ nm; ...
Only 603 nm is in the visible region; the color for this wavelength is orange.

EVALUATE: The dominant color of the reflected light depends on the thickness of the film. If the bubble has varying thickness at different points, these points will appear to be different colors when the light reflected from the bubble is viewed.

35.37 IDENTIFY and **SET UP:** Apply Eq.(35.19) and calculate y for $m = 1800$.
EXECUTE: Eq.(35.19): $y = m(\lambda/2) = 1800(633 \times 10^{-9}$ m$)/2 = 5.70 \times 10^{-4}$ m $= 0.570$ mm

EVALUATE: A small displacement of the mirror corresponds to many wavelengths and a large number of fringes cross the line.

Problems

35.39 IDENTIFY and **SET UP:** The only effect of the water is to change the wavelength λ_0 to λ. Use Eq.(35.5) to calculate the angular poisition θ of the dark lines. The distance on the screen is then given by $y = R \tan \theta$.

EXECUTE: $\lambda = \lambda_0/n = \dfrac{500 \times 10^{-9} \text{ m}}{1.333} = 375 \times 10^{-9}$ m

$\theta_1 \approx \sin \theta_1 = \dfrac{3\lambda}{2d} = \dfrac{3(375 \times 10^{-9} \text{ m})}{2(0.450 \times 10^{-3} \text{ m})} = 1.250 \times 10^{-3}$ rad

$\theta_2 \approx \sin \theta_2 = \dfrac{5\lambda}{2d} = \dfrac{5(375 \times 10^{-9} \text{ m})}{2(0.450 \times 10^{-3} \text{ m})} = 2.083 \times 10^{-3}$ rad

$y_1 \approx R\theta_1 = (0.750 \text{ m})(1.250 \times 10^{-3} \text{ rad}) = 9.38 \times 10^{-4}$ m

$y_2 \approx R\theta_2 = (0.750 \text{ m})(2.083 \times 10^{-3} \text{ rad}) = 1.562 \times 10^{-3}$ m

$\Delta y = y_2 - y_1 = 1.562 \times 10^{-3}$ m $- 9.38 \times 10^{-4}$ m $= 6.24 \times 10^{-4}$ m $= 0.62$ mm

EVALUATE: In Exercise 35.11 the separation is 0.83 mm. In water the wavelength is smaller and the dark lines in the interference pattern are closer together. For smaller λ a smaller change in path difference is needed to move from one dark line to another.

35.41 a) IDENTIFY and **SET UP:** There must be destructive interference between the sound waves from the two speakers.

b) For destructive interference the path difference is a half-integer number of wavelengths. For constructive interference it is an integer number of wavelengths, so the change in path length must be $\lambda/2$.

EXECUTE: $\lambda/2 = 0.398$ m and $\lambda = 0.796$ m.

$$v = f\lambda \text{ so } f = \frac{v}{\lambda} = \frac{340 \text{ m/s}}{0.796 \text{ m}} = 427 \text{ Hz}$$

c) The change in path length must equal λ to go from one point of constructive interference to the next, so the speakers must be moved 0.796 m.

EVALUATE: The wavelength of audible sound waves in air is on the order of one meter. Midway between speaker positions that give maximum intensity are positions that give minimum intensity.

35.43 IDENTIFY: The phase difference between the output of the sources and the additional phase difference due to the path difference combines to produce a total phase difference that results in destructive interference. The output phase difference of the sources corresponds to a $\lambda/6$ phase difference.

SET UP: At points on the same side of the centerline as point A, the path from B is longer than the path from A, and the path difference $d\sin\theta$ puts speaker A ahead of speaker B in phase. Constructive interference occurs when
$d\sin\theta - \lambda/6 = (m + \frac{1}{2})\lambda$, $m = 0, 1, 2, \ldots$
EXECUTE: $\sin\theta = (m + \frac{2}{3})(\lambda/d) = (m + \frac{2}{3})(0.2381)$, $m = 0, 1, 2, \ldots$
$m = 0$, 9.13°; $m = 1$, 23.4°; $m = 2$, 39.4°; $m = 3$, 60.8°; $m = 4$, no solution

SET UP: At points on the other side of the centerline, the path from A is longer than the path from B, and the path difference $d\sin\theta$ puts speaker A behind of speaker B in phase. Constructive interference occurs when
$d\sin\theta + \lambda/6 = (m + \frac{1}{2})\lambda$, $m = 0, 1, 2, \ldots$
EXECUTE: $\sin\theta = (m + \frac{1}{3})(\lambda/d) = (m + \frac{1}{3})(0.2381)$, $m = 0, 1, 2, \ldots$
$m = 0$, 4.55°; $m = 1$, 18.5°; $m = 2$, 33.7°; $m = 3$, 52.5°; $m = 4$, no solution

EVALUATE: The directions for which there is destructive interference are not symmetrically placed on about the centerline, like they are for sources emitting in phase.

35.49 IDENTIFY and SET UP: Consider interference between rays reflected from the upper and lower surfaces of the film to relate the thickness of the film to the wavelengths for which there is destructive interference. The thermal expansion of the film changes the thickness of the film when the temperature changes.

EXECUTE: For this film on this glass, there is a net $\lambda/2$ phase change due to reflection and the condition for destructive interference is $2t = m(\lambda/n)$, where $n = 1.750$.

Smallest nonzero thickness is given by $t = \lambda/2n$.
At 20.0°C, $t_0 = (582.4 \text{ nm})/[(2)(1.750)] = 166.4$ nm.
At 170°C, $t_0 = (588.5 \text{ nm})/[(2)(1.750)] = 168.1$ nm.

$t = t_0(1 + \alpha \,\Delta T)$ so
$\alpha = (t - t_0)/(t_0\,\Delta T) = (1.7\ \text{nm})/[(166.4\ \text{nm})(150\text{C}^\circ)] = 6.8 \times 10^{-5}\ (\text{C}^\circ)^{-1}$

EVALUATE: When the film is heated its thickness increases, and it takes a larger wavelength in the film to equal $2t$. The value we calculated for α is the same order of magnitude as those given in Table 17.1.

35.53 IDENTIFY: Consider the phase difference due to the path difference and due to the reflection of one ray from the glass surface.

a) SET UP:

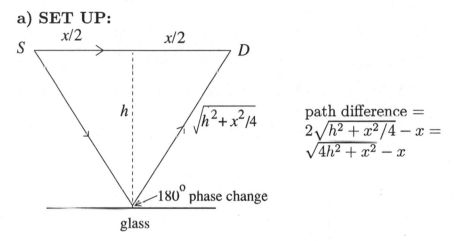

path difference =
$2\sqrt{h^2 + x^2/4} - x =$
$\sqrt{4h^2 + x^2} - x$

Since there is a 180° phase change for the reflected ray, the condition for constructive interference is path difference $= (m + \frac{1}{2})\lambda$ and the condition for destructive interference is path difference $= m\lambda$.

b) EXECUTE: Constructive interference: $(m + \frac{1}{2})\lambda = \sqrt{4h^2 + x^2} - x$ and

$\lambda = \dfrac{\sqrt{4h^2 + x^2} - x}{m + \frac{1}{2}}$. Longest λ is for $m = 0$ and then

$\lambda = 2(\sqrt{4h^2 + x^2} - x) = 2(\sqrt{4(0.24\ \text{m})^2 + (0.14\ \text{m})^2} - 0.14\ \text{m}) = 0.72\ \text{m}$

EVALUATE: For $\lambda = 0.72$ m the path difference is $\lambda/2$.

35.55 IDENTIFY: Consider interference between the rays reflected at the upper and lower surfaces of the plate.
SET UP:

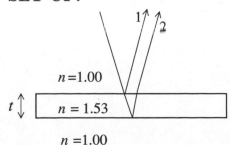

Ray (1) undergoes a 180° phase change on reflection at the top surface of the glass.

Ray (2) has no phase change on reflection from the lower surface of the glass.

a) Intensified in the reflected beam means constructive interference for the reflected light. The reflections produce a net phase difference of 180°, so the condition for constructive interference is $2t = (m + \frac{1}{2})\lambda$, $m = 0, 1, 2, \ldots$ and $\lambda = 2t/(m + \frac{1}{2})$.

λ is the wavelength in the glass plate: $\lambda = \lambda_0/n$.

EXECUTE: $\dfrac{\lambda_0}{n} = \dfrac{2t}{m + \frac{1}{2}}$ and $\lambda_0 = \dfrac{2tn}{m + \frac{1}{2}} = \dfrac{2(0.485 \times 10^{-6}\text{ m})(1.53)}{m + \frac{1}{2}}$

$= \dfrac{1484 \text{ nm}}{m + \frac{1}{2}}$.

$m = 0$ gives $\lambda_0 = 2968$ nm; $m = 1$ gives $\lambda_0 = 989$ nm; $m = 2$ gives $\lambda_0 = 594$ nm; $m = 3$ gives $\lambda_0 = 424$ nm; $m = 4$ gives $\lambda_0 = 330$ nm; $\ldots$

The wavelengths 424 nm and 594 nm are within the limits of the visible spectrum.

b) SET UP: Light that is not reflected is transmitted, so "intensified in the transmitted light" means destructive interference in the reflected light. The condition for destructive interference between the light reflected at the top and at the bottom of the oil film is $2t = m\lambda_0/n$.

EXECUTE: $\lambda_0 = \dfrac{2tn}{m} = \dfrac{2(0.485 \times 10^{-6}\text{ m})(1.53)}{m} = \dfrac{1484 \text{ nm}}{m}$

$m = 1$ gives $\lambda_0 = 1484$ nm; $m = 2$ gives $\lambda_0 = 742$ nm; $m = 3$ gives $\lambda_0 = 495$ nm; $m = 4$ gives $\lambda_0 = 371$ nm; $\ldots$

The only wavelength within the visible spectrum is 495 nm.

EVALUATE: There is minimum transmitted intensity for wavelengths for which the reflected intensity is maximum, and vice versa.

35.57 IDENTIFY: This problem deals with Newton's rings (Sect.35.4). The interference is between rays reflecting from the top and bottom edges of the air that is between the lens and the plate.

SET UP:

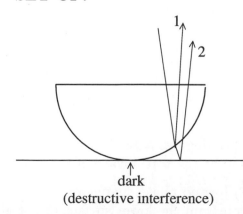

dark
(destructive interference)

Ray (1) does not undergo any phase change on reflection.

Ray (2) does undergo a 180° phase change on reflection.

EXECUTE: The path difference $2t$, where t is the thickness of the air wedge, must satisfy

$2t = (m + \frac{1}{2})\lambda$, $m = 0, 1, 2, \ldots$ for constructive interference

Second bright ring means $m = 1$ and $t = \dfrac{3\lambda}{4} = \dfrac{3(580 \times 10^{-9} \text{ m})}{4} = 4.35 \times 10^{-7}$ m.

Now must relate t to the diameter of the ring:

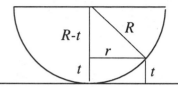

The radius of the ring is r.
$$r^2 + (R - t)^2 = R^2$$

$r = \sqrt{R^2 - (R - t)^2} = \sqrt{R^2 - R^2 + 2Rt - t^2} = \sqrt{2Rt - t^2}$

But $R = 0.952$ m $\gg t$, so we can neglect t^2 relative to $2Rt$:

$r = \sqrt{2Rt} = \sqrt{2(0.952 \text{ m})(4.35 \times 10^{-7} \text{ m})} = 0.910 \times 10^{-3}$ m

This is the radius. The diameter of the ring is $2r = 1.82 \times 10^{-3}$ m $= 1.82$ mm.

EVALUATE: For any bright ring $t = (m + \frac{1}{2})\lambda/2$ and the change in t from one ring to the next is a constant $\lambda/2$. But r is proportional to $\sqrt{t}$, so the rings aren't equally spaced.

35.59 a) IDENTIFY: The wavelength in the glass is decreased by a factor of $1/n$, so for light through the upper slit a shorter path is needed to produce the same phase at the screen. Therefore, the interference pattern is shifted downward on the screen.

b) SET UP: Consider the total phase difference produced by the path length difference and also by the different wavelength in the glass.

EXECUTE: At a point on the screen located by the angle θ the difference in path length is $d \sin \theta$. This introduces a phase difference of $\phi = \left(\dfrac{2\pi}{\lambda_0}\right)(d \sin \theta)$, where λ_0 is the wavelength of the light in air or vacuum.

In the thickness L of glass the number of wavelengths is $\dfrac{L}{\lambda} = \dfrac{nL}{\lambda_0}$. A corresponding length L of the path of the ray through the lower slit, in air, contains L/λ_0 wavelenths. The phase difference this introduces is $\phi = 2\pi \left(\dfrac{nL}{\lambda_0} - \dfrac{L}{\lambda_0}\right)$ and $\phi = 2\pi(n - 1)(L/\lambda_0)$.

The total phase difference is the sum of these two,

$\left(\dfrac{2\pi}{\lambda_0}\right)(d \sin \theta) + 2\pi(n - 1)(L/\lambda_0) = (2\pi/\lambda_0)(d \sin \theta + L(n - 1))$.

Eq.(35.10) then gives $I = I_0 \cos^2\left[\left(\dfrac{\pi}{\lambda_0}\right)(d \sin \theta + L(n - 1))\right]$.

c) Maxima means $\cos \phi/2 = +1$ and $\phi/2 = m\pi$, $m = 0, \pm1, \pm2, \ldots$

$(\pi/\lambda_0)(d \sin \theta + L(n-1)) = m\pi$

$d \sin \theta + L(n-1) = m\lambda_0$

$\sin \theta = \dfrac{m\lambda_0 - L(n-1)}{d}$

EVALUATE: When $L \to 0$ or $n \to 1$ the effect of the plate goes away and the maxima are located by Eq.(35.4).

CHAPTER 36
DIFFRACTION

Exercises

36.1 **IDENTIFY:** Use $y = x \tan \theta$ to calculate the angular position θ of the first minimum. The minima are located by Eq.(36.2): $\sin \theta = \dfrac{m\lambda}{a}$, $m = \pm 1, \pm 2, \ldots$ First minimum means $m = 1$ and $\sin \theta_1 = \lambda/2$ and $\lambda = a \sin \theta_1$. Use this equation to calculate λ.

SET UP:

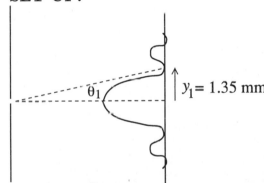

EXECUTE:
$$y_1 = x \tan \theta_1$$

$$\tan \theta_1 = \frac{y_1}{x} =$$

$$\frac{1.35 \times 10^{-3} \text{ m}}{2.00 \text{ m}} = 0.675 \times 10^{-3}$$

$$\theta_1 = 0.675 \times 10^{-3} \text{ rad}$$

$y_1 = 1.35$ mm

$$\lambda = a \sin \theta_1 = (0.750 \times 10^{-3} \text{ m}) \sin(0.675 \times 10^{-3} \text{ rad}) = 506 \text{ nm}$$

EVALUATE: θ_1 is small so the approximation used to obtain Eq.(36.3) is valid and this equation could have been used.

36.7 **IDENTIFY** and **SET UP:** $v = f\lambda$ gives λ. The person hears no sound at angles corresponding to diffraction minima. The diffraction minima are located by $\sin \theta = m\lambda/a$, $m = \pm 1, \pm 2, \ldots$ Solve for θ.

EXECUTE: $\lambda = v/f = (344 \text{ m/s})/(1250 \text{ Hz}) = 0.2752 \text{ m}; \qquad a = 1.00 \text{ m}$
$m = \pm 1, \theta = \pm 16.0°; m = \pm 2, \theta = \pm 33.4°; m = \pm 3, \theta = \pm 55.6°;$ no solution for larger m

EVALUATE: $\lambda/a = 0.28$ so for the large wavelength sound waves diffraction by the doorway is a large effect. Diffraction would not be observable for visible light because its wavelength is much smaller and $\lambda/a << 1$.

36.11 **IDENTIFY:** Calculate the angular positions of the minima and use $y = x \tan \theta$

to calculate the distance on the screen between them.

a) SET UP:

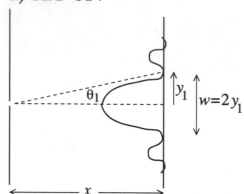

EXECUTE:
The first minimum is located by

$$\sin\theta_1 = \frac{\lambda}{a} =$$
$$\frac{633 \times 10^{-9}\ \text{m}}{0.350 \times 10^{-3}\ \text{m}} = 1.809 \times 10^{-3}$$

$$\theta_1 = 1.809 \times 10^{-3}\ \text{rad}$$

$y_1 = x\tan\theta_1 = (3.00\ \text{m})\tan(1.809 \times 10^{-3}\ \text{rad}) = 5.427 \times 10^{-3}\ \text{m}$

$w = 2y_1 = 2(5.427 \times 10^{-3}\ \text{m}) = 1.09 \times 10^{-2}\ \text{m} = 10.9\ \text{mm}$

b) SET UP:

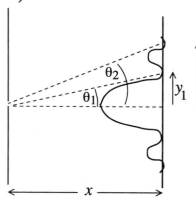

EXECUTE:
$$w = y_2 - y_1$$
$$y_1 = 5.427 \times 10^{-3}\ \text{m}\ \text{(part (a))}$$

$$\sin\theta_2 = \frac{2\lambda}{a} = 3.618 \times 10^{-3}$$

$$\theta_2 = 3.618 \times 10^{-3}\ \text{rad}$$
$$y_2 = x\tan\theta_2 = 1.085 \times 10^{-2}\ \text{m}$$

$w = y_2 - y_1 = 1.085 \times 10^{-2}\ \text{m} - 5.427 \times 10^{-3}\ \text{m} = 5.4 \times 10^{-3}\ \text{m} = 5.4\ \text{mm}$

EVALUATE: The central bright fringe is twice as wide as the other bright fringes.

36.13 a) IDENTIFY: Use Eq.(36.2) with $m = 1$ to locate the angular position of the first minimum and then use $y = x\tan\theta$ to find its distance from the centef of the screen.

SET UP:

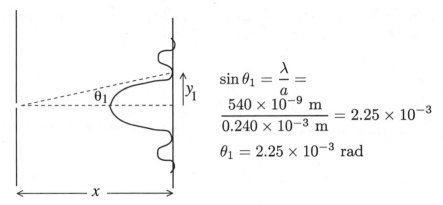

$$\sin\theta_1 = \frac{\lambda}{a} =$$

$$\frac{540 \times 10^{-9}\ \text{m}}{0.240 \times 10^{-3}\ \text{m}} = 2.25 \times 10^{-3}$$

$$\theta_1 = 2.25 \times 10^{-3}\ \text{rad}$$

$$y_1 = x\tan\theta_1 = (3.00\ \text{m})\tan(2.25 \times 10^{-3}\ \text{rad}) = 6.75 \times 10^{-3}\ \text{m} = 6.75\ \text{mm}$$

b) IDENTIFY and SET UP: Use Eqs.(36.5) and (36.6) to calculate the intensity at this point.

EXECUTE: Midway between the center of the central maximum and the first minimum implies $y = \frac{1}{2}(6.75\ \text{mm}) = 3.375 \times 10^{-3}\ \text{m}$.

$$\tan\theta = \frac{y}{x} = \frac{3.375 \times 10^{-3}\ \text{m}}{3.00\ \text{m}} = 1.125 \times 10^{-3}; \theta = 1.125 \times 10^{-3}\ \text{rad}$$

The phase angle β at this point on the screen is

$$\beta = \left(\frac{2\pi}{\lambda}\right) a\sin\theta = \frac{2\pi}{540 \times 10^{-9}\ \text{m}}(0.240 \times 10^{-3}\ \text{m})\sin(1.125 \times 10^{-3}\ \text{rad}) = \pi.$$

Then $I = I_0 \left(\dfrac{\sin\beta/2}{\beta/2}\right)^2 = (6.00 \times 10^{-6}\ \text{W/m}^2)\left(\dfrac{\sin\pi/2}{\pi/2}\right)^2$

$$I = \left(\frac{4}{\pi^2}\right)(6.00 \times 10^{-6}\ \text{W/m}^2) = 2.43 \times 10^{-6}\ \text{W/m}^2.$$

EVALUATE: The intensity at this point midway between the center of the central maximum and the first minimum is less than half the maximum intensity. Compare this result to the corresponding one for the two-slit pattern, Exercises 35.23 and 35.25.

36.15 IDENTIFY and SET UP: Eq.(36.6): $\beta = \left(\dfrac{2\pi}{\lambda}\right) a\sin\theta$. β, a and θ are given; solve for λ.

EXECUTE:

$$\lambda = \left(\frac{2\pi}{\beta}\right) a\sin\theta = \left(\frac{2\pi}{(\pi/2)\ \text{rad}}\right)(0.320 \times 10^{-3}\ \text{m})\sin 0.24° = 5.4\ \mu\text{m}$$

EVALUATE: For this λ, the first minimum is located by $\theta \approx \sin\theta = \lambda/a = 0.0169$ rad $= 0.97°$ and at this point $\beta = 2\pi$ rad. The point where $\beta = \pi/2$ rad is within the first maximum. Note that in Eq.(36.6), β is in radians.

36.17 IDENTIFY and **SET UP:** Use Eq.(36.6) to calculate λ and use Eq.(36.5) to calculate I. $\theta = 3.25°$, $\beta = 56.0$ rad, $a = 0.105 \times 10^{-3}$ m.

a) EXECUTE: $\beta = \left(\dfrac{2\pi}{\lambda}\right) a \sin\theta$ so

$$\lambda = \frac{2\pi a \sin\theta}{\beta} = \frac{2\pi(0.105 \times 10^{-3} \text{ m})\sin 3.25°}{56.0 \text{ rad}} = 668 \text{ nm}$$

b) $I = I_0 \left(\dfrac{\sin\beta/2}{\beta/2}\right)^2 = I_0\left(\dfrac{4}{\beta^2}\right)(\sin(\beta/2))^2 = I_0\dfrac{4}{(56.0 \text{ rad})^2}[\sin(28.0 \text{ rad})]^2 = 9.36 \times 10^{-5} I_0$

EVALUATE: At the first minimum $\beta = 2\pi$ rad and at the point considered in the problem $\beta = 17.8\pi$ rad, so the point is well outside the central maximum. Since β is close to $m\pi$ with $m = 18$, this point is near one of the minima. The intensity here is much less than I_0.

36.19 a) IDENTIFY and **SET UP:** The interference fringes (maxima) are located by $d\sin\theta = m\lambda$, with $m = 0, \pm 1, \pm 2, \ldots$. The intensity I in the diffraction pattern is given by $I = I_0\left(\dfrac{\sin\beta/2}{\beta/2}\right)^2$, with $\beta = \left(\dfrac{2\pi}{\lambda}\right)a\sin\theta$.

We want $m = \pm 3$ in the first equation to give θ that makes $I = 0$ in the second equation.

EXECUTE: $d\sin\theta = m\lambda$ gives $\beta = \left(\dfrac{2\pi}{\lambda}\right)a\left(\dfrac{3\lambda}{d}\right) = 2\pi(3a/d)$.

$I = 0$ says $\dfrac{\sin\beta/2}{\beta/2} = 0$ so $\beta = 2\pi$ and then $2\pi = 2\pi(3a/d)$ and $(d/a) = 3$.

b) IDENTIFY and **SET UP:** Fringes $m = 0, \pm 1, \pm 2$ are within the central diffraction maximum and the $m = \pm 3$ fringes coincide with the first diffraction minimum.

Find the value of m for the fringes that coincide with the second diffraction minimum.

EXECUTE: Second minimum implies $\beta = 4\pi$.

$\beta = \left(\dfrac{2\pi}{\lambda}\right)a\sin\theta = \left(\dfrac{2\pi}{\lambda}\right)a\left(\dfrac{m\lambda}{d}\right) = 2\pi m(a/d) = 2\pi(m/3)$

Then $\beta = 4\pi$ says $4\pi = 2\pi(m/3)$ and $m = 6$.

Therefore the $m = +4$ and $m = +5$ fringes are contained within the first diffraction maximum on one side of the central maximum; two fringes.

EVALUATE: The central maximum is twice as wide as the other maxima so it contains more fringes.

36.21 **a) IDENTIFY** and **SET UP:** If the slits are very narrow then the central maximum of the diffraction pattern for each slit completely fills the screen and the intensity distribution is given solely by the two-slit interference. The maxima are given by

$d\sin\theta = m\lambda$ so $\sin\theta = m\lambda/d$. Solve for θ.

EXECUTE: 1st order maximum: $m = 1$, so $\sin\theta = \dfrac{\lambda}{d} = \dfrac{580\times 10^{-9}\text{ m}}{0.530\times 10^{-3}\text{ m}} = $
1.094×10^{-3}; $\theta = 0.0627°$

2nd order maximum: $m = 2$, so $\sin\theta = \dfrac{2\lambda}{d} = 2.188\times 10^{-3}$; $\theta = 0.125°$

b) IDENTIFY and **SET UP:** The intensity is given by Eq.(36.12):

$I = I_0\cos^2(\phi/2)\left(\dfrac{\sin\beta/2}{\beta/2}\right)^2$. Calculate ϕ and β at each θ from part (a).

EXECUTE:
$\phi = \left(\dfrac{2\pi d}{\lambda}\right)\sin\theta = \left(\dfrac{2\pi d}{\lambda}\right)\left(\dfrac{m\lambda}{d}\right) = 2\pi m$, so $\cos^2(\phi/2) = \cos^2(m\pi) = 1$
(Since the angular positions in part (a) correspond to interference maxima.)

$\beta = \left(\dfrac{2\pi a}{\lambda}\right)\sin\theta =$

$\left(\dfrac{2\pi a}{\lambda}\right)\left(\dfrac{m\lambda}{d}\right) = 2\pi m(a/d) = m2\pi\left(\dfrac{0.320\text{ mm}}{0.530\text{ mm}}\right) = m(3.794\text{ rad})$

1st order maximum: $m = 1$, so $I = I_0(1)\left(\dfrac{\sin(3.794/2)\text{ rad}}{(3.794/2)\text{ rad}}\right)^2 = 0.249 I_0$

2nd order maximum: $m = 2$, so $I = I_0(1)\left(\dfrac{\sin 3.794\text{ rad}}{3.794\text{ rad}}\right)^2 = 0.0256 I_0$

EVALUATE: The first diffraction minimum is at an angle θ given by $\sin\theta = \lambda/a$ so $\theta = 0.104°$. The first order fringe is within the central maximum and the second order fringe is inside the first diffraction maximum on one side of the central maximum. The intensity here at this second fringe is much less than I_0.

36.23 **IDENTIFY** and **SET UP:** The phasor diagrams are similar to those in Fig.36.13. An interference minimum occurs when the phasors add to zero.

EXECUTE:
(i)

There is destructive interference between the light through slits 1 and 3 and between 2 and 4.

(ii)

3 ⇄ 4,2 1→ $\phi = \pi$

There is destructive interference between the light through slits 1 and 2 and between 3 and 4.

(iii)

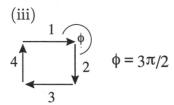 $\phi = 3\pi/2$

There is destructive interference between the light through slits 1 and 3 and between 2 and 4.

EVALUATE: Maxima occur when $\phi = 0$, 2π, 4π, etc. Our diagrams show that there are three minima between the maxima at $\phi = 0$ and $\phi = 2\pi$. This agrees with the general result that for N slits there are $N - 1$ minima between each pair of principal maxima.

36.25 IDENTIFY and **SET UP:** The interference <u>maxima</u> are at angles θ_{m_i} given by $\sin \theta_{m_i} = \dfrac{m_i \lambda}{d}$.

The diffraction <u>minima</u> are at angles θ_{m_d} given by $\sin \theta_{m_d} = \dfrac{m_d \lambda}{a}$.

The m_i-th maximum coincides with the m_d-th minimum when $\theta_{m_i} = \theta_{m_d}$.

EXECUTE:

a) The m_i-th interference maximum coincides with the m_d-th diffraction minimum if $m_i(\lambda/d) = m_d(\lambda/a)$, or $m_i = m_d(d/a)$.

If $m_i = 3$ coincides with $m_d = 1$, then $3 = d/a$ and $a = d/3 = 0.840$ mm$/3 = 0.280$ mm.

b) With $d/a = 3$ the equation in part (a) becomes $m_i = 3m_d$. m_d takes on the values 1, 2, 3, 4, ..., so the other interference maxima which are missing because they coincide with a diffraction minimum are $m_i = 6$, 9, 12, ...

c) The wavelength λ does not appear in the equation $m_i = m_d(d/a)$ from part (a) so changing the wavelength will not affect which interference maxima are missing; $m_i = 3$, 6, 9, 12, ... will still be the ones missing.

EVALUATE: Which interference maximum coincides with a particular diffraction minimum depends only on the ratio d/a. To have missing fringes, d/a must be an integer.

36.27 **IDENTIFY** and **SET UP:** The bright bands are at angles θ given by $d\sin\theta = m\lambda$. Solve for d and then solve for θ for the specified order.

EXECUTE:

a) $\theta = 78.4°$ for $m = 3$ and $\lambda = 681$ nm, so $d = m\lambda/\sin\theta = 2.086 \times 10^{-4}$ cm

The number of slits per cm is $1/d = 4790$ slits/cm

b) 1st order: $m = 1$, so $\sin\theta = \lambda/d = (681 \times 10^{-9}$ m$)/(2.086 \times 10^{-6}$ m$)$ and $\theta = 19.1°$

2nd order: $m = 2$, so $\sin\theta = 2\lambda/d$ and $\theta = 40.8°$

c) For $m = 4$, $\sin\theta = 4\lambda/d$ is greater than 1.00, so there is no 4th-order bright band.

EVALUATE: The angular position of the bright bands for a particular wavelength increases as the order increases.

36.29 **IDENTIFY** and **SET UP:** Calculate d for the grating. Use Eq.(36.13) to calculate θ for the longest wavelength in the visible spectrum and verify that θ is small. Then use Eq.(36.3) to relate the linear separation of lines on the screen to the difference in wavelength.

EXECUTE:

a) $d - \left(\frac{1}{900}\right)$ cm $= 1.111 \times 10^{-5}$ m

For $\lambda = 700$ nm, $\lambda/d = 6.3 \times 10^{-2}$. The first-order lines are located at $\sin\theta = \lambda/d$; $\sin\theta$ is small enough for $\sin\theta \approx \theta$ to be an excellent approximation.

b) $y = x\lambda/d$, where $x = 2.50$ m.

The distance on the screen between 1st order bright bands for two different wavelengths is

$\Delta y = x(\Delta\lambda)/d$, so $\Delta\lambda = d(\Delta y)/x = (1.111 \times 10^{-5}$ m$)(3.00 \times 10^{-3}$ m$)/(2.50$ m$) = 13.3$ nm

EVALUATE: The smaller d is (greater number of lines per cm) the smaller the $\Delta\lambda$ that can be measured.

36.35 **IDENTIFY** and **SET UP:** Use Eq.(36.13) to calculate the angular position of each line.

EXECUTE: 4000 lines/cm means 4.00×10^5 lines/m.

The slit spacing is $d = \dfrac{1}{4.00 \times 10^5}$ m $= 2.50 \times 10^{-6}$ m.

a) The line positions are given by $\sin\theta = m\lambda/d$.

first order means $m = 1$

$$\sin \theta_\alpha = \frac{\lambda_\alpha}{d} = \frac{656 \times 10^{-9} \text{ m}}{2.50 \times 10^{-6} \text{ m}} = 0.2624 \text{ and } \theta_\alpha = 15.21°.$$

$$\sin \theta_\beta = \frac{\lambda_\beta}{d} = \frac{486 \times 10^{-9} \text{ m}}{2.50 \times 10^{-6} \text{ m}} = 0.1944 \text{ and } \theta_\beta = 11.21°.$$

The angular separation is $\theta_\alpha - \theta_\beta = 15.21° - 11.21° = 4.0°$.

b) second order means $m = 2$

$\sin \theta_\alpha = 2\lambda_\alpha/d = 0.5248$ and $\theta_\alpha = 31.65°$

$\sin \theta_\beta = 2\lambda_\beta/d = 0.3888$ and $\theta_\beta = 22.88°$

The angular separation is $\theta_\alpha - \theta_\beta = 31.65° - 22.88° = 8.8°$.

EVALUATE: The angular separation is larger in higher orders.

36.37 IDENTIFY and **SET UP:** The maxima occur at angles θ given by Eq.(36.16), $2d \sin \theta = m\lambda$, where d is the spacing between adjacent atomic planes. Solve for d.
EXECUTE: second order says $m = 2$.

$$d = \frac{m\lambda}{2 \sin \theta} = \frac{2(0.0850 \times 10^{-9} \text{ m})}{2 \sin 21.5°} = 2.32 \times 10^{-10} \text{ m} = 0.232 \text{ nm}$$

EVALUATE: Our result is similar to d calculated in Example 36.5.

36.43 IDENTIFY and **SET UP:** The angular size of the first dark ring is given by $\sin \theta_1 = 1.22\lambda/D$ (Eq.36.17). Calculate θ_1, and then the diameter of the ring on the screen is $2(4.5 \text{ m}) \tan \theta_1$.

EXECUTE: $\sin \theta_1 = 1.22 \left(\frac{620 \times 10^{-9} \text{ m}}{7.4 \times 10^{-6} \text{ m}} \right) = 0.1022; \quad \theta_1 = 0.1024 \text{ rad}$

The radius of the Airy disk (central bright spot) is $r = (4.5 \text{ m}) \tan \theta_1 = 0.462 \text{ m}$. The diameter is $2r = 0.92 \text{ m} = 92 \text{ cm}$.

EVALUATE: $\lambda/D = 0.084$. For this small D the central diffraction maximum is broad.

36.45 IDENTIFY and **SET UP:** Resolved by Rayleigh's criterion means angular separation θ of the objects equals $1.22\lambda/D$. The angular separation θ of the objects is their linear separation divided by their distance from the telescope.

EXECUTE: $\theta = \frac{250 \times 10^3 \text{ m}}{5.93 \times 10^{11} \text{ m}}$, where 5.93×10^{11} m is the distance from earth to Jupiter.

Thus $\theta = 4.216 \times 10^{-7}$.

Then $\theta = 1.22\frac{\lambda}{D}$ and $D = \frac{1.22\lambda}{\theta} = \frac{1.22(500 \times 10^{-9} \text{ m})}{4.216 \times 10^{-7}} = 1.45 \text{ m}$

EVALUATE: This is a very large telescope mirror. The greater the angular resolution the greater the diameter the lens or mirror must be.

Problems

36.51 a) IDENTIFY and **SET UP:** The intensity in the diffraction pattern is given by Eq.(36.5): $I = I_0 \left(\dfrac{\sin \beta/2}{\beta/2} \right)^2$, where $\beta = \left(\dfrac{2\pi}{\lambda} \right) a \sin \theta$. Solve for θ that gives $I = \frac{1}{2}I_0$.

EXECUTE: $I = \frac{1}{2}I_0$ so $\dfrac{\sin \beta/2}{\beta/2} = \dfrac{1}{\sqrt{2}}$

Let $x = \beta/2$; the equation for x is $\dfrac{\sin x}{x} = \dfrac{1}{\sqrt{2}} = 0.7071$.

Use trial and error to find the value of x that is a solution to this equation.

x	$(\sin x)/x$
1.0 rad	0.841
1.5 rad	0.665
1.2 rad	0.777
1.4 rad	0.7039
1.39 rad	0.7077; thus $x = 1.39$ rad and $\beta = 2x = 2.78$ rad

$\Delta\theta = |\theta_+ - \theta_-| = 2\theta_+$

$\sin\theta_+ = \dfrac{\lambda\beta}{2\pi a} = \dfrac{\lambda}{a}\left(\dfrac{2.78\text{ rad}}{2\pi\text{ rad}} \right) = 0.4425 \left(\dfrac{\lambda}{a} \right)$

(i) For $\dfrac{a}{\lambda} = 2$, $\sin\theta_+ = 0.4425(\frac{1}{2}) = 0.2212$; $\theta_+ = 12.78°$; $\Delta\theta = 2\theta_+ = 25.6°$

(ii) For $\dfrac{a}{\lambda} = 5$, $\sin\theta_+ = 0.4425(\frac{1}{5}) = 0.0885$; $\theta_+ = 5.077°$; $\Delta\theta = 2\theta_+ = 10.2°$

(iii) For $\dfrac{a}{\lambda} = 10$, $\sin\theta_+ = 0.4425(\frac{1}{10}) = 0.04425$; $\theta_+ = 2.536°$; $\Delta\theta = 2\theta_+ = 5.1°$

b) IDENTIFY and **SET UP:** $\sin\theta_0 = \dfrac{\lambda}{a}$ locates the first minimum. Solve for θ_0.

EXECUTE:
(i) For $\dfrac{a}{\lambda} = 2$, $\sin\theta_0 = \frac{1}{2}$; $\theta_0 = 30.0°$; $2\theta_0 = 60.0°$

(ii) For $\dfrac{a}{\lambda} = 5$, $\sin\theta_0 = \frac{1}{5}$; $\theta_0 = 11.54°$; $2\theta_0 = 23.1°$

(iii) For $\dfrac{a}{\lambda} = 10$, $\sin\theta_0 = \frac{1}{10}$; $\theta_0 = 5.74°$; $2\theta_0 = 11.5°$

EVALUATE: Either definition of the width shows that the central maximum gets narrower as the slit gets wider.

36.53 IDENTIFY and **SET UP:** $\sin\theta = \lambda/a$ locates the first dark band. In the liquid the wavelength changes and this changes the angular position of the first diffraction minimum.

EXECUTE: $\sin\theta_{air} = \dfrac{\lambda_{air}}{a}$; $\sin\theta_{liquid} = \dfrac{\lambda_{liquid}}{a}$

$\lambda_{liquid} = \lambda_{air}\left(\dfrac{\sin\theta_{liquid}}{\sin\theta_{air}}\right) = 0.4836$

$\lambda = \lambda_{air}/n$ (Eq.33.5), so $n = \lambda_{air}/\lambda_{liquid} = 1/0.4836 = 2.07$

EVALUATE: Light travels faster in air and n must be > 1.00. The smaller λ in the liquid reduces θ that located the first dark band.

36.55 a) IDENTIFY and **SET UP:** The angular position of the first minimum is given by $a\sin\theta = m\lambda$ (Eq.36.2), with $m = 1$. The distance of the minimum from the center of the pattern is given by $y = x\tan\theta$.

$\sin\theta = \dfrac{\lambda}{a} = \dfrac{540 \times 10^{-9}\text{ m}}{0.360 \times 10^{-3}\text{ m}} = 1.50 \times 10^{-3}$; $\theta = 1.50 \times 10^{-3}$ rad

$y_1 = x\tan\theta = (1.20\text{ m})\tan(1.50 \times 10^{-3}\text{ rad}) = 1.80 \times 10^{-3}\text{ m} = 1.80$ mm.

(Note that θ is small enough for $\theta \approx \sin\theta \approx \tan\theta$, and Eq.(36.3) applies.)

b) IDENTIFY and **SET UP:** Find the phase angle β where $I = I_0/2$. Then use Eq.(36.6) to solve for θ and $y = x\tan\theta$ to find the distance.

EXECUTE: From part (a) of Problem 36.51, $I = \frac{1}{2}I_0$ when $\beta = 2.78$ rad.

$\beta = \left(\dfrac{2\pi}{\lambda}\right)a\sin\theta$ (Eq.(36.6)), so $\sin\theta = \dfrac{\beta\lambda}{2\pi a}$.

$y = x\tan\theta \approx x\sin\theta \approx \dfrac{\beta\lambda x}{2\pi a} = \dfrac{(2.78\text{ rad})(540 \times 10^{-9}\text{ m})(1.20\text{ m})}{2\pi(0.360 \times 10^{-3}\text{ m})} =$

$7.96 \times 10^{-4}\text{ m} = 0.796$ mm

EVALUATE: The point where $I = I_0/2$ is not midway between the center of the central maximum and the first minimum; see Exercise 36.13.

36.57 IDENTIFY and **SET UP:** Relate the phase difference between adjacent slits to the sum of the phasors for all slits. The phase difference between adjacent slits is

$\phi = \dfrac{2\pi d}{\lambda}\sin\theta \approx \dfrac{2\pi d\theta}{\lambda}$ when θ is small and $\sin\theta \approx \theta$. Thus $\theta = \dfrac{\lambda\phi}{2\pi d}$.

EXECUTE: A principal maximum occurs when $\phi = \phi_{\max} = m2\pi$, where m is an integer, since then all the phasors add. The first minima on either side of the mth principal maximum occurs when $\phi = \phi_{\min}^{\pm} = m2\pi \pm (2\pi/N)$ and the phasor diagram for N slits forms a closed loop and the resultant phasor is zero.

The angular position of a principal maximum is $\theta = \left(\dfrac{\lambda}{2\pi d}\right)\phi_{\max}$. The angular position of the adjacent minimum is $\theta_{\min}^{\pm} = \left(\dfrac{\lambda}{2\pi d}\right)\phi_{\min}^{\pm}$.

$\theta_{\min}^{+} = \left(\dfrac{\lambda}{2\pi d}\right)\left(\phi_{\max} + \dfrac{2\pi}{N}\right) = \theta + \left(\dfrac{\lambda}{2\pi d}\right)\left(\dfrac{2\pi}{N}\right) = \theta + \dfrac{\lambda}{Nd}$

$\theta_{\min}^{-} = \left(\dfrac{\lambda}{2\pi d}\right)\left(\phi_{\max} - \dfrac{2\pi}{N}\right) = \theta - \dfrac{\lambda}{Nd}$

The angular width of the principal maximum is $\theta_{\min}^{+} - \theta_{\min}^{-} = \dfrac{2\lambda}{Nd}$, as was to be shown.

EVALUATE: The angular width of each principal maximum decreases like $1/N$ as N increases.

36.63 IDENTIFY and **SET UP:** The condition for an intensity maximum is $d\sin\theta = m\lambda$, $m = 0, \pm1, \pm2, \ldots$ Third order means $m = 3$. The longest observable wavelength is the one that gives $\theta = 90°$ and hence $\sin\theta = 1$.

EXECUTE: 6500 lines/cm so 6.50×10^5 lines/m and $d = \dfrac{1}{6.50 \times 10^5}$ m $= 1.538 \times 10^{-6}$ m

$\lambda = \dfrac{d\sin\theta}{m} = \dfrac{(1.538 \times 10^{-6}\text{ m})(1)}{3} = 5.13 \times 10^{-7}$ m $= 513$ nm

EVALUATE: The longest wavelength that can be obtained decreases as the order increases.

36.69 IDENTIFY and **SET UP:** Rayleigh's criterion says that the two objects are resolved if the center of one diffraction pattern coincides with the first minimum of the other.

By Eq.(36.2) the angular position of the first minimum relative to the center of the central maximum is $\sin\theta = \lambda/a$, where a is the slit width. Hence if the objects are resolved according to Rayleigh's criterion, the angular separation between centers of the images of the two objects must be at least λ/a.

But as discussed in Example 36.6, the angular separation of the image points equals the angular separation of the object points. The angular separation of the object points is y/s, where $y = 2.50$ m is the linear separation of the two points and s is their distance from the observer.

EXECUTE: $\dfrac{y}{s} = \dfrac{\lambda}{a}$ and $s = \dfrac{ya}{\lambda} = \dfrac{(2.50 \text{ m})(0.350 \times 10^{-3} \text{ m})}{600 \times 10^{-9} \text{ m}} = 1.46$ km.

EVALUATE: The smaller the slit width, the closer to the telescope the objects must be to be resolved. Narrower slit means a wider central diffraction pattern for each object.

36.71 **IDENTIFY** and **SET UP:** Resolved by Rayleigh's criterion means the angular separation θ of the objects is given by $\theta = 1.22\lambda/D$. $\theta = y/s$, where $y = 75.0$ m is the distance between the two objects and s is their distance from the astronaut (her altitude).

EXECUTE: $\dfrac{y}{s} = 1.22\dfrac{\lambda}{D}$

$s = \dfrac{yD}{1.22\lambda} = \dfrac{(75.0 \text{ m})(4.00 \times 10^{-3} \text{ m})}{1.22(500 \times 10^{-9} \text{ m})} = 4.92 \times 10^{5} \text{ m} = 492$ km

EVALUATE: In practice, this diffraction limit of resolution is not achieved. Defects of vision and distortion by the earth's atmosphere limit the resolution more than diffraction does.

CHAPTER 37
RELATIVITY

Exercises 1, 3, 5, 9, 13, 19, 21, 23, 25, 27, 33, 35, 37, 39, 43, 45
Problems 49, 51, 57, 59, 63, 65, 67

Exercises

37.1 **IDENTIFY** and **SET UP:** Consider the distance A to O' and B to O' as observed by an observer on the ground.

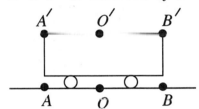

EXECUTE: Simultaneous to observer on train means light pulses from A' and B' arrive at O' at the same time. To observer at O light from A' has a longer distance to travel than light from B' so O will conclude that the pulse from $A(A')$ started before the pulse at $B(B')$. To observer at O bolt A appeared to strike first.

EVALUATE: Section 37.2 shows that if they are simultaneous to the observer on the ground then an observer on the train measures that the bolt at B' struck first.

37.3 **IDENTIFY** and **SET UP:** The clock on the plane measures the proper time Δt_0. $\Delta t = 4.00$ h $= 4.00$ h $(3600$ s$/1$ h$) = 1.44 \times 10^4$ s.

$$\Delta t = \frac{\Delta t_0}{\sqrt{1 - u^2/c^2}} \text{ and } \Delta t_0 = \Delta t\sqrt{1 - u^2/c^2}$$

EXECUTE: $\dfrac{u}{c}$ small so $\sqrt{1 - u^2/c^2} = (1 - u^2/c^2)^{1/2} \approx 1 - \dfrac{1}{2}\dfrac{u^2}{c^2}$; thus $\Delta t_0 = \Delta t\left(1 - \dfrac{1}{2}\dfrac{u^2}{c^2}\right)$

The difference in the clock readings is

$$\Delta t - \Delta t_0 = \frac{1}{2}\frac{u^2}{c^2}\Delta t = \frac{1}{2}\left(\frac{250 \text{ m/s}}{2.998 \times 10^8 \text{ m/s}}\right)^2 (1.44 \times 10^4 \text{ s}) = 5.01 \times 10^{-9} \text{ s. The}$$

clock on the plane has the shorter elapsed time.

EVALUATE: Δt_0 is always less than Δt; our results agree with this. The speed of the plane is much less than the speed of light, so the difference in the reading of the two clocks is very small.

37.5 **a) IDENTIFY** and **SET UP:** $\Delta t_0 = 2.60 \times 10^{-8}$ s; $\Delta t = 4.20 \times 10^{-7}$ s.
In the lab frame the pion is created and decays at different points, so this time is not the proper time.

EXECUTE: $\Delta t = \dfrac{\Delta t_0}{\sqrt{1 - u^2/c^2}}$ says $1 - \dfrac{u^2}{c^2} = \left(\dfrac{\Delta t_0}{\Delta t}\right)^2$

$\dfrac{u}{c} = \sqrt{1 - \left(\dfrac{\Delta t_0}{\Delta t}\right)^2} = \sqrt{1 - \left(\dfrac{2.60 \times 10^{-8} \text{ s}}{4.20 \times 10^{-7} \text{ s}}\right)^2} = 0.998; \ u = 0.998c$

EVALUATE: $u << c$, as it must be, but u/c is close to unity and the time dilation effects are large.

b) IDENTIFY and **SET UP:** The speed in the laboratory frame is $u = 0.998c$; the time measured in this frame is Δt, so the distance as measured in this frame is $d = u\Delta t$

EXECUTE: $d = (0.998)(2.998 \times 10^8 \text{ m/s})(4.20 \times 10^{-7} \text{ s}) = 126$ m

EVALUATE: The distance measured in the pion's frame will be different because the time measured in the pion's frame is different (shorter).

37.9 **a) IDENTIFY** and **SET UP:** The distance measured in the earth's frame is the proper length $l_0 = 55.0 \times 10^3$ m. Use Eq.(37.16) to calculate l, the distance in the muon's frame.

EXECUTE: $l = l_0\sqrt{1 - u^2/c^2} = (55.0 \times 10^3 \text{ m})\sqrt{1 - (0.9860c/c)^2} = 9.17 \times 10^3$ m $= 9.17$ km

b) IDENTIFY and **SET UP:** Use the lifetime measured in the muon's frame as the time of travel to calculate the distance traveled as measured in that frame.

EXECUTE: $d = u\,\Delta t = (0.9860)(2.998 \times 10^8 \text{ m/s})(2.20 \times 10^{-6} \text{ s}) = 650$ m $= 0.650$ km

The muon's original height as measured in the muon's frame (part (a)) is 9.17 km, so the fraction is $\dfrac{0.650 \text{ km}}{9.17 \text{ km}} = 0.0709$.

c) IDENTIFY and **SET UP:** The lifetime measured in the muon's frame is the proper time; solve for Δt, the lifetime in the earth's frame. $\Delta t_0 = 2.20 \times 10^{-6}$ s; $\Delta t = ?$

EXECUTE: $\Delta t = \dfrac{\Delta t_0}{\sqrt{1 - u^2/c^2}} = \dfrac{2.20 \times 10^{-6} \text{ s}}{\sqrt{1 - (0.9860c/c)^2}} = 1.32 \times 10^{-5}$ s $= 13.2 \ \mu$s

Use the lifetime in the earth's frame to find the distance traveled in that frame:

$d = u \Delta t = (0.9860)(2.998 \times 10^8 \text{ m/s})(1.32 \times 10^{-5} \text{ s}) = 3.90 \times 10^3 \text{ m} = 3.90 \text{ km}$

The fraction is $\dfrac{3.90 \text{ km}}{55.0 \text{ km}} = 0.0709$, the same fraction as in the muon's frame.

EVALUATE: In the earth's frame the muon lives longer and travels farther. In the muon's frame its lifetime is shortened, but the distance between where it is created and the surface of the earth is shortened by the same factor.

37.13 **IDENTIFY** and **SET UP:** $l = l_0 \sqrt{1 - u^2/c^2}$. The length measured when the spacecraft is moving is $l = 74.0$ m; l_0 is the length measured in a frame at rest relative to the spacecraft.

EXECUTE: $l_0 = \dfrac{l}{\sqrt{1 - u^2/c^2}} = \dfrac{74.0 \text{ m}}{\sqrt{1 - (0.600c/c)^2}} = 92.5 \text{ m}.$

EVALUATE: $l_0 > l$. The moving spacecraft appears to an observer on the planet to be shortened along the direction of motion.

37.19 **IDENTIFY** and **SET UP:** Use the Lorentz velocity transformation equation, Eq.(37.22): $v'_x = \dfrac{v_x - u}{1 - uv_x/c^2}.$

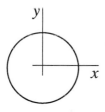 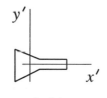

pursuit ship   cruiser

Tatooine

S = Tatooine frame
S' = pursuit spacecraft frame
The object is the cruiser.

With the coordinates shown, each ship is moving in the positive coordinate direction in the Tatooine frame.

u is the velocity of the pursuit spacecraft relative to Tatooine; $u = +0.800c$. This is the velocity of frame S' relative to frame S.

$v_x = +0.600c$, the velocity of the object in frame S.

$v'_x = ?$ (velocity of the cruiser relative to the pursuit spacecraft, the velocity of the object in frame S).

EXECUTE: $v'_x = \dfrac{v_x - u}{1 - uv_x/c^2} = \dfrac{0.600c - 0.800c}{1 - (0.800c)(0.600c)/c^2} = \dfrac{-0.200c}{0.520} = -0.385c$

The cruiser is moving toward the pursuit spacecraft with a speed of $0.385c = 1.15 \times 10^8$ m/s.

EVALUATE: The incorrect Galilean expression for the relative velocity gives that the cruiser is moving toward the pursuit spacecraft with a speed of $0.200c$. The correct relativistic expression differs from this by nearly a factor of 2.

37.21 IDENTIFY and SET UP:

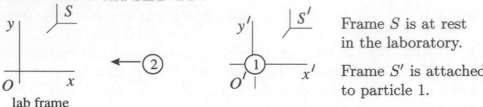

Frame S is at rest in the laboratory.

Frame S' is attached to particle 1.

u is the speed of S' relative to S; this is the speed of particle 1 as measured in the laboratory. Thus $u = +0.650c$. The speed of particle 2 in S' is $0.950c$. Also, since the two particles move in opposite directions, 2 moves in the $-x'$ direction and $v'_x = -0.950c$.

We want to calculate v_x, the speed of particle 2 in frame S; use Eq.(37.23).

EXECUTE: $v_x = \dfrac{v'_x + u}{1 + uv'_x/c^2} = \dfrac{-0.950c + 0.650c}{1 + (0.950c)(-0.650c)/c^2} = \dfrac{-0.300c}{1 - 0.6175} =$

$-0.784c$. The speed of the second particle, as masured in the laboratory, is $0.784c$.

EVALUATE: The incorrect Galilean expression for the relative velocity gives that the speed of the second particle in the lab frame is $0.300c$. The correct relativistic calculation gives a result more than twice this.

37.23 IDENTIFY and SET UP:

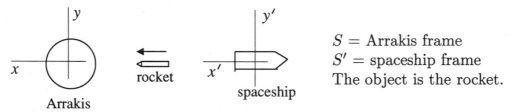

S = Arrakis frame
S' = spaceship frame
The object is the rocket.

u is the velocity of the spaceship relative to Arrakis.

$v_x = +0.360c;\quad v'_x = +0.920c$

(In each frame the rocket is moving in the positive coordinate direction.)

Use the Lorentz velocity transformation equation, Eq.(37.22): $v'_x = \dfrac{v_x - u}{1 - uv_x/c^2}$.

EXECUTE: $v'_x = \dfrac{v_x - u}{1 - uv_x/c^2}$ so $v'_x - u\left(\dfrac{v_x v'_x}{c^2}\right) = v_x - u$ and $u\left(1 - \dfrac{v_x v'_x}{c^2}\right) =$

$v_x - v'_x$

$u = \dfrac{v_x - v'_x}{1 - v_x v'_x/c^2} = \dfrac{0.360c - 0.920c}{1 - (0.360c)(0.920c)/c^2} = -\dfrac{0.560c}{0.6688} = -0.837c$

The speed of the spacecraft relative to Arrakis is $0.837c = 2.51\times10^8$ m/s. The minus sign in our result for u means that the spacecraft is moving in the $-x$-direction, so it is moving away from Arrakis.

EVALUATE: The incorrect Galilean expression also says that the spacecraft is moving away from Arrakis, but with speed $0.920c - 0.360c = 0.560c$.

37.25 **IDENTIFY** and **SET UP:** Source and observer are approaching, so use Eq.(37.25): $f = \sqrt{\dfrac{c+u}{c-u}} f_0$. Solve for u, the speed of the light source relative to the observer.

a) **EXECUTE:** $f^2 = \left(\dfrac{c+u}{c-u}\right) f_0^2$

$(c-u)f^2 = (c+u)f_0^2$ and $u = \dfrac{c(f^2 - f_0^2)}{f^2 + f_0^2} = c\left(\dfrac{(f/f_0)^2 - 1}{(f/f_0)^2 + 1}\right)$

$\lambda_0 = 675$ nm, $\quad \lambda = 575$ nm

$u = \left(\dfrac{(675 \text{ nm}/575 \text{ nm})^2 - 1}{(675 \text{ nm}/575 \text{ nm})^2 + 1}\right) c = 0.159c = (0.159)(2.998 \times 10^8 \text{ m/s}) =$
4.77×10^7 m/s; definitely speeding

b) 4.77×10^7 m/s $= (4.77 \times 10^7 \text{ m/s})(1 \text{ km}/1000 \text{ m})(3600 \text{ s}/1 \text{ h}) =$
1.72×10^8 km/h. Your fine would be $\$1.72 \times 10^8$ (172 million dollars).

EVALUATE: The source and observer are approaching, so $f > f_0$ and $\lambda < \lambda_0$. Our result gives $u < c$, as it must.

37.27 **IDENTIFY** and **SET UP:** If $\vec{F}$ is parallel to $\vec{v}$ then $\vec{F}$ changes the magnitude of $\vec{v}$ and not its direction.

$F = \dfrac{dp}{dt} = \dfrac{d}{dt}\left(\dfrac{mv}{\sqrt{1 - v^2/c^2}}\right)$

Use the chain rule to evaluate the derivative: $\dfrac{d}{dt} f(v(t)) = \dfrac{df}{dv}\dfrac{dv}{dt}$.

EXECUTE: $F = \dfrac{m}{(1 - v^2/c^2)^{1/2}}\left(\dfrac{dv}{dt}\right) + \dfrac{mv}{(1 - v^2/c^2)^{3/2}}\left(-\dfrac{1}{2}\right)\left(-\dfrac{2v}{c^2}\right)\left(\dfrac{dv}{dt}\right)$

$F = \dfrac{dv}{dt}\dfrac{m}{(1 - v^2/c^2)^{3/2}}\left(1 - \dfrac{v^2}{c^2} + \dfrac{v^2}{c^2}\right) = \dfrac{dv}{dt}\dfrac{m}{(1 - v^2/c^2)^{3/2}}$

But $\dfrac{dv}{dt} = a$, so $a = (F/m)(1 - v^2/c^2)^{3/2}$.

EVALUATE: Our result agrees with Eq.(37.30).

b) **IDENTIFY** and **SET UP:** If $\vec{F}$ is perpendicular to $\vec{v}$ then $\vec{F}$ changes the direction of $\vec{v}$ and not its magnitude.

$$\vec{F} = \frac{d}{dt}\left(\frac{m\vec{v}}{\sqrt{1 - v^2/c^2}}\right).$$

$\vec{a} = d\vec{v}/dt$ but the magnitude of v in the denominator of Eq.(37.29) is constant.

EXECUTE: $F = \dfrac{ma}{\sqrt{1 - v^2/c^2}}$ and $a = (F/m)(1 - v^2/c^2)^{1/2}$.

EVALUATE: This result agrees with Eq.(37.33).

37.33 IDENTIFY and **SET UP:** Eq.37.37: $K = \frac{1}{2}mv^2 + \frac{3}{8}mv^4/c^2$

We want $\dfrac{K - \frac{1}{2}mv^2}{\frac{1}{2}mv^2} = 0.020$. Solve for v/c.

EXECUTE: $\dfrac{\frac{3}{8}mv^4/c^2}{\frac{1}{2}mv^2} = 0.020$.

$\frac{3}{4}(v^2/c^2) = 0.020$ and $v = \sqrt{\frac{4}{3}(0.020)}c = 0.16c = 4.8 \times 10^7$ m/s

EVALUATE: With v specified, K is always larger than the Newtonian value. Our calculation gives $v < c$, as it must.

37.35 IDENTIFY: Use $E = mc^2$ to relate the mass increase to the energy increase.

a) SET UP: Your total energy E increases because your gravitational potential energy mgy increases.

EXECUTE: $\Delta E = mg\,\Delta y$

$\Delta E = (\Delta m)c^2$ so $\Delta m = \Delta E/c^2 = mg(\Delta y)/c^2$

$\Delta m/m = (g\,\Delta y)/c^2 = (9.80 \text{ m/s}^2)(30 \text{ m})/(2.998 \times 10^8 \text{ m/s})^2 = 3.3 \times 10^{-13}\%$

This increase is much, much too small to be noticed.

b) SET UP: The energy increases because potential energy is stored in the compressed spring.

EXECUTE: $\Delta E = \Delta U = \frac{1}{2}kx^2 = \frac{1}{2}(2.00 \times 10^4 \text{ N/m})(0.060 \text{ m})^2 = 36.0$ J

$\Delta m = (\Delta E)/c^2 = 4.0 \times 10^{-16}$ kg

Energy increases so mass increases. The mass increase is much, much too small to be noticed.

EVALUATE: In both cases the energy increase corresponds to a mass increase. But since c^2 is a very large number the mass increase is very small.

37.37 IDENTIFY and **SET UP:** Use Eqs.(37.38) and (37.39).

EXECUTE:

a) $E = mc^2 + K$, so $E = 4.00mc^2$ means $K = 3.00mc^2 = 4.50 \times 10^{-10}$ J

b) $E^2 = (mc^2)^2 + (pc)^2$; $E = 4.00mc^2$, so $15.0(mc^2)^2 = (pc)^2$

$p = \sqrt{15}mc = 1.94 \times 10^{-18}$ kg · m/s

c) $E = mc^2/\sqrt{1 - v^2/c^2}$

$E = 4.00mc^2$ gives $1 - v^2/c^2 = 1/16$ and $v = \sqrt{15/16}c = 0.968c$

EVALUATE: The speed is close to c since the kinetic energy is greater than the rest energy. Nonrelativistic expressions relating E, K p and v will be very inaccurate.

37.39 IDENTIFY and **SET UP:** The total energy is given in terms of the momentum by Eq.(37.39). In terms of the total energy E, the kinetic energy K is $K = E - mc^2$ (from Eq.37.38). The rest energy is mc^2.

EXECUTE:

a) $E = \sqrt{(mc^2)^2 + (pc)^2} =$

$\sqrt{[(6.64 \times 10^{-27})(2.998 \times 10^8)^2]^2 + [(2.10 \times 10^{-18})(2.998 \times 10^8)]^2}$ J

$E = 8.67 \times 10^{-10}$ J

b) $mc^2 = (6.64 \times 10^{-27}$ kg$)(2.998 \times 10^8$ m/s$)^2 = 5.97 \times 10^{-10}$ J

$K = E - mc^2 = 8.67 \times 10^{-10}$ J $- 5.97 \times 10^{-10}$ J $= 2.70 \times 10^{-10}$ J

c) $\dfrac{K}{mc^2} = \dfrac{2.70 \times 10^{-10} \text{ J}}{5.97 \times 10^{-10} \text{ J}} = 0.452$

EVALUATE: The incorrect nonrelativistic expressions for K and p give $K = p^2/2m = 3.3 \times 10^{-10}$ J;the correct relativistic value is less than this.

37.43 IDENTIFY and **SET UP:** Use Eq.(23.12) and conservation of energy to relate the potential difference to the kinetic energy gained by the electron. Use Eq.(37.36) to calculate the kinetic energy from the speed.

EXECUTE:

a) $K = q\,\Delta V = e\,\Delta V$

$K = mc^2 \left(\dfrac{1}{\sqrt{1 - v^2/c^2}} - 1 \right) = 4.025mc^2 = 3.295 \times 10^{-13}$ J $= 2.06$ MeV

$\Delta V = K/e = 2.06 \times 10^6$ V

b) From part (a), $K = 3.30 \times 10^{-13}$ J $= 2.06$ MeV

EVALUATE: The speed is close to c and the kinetic energy is four times the rest mass.

37.45 IDENTIFY and **SET UP:** 0.420 MeV is the kinetic energy of the electron.

Use Eq.(37.38) to calculate E and v.

EXECUTE:

a) $K = 0.420$ MeV $= 4.20 \times 10^5$ eV

b) $E = K + mc^2$

For an electron $mc^2 = (9.109 \times 10^{-31}$ kg$)(2.998 \times 10^8$ m/s$)^2 = 8.187 \times 10^{-14}$ J$(1$ eV$/1.602 \times 10^{-19}$ J$)$

$mc^2 = 5.110 \times 10^5$ eV $= 0.511$ MeV

Then $E = K + mc^2 = 0.420$ MeV $+ 0.511$ MeV $= 0.931$ MeV $= 9.31 \times 10^5$ eV

c) $E = \dfrac{mc^2}{\sqrt{1 - v^2/c^2}}$ so $1 - \dfrac{v^2}{c^2} = \left(\dfrac{mc^2}{E}\right)^2$

$v = c\sqrt{1 - \left(\dfrac{mc^2}{E}\right)^2} = (2.998 \times 10^8 \text{ m/s})\sqrt{1 - \left(\dfrac{0.511 \text{ MeV}}{0.931 \text{ MeV}}\right)^2} = 2.51 \times 10^8$ m/s

d) The classical relation between speed and kinetic energy is $K = \frac{1}{2}mv^2$ so

$v = \sqrt{\dfrac{2K}{m}} = \sqrt{\dfrac{2(4.20 \times 10^5 \text{ eV})(1.602 \times 10^{-19} \text{ J/1 eV})}{9.109 \times 10^{-31} \text{ kg}}} = 3.84 \times 10^8$ m/s

The classical result is too large by about 50%.

EVALUATE: The kinetic energy is nearly as large as the rest energy, so relativistic effects are large. The kinetic energy is larger than $\frac{1}{2}mv^2$, so the speed calculated using $K = \frac{1}{2}mv^2$ is larger than the correct value.

Problems

37.49 a) **IDENTIFY** and **SET UP:** $\Delta t_0 = 2.60 \times 10^{-8}$ s is the proper time, measured in the pion's frame.

The time measured in the lab must satisfy $d = c\,\Delta t$, where $u \approx c$. Calculate Δt and then use Eq.(37.6) to calculate u.

EXECUTE: $\Delta t = \dfrac{d}{c} = \dfrac{1.20 \times 10^3 \text{ m}}{2.998 \times 10^8 \text{ m/s}} = 4.003 \times 10^{-6}$ s

$\Delta t = \dfrac{\Delta t_0}{\sqrt{1 - u^2/c^2}}$ so $(1 - u^2/c^2)^{1/2} = \dfrac{\Delta t_0}{\Delta t}$ and $(1 - u^2/c^2) = \left(\dfrac{\Delta t_0}{\Delta t}\right)^2$

Write $u = (1 - \Delta)c$ so that $(u/c)^2 = (1 - \Delta)^2 = 1 - 2\Delta + \Delta^2 \approx 1 - 2\Delta$ since Δ is small.

Using this in the above gives $1 - (1 - 2\Delta) = \left(\dfrac{\Delta t_0}{\Delta t}\right)^2$

$$\Delta = \frac{1}{2}\left(\frac{\Delta t_0}{\Delta t}\right)^2 = \frac{1}{2}\left(\frac{2.60 \times 10^{-8} \text{ s}}{4.003 \times 10^{-6} \text{ s}}\right)^2 = 2.11 \times 10^{-5}$$

EVALUATE: An alternative calculation is to say that the length of the tube must contract relative to the moving pion so that the pion travels that length before decaying. The contracted length must be

$$l = c\,\Delta t_0 = (2.998 \times 10^8 \text{ m/s})(2.60 \times 10^{-8} \text{ s}) = 7.79 \text{ m}.$$

$$l = l_0\sqrt{1 - u^2/c^2} \text{ so } 1 - u^2/c^2 = \left(\frac{l}{l_0}\right)^2$$

Then $u = (1-\Delta)c$ gives $\Delta = \frac{1}{2}\left(\frac{l}{l_0}\right)^2 = \frac{1}{2}\left(\frac{7.79 \text{ m}}{1.20 \times 10^3 \text{ m}}\right)^2 = 2.11 \times 10^{-5}$, which checks.

b) IDENTIFY and **SET UP:** $E = \gamma mc^2$ (Eq.(37.38)).

EXECUTE: $\gamma = \dfrac{1}{\sqrt{1 - u^2/c^2}} = \dfrac{1}{\sqrt{2\Delta}} = \dfrac{1}{\sqrt{2(2.11 \times 10^{-5})}} = 154$

$E = 154(139.6 \text{ MeV}) = 2.15 \times 10^4 \text{ MeV} = 21.5 \text{ GeV}$

EVALUATE: The total energy is 154 times the rest energy.

37.51 IDENTIFY and **SET UP:** There must be a length contraction such that the length a becomes the same as b; $l_0 = a$, $l = b$. l_0 is the distance measured by an observer at rest relative to the spacecraft. Use Eq.(37.16) and solve for u.

EXECUTE: $\dfrac{l}{l_0} = \sqrt{1 - u^2/c^2}$ so $\dfrac{b}{a} = \sqrt{1 - u^2/c^2}$;

$a = 1.40b$ gives $b/1.40b = \sqrt{1 - u^2/c^2}$ and thus $1 - u^2/c^2 = 1/(1.40)^2$

$u = \sqrt{1 - 1/(1.40)^2}\,c = 0.700c = 2.10 \times 10^8 \text{ m/s}$

EVALUATE: A length on the spacecraft in the direction of the motion is shortened. A length perpendicular to the motion is unchanged.

37.57 IDENTIFY and **SET UP:** $E = mc^2$; the mass increase is due to the increase in energy, equal to heat flow into the ice to melt it. The amount of heat energy is given by Eq.(17.20).

EXECUTE: $E = Q = mL_f = (4.00 \text{ kg})(334 \times 10^3 \text{ J/kg}) = 1.336 \times 10^6 \text{ J}$

$m = \dfrac{E}{c^2} = \dfrac{1.336 \times 10^6 \text{ J}}{(2.998 \times 10^8 \text{ m/s})^2} = 1.49 \times 10^{-11} \text{ kg}$

EVALUATE: The mass increase is very, very small.

37.59 IDENTIFY and **SET UP:** In crown glass the speed of light is $v = \dfrac{c}{n}$. Calculate the kinetic energy of an electron that has this speed:

EXECUTE: $v = \dfrac{2.998 \times 10^8 \text{ m/s}}{1.52} = 1.972 \times 10^8 \text{ m/s}.$

$K = mc^2(\gamma - 1)$

$mc^2 = (9.109 \times 10^{-31} \text{ kg})(2.998 \times 10^8 \text{ m/s})^2 = 8.187 \times 10^{-14}$ J(1 eV/1.602 $\times$ 10^{-19} J) = 0.5111 MeV

$\gamma = \dfrac{1}{\sqrt{1 - v^2/c^2}} = \dfrac{1}{\sqrt{1 - ((1.972 \times 10^8 \text{ m/s})/(2.998 \times 10^8 \text{ m/s}))^2}} = 1.328$

$K = mc^2(\gamma - 1) = (0.5111 \text{ MeV})(1.328 - 1) = 0.168 \text{ MeV}$

EVALUATE: No object can travel faster than the speed of light in vacuum but there is nothing that prohibits an object from traveling faster than the speed of light in some material.

37.63 IDENTIFY and **SET UP:** Use Eq.(37.30),with $a = dv/dt$, to obtain an expression for dv/dt. Separate the variables v and t and integrate to obtain an expression for $v(t)$. In this expression, let $t \to \infty$.

EXECUTE: $a = \dfrac{dv}{dt} = \dfrac{F}{m}(1 - v^2/c^2)^{3/2}$. (One-dimensional motion is assumed, and all the F, v, and a refer to x-components.)

$\dfrac{dv}{(1 - v^2/c^2)^{3/2}} = \left(\dfrac{F}{m}\right) dt$

Integrate from $t = 0$, when $v = 0$, to time t, when the velocity is v.

$\displaystyle\int_0^v \dfrac{dv}{(1 - v^2/c^2)^{3/2}} = \int_0^t \left(\dfrac{F}{m}\right) dt$

Since F is constant, $\displaystyle\int_0^t \left(\dfrac{F}{m}\right) dt = \dfrac{Ft}{m}.$

In the velocity integral make the change of variable $y = v/c$; then $dy = dv/c$.

$\displaystyle\int_0^v \dfrac{dv}{(1 - v^2/c^2)^{3/2}} = c \int_0^{v/c} \dfrac{dy}{(1 - y^2)^{3/2}} = c \left[\dfrac{y}{(1 - y^2)^{1/2}}\right]_0^{v/c} = \dfrac{v}{\sqrt{1 - v^2/c^2}}$

Thus $\dfrac{v}{\sqrt{1 - v^2/c^2}} = \dfrac{Ft}{m}.$

Solve this equation for v:

$\dfrac{v^2}{1 - v^2/c^2} = \left(\dfrac{Ft}{m}\right)^2$ and $v^2 = \left(\dfrac{Ft}{m}\right)^2 (1 - v^2/c^2)$

$v^2 \left(1 + \left(\dfrac{Ft}{mc}\right)^2\right) = \left(\dfrac{Ft}{m}\right)^2$ so $v = \dfrac{(Ft/m)}{\sqrt{1 + (Ft/mc)^2}} = c\dfrac{Ft}{\sqrt{m^2c^2 + F^2t^2}}$

As $t \to \infty$, $\dfrac{Ft}{\sqrt{m^2c^2 + F^2t^2}} \to \dfrac{Ft}{\sqrt{F^2t^2}} \to 1$, so $v \to c$.

EVALUATE: Note that $\dfrac{Ft}{\sqrt{m^2c^2 + F^2t^2}}$ is always less than 1, so $v < c$ always and v approaches c only when $t \to \infty$.

37.65 **a) IDENTIFY** and **SET UP:** Use the Lorentz coordinate transformation (Eq.37.21) for (x_1, t_1) and (x_2, t_2):

$$x_1' = \frac{x_1 - ut_1}{\sqrt{1 - u^2/c^2}}, \qquad x_2' = \frac{x_2 - ut_2}{\sqrt{1 - u^2/c^2}}$$

$$t_1' = \frac{t_1 - ux_1/c^2}{\sqrt{1 - u^2/c^2}}, \qquad t_2' = \frac{t_2 - ux_2/c^2}{\sqrt{1 - u^2/c^2}}$$

Same point in S' implies $x_1' = x_2'$. What then is $\Delta t' = t_2' - t_1'$?

EXECUTE: $x_1' = x_2'$ implies $x_1 - ut_1 = x_2 - ut_2$

$u(t_2 - t_1) = x_2 - x_1$ and $u = \dfrac{x_2 - x_1}{t_2 - t_1} = \dfrac{\Delta x}{\Delta t}$

From the time transformation equations,

$$\Delta t' = t_2' - t_1' = \frac{1}{\sqrt{1 - u^2/c^2}}(\Delta t - u\,\Delta x/c^2)$$

Using the result that $u = \dfrac{\Delta x}{\Delta t}$ gives

$$\Delta t' = \frac{1}{\sqrt{1 - (\Delta x)^2/((\Delta t)^2 c^2)}}(\Delta t - (\Delta x)^2/((\Delta t)c^2))$$

$$\Delta t' = \frac{\Delta t}{\sqrt{(\Delta t)^2 - (\Delta x)^2/c^2}}(\Delta t - (\Delta x)^2/((\Delta t)c^2))$$

$$\Delta t' = \frac{(\Delta t)^2 - (\Delta x)^2/c^2}{\sqrt{(\Delta t)^2 - (\Delta x)^2/c^2}} = \sqrt{(\Delta t)^2 - (\Delta x/c)^2}, \text{ as was to be shown.}$$

This equation doesn't have a physical solution (because of a negative square root) if $(\Delta x/c)^2 > (\Delta t)^2$ or $\Delta x \geq c\,\Delta t$.

b) IDENTIFY and **SET UP:** Now require that $t_2' = t_1'$ (the two events are simultaneous in S') and use the Lorentz coordinate transformation equations.

EXECUTE: $t_1' = t_2'$ implies $t_1 - ux_1/c^2 = t_2 - ux_2/c^2$

$t_2 - t_1 = \left(\dfrac{x_2 - x_1}{c^2}\right)u$ so $\Delta t = \left(\dfrac{\Delta x}{c^2}\right)u$ and $u = \dfrac{c^2\,\Delta t}{\Delta x}$

From the Lorentz transformation equations,

$$\Delta x' = x_2' - x_1' = \left(\frac{1}{\sqrt{1 - u^2/c^2}} \right) (\Delta x - u\,\Delta t).$$

Using the result that $u = c^2\,\Delta t/\Delta x$ gives

$$\Delta x' = \frac{1}{\sqrt{1 - c^2(\Delta t)^2/(\Delta x)^2}}(\Delta x - c^2(\Delta t)^2/\Delta x)$$

$$\Delta x' = \frac{\Delta x}{\sqrt{(\Delta x)^2 - c^2(\Delta t)^2}}(\Delta x - c^2(\Delta t)^2/\Delta x)$$

$$\Delta x' = \frac{(\Delta x)^2 - c^2(\Delta t)^2}{\sqrt{(\Delta x)^2 - c^2(\Delta t)^2}} = \sqrt{(\Delta x)^2 - c^2(\Delta t)^2}$$

c) **IDENTIFY** and **SET UP:** The result from part (b) is
$\Delta x' = \sqrt{(\Delta x)^2 - c^2(\Delta t)^2}$
Solve for Δt: $(\Delta x')^2 = (\Delta x)^2 - c^2(\Delta t)^2$

EXECUTE: $\Delta t = \dfrac{\sqrt{(\Delta x)^2 - (\Delta x')^2}}{c} = \dfrac{\sqrt{(5.00 \text{ m})^2 - (2.50 \text{ m})^2}}{2.998 \times 10^8 \text{ m/s}} = 1.44 \times 10^{-8}$ s

EVALUATE: This provides another illustration of the concept of simultaneity (Section 37.2): events observed to be simultaneous in one frame are not simultaneous in another frame that is moving relative to the first.

37.67 **IDENTIFY** and **SET UP:** An increase in wavelength corresponds to a decrease in frequency ($f = c/\lambda$), so the atoms are moving away from the earth.

Receding, so use Eq.(37.26): $f = \sqrt{\dfrac{c - u}{c + u}}\, f_0$

EXECUTE: Solve for u: $(f/f_0)^2(c + u) = c - u$ and $u = c\left(\dfrac{1 - (f/f_0)^2}{1 + (f/f_0)^2} \right)$

$f = c/\lambda$, $f_0 = c/\lambda_0$ so $f/f_0 = \lambda_0/\lambda$

$$u = c\left(\frac{1 - (\lambda_0/\lambda)^2}{1 + (\lambda_0/\lambda)^2} \right) = c\left(\frac{1 - (656.3/953.4)^2}{1 + (656.3/953.4)^2} \right) = 0.357c = 1.07 \times 10^8 \text{ m/s}$$

EVALUATE: The relative speed is large, 36% of c. The cosmological implications of such observations will be discussed in Section 44.6.

CHAPTER 38
PHOTONS, ELECTRONS, AND ATOMS

Exercises 3, 5, 9, 11, 13, 17, 19, 21, 23, 25, 29, 31, 35, 37, 43
Problems 51, 57, 59, 61, 63, 65, 69, 71, 73, 75

Exercises

38.3 **IDENTIFY** and **SET UP:** Eq.(38.2) relates the photon energy and wavelength. $c = f\lambda$ relates speed, frequency and wavelength for an electromagnetic wave.

EXECUTE:

a) $E = hf$ so $f = \dfrac{E}{h} = \dfrac{(2.45 \times 10^6 \text{ eV})(1.602 \times 10^{-19} \text{ J/1 eV})}{6.626 \times 10^{-34} \text{ J} \cdot \text{s}} = 5.92 \times 10^{20}$ Hz

b) $c = f\lambda$ so $\lambda = \dfrac{c}{f} = \dfrac{2.998 \times 10^8 \text{ m/s}}{5.92 \times 10^{20} \text{ Hz}} = 5.06 \times 10^{-13}$ m

c) **EVALUATE:** λ is comparable to a nuclear radius. Note that in doing the calculation the energy in MeV was converted to the SI unit of joules.

38.5 **IDENTIFY** and **SET UP:** Eq.(38.3): $\frac{1}{2}mv_{\text{max}}^2 = hf - \phi = \dfrac{hc}{\lambda} - \phi$. Take the work function ϕ from Table 38.1. Solve for v_{max}. Note that we wrote f as c/λ.

EXECUTE: $\frac{1}{2}mv_{\text{max}}^2 = \dfrac{(6.626 \times 10^{-34} \text{ J} \cdot \text{s})(2.998 \times 10^8 \text{ m/s})}{235 \times 10^{-9} \text{ m}} - (5.1 \text{ eV})(1.602 \times 10^{-19} \text{ J/1 eV})$

$\frac{1}{2}mv_{\text{max}}^2 = 8.453 \times 10^{-19} \text{ J} - 8.170 \times 10^{-19} \text{ J} = 2.83 \times 10^{-20}$ J

$v_{\text{max}} = \sqrt{\dfrac{2(2.83 \times 10^{-20} \text{ J})}{9.109 \times 10^{-31} \text{ kg}}} = 2.49 \times 10^5$ m/s

EVALUATE: The work function in eV was converted to joules for use in Eq.(38.3). A photon with $\lambda = 235$ nm has energy greater than the work function for the surface.

38.9 **IDENTIFY:** Protons have mass and photons are massless.

a) **SET UP:** For a particle with mass, $K = p^2/2m$.

EXECUTE: $p_2 = 2p_1$ means $K_2 = 4K_1$.

b) **SET UP:** For a photon, $E = pc$.

EXECUTE: $p_2 = 2p_1$ means $E_2 = 2E_1$.

EVALUATE: The relation between E and p is different for particles with mass and particles without mass.

38.11 a) IDENTIFY: First use Eq.(38.4) to find the work function ϕ.

SET UP: $eV_0 = hf - \phi$ so $\phi = hf - eV_0 = \dfrac{hc}{\lambda} - eV_0$

EXECUTE:

$\phi = \dfrac{(6.626 \times 10^{-34} \text{ J} \cdot \text{s})(2.998 \times 10^8 \text{ m/s})}{254 \times 10^{-9} \text{ m}} - (1.602 \times 10^{-19})(0.181 \text{ V})$

$\phi = 7.821 \times 10^{-19} \text{ J} - 2.900 \times 10^{-20} \text{ J} = 7.531 \times 10^{-19} \text{ J}(1 \text{ eV}/1.602 \times 10^{-19} \text{ J}) = 4.70 \text{ eV}$

IDENTIFY and **SET UP:** The threshold frequency f_{th} is the smallest frequency that still produces photoelectrons. It corresponds to $K_{max} = 0$ in Eq.(38.3), so $hf_{th} = \phi$.

EXECUTE: $f = \dfrac{c}{\lambda}$ says $\dfrac{hc}{\lambda_{th}} = \phi$

$\lambda_{th} = \dfrac{hc}{\phi} = \dfrac{(6.626 \times 10^{-34} \text{ J} \cdot \text{s})(2.998 \times 10^8 \text{ m/s})}{7.531 \times 10^{-19} \text{ J}} = 2.64 \times 10^{-7} \text{ m} = 264 \text{ nm}$

b) EVALUATE: As calculated in part (a), $\phi = 4.70$ eV. This is the value given in Table 38.1 for copper.

38.13 IDENTIFY and **SET UP:** A photon has zero rest mass, so its energy and momentum are related by Eq.(37.40). Eq.(38.5) then relates its momentum and wavelength.

EXECUTE:

a) $E = pc = (8.24 \times 10^{-28} \text{ kg} \cdot \text{m/s})(2.998 \times 10^8 \text{ m/s}) = 2.47 \times 10^{-19} \text{ J} = (2.47 \times 10^{-19} \text{ J})(1 \text{ eV}/1.602 \times 10^{-19} \text{ J}) = 1.54 \text{ eV}$

b) $p = \dfrac{h}{\lambda}$ so $\lambda = \dfrac{h}{p} = \dfrac{6.626 \times 10^{-34} \text{ J} \cdot \text{s}}{8.24 \times 10^{-28} \text{ kg} \cdot \text{m/s}} = 8.04 \times 10^{-7} \text{ m} = 804 \text{ nm}$

EVALUATE: This wavelength is longer than visible wavelengths; it is in the infrared region of the electromagnetic spectrum.

To check our result we could verify that the same E is given by Eq.(38.2), using the λ we have calculated.

38.17 IDENTIFY and **SET UP:** Balmer's formula is $\dfrac{1}{\lambda} = R\left(\dfrac{1}{2^2} - \dfrac{1}{n^2}\right)$.

For the H_γ spectral line $n = 5$. Once we have λ, calculate f from $f = c/\lambda$ and E from Eq.(38.2).

EXECUTE:

a) $\frac{1}{\lambda} = R\left(\frac{1}{2^2} - \frac{1}{5^2}\right) = R\left(\frac{25-4}{100}\right) = R\left(\frac{21}{100}\right).$

Thus $\lambda = \frac{100}{21R} = \frac{100}{21(1.097 \times 10^7)}$ m $= 4.341 \times 10^{-7}$ m $= 434.1$ nm.

b) $f = \frac{c}{\lambda} = \frac{2.998 \times 10^8 \text{ m/s}}{4.341 \times 10^{-7} \text{ m}} = 6.906 \times 10^{14}$ Hz

c) $E = hf = (6.626 \times 10^{-34} \text{ J} \cdot \text{s})(6.906 \times 10^{14} \text{ Hz}) = 4.576 \times 10^{-19}$ J $= 2.856$ eV

EVALUATE: Section 38.3 shows that the longest wavelength in the Balmer series (H_α) is 656 nm and the shortest is 365 nm. Our result for H_γ falls within this range. The photon energies for hydrogen atom transitions are in the eV range, and our result is of this order.

38.19 IDENTIFY: Use Eq.(38.6). We know λ for the transition from each excited level to the ground state. From the corresponding transition energies calculate the energy difference between the two excited levels.

SET UP: Call the two lowest excited levels level 1 and level 2. If λ is the wavelength shown in the figure for the transition from one of these levels to the ground state then the transition energy is $\Delta E = hc/\lambda$.

The difference in energy between these two levels is

$$\Delta E_1 - \Delta E_2 = hc\left(\frac{1}{\lambda_1} - \frac{1}{\lambda_2}\right) = hc\left(\frac{\lambda_2 - \lambda_1}{\lambda_1 \lambda_2}\right).$$

EXECUTE: $\Delta E_1 - \Delta E_2 =$

$(4.136 \times 10^{-15} \text{ eV} \cdot \text{s})(2.998 \times 10^8 \text{ m/s})\left(\frac{(589.6 \times 10^{-9} \text{ m} - 589.0 \times 10^{-9} \text{ m})}{(589.6 \times 10^{-9} \text{ m})(589.0 \times 10^{-9} \text{ m})}\right) =$

0.002 eV

EVALUATE: These two excited levels have nearly the same energy. We knew this would be the case because the transition wavelengths are almost the same.

38.21 a) IDENTIFY: If the particles are treated as point charges, $U = \frac{1}{4\pi\epsilon_0}\frac{q_1 q_2}{r}$.

SET UP: $q_1 = 2e$ (alpha particle); $q_2 = 82e$ (gold nucleus); r is given so we can solve for U.

EXECUTE:

$U = (8.987 \times 10^9 \text{ N} \cdot \text{m}^2/\text{C}^2)\dfrac{(2)(82)(1.602 \times 10^{-19} \text{ C})^2}{6.50 \times 10^{-14} \text{ m}} = 5.82 \times 10^{-13}$ J

$U = 5.82 \times 10^{-13}$ J$(1 \text{ eV}/1.602 \times 10^{-19} \text{ J}) = 3.63 \times 10^6$ eV $= 3.63$ MeV

b) **IDENTIFY:** Apply conservation of energy: $K_1 + U_1 = K_2 + U_2$.

SET UP: Let point 1 be the initial position of the alpha particle and point 2 be where the alpha particle momentarily comes to rest. Alpha particle is initially far from the lead nucleus implies $r_1 \approx \infty$ and $U_1 = 0$. Alpha particle stops implies $K_2 = 0$.

EXECUTE: Conservation of energy thus says $K_1 = U_2 = 5.82 \times 10^{-13}$ J = 3.63 MeV.

c) $K = \frac{1}{2}mv^2$ so $v = \sqrt{\dfrac{2K}{m}} = \sqrt{\dfrac{2(5.82 \times 10^{-13} \text{ J})}{6.64 \times 10^{-27} \text{ kg}}} = 1.32 \times 10^7$ m/s

EVALUATE: $v/c = 0.44$, so it is ok to use the nonrelativistic expression to relate K and v. When the alpha particle stops, all its initial kinetic enrgy has been converted to electrostatic potential energy.

38.23 **IDENTIFY:** The force between the electron and the nucleus in Be^{3+} is $F = \dfrac{1}{4\pi\epsilon_0} \dfrac{Ze^2}{r^2}$, where $Z = 4$ is the nuclear charge. All the equations for the hydrogen atom apply to Be^{+3} if we replace e^2 by Ze^2.

a) **SET UP:** Modify Eq.(38.18).

EXECUTE: $E_n = -\dfrac{1}{\epsilon_0} \dfrac{me^4}{8n^2h^2}$ (hydrogen) becomes

$E_n = -\dfrac{1}{\epsilon_0} \dfrac{m(Ze^2)^2}{8n^2h^2} = Z^2\left(-\dfrac{1}{\epsilon_0} \dfrac{me^4}{8n^2h^2}\right) = Z^2\left(-\dfrac{13.60 \text{ eV}}{n^2}\right)$ (for Be^{3+})

The ground-level energy of Be^{3+} is $E_1 = 16\left(-\dfrac{13.60 \text{ eV}}{1^2}\right) = -218$ eV.

EVALUATE: The ground-level energy of Be^{3+} is $Z^2 = 16$ times the ground-level energy of H.

b) **SET UP:** The ionization energy is the energy difference between the $n \to \infty$ level energy and the $n = 1$ level energy.

EXECUTE: The $n \to \infty$ level energy is zero, so the ionization energy of Be^{3+} is 218 eV.

EVALUATE: This is 16 times the ionization energy of hydrogen.

c) **SET UP:** $\dfrac{1}{\lambda} = R\left(\dfrac{1}{n_1^2} - \dfrac{1}{n_2^2}\right)$ just as for hydrogen but now R has a diferent value.

EXECUTE: $R_H = \dfrac{me^4}{8\epsilon_0 h^3 c} = 1.097 \times 10^7$ m^{-1} for hydrogen becomes

$$R_{Be} = Z^2 \frac{me^4}{8\epsilon_0 h^3 c} = 16(1.097 \times 10^7 \text{ m}^{-1}) = 1.755 \times 10^8 \text{ m}^{-1} \text{ for Be}^{3+}.$$

For $n = 2$ to $n = 1$, $\frac{1}{\lambda} = R_{Be}\left(\frac{1}{1^2} - \frac{1}{2^2}\right) = 3R/4.$

$\lambda = 4/(3R) = 4/(3(1.755 \times 10^8 \text{ m}^{-1})) = 7.60 \times 10^{-9} \text{ m} = 7.60 \text{ nm}.$

EVALUATE: This wavelength is smaller by a factor of 16 compared to the wavelength for the corresponding transition in the hydrogen atom.

d) SET UP: Modify Eq. (38.12): $r_n = \varepsilon_0 \dfrac{n^2 h^2}{\pi m e^2}$ (hydrogen).

EXECUTE: $r_n = \varepsilon_0 \dfrac{n^2 h^2}{\pi m(Z e^2)}$ (Be^{3+}).

EVALUATE: For a given n the orbit radius for Be^{3+} is smaller by a factor of $Z = 4$ compared to the corresponding radius for hydrogen.

38.25 IDENTIFY and **SET UP:** Use the energy to calculate n for this state. Then use the Bohr equation, Eq.(38.10), to calculate L.

EXECUTE: $E_n = -(13.6 \text{ eV})/n^2$, so this state has $n = \sqrt{13.6/1.51} = 3$. In the Bohr model. $L = n\hbar$ so for this state $L = 3\hbar = 3.16 \times 10^{-34} \text{ kg}\cdot\text{m}^2/\text{s}.$

EVALUATE: We will find in Section 41.1 that the modern quantum mechanical description gives a different result.

38.29 IDENTIFY: Apply Eq.(38.21): $\dfrac{n_{5s}}{n_{3p}} = e^{-(E_{5s} - E_{3p})/kT}$

SET UP: From Fig.38.24a, $E_{5s} = 20.66$ eV and $E_{3p} = 18.70$ eV

EXECUTE: $E_{5s} - E_{3p} = 20.66 \text{ eV} - 18.70 \text{ eV} = 1.96 \text{ eV}(1.602 \times 10^{-19} \text{ J}/1 \text{ eV}) = 3.140 \times 10^{-19} \text{ J}$

a) $\dfrac{n_{5s}}{n_{3p}} = e^{-(3.140 \times 10^{-19} \text{ J})/[(1.38 \times 10^{-23} \text{ J/K})(300 \text{ K})]} = e^{-75.79} = 1.2 \times 10^{-33}$

b) $\dfrac{n_{5s}}{n_{3p}} = e^{-(3.140 \times 10^{-19} \text{ J})/[(1.38 \times 10^{-23} \text{ J/K})(600 \text{ K})]} = e^{-37.90} = 3.5 \times 10^{-17}$

c) $\dfrac{n_{5s}}{n_{3p}} = e^{-(3.140 \times 10^{-19} \text{ J})/[(1.38 \times 10^{-23} \text{ J/K})(1200 \text{ K})]} = e^{-18.95} = 5.9 \times 10^{-9}$

d) EVALUATE: At each of these temperatures the number of atoms in the $5s$ excited state, the initial state for the transition that emits 632.8 nm radiation, is quite small. The ratio increases as the temperature increases.

38.31 IDENTIFY and **SET UP:** The number of photons emitted each second is the total energy emitted divided by the energy of one photon. The energy of one photon is given by Eq.(38.2). $E = Pt$ gives the energy emitted by the laser in time t.

EXECUTE: In 1.00 s the energy emitted by the laser is

$(7.50 \times 10^{-3} \text{ W})(1.00 \text{ s}) = 7.50 \times 10^{-3} \text{ J}.$

The energy of each photon is

$$E = \frac{hc}{\lambda} = \frac{(6.626 \times 10^{-34} \text{ J} \cdot \text{s})(2.998 \times 10^{8} \text{ m/s})}{10.6 \times 10^{-6} \text{ m}} = 1.874 \times 10^{-20} \text{ J}.$$

Therefore $\dfrac{7.50 \times 10^{-3} \text{ J/s}}{1.874 \times 10^{-20} \text{ J/photon}} = 4.00 \times 10^{17}$ photons/s

EVALUATE: The number of photons emitted per second is extremely large.

38.35 **IDENTIFY:** The shortest wavelength x rays are those for which the kinetic energy of a photon is converted entirely to the photon energy $hf = hc/\lambda$.

SET UP: The kinetic energy K of an electron after acceleration is $K = q\,\Delta V = (1.602 \times 10^{-19} \text{ C})(15.0 \times 10^{3} \text{ V}) = 2.403 \times 10^{-15} \text{ J}.$

EXECUTE: $\dfrac{hc}{\lambda} = K$ gives

$$\lambda = \frac{hc}{K} = \frac{(6.626 \times 10^{-34} \text{ J} \cdot \text{s})(2.998 \times 10^{8} \text{ m/s})}{2.403 \times 10^{-15} \text{ J}} = 8.27 \times 10^{-11} \text{ m} = 0.0827 \text{ nm}.$$

EVALUATE: Typical x-ray wavelengths are 0.001 to 1 nm, and our results are in this range.

38.37 **IDENTIFY:** Apply Eq.(38.23): $\lambda' - \lambda = \dfrac{h}{mc}(1 - \cos\phi) = \lambda_c(1 - \cos\phi)$

SET UP: Solve for λ': $\lambda' = \lambda + \lambda_c(1 - \cos\phi)$

The largest λ' corresponds to $\phi = 180°$, so $\cos\phi = -1$.

EXECUTE: $\lambda' = \lambda + 2\lambda_c = 0.0665 \times 10^{-9} \text{ m} + 2(2.426 \times 10^{-12} \text{ m}) = 7.135 \times 10^{-11} \text{ m} = 0.0714 \text{ nm}.$

This wavelength occurs at a scattering angle of $\phi = 180°$.

EVALUATE: The incident photon transfers some of its energy and momentum to the electron from which it scatters. Since the photon loses energy its wavelength increases, $\lambda' > \lambda$.

38.43 **IDENTIFY** and **SET UP:** The wavelength λ_m where the Planck distribution peaks is given by Eq.(38.30).

EXECUTE: $\lambda_m = \dfrac{2.90 \times 10^{-3} \text{ m} \cdot \text{K}}{2.728 \text{ K}} = 1.06 \times 10^{-3} \text{ m} = 1.06 \text{ mm}.$

EVALUATE: This wavelength is in the microwave portion of the electromagnetic spectrum. This radiation is often referred to as the "microwave background" (Section 44.7). Note that in Eq.(38.30), T must be in kelvins.

Problems

38.51 **IDENTIFY** and **SET UP:** Use $c = f\lambda$ to relate frequency and wavelength and use $E = hf$ to relate photon energy and frequency.

EXECUTE:

a) One photon dissociates one AgBr molecule, so we need to find the energy required to dissociate a single molecule. The problem states that it requires 1.00×10^5 J to dissociate one mole of AgBr, and one mole contains Avogadro's number (6.02×10^{23}) of molecules, so the energy required to dissociate one AgBr is

$$\frac{1.00 \times 10^5 \text{ J/mol}}{6.02 \times 10^{23} \text{ molecules/mol}} = 1.66 \times 10^{-19} \text{ J/molecule.}$$

The photon is to have this energy, so

$E = 1.66 \times 10^{-19} \text{ J}(1\text{eV}/1.602 \times 10^{-19} \text{ J}) = 1.04 \text{ eV.}$

b) $E = \dfrac{hc}{\lambda}$ so $\lambda = \dfrac{hc}{E} = \dfrac{(6.626 \times 10^{-34} \text{ J} \cdot \text{s})(2.998 \times 10^8 \text{ m/s})}{1.66 \times 10^{-19} \text{ J}} = 1.20 \times 10^{-6} \text{ m} = 1200 \text{ nm}$

c) $c = f\lambda$ so $f = \dfrac{c}{\lambda} = \dfrac{2.998 \times 10^8 \text{ m/s}}{1.20 \times 10^{-6} \text{ m}} = 2.50 \times 10^{14} \text{ Hz}$

d) $E = hf = (6.626 \times 10^{-34} \text{ J} \cdot \text{s})(100 \times 10^6 \text{ Hz}) = 6.63 \times 10^{-26} \text{ J}$

$E = 6.63 \times 10^{-26} \text{ J}(1 \text{ eV}/1.602 \times 10^{-19} \text{ J}) = 4.14 \times 10^{-7} \text{ eV}$

e) **EVALUATE:** A photon with frequency $f = 100$ MHz has too little energy, by a large factor, to dissociate a AgBr molecule. The photons in the visible light from a firefly do individually have enough energy to dissociate AgBr. The huge number of 100 MHz photons can't compensate for the fact that individually they have too little energy.

38.57 a) **IDENTIFY:** Apply the photoelectric effect equation, Eq.(38.4).

SET UP: $eV_0 = hf - \phi = (hc/\lambda) - \phi.$

Call the stopping potential V_{01} for λ_1 and V_{02} for λ_2. Thus $eV_{01} = (hc/\lambda_1) - \phi$ and $eV_{02} = (hc/\lambda_2) - \phi$. Note that the work function ψ is a property of the material and is independent of the wavelength of the light.

EXECUTE: Subtracting one equation from the other gives

$e(V_{02} - V_{01}) = hc\left(\dfrac{\lambda_1 - \lambda_2}{\lambda_1 \lambda_2}\right).$

b) $\Delta V_0 = \dfrac{(6.626 \times 10^{-34} \text{ J} \cdot \text{s})(2.998 \times 10^8 \text{ m/s})}{1.602 \times 10^{-19} \text{ C}} \left(\dfrac{295 \times 10^{-9} \text{ m} - 265 \times 10^{-9} \text{ m}}{(295 \times 10^{-9} \text{ m})(265 \times 10^{-9} \text{ m})} \right)$

$= 0.476$ V.

EVALUATE: $e\,\Delta V_0$, which is 0.476 eV, is the increase in photon energy from 295 nm to 265 nm. The stopping potential increases when λ decreases because the photon energy increases when the wavelength decreases.

38.59   **IDENTIFY** and **SET UP:** $\lambda' = \lambda + \dfrac{h}{mc}(1 - \cos\phi)$

$\phi = 180°$ so $\lambda' = \lambda + \dfrac{2h}{mc} = 0.09485$ m. Use Eq.(38.5) to calculate the momentum of the scattered photon. Apply conservation of energy to the collision to calculate the kinetic energy of the electron after the scattering. The energy of the photon is given by Eq.(38.2).

EXECUTE:

a) $p' = h/\lambda' = 6.99 \times 10^{-24}$ kg·m/s.

b) $E = E' + E_e; \qquad hc/\lambda = hc/\lambda' + E_e$

$E_e = hc\left(\dfrac{1}{\lambda} - \dfrac{1}{\lambda'}\right) = (hc)\dfrac{\lambda' - \lambda}{\lambda\lambda'} = 1.129 \times 10^{-16} \text{ J} = 705 \text{ eV}$

EVALUATE: The energy of the incident photon is 13.8 keV, so only about 5% of its energy is transferred to the electron. This corresponds to a fractional shift in the photon's wavelength that is also 5%.

38.61   **a) IDENTIFY** and **SET UP:** Apply Eq.(38.20): $m_r = \dfrac{m_1 m_2}{m_1 + m_2} = \dfrac{207 m_e m_p}{207 m_e + m_p}$

EXECUTE: $m_r = \dfrac{207(9.109 \times 10^{-31} \text{ kg})(1.673 \times 10^{-27} \text{ kg})}{207(9.109 \times 10^{-31} \text{ kg}) + 1.673 \times 10^{-27} \text{ kg}} = 1.69 \times 10^{-28}$ kg

We have used m_e to denote the electron mass.

b) IDENTIFY: In Eq.(38.18) replace $m = m_e$ by m_r: $E_n = -\dfrac{1}{\varepsilon_0^2}\dfrac{m_r e^4}{8n^2 h^2}$.

SET UP: Write as $E_n = \left(\dfrac{m_r}{m_H}\right)\left(-\dfrac{1}{\varepsilon_0^2}\dfrac{m_H e^4}{8n^2 h^2}\right)$, since we know that $\dfrac{1}{\varepsilon_0^2}\dfrac{m_H e^4}{8h^2} = $ 13.60 eV.

Here m_H denotes the reduced mass for the hydrogen atom; $m_H = 0.99946(9.109 \times 10^{-31} \text{ kg}) = 9.104 \times 10^{-31}$ kg.

EXECUTE: $E_n = \left(\dfrac{m_r}{m_H}\right)\left(-\dfrac{13.60 \text{ eV}}{n^2}\right)$

$E_1 = \dfrac{1.69 \times 10^{-28} \text{ kg}}{9.104 \times 10^{-31} \text{ kg}}(-13.60 \text{ eV}) = 186(-13.60 \text{ eV}) = -2.53 \text{ keV}$

c) SET UP: From part (b), $E_n = \left(\dfrac{m_r}{m_H}\right)\left(-\dfrac{R_H ch}{n^2}\right)$, where $R_H = 1.097 \times 10^7$ m^{-1} is the Rydberg constant for the hydrogen atom.

Use this result in $\dfrac{hc}{\lambda} = E_i - E_f$ to find an expression for $1/\lambda$.

The initial level for the transition is the $n_i = 2$ level and the final level is the $n_f = 1$ level.

EXECUTE: $\dfrac{hc}{\lambda} = \dfrac{m_r}{m_H}\left(-\dfrac{R_H ch}{n_i^2} - \left(-\dfrac{R_H ch}{n_f^2}\right)\right)$

$$\dfrac{1}{\lambda} = \dfrac{m_r}{m_H} R_H \left(\dfrac{1}{n_f^2} - \dfrac{1}{n_i^2}\right)$$

$$\dfrac{1}{\lambda} = \dfrac{1.69 \times 10^{-28}\ \text{kg}}{9.104 \times 10^{-31}\ \text{kg}}(1.097 \times 10^7\ \text{m}^{-1})\left(\dfrac{1}{1^2} - \dfrac{1}{2^2}\right) = 1.527 \times 10^9\ \text{m}^{-1}$$

$$\lambda = 0.655\ \text{nm}$$

EVALUATE: From Example 38.6 the wavelength of the radiation emitted in this transition in hydrogen is 122 nm. The wavelength for muonium is $\dfrac{m_H}{m_r} = 5.39 \times 10^{-3}$ times this. The reduced mass for hydrogen is very close to the electron mass because the electron mass is much less than the proton mass: $m_p/m_e = 1836$. The muon mass is $207m_e = 1.886 \times 10^{-28}$ kg. The proton is only about 10 times more massive than the muon, so the reduced mass is somewhat smaller than the muon mass. The muon-proton atom has much more strongly bound energy levels and much shorter wavelengths in its spectrum than for hydrogen.

38.63 a) IDENTIFY and **SET UP:** The photon energy is given to the electron in the atom. Some of this energy overcomes the binding energy of the atom and what is left appears as kinetic energy of the free electron. Apply $hf = E_f - E_i$, the energy given to the electron in the atom when a photon is absorbed.

EXECUTE:

The energy of one photon is $\dfrac{hc}{\lambda} = \dfrac{(6.626 \times 10^{-34}\ \text{J}\cdot\text{s})(2.998 \times 10^8\ \text{m/s})}{85.5 \times 10^{-9}\ \text{m}}$

$\dfrac{hc}{\lambda} = 2.323 \times 10^{-18}\ \text{J}(1\ \text{eV}/1.602 \times 10^{-19}\ \text{J}) = 14.50\ \text{eV}.$

The final energy of the electron is $E_f = E_i + hf$. In the ground state of the hydrogen atom the energy of the electron is $E_i = -13.60$ eV. Thus $E_f = -13.60\ \text{eV} + 14.50\ \text{eV} = 0.90\ \text{eV}.$

b) EVALUATE: At thermal equilibrium a few atoms will be in the $n = 2$ excited levels, which have an energy of $-13.6\ \text{eV}/4 = -3.40$ eV, 10.2 eV greater than the energy of the ground state. If an electron with $E = -3.40$ eV gains 14.5 eV from the absorbed photon, it will end up with 14.5 eV − 3.4 eV = 11.1 eV of kinetic energy.

38.65 IDENTIFY: Bohr's angular momentum equation: $L = mvr = n(h/2\pi)$, so $v = \dfrac{nh}{2\pi mr}$.

a) SET UP: Apply Newton's 2nd law to the circular motion and combine with the Bohr equation.

EXECUTE: $\sum \vec{F} = m\vec{a}$ gives $Dr = m(v^2/r)$ and $r = \sqrt{(m/D)}v$.

Use the Bohr equation to replace v: $r = \sqrt{\dfrac{m}{D}}\dfrac{nh}{2\pi mr}$.

$r^2 = \dfrac{nh}{2\pi D^{1/2}m^{1/2}}$ and $r_n = \left(\dfrac{n^2h^2}{4\pi^2 mD}\right)^{1/4}$

b) SET UP: The force has the same dependence on position as $F = -kx$ for a one-dimensional simple harmonic oscillator. For $F = -kx$ the potential energy is $U = \frac{1}{2}kx^2$, so for $F = -Dr$ it is $U = \frac{1}{2}Dr^2$. (This does give $U = 0$ when $r = 0$.) $E = K + U$. Replace v and r by the results from part (a).

EXECUTE: $E = \frac{1}{2}mv^2 + \frac{1}{2}Dr^2$

From part (a) $v = \sqrt{\dfrac{D}{m}}r$, so $E = \frac{1}{2}m\left(\dfrac{D}{m}r^2\right) + \frac{1}{2}Dr^2 = Dr^2$

Use the result for r obtained in part (a):

$E_n = D\dfrac{nh}{2\pi\sqrt{m}\sqrt{D}} = \sqrt{\dfrac{D}{m}}\dfrac{nh}{2\pi}$

c) SET UP: The photon energy equals the energy change for the particle when it undergoes a transition from one energy level to another.

EXECUTE: $\Delta E = E_i - E_f = (n_i - n_f)\sqrt{\dfrac{D}{m}}\dfrac{h}{2\pi}$

$n_i - n_f$ can be any positive integer, so can write the possible photon energies as $n\sqrt{\dfrac{D}{m}}\dfrac{h}{2\pi}$, where $n = 1, 2, \ldots$

d) EVALUATE: This could describe a charged mass attached to a spring and traveling in a circle. Such spring type forces describe the vibrational motion of atoms in molecules.

38.69 IDENTIFY: Apply conservation of energy and conservation of linear momentum to the system of atom plus photon.

a) SET UP: Let E_{tr} be the transition energy, E_{ph} be the energy of the photon with wavelength λ', and E_r be the kinetic energy of the recoiling atom.

Conservation of energy gives $E_{ph} + E_r = E_{tr}$.

$E_{ph} = \dfrac{hc}{\lambda'}$ so $\dfrac{hc}{\lambda'} = E_{tr} - E_r$ and $\lambda' = \dfrac{hc}{E_{tr} - E_r}$.

EXECUTE: If the recoil energy is neglected then the photon wavelength is $\lambda = hc/E_{tr}$.

$$\Delta\lambda = \lambda' - \lambda = hc\left(\frac{1}{E_{tr} - E_r} - \frac{1}{E_{tr}}\right) = \left(\frac{hc}{E_{tr}}\right)\left(\frac{1}{1 - E_r/E_{tr}} - 1\right)$$

$$\frac{1}{1 - E_r/E_{tr}} = \left(1 - \frac{E_r}{E_{tr}}\right)^{-1} \approx 1 + \frac{E_r}{E_{tr}} \text{ since } \frac{E_r}{E_{tr}} << 1$$

(We have used the binomial theorem, Appendix B.)

Thus $\Delta\lambda = \dfrac{hc}{E_{tr}}\left(\dfrac{E_r}{E_{tr}}\right)$, or since $E_{tr} = hc/\lambda$, $\Delta\lambda = \left(\dfrac{E_r}{hc}\right)\lambda^2$.

SET UP: Use conservation of linear momentum to find E_r:

Assuming that the atom is initially at rest, the momentum p_r of the recoiling atom must be equal in magnitude and opposite in direction to the momentum $p_{ph} = h/\lambda$ of the emitted photon: $h/\lambda = p_r$.

EXECUTE: $E_r = \dfrac{p_r^2}{2m}$, where m is the mass of the atom, so $E_r = \dfrac{h^2}{2m\lambda^2}$.

Use this result in the above equation:

$$\Delta\lambda = \left(\frac{E_r}{hc}\right)\lambda^2 = \left(\frac{h^2}{2m\lambda^2}\right)\left(\frac{\lambda^2}{hc}\right) = \frac{h}{2mc};$$

note that this result for $\Delta\lambda$ is independent of the atomic transition energy.

b) For a hydrogen atom $m = m_p$ and

$$\Delta\lambda = \frac{h}{2m_p c} = \frac{6.626 \times 10^{-34} \text{ J}\cdot\text{s}}{2(1.673 \times 10^{-27} \text{ kg})(2.998 \times 10^8 \text{ m/s})} = 6.61 \times 10^{-16} \text{ m}$$

EVALUATE: The correction is independent of n. The wavelengths of photons emitted in hydrogen atom transitions are on the order of $100 \text{ nm} = 10^{-7}$ m, so the recoil correction is exceedingly small.

38.71 IDENTIFY: Apply the Compton scattering formula

$$\lambda' - \lambda = \Delta\lambda = \frac{h}{mc}(1 - \cos\phi) = \lambda_c(1 - \cos\phi)$$

a) SET UP: Largest $\Delta\lambda$ is for $\phi = 180°$.

EXECUTE: For $\phi = 180°$, $\Delta\lambda = 2\lambda_c = 2(2.426 \text{ pm}) = 4.85 \text{ pm}$.

b) SET UP: $\lambda' - \lambda = \lambda_c(1 - \cos\phi)$

Wavelength doubles implies $\lambda' = 2\lambda$ so $\lambda' - \lambda = \lambda$. Thus $\lambda = \lambda_c(1 - \cos\phi)$. λ is related to E by Eq.(38.2).

EXECUTE: $E = hc/\lambda$, so smallest energy photon means largest wavelength photon, so $\phi = 180°$ and $\lambda = 2\lambda_c = 4.85$ pm.

Then $E = \dfrac{hc}{\lambda} = \dfrac{(6.626 \times 10^{-34} \text{ J} \cdot \text{s})(2.998 \times 10^8 \text{ m/s})}{4.85 \times 10^{-12} \text{ m}} =$

4.096×10^{-14} J$(1 \text{ eV}/1.602 \times 10^{-19} \text{ J}) = 0.256$ MeV.

EVALUATE: Any photon Compton scattered at $\phi = 180°$ has a wavelength increase of $2\lambda_c = 4.85$ pm. 4.85 pm is near the short-wavelength end of the range of x-ray wavelengths.

38.73 **a) IDENTIFY** and **SET UP:** Conservation of energy applied to the collision gives $E_\lambda = E_{\lambda'} + E_e$, where E_e is the kinetic energy of the electron after the collision and E_λ and $E_{\lambda'}$ are the energies of the photon before and after the collision. The energy of a photon is related to its wavelength according to Eq.(38.2).

EXECUTE: $E_e = hc\left(\dfrac{1}{\lambda} - \dfrac{1}{\lambda'}\right) = hc\left(\dfrac{\lambda' - \lambda}{\lambda\lambda'}\right)$

$E_e = (6.626 \times 10^{-34} \text{ J}\cdot\text{s})(2.998 \times 10^8 \text{ m/s})\left(\dfrac{0.0032 \times 10^{-9} \text{ m}}{(0.1100 \times 10^{-9} \text{ m})(0.1132 \times 10^{-9} \text{ m})}\right)$

$E_e = 5.105 \times 10^{-17}$ J $= 319$ eV

$E_e = \frac{1}{2}mv^2$ so $v = \sqrt{\dfrac{2E_e}{m}} = \sqrt{\dfrac{2(5.105 \times 10^{-17} \text{ J})}{9.109 \times 10^{-31} \text{ kg}}} = 1.06 \times 10^7$ m/s

b) The wavelength λ of a photon with energy E_e is given by $E_e = hc/\lambda$ so

$\lambda = \dfrac{hc}{E_e} = \dfrac{(6.626 \times 10^{-34} \text{ J} \cdot \text{s})(2.998 \times 10^8 \text{ m/s})}{5.105 \times 10^{-17} \text{ J}} = 3.89$ nm

EVALUATE: Only a small portion of the incident photon's energy is transferred to the struck electron; this is why the wavelength calculated in part (b) is much larger than the wavelength of the incident photon in the Compton scattering.

38.75 **IDENTIFY** and **SET UP:** Find the average change in wavelength for one scattering and use that in $\Delta\lambda$ in Eq.(38.23) to calculate the average scattering angle ϕ.

EXECUTE:

a) The wavelength of a 1 MeV photon is

$\lambda = \dfrac{hc}{E} = \dfrac{(4.136 \times 10^{-15} \text{ eV} \cdot \text{s})(2.998 \times 10^8 \text{ m/s})}{1 \times 10^6 \text{ eV}} = 1 \times 10^{-12}$ m

The total change in wavelength therefore is

500×10^{-9} m $- 1 \times 10^{-12}$ m $= 500 \times 10^{-9}$ m.

If this shift is produced in 10^{26} Compton scattering events, the wavelength shift in each scattering event is $\Delta\lambda = \dfrac{500 \times 10^{-9} \text{ m}}{1 \times 10^{26}} = 5 \times 10^{-33}$ m.

b) Use this $\Delta\lambda$ in $\Delta\lambda = \dfrac{h}{mc}(1 - \cos\phi)$ and solve for ϕ. We anticipate that ϕ will be very small, since $\Delta\lambda$ is much less than h/mc, so can use $\cos\phi \approx 1 - \phi^2/2$.

$$\Delta\lambda = \frac{h}{mc}\left(1 - \left(1 - \phi^2/2\right)\right) = \frac{h}{2mc}\phi^2$$

$$\phi = \sqrt{\frac{2\,\Delta\lambda}{(h/mc)}} = \sqrt{\frac{2(5 \times 10^{-33} \text{ m})}{2.426 \times 10^{-12} \text{ m}}} = 6.4 \times 10^{-11} \text{ rad} = (4 \times 10^{-9})°$$

ϕ in radians is much less than 1 so the approximation we used is valid.

c) IDENTIFY and SET UP: We know the total transit time and the total number of scatterings, so we can calculate the average time between scatterings.

EXECUTE: The total time to travel from the core to the surface is $(10^6$ y$)(3.156 \times 10^7$ s/y$) = 3.2 \times 10^{13}$ s. There are 10^{26} scatterings during this time, so the average time between scaterings is $t = \dfrac{3.2 \times 10^{13} \text{ s}}{10^{26}} = 3.2 \times 10^{-13}$ s.

The distance light travels in this time is

$d = ct = (3.0 \times 10^8 \text{ m/s})(3.2 \times 10^{-13} \text{ s}) = 0.1$ mm

EVALUATE: The photons are on the average scattered through a very small angle in each scattering event. The average distance a photon travels between scatterings is very small.

CHAPTER 39
THE WAVE NATURE OF PARTICLES

Exercises 5, 7, 9, 15, 17, 21, 25, 27, 29, 33
Problems 39, 45, 47, 49, 53, 55, 59, 63, 65

Exercises

39.5 **IDENTIFY** and **SET UP:** The de Broglie wavelength is $\lambda = \dfrac{h}{p} = \dfrac{h}{mv}$.

In the Bohr model, $mvr_n = n(h/2\pi)$, so $mv = nh/(2\pi r_n)$. Combine these two expressions and obtain an equation for λ in terms of n.

Then $\lambda = h\left(\dfrac{2\pi r_n}{nh}\right) = \dfrac{2\pi r_n}{n}$.

EXECUTE:

a) For $n = 1$, $\lambda = 2\pi r_1$ with $r_1 = a_0 = 0.529 \times 10^{-10}$ m, so

$\lambda = 2\pi(0.529 \times 10^{-10}$ m$) = 3.32 \times 10^{-10}$ m

$\lambda = 2\pi r_1$; the de Broglie wavelength equals the circumference of the orbit.

b) For $n = 4$, $\lambda = 2\pi r_4/4$.

$r_n = n^2 a_0$ so $r_4 = 16a_0$.

$\lambda = 2\pi(16a_0)/4 = 4(2\pi a_0) = 4(3.32 \times 10^{-10}$ m$) = 1.33 \times 10^{-9}$ m

$\lambda = 2\pi r_4/4$; the de Broglie wavelength is $\dfrac{1}{n} = \dfrac{1}{4}$ times the circumference of the orbit.

EVALUATE: As n increases the momentum of the electron increases and its de Broglie wavelength decreases. For any n, the circumference of the orbits equals an integer number of de Broglie wavelengths.

39.7 **IDENTIFY** and **SET UP:** Use Eq.(39.1).

EXECUTE: $\lambda = \dfrac{h}{p} = \dfrac{h}{mv} = \dfrac{6.626 \times 10^{-34} \text{ J} \cdot \text{s}}{(5.00 \times 10^{-3} \text{ kg})(340 \text{ m/s})} = 3.90 \times 10^{-34}$ m

EVALUATE: This wavelength is extremely short; the bullet will not exhibit wave-like properties.

39.9 **IDENTIFY** and **SET UP:** A photon has zero mass and its energy and wavelength are related by Eq.(38.2). An electron has mass. Its energy is related to its momentum by $E = p^2/2m$ and its wavelength is related to its momentum by Eq.(39.1).

EXECUTE:

a) photon

$$E = \frac{hc}{\lambda} \text{ so } \lambda = \frac{hc}{E} = \frac{(6.626 \times 10^{-34} \text{ J} \cdot \text{s})(2.998 \times 10^8 \text{ m/s})}{(20.0 \text{ eV})(1.602 \times 10^{-19} \text{ J/eV})} = 62.0 \text{ nm}$$

electron

$$E = p^2/(2m) \text{ so } p = \sqrt{2mE} =$$
$$\sqrt{2(9.109 \times 10^{-31} \text{ kg})(20.0 \text{ eV})(1.602 \times 10^{-19} \text{ J/eV})} = 2.416 \times 10^{-24} \text{ kg·m/s}$$
$$\lambda = h/p = 0.274 \text{ nm}$$

b) photon $E = hc/\lambda = 7.946 \times 10^{-19} \text{ J} = 4.96 \text{ eV}$

electron $\lambda = h/p$ so $p = h/\lambda = 2.650 \times 10^{-27} \text{ kg} \cdot \text{m/s}$

$E = p^2/(2m) = 3.856 \times 10^{-24} \text{ J} = 2.41 \times 10^{-5} \text{ eV}$

c) EVALUATE: You should use a probe of wavelength approximately 250 nm. An electron with $\lambda = 250$ nm has much less energy than a photon with $\lambda = 250$ nm, so is less likely to damage the molecule.

Note that $\lambda = h/p$ applies to all particles, those with mass and those with zero mass. $E = hf = hc/\lambda$ applies only to photons and $E = p^2/2m$ applies only to particles with mass.

39.15 IDENTIFY and **SET UP:** Since the alpha particles are scattered from the surface plane of the crystal Eq.(39.4) applies: $d \sin\theta = m\lambda$.

$m = 1$ implies $\sin\theta = \lambda/d$. Calculate the wavelength λ of the particles using the de Broglie relation: $\lambda = h/p$.

EXECUTE: $E = \frac{1}{2}mv^2 = p^2/2m$ so $p = \sqrt{2mE}$ and

$$\lambda = \frac{h}{\sqrt{2mE}} = \frac{6.626 \times 10^{-34} \text{ J} \cdot \text{s}}{\sqrt{2(6.64 \times 10^{-27} \text{ kg})(840 \text{ eV})(1.602 \times 10^{-19} \text{ eV/1 eV})}} =$$
$$4.957 \times 10^{-13} \text{ m}$$

$$\sin\theta = \frac{\lambda}{d} = \frac{4.957 \times 10^{-13} \text{ m}}{0.0834 \times 10^{-9} \text{ m}} = 5.94 \times 10^{-3} \text{ and } \theta = 0.341°$$

EVALUATE: The more massive and more energetic alpha particles have a much shorter wavelength than the electrons in Example 39.2 so the angle θ is much smaller than in that example.

39.17 a) IDENTIFY and **SET UP:** Use $\Delta x \Delta p_x \geq h/2\pi$ to calculate Δx and obtain Δv_x from this.

EXECUTE: $\Delta p_x \geq \dfrac{h}{2\pi \Delta x} = \dfrac{6.626 \times 10^{-34} \text{ J} \cdot \text{s}}{2\pi(1.00 \times 10^{-6} \text{ m})} = 1.055 \times 10^{-28} \text{ kg} \cdot \text{m/s}$

$$\Delta v_x = \frac{\Delta p_x}{m} = \frac{1.055 \times 10^{-28} \text{ kg} \cdot \text{m/s}}{1200 \text{ kg}} = 8.79 \times 10^{-32} \text{ m/s}$$

b) EVALUATE: Even for this very small Δx the minimum Δv_x required by the Heisenberg uncertainty principle is very small. The uncertainty principle does not impose any practical limit on the simultaneous measurements of the positions and velocities of ordinary objects.

39.21 IDENTIFY and SET UP: Use $\Delta x \Delta p_x \geq h/2\pi$ to calculate Δp_x. The kinetic energy is related to the momentum by $K = p^2/2m$.

a) EXECUTE: $\Delta x \approx (0.215 \text{ nm})/2 = 0.1075 \times 10^{-9} \text{ m}$

$$\Delta p_x \geq \frac{h}{2\pi \Delta x} = \frac{6.626 \times 10^{-34} \text{ J} \cdot \text{s}}{2\pi(0.1075 \times 10^{-9} \text{ m})} = 9.8 \times 10^{-25} \text{ kg} \cdot \text{m/s}$$

b) $K = \dfrac{p^2}{2m} = \dfrac{(9.8 \times 10^{-25} \text{ kg} \cdot \text{m/s})^2}{2(9.75 \times 10^{-26} \text{ kg})} = 4.9 \times 10^{-24} \text{ J} = 3.1 \times 10^{-5} \text{ eV}$

c) The number of atoms in 1.00 kg is $N = \dfrac{1.00 \text{ kg}}{9.75 \times 10^{-26} \text{ kg}} = 1.03 \times 10^{25}$.

$K_{\text{tot}} = NK = (1.03 \times 10^{25})(4.9 \times 10^{-24} \text{ J}) = 50 \text{ J}$

d) $K_{\text{tot}} = mgy$

$$y = \frac{K_{\text{tot}}}{mg} = \frac{50 \text{ J}}{(1.00 \text{ kg})(9.80 \text{ m/s}^2)} = 5.1 \text{ m}$$

e) EVALUATE: The kinetic energy cannot become zero because then the x-component of the momentum and the uncertainty in the x-component of the momentum of the atoms in the crystal would be zero and this would violate the Heisneberg uncertainty principle.

39.25 IDENTIFY and SET UP: Find the uncertainty ΔE in the particle's energy: $E = mc^2$ so $\Delta E = (\Delta m)c^2$. Then use the energy uncertainty principle $\Delta E \Delta t \geq h/2\pi$ to estimate the lifetime.

EXECUTE: $m = 4.50 m_p$; $\Delta m = (0.145)m = 0.145(4.50 m_p) = (0.6525)m_p = 0.6525(1.673 \times 10^{-27} \text{ kg}) = 1.092 \times 10^{-27} \text{ kg}$.

Then $\Delta E = (\Delta m)c^2 = (1.092 \times 10^{-27} \text{ kg})(2.998 \times 10^8 \text{ m/s})^2 = 9.815 \times 10^{-11} \text{ J}$.

$$\Delta t \approx \frac{h}{2\pi \Delta E} = \frac{6.626 \times 10^{-34} \text{ J} \cdot \text{s}}{2\pi(9.815 \times 10^{-11} \text{ J})} = 1.1 \times 10^{-24} \text{ s}$$

EVALUATE: The shorter the lifetime of the particle, the greater the uncertainty in its mass and energy.

39.27 **IDENTIFY** and **SET UP:** Find the energy and momentum of the particle after it has been accelerated. Then use Eq.(39.1) to calculate λ.

EXECUTE:

a) The relation between the kinetic energy K of the particle of charge q and the potential difference through which it has been accelerated is $K = |q|\,\Delta V$.

And $K = p^2/2m$, so $p = \sqrt{2mK} = \sqrt{2m|q|\,\Delta V}$.

The de Broglie wavelength is $\lambda = \dfrac{h}{p} = \dfrac{h}{\sqrt{2m|q|\,\Delta V}} =$

$$\frac{6.626 \times 0^{-34} \text{ J} \cdot \text{s}}{\sqrt{2(9.109 \times 10^{-31} \text{ kg})(1.602 \times 10^{-19} \text{ C})(800 \text{ V})}} = 4.34 \times 10^{-11} \text{ m} = 43.4 \text{ pm}$$

b) The only change is the mass m of the particle:

$$\lambda = \frac{h}{\sqrt{2m|q|\,\Delta V}} = \frac{6.626 \times 10^{-34} \text{ J} \cdot \text{s}}{\sqrt{2(1.673 \times 10^{-27} \text{ kg})(1.602 \times 10^{-19} \text{ C})(800 \text{ V})}} =$$
1.01×10^{-12} m = 1.01 pm

EVALUATE: The proton wavelength is smaller than the electron wavelength by a factor of $\sqrt{m_e/m_p} = 1/\sqrt{1836}$. Both particles have the same magnitude of charge so gain the same amount of kinetic energy when acclerated through the same magnitude of potential difference. But the more massive proton has greater momentum than the electron when they have the same kinetic energy.

39.29 **IDENTIFY** and **SET UP:** $\psi(x) = A \sin kx$. The position probability density is given by $|\psi(x)|^2 = A^2 \sin^2 kx$.

EXECUTE:

a) The probability is highest where $\sin kx = 1$ so $kx = 2\pi x/\lambda = n\pi/2$, $n = 1, 3, 5, \ldots$.

$x = n\lambda/4$, $n = 1, 3, 5, \ldots$ so $x = \lambda/4, 3\lambda/4, 5\lambda/4, \ldots$

b) The probability of finding the particle is zero where $|\psi|^2 = 0$, which occurs where $\sin kx = 0$ and $kx = 2\pi x/\lambda = n\pi$, $n = 0, 1, 2, \ldots$

$x = n\lambda/2$, $n = 0, 1, 2, \ldots$ so $x = 0, \lambda/2, \lambda, 3\lambda/2, \ldots$

EVALUATE: The situation is analogous to a standing wave, with the probability analagous to the square of the amplitude of the standing wave.

39.33 **IDENTIFY** and **SET UP:** The probability P that the particle will be found in a volume ΔV centered around the point (x_1, y_1, z_1) is $|\psi(x_1, y_1, z_1)|^2 \Delta V$.

EXECUTE:

a) At the point $(L/4, L/4, L/4)$ the wavefunction has the value
$\psi = (2/L)^{3/2} \sin(\pi/4)^3$

$$P = |\psi|^2 \, \Delta V = (2/L)^3 \sin(\pi/4)^6 (0.01L)^3 = 2^3 (0.01)^3 (\sin \pi/4)^6 = 1.0 \times 10^{-6}$$

b) At the point $(L/2, L/2, L/2)$ the wavefunction has the value
$$\psi = (2/L)^{3/2} \sin(\pi/2)^3 = (2/L)^{3/2}$$
$$P = |\psi|^2 \, \Delta V = (2/L)^3 (0.01L)^3 = 2^3 (0.01)^3 = 8.0 \times 10^{-6}$$

EVALUATE: The probability that the particle will be found anywhere within the region $0 \le x \le L$, $0 \le y \le L$, and $0 \le z \le L$ is unity.

Problems

39.39 IDENTIFY and **SET UP:** Use the information given about the diffraction pattern for the photons to calculate the slit width a. Use Eq.(36.1), that locates the first dark band. Use Eq.(39.1) to find λ for the electrons. Use this λ in Eq.(36.1) to find the angular position of the first diffraction minimum; no electrons will be detected at this diffraction minimum.

EXECUTE:

a) The first dark band is located by $\sin \theta = \lambda/a$
$$a = \frac{\lambda}{\sin \theta} = \frac{150 \text{ nm}}{\sin 25.0°} = 355 \text{ nm}$$

b) Find λ for the electrons.
$$E = \frac{hc}{\lambda_{\text{photon}}} = 1.324 \times 10^{-18} \text{ J}$$
$$E = p^2/(2m) \text{ so } p = \sqrt{2mE} = 1.553 \times 10^{-24} \text{ kg} \cdot \text{m/s}$$
$$\lambda = h/p = 4.266 \times 10^{-10} \text{ m}$$

No electrons at locations of minima in the diffraction pattern. The angular position of these minima are given by:
$$\sin \theta = m\lambda/a = m(4.266 \times 10^{-10} \text{ m})/(355 \times 10^{-9} \text{ m}) = m(0.00120), \quad m = \pm 1, \pm 2, \pm 3, \ldots$$

$m = \pm 1, \theta = 0.0689°; \quad m = \pm 2, \theta = 0.138°; \quad m = \pm 3, \theta = 0.207°; \ldots$

EVALUATE: When a photon and an electron have the same wavelength the electron has a much smaller λ and for the same slit λ/a is much smaller. So, θ for the diffraction minima are much smaller.

39.45 IDENTIFY and **SET UP:** Use the expression derived in Problem 39.44:
$$\lambda = \frac{hc}{\sqrt{K(K + 2mc^2)}}.$$

EXECUTE:

a) With $K = 3mc^2$ this becomes $\lambda = \dfrac{hc}{\sqrt{3mc^2(3mc^2 + 2mc^2)}} = \dfrac{h}{\sqrt{15}mc}$.

b) (i) $K = 3mc^2 = 3(9.109 \times 10^{-31} \text{ kg})(2.998 \times 10^8 \text{ m/s})^2 = 2.456 \times 10^{-13}$ J $=$ 1.53 MeV

$\lambda = \dfrac{h}{\sqrt{15}mc} = \dfrac{6.626 \times 10^{-34} \text{ J} \cdot \text{s}}{\sqrt{15}(9.109 \times 10^{-31} \text{ kg})(2.998 \times 10^8 \text{ m/s})} = 6.26 \times 10^{-13}$ m

(ii) K is proportional to m, so for a proton
$K = (m_\text{p}/m_\text{e})(1.53 \text{ MeV}) = 1836(1.53 \text{ MeV}) = 2810$ MeV

λ is proportional to $1/m$, so for a proton
$\lambda = (m_\text{e}/m_\text{p})(6.26 \times 10^{-13} \text{ m}) = (1/1836)(6.26 \times 10^{-13} \text{ m}) = 3.41 \times 10^{-16}$ m

EVALUATE: The proton has a larger rest mass energy so its kinetic energy is larger when $K = 3mc^2$. The proton also has a larger momentum so has a smaller λ.

39.47 IDENTIFY and **SET UP:** Use Eqs.(39.1) and (39.11).
EXECUTE: $\Delta x = 0.40\lambda = 0.40(h/p)$
$\Delta x \Delta p_x \geq h/2\pi$. So $(\Delta p_x)_\text{min} = h/(2\pi \Delta x)$ (as in Example 39.3).
$(\Delta p_x)_\text{min} = \dfrac{h}{2\pi(0.40h/p)} = \dfrac{p}{2\pi(0.40)} = 0.40p$

EVALUATE: This not a general result but is true only for the special case of 40%. If in general $\Delta x/x = a$, where a is some constant, then $\Delta p/p = 1/(2\pi a)$. Only for $a = 0.40$ is $a = 1/(2\pi a)$.

39.49 a) IDENTIFY and **SET UP:** $\Delta x \Delta p_x \geq h/2\pi$
Estimate Δx as $\Delta x \approx 5.0 \times 10^{-15}$ m.

EXECUTE: Then the minimum allowed Δp_x is
$\Delta p_x \approx \dfrac{h}{2\pi \Delta x} = \dfrac{6.626 \times 10^{-34} \text{ J} \cdot \text{s}}{2\pi(5.0 \times 10^{-15} \text{ m})} = 2.1 \times 10^{-20}$ kg $\cdot$ m/s

b) IDENTIFY and **SET UP:** Assume $p \approx 2.1 \times 10^{-20}$ kg $\cdot$ m/s. Use Eq.(37.39) to calculate E, and then $K = E - mc^2$.

EXECUTE: $E = \sqrt{(mc^2)^2 + (pc)^2}$
$mc^2 = (9.109 \times 10^{-31} \text{ kg})(2.998 \times 10^8 \text{ m/s})^2 = 8.187 \times 10^{-14}$ J
$pc = (2.1 \times 10^{-20} \text{ kg} \cdot \text{m/s})(2.998 \times 10^8 \text{ m/s}) = 6.296 \times 10^{-12}$ J
$E = \sqrt{(8.187 \times 10^{-14} \text{ J})^2 + (6.296 \times 10^{-12} \text{ J})^2} = 6.297 \times 10^{-12}$ J

$K = E - mc^2 = 6.297 \times 10^{-12} \text{ J} - 8.187 \times 10^{-14} \text{ J} =$

6.215×10^{-12} J$(1$ eV$/1.602 \times 10^{-19}$ J$) = 39$ MeV

c) **IDENTIFY** and **SET UP:** The Coulomb potential energy for a pair of point charges is given by Eq.(23.9). The proton has charge $+e$ and the electron has charge $-e$.

EXECUTE: $U = -\dfrac{ke^2}{r} = -\dfrac{(8.988 \times 10^9 \text{ N} \cdot \text{m}^2/\text{C}^2)(1.602 \times 10^{-19} \text{ C})^2}{5.0 \times 10^{-15} \text{ m}} =$
-4.6×10^{-14} J $= -0.29$ MeV

EVALUATE: The kinetic energy of the electron required by the uncertainty principle would be much larger than the magnitude of the negative Coulomb potential energy. The total energy of the electron would be large and positive and the electron could not be bound within the nucleus.

39.53 **IDENTIFY** and **SET UP:** Use Eq.(39.1) to relate your wavelength and speed.

EXECUTE:

a) $\lambda = \dfrac{h}{mv}$, so $v = \dfrac{h}{m\lambda} = \dfrac{6.626 \times 10^{-34} \text{ J} \cdot \text{s}}{(60.0 \text{ kg})(1.0 \text{ m})} = 1.1 \times 10^{-35}$ m/s

b) $t = \dfrac{\text{distance}}{\text{velocity}} = \dfrac{0.80 \text{ m}}{1.1 \times 10^{-35} \text{ m/s}} = 7.3 \times 10^{34}$ s$(1$ y$/3.156 \times 10^7$ s$) =$
2.3×10^{27} y

Since you walk through doorways much more quickly than this, you will not experience diffraction effects.

EVALUATE: A 1 kg object moving at 1 m/s has a de Broglie wavelength $\lambda = 6.6 \times 10^{-34}$ m, which is exceedingly small. An object like you has a very, very small λ at ordinary speeds and does not exhibit wavelike properties.

39.55 **IDENTIFY** and **SET UP:** The energy of the photon equals the transition energy of the atom, so the uncertainty in the energy of the excited state equals the uncertainty in the energy of the photon. Use Eq.(39.13) to estimate the energy uncertainty.

EXECUTE: $h = 6.63 \times 10^{-22}$ J $\cdot$ s

$\Delta E \Delta t \geq h/2\pi$ so $\Delta E \approx \dfrac{h}{2\pi \Delta t} = \dfrac{6.63 \times 10^{-22} \text{ J} \cdot \text{s}}{2\pi (2.24 \times 10^{-3} \text{ s})} =$
4.71×10^{-20} J$(1$ eV$/1.602 \times 10^{-19}$ J$) = 0.294$ eV

EVALUATE: The minimum uncertainty in the photon's energy is 6.5% of its energy. With our value of $h = 6.63 \times 10^{-34}$ J$\cdot$s, the fractional uncertainty is 10^{-13}.

39.59 a) **IDENTIFY** and **SET UP:** $U = A|x|$. Eq.(7.17) relates force and potential. The slope of the function $A|x|$ is not continuous at $x = 0$ so we must consider the regions $x > 0$ and $x < 0$ separately.

EXECUTE: For $x > 0$, $|x| - x$ so $U = Ax$ and $F = -\dfrac{d(Ax)}{dx} = -A$.

For $x < 0$, $|x| = -x$ so $U = -Ax$ and $F = -\dfrac{d(-Ax)}{dx} = +A$.

We can write this result as $F = -A|x|/x$, valid for all x except for $x = 0$.

b) IDENTIFY and **SET UP:** Use the uncertainty principle, expressed as $\Delta p\,\Delta x \approx h$, and as in problem 39.48 estimate Δp by p and Δx by x. Use this to write the energy E of the particle as a function of x. Find the value of x that gives the minimum E and then find the minimum E.

EXECUTE: $E = K + U = \dfrac{p^2}{2m} + A|x|$

$px \approx h$, so $p \approx h/x$

Then $E \approx \dfrac{h^2}{2mx^2} + A|x|$.

For $x > 0$, $E = \dfrac{h^2}{2mx^2} + Ax$.

To find the value of x that gives minimum E set $\dfrac{dE}{dx} = 0$.

$0 = \dfrac{-2h^2}{2mx^3} + A$

$x^3 = \dfrac{h^2}{mA}$ and $x = \left(\dfrac{h^2}{mA}\right)^{1/3}$

With this x the minimum E is

$E = \dfrac{h^2}{2m}\left(\dfrac{mA}{h^2}\right)^{2/3} + A\left(\dfrac{h^2}{mA}\right)^{1/3} = \dfrac{1}{2}h^{2/3}m^{-1/3}A^{2/3} + h^{2/3}m^{-1/3}A^{2/3}$

$E = \dfrac{3}{2}\left(\dfrac{h^2 A^2}{m}\right)^{1/3}$

EVALUATE: The potential well is shaped like a V. The larger A is the steeper the slope of U and the smaller the region to which the particle is confined and the greater is its energy. Note that for the x that minimizes E, $2K = U$.

39.63 a) IDENTIFY and **SET UP:** Let the y-direction be from the thrower to the catcher, and let the x-direction be horizontal and perpendicular to the y-direction. A cube with volume $V = 125$ cm$^3 = 0.125 \times 10^{-3}$ m^3 has side length $l - V^{1/3} - (0.125 \times 10^{-3}$ m$^3)^{1/3} = 0.050$ m. Thus estimate Δx as $\Delta x \approx 0.050$ m. Use the uncertainty principle to estimate Δp_x.

EXECUTE:

$\Delta x \Delta p_x \geq h/2\pi$ then gives $\Delta p_x \approx \dfrac{h}{2\pi \, \Delta x} = \dfrac{0.0663 \text{ J} \cdot \text{s}}{2\pi(0.050 \text{ m})} = 0.21 \text{ kg} \cdot \text{m/s}$

(The value of h in this other universe has been used.)

b) IDENTIFY and **SET UP:** $\Delta x = (\Delta v_x)t$ is the uncertainty in the x-coordinate of the ball when it reaches the catcher, where t is the time it takes the ball to reach the second student. Obtain Δv_x from Δp_x.

EXECUTE:

The uncertainty in the ball's horizontal velocity is

$\Delta v_x = \dfrac{\Delta p_x}{m} = \dfrac{0.21 \text{ kg} \cdot \text{m/s}}{0.25 \text{ kg}} = 0.84 \text{ m/s}$

The time it takes the ball to travel to the second student is $t = \dfrac{12 \text{ m}}{6.0 \text{ m/s}} = 2.0 \text{ s}$.

The uncertainty in the x-coordinate of the ball when it reaches the second student that is introduced by Δv_x is $\Delta x = (\Delta v_x)t = (0.84 \text{ m/s})(2.0 \text{ s}) = 1.7 \text{ m}$.

The ball could miss the second student by about 1.7 m.

EVALUATE: A game of catch would be very different in this universe. We don't notice the effects of the uncertainty principle in everyday life because h is so small.

39.65 a) IDENTIFY and **SET UP:** The probability is $P = |\psi|^2 \, dV$ with $dV = 4\pi r^2 \, dr$

EXECUTE: $|\psi|^2 = A^2 e^{-2\alpha r^2}$ so $P = 4\pi A^2 r^2 e^{-2\alpha r^2} \, dr$

b) IDENTIFY and **SET UP:** P is maximum where $\dfrac{dP}{dr} = 0$

EXECUTE: $\dfrac{d}{dr}\left(r^2 e^{-2\alpha r^2} \right) = 0$

$2r e^{-2\alpha r^2} - 4\alpha r^3 e^{-2\alpha r^2} = 0$ and this reduces to $2r - 4\alpha r^3 = 0$

$r = 0$ is a solution of the equation but corresponds to a minimum not a maximum. Seek r not equal to 0 so divide by r and get $2 - 4\alpha r^2 = 0$

This gives $r = \dfrac{1}{\sqrt{2\alpha}}$ (We took the positive square root since r must be positive.)

EVALUATE: This is different from the value of r, $r = 0$, where $|\psi|^2$ is a maximum. At $r = 0$ $|\psi|^2$ has a maximum but the volume element $dV = 4\pi r^2 dr$ is zero here so P does not have a maximum at $r = 0$.

CHAPTER 40
QUANTUM MECHANICS

Exercises

40.1 **IDENTIFY** and **SET UP:** The energy levels for a particle in a box are given by $E_n = \dfrac{n^2 h^2}{8mL^2}$.

EXECUTE:

a) The lowest level is for $n = 1$, and

$$E_1 = \frac{(1)(6.626 \times 10^{-34} \text{ J} \cdot \text{s})^2}{8(0.20 \text{ kg})(1.5 \text{ m})^2} = 1.2 \times 10^{-67} \text{ J}.$$

b) $E = \frac{1}{2}mv^2$ so $v = \sqrt{\dfrac{2E}{m}} = \sqrt{\dfrac{2(1.2 \times 10^{-67} \text{ J})}{0.20 \text{ kg}}} = 1.1 \times 10^{-33}$ m/s.

If the ball has this speed the time it would take it to travel from one side of the table to the other is $t = \dfrac{1.5 \text{ m}}{1.1 \times 10^{-33} \text{ m/s}} = 1.4 \times 10^{33}$ s.

c) $E_1 = \dfrac{h^2}{8mL^2}$, $E_2 = 4E_1$,

so $\Delta E = E_2 - E_1 = 3E_1 = 3(1.2 \times 10^{-67} \text{ J}) = 3.6 \times 10^{-67}$ J

d) EVALUATE: No, quantum mechanical effects are not important for the game of billiards. The discrete, quantized nature of the energy levels is completely unobservable.

40.3 **IDENTIFY** and **SET UP:** Eq.(40.9) gives the energy levels. Use this to obtain an expression for $E_2 - E_1$ and use the value given for this energy difference to solve for L.

EXECUTE: Ground state energy is $E_1 = \dfrac{h^2}{8mL^2}$; first excited state energy is $E_2 = \dfrac{4h^2}{8mL^2}$.

The energy separation between these two levels is $\Delta E = E_2 - E_1 = \dfrac{3h^2}{8mL^2}$.

This gives $L = h\sqrt{\dfrac{3}{8m\,\Delta E}} =$

$$L = 6.626 \times 10^{-34} \text{ J} \cdot \text{s} \sqrt{\frac{3}{8(9.109 \times 10^{-31} \text{ kg})(3.0 \text{ eV})(1.602 \times 10^{-19} \text{ J/1 eV})}} =$$
6.1×10^{-10} m $= 0.61$ nm.

EVALUATE: This energy difference is typical for an atom and L is comparable to the size of an atom.

40.7   **IDENTIFY** and **SET UP:** For the $n = 2$ first excited state the normalized wave function is given by Eq.(40.13). $\psi_2(x) = \sqrt{\frac{2}{L}} \sin\left(\frac{2\pi x}{L}\right)$.

$|\psi_2(x)|^2 \, dx = \frac{2}{L} \sin^2\left(\frac{2\pi x}{L}\right) dx$. Examine $|\psi_2(x)|^2 \, dx$ and find where it is zero and where it is maximum.

EXECUTE:

a) $|\psi_2|^2 \, dx = 0$ implies $\sin\left(\frac{2\pi x}{L}\right) = 0$

$\frac{2\pi x}{L} = m\pi$, $m = 0, 1, 2, \ldots$; $x = m(L/2)$

For $m = 0$, $x = 0$; for $m = 1$, $x = L/2$; for $m = 2$, $x = L$

The probability of finding the particle is zero at $x = 0$, $L/2$, and L.

b) $|\psi_2|^2 \, dx$ is maximum when $\sin\left(\frac{2\pi x}{L}\right) = \pm 1$

$\frac{2\pi x}{L} = m(\pi/2)$, $m = 1, 3, 5, \ldots$; $x = m(L/4)$

For $m = 1$, $x = L/4$; for $m = 3$, $x = 3L/4$

The probability of finding the particle is largest at $x = L/4$ and $3L/4$.

c) EVALUATE: The answers to part (a) coresspond to the zeros of $|\psi|^2$ shown in Fig.40.5 and the answers to part (b) correspond to the two values of x where $|\psi|^2$ in the figure is maximum.

40.11   **a) IDENTIFY** and **SET UP:** $\psi = A \cos kx$. Calculate $d\psi^2/dx^2$ and substitute into Eq.(40.3) to see if this equation is satisfied.

EXECUTE: Eq.(40.3): $-\dfrac{h^2}{8\pi^2 m} \dfrac{d^2\psi}{dx^2} = E\psi$

$\dfrac{d\psi}{dx} = A(-k \sin kx) = -Ak \sin kx$

$\dfrac{d^2\psi}{dx^2} = -Ak(k \cos kx) = -Ak^2 \cos kx$

Thus Eq.(40.3) requires $-\dfrac{h^2}{8\pi^2 m}(-Ak^2 \cos kx) = E(A\cos kx)$.

This says $\dfrac{h^2 k^2}{8\pi^2 m} = E$; $k = \dfrac{\sqrt{2mE}}{(h/2\pi)} = \dfrac{\sqrt{2mE}}{\hbar}$

$\psi = A\cos kx$ is a solution to Eq.(40.3) if $k = \dfrac{\sqrt{2mE}}{\hbar}$.

b) EVALUATE: The wave function for a particle in a box with rigid walls at $x = 0$ and $x = L$ must satisfy the boundry conditions $\psi = 0$ at $x = 0$ and $\psi = 0$ at $x = L$.

$\psi(0) = A\cos 0 = A$, since $\cos 0 = 1$.

Thus ψ is not 0 at $x = 0$ and this wave function isn't acceptable because it doesn't satisfy the required boundary condition, even though it is a solution to the Schrödinger equation.

40.17 IDENTIFY: Find the transition energy ΔE and set it equal to the energy of the absorbed photon. Use $E - hc/\lambda$ to find the wavelength of the photon.

SET UP: $U_0 = 6E_\infty$, as in Fig.40.8, so $E_1 = 0.625E_\infty$ and $E_3 = 5.09E_\infty$ with $E_\infty = \dfrac{\pi^2 \hbar^2}{2mL^2}$. In this problem the particle bound in the well is a proton, so $m = 1.673 \times 10^{-27}$ kg.

EXECUTE:

$E_\infty = \dfrac{\pi^2 \hbar^2}{2mL^2} = \dfrac{\pi^2 (1.055 \times 10^{-34} \text{ J}\cdot\text{s})^2}{2(1.673 \times 10^{-27} \text{ kg})(4.0 \times 10^{-15} \text{ m})^2} = 2.052 \times 10^{-12}$ J.

The transition energy is $\Delta E = E_3 - E_1 = (5.09 - 0.625)E_\infty = 4.465E_\infty$.
$\Delta E = 4.465(2.052 \times 10^{-12} \text{ J}) = 9.162 \times 10^{-12}$ J

The wavelength of the photon that is absorbed is related to the transition energy by $\Delta E = hc/\lambda$, so

$\lambda = \dfrac{hc}{\Delta E} = \dfrac{(6.626 \times 10^{-34} \text{ J}\cdot\text{s})(2.998 \times 10^8 \text{ m/s})}{9.162 \times 10^{-12} \text{ J}} = 2.2 \times 10^{-14}$ m $= 22$ fm.

EVALUTE: The wavelength of the photon is comparable to the size of the box.

40.23 IDENTIFY and **SET UP:** Use Eq.(39.1), where $K = p^2/2m$ and $E = K + U$.
EXECUTE: $\lambda = h/p - h/\sqrt{2mK}$, so $\lambda\sqrt{K}$ is constant
$\lambda_1\sqrt{K_1} = \lambda_2\sqrt{K_2}$; λ_1 and K_1 are for $x > L$ where $K_1 = 2U_0$ and λ_2 and K_2 are for $0 < x < L$ where $K_2 = E - U_0 = U_0$

$\dfrac{\lambda_1}{\lambda_2} = \sqrt{\dfrac{K_2}{K_1}} = \sqrt{\dfrac{U_0}{2U_0}} = \dfrac{1}{\sqrt{2}}$

EVALUATE: When the particle is passing over the barrier its kinetic energy is less and its wavelength is larger.

40.25 IDENTIFY and **SET UP:** The probability is $T = Ae^{-2\kappa L}$, with
$A = 16\dfrac{E}{U_0}\left(1 - \dfrac{E}{U_0}\right)$ and $\kappa = \dfrac{\sqrt{2m(U_0 - E)}}{\hbar}$.

$E = 32$ eV, $U_0 = 41$ eV, $L = 0.25 \times 10^{-9}$ m. Calculate T.

EXECUTE:

a) $A = 16\dfrac{E}{U_0}\left(1 - \dfrac{E}{U_0}\right) = 16\dfrac{32}{41}\left(1 - \dfrac{32}{41}\right) = 2.741.$

$\kappa = \dfrac{\sqrt{2m(U_0 - E)}}{\hbar}$

$\kappa = \dfrac{\sqrt{2(9.109 \times 10^{-31} \text{ kg})(41 \text{ eV} - 32 \text{ eV})(1.602 \times 10^{-19} \text{ J/eV})}}{1.055 \times 10^{-34} \text{ J} \cdot \text{s}} = $

$1.536 \times 10^{10} \text{ m}^{-1}$

$T = Ae^{-2\kappa L} = (2.741)e^{-2(1.536 \times 10^{10} \text{ m}^{-1})(0.25 \times 10^{-9} \text{ m})} = 2.741e^{-7.68} = 0.0013$

b) The only change is the mass m, which appears in κ.

$\kappa = \dfrac{\sqrt{2m(U_0 - E)}}{\hbar}$

$\kappa = \dfrac{\sqrt{2(1.673 \times 10^{-27} \text{ kg})(41 \text{ eV} - 32 \text{ eV})(1.602 \times 10^{-19} \text{ J/eV})}}{1.055 \times 10^{-34} \text{ J} \cdot \text{s}} = $

$6.584 \times 10^{11} \text{ m}^{-1}$

Then

$T = Ae^{-2\kappa L} = (2.741)e^{-2(6.584 \times 10^{11} \text{ m}^{-1})(0.25 \times 10^{-9} \text{ m})} = 2.741e^{-392.2} = 10^{-143}$

EVALUATE: The more massive proton has a much smaller probability of tunneling than the electron does.

40.27 IDENTIFY and **SET UP:** The energy levels are given by Eq.(40.26), where $\omega = \sqrt{\dfrac{k'}{m}}$.

EXECUTE: $\omega = \sqrt{\dfrac{k'}{m}} = \sqrt{\dfrac{110 \text{ N/m}}{0.250 \text{ kg}}} = 21.0$ rad/s

The ground state energy is given by Eq.(40.26):
$E_0 = \frac{1}{2}\hbar\omega = \frac{1}{2}(1.055 \times 10^{-34} \text{ J} \cdot \text{s})(21.0 \text{ rad/s}) = $
$1.11 \times 10^{-33} \text{ J}(1 \text{ eV}/1.602 \times 10^{-19} \text{ J}) = 6.93 \times 10^{-15}$ eV
$E_n = (n + \frac{1}{2})\hbar\omega; \quad E_{(n+1)} = (n + 1 + \frac{1}{2})\hbar\omega$

The energy separation between these adjacent levels is
$\Delta E = E_{n+1} - E_n = \hbar\omega = 2E_0 = 2(1.11 \times 10^{-33} \text{ J}) = 2.22 \times 10^{-33} \text{ J} = 1.39 \times 10^{-14} \text{ eV}$

EVALUATE: These energies are extremely small; quantum effects are not important for this oscillator.

40.29 IDENTIFY and **SET UP:** The photon wavelength λ is related to the transition energy by $\Delta E = hc/\lambda$. The energies are given by Eq.(40.26). Solve for k'.

EXECUTE: Ground state energy is $E_0 = \frac{1}{2}\hbar\omega$; first excited state energy is $E_1 = \frac{3}{2}\hbar\omega$, so the transition energy is $\Delta E = (\frac{3}{2} - \frac{1}{2})\hbar\omega = \hbar\omega = \dfrac{h}{2\pi}\sqrt{k'/m}$.

Equating this to $\Delta E = hc/\lambda$ gives $\dfrac{hc}{\lambda} = \dfrac{h}{2\pi}\sqrt{k'/m}$.

Thus $k' = m\left(\dfrac{2\pi c}{\lambda}\right)^2 = (9.4 \times 10^{-26} \text{ kg})\left(\dfrac{2\pi(2.998 \times 10^8 \text{ m/s})}{525 \times 10^{-6} \text{ m}}\right)^2 = 1.2 \text{ N/m}.$

EVALUATE: Comparing to Example 40.6, the wavelength of the photon is larger in this problem, so ΔE is smaller and this corresponds to a smaller k'.

40.31 IDENTIFY and **SET UP:** Calculate ω and use Eq.(40.26) for the energy levels of the oscillator. The wavelength of the photon is related to the transition energy ΔE by $\Delta E = hc/\lambda$.

EXECUTE:

a) $E = (n + \frac{1}{2})\hbar\omega$

For $\Delta n = 1$, $\Delta E = \hbar\omega = \hbar\sqrt{k'/m} = 1.544 \times 10^{-21} \text{ J}$

$\Delta E = hc/\lambda$ so $\lambda = (hc)/\Delta E = 129 \ \mu\text{m}$

b) $E_0 = \frac{1}{2}\hbar\omega = \frac{1}{2}(1.544 \times 10^{-21} \text{ J}) = 4.82 \text{ meV}$

EVALUATE: The wavelength we calculated is similar to that found in Example 40.6. Note that ΔE for $\Delta n = 1$ does not depend on n; λ for the $n = 2$ to $n = 1$ transition is the same as λ for $n = 3$ to $n = 2$.

40.33 IDENTIFY and **SET UP:** Use the energies given in Eq.(40.26) to solve for the amplitude A and maximum speed $v_{\max}$ of the oscillator. Use these to estimate Δx and Δp_x and compute the uncertainty product $\Delta x \, \Delta p_x$.

EXECUTE: The total energy of a Newtonian oscillator is given by $E = \frac{1}{2}k'A^2$ where k' is the force constant and A is the amplitude of the oscillator. Set this equal to the energy $E = (n + \frac{1}{2})\hbar\omega$ of an excited level that has quantum number

n, where $\omega = \sqrt{\dfrac{k'}{m}}$, and solve for A:

$$\tfrac{1}{2}k'A^2 = (n + \tfrac{1}{2})\hbar\omega$$

$$A = \sqrt{\frac{(2n+1)\hbar\omega}{k'}}$$

The total energy of the Newtonian oscillator can also be written as $E = \tfrac{1}{2}mv_{max}^2$. Set this equal to $E = (n + \tfrac{1}{2})\hbar\omega$ and solve for v_{max}:

$$\tfrac{1}{2}mv_{max}^2 = (n + \tfrac{1}{2})\hbar\omega$$

$$v_{max} = \sqrt{\frac{(2n+1)\hbar\omega}{m}}$$

Thus the maximum linear momentum of the oscillator is

$$p_{max} = mv_{max} = \sqrt{(2n+1)\hbar m\omega}.$$

Assume that A represents the uncertainty Δx in position and that p_{max} is the corresponding uncertainty Δp_x in momentum. Then the uncertainty product is

$$\Delta x \Delta p_x = \sqrt{\frac{(2n+1)\hbar\omega}{k'}}\sqrt{(2n+1)\hbar m\omega} = (2n+1)\hbar\omega\sqrt{\frac{m}{k'}} = (2n+1)\hbar\omega\left(\frac{1}{\omega}\right) = (2n+1)\hbar.$$

EVALUATE: For $n = 1$ this gives $\Delta x \Delta p_x = 3\hbar$, in agreement with the result derived in Section 40.4. The uncertainty product $\Delta x \Delta p_x$ increases with n.

Problems

40.35 **IDENTIFY:** The probability of the particle being between x_1 and x_2 is $\displaystyle\int_{x_1}^{x_2} |\psi|^2 \, dx$, where ψ is the normalized wavelength for the particle.

a) **SET UP:** The normalized wave function for the ground state is

$$\psi_1 = \sqrt{\frac{2}{L}} \sin\left(\frac{\pi x}{L}\right).$$

EXECUTE: The probability P of the particle being between $x = L/4$ and $x = 3L/4$ is

$$P = \int_{L/4}^{3L/4} |\psi_1|^2 \, dx = \frac{2}{L}\int_{L/4}^{3L/4} \sin^2\left(\frac{\pi x}{L}\right) \, dx.$$

Let $y = \pi x/L$; $dx = (L/\pi)\,dy$ and the integration limits become $\pi/4$ and $3\pi/4$.

$$P = \frac{2}{L}\left(\frac{L}{\pi}\right)\int_{\pi/4}^{3\pi/4} \sin^2 y \, dy = \frac{2}{\pi}\left[\frac{1}{2}y - \frac{1}{4}\sin 2y\right]_{\pi/4}^{3\pi/4}$$

$$P = \frac{2}{\pi}\left[\frac{3\pi}{8} - \frac{\pi}{8} - \frac{1}{4}\sin\left(\frac{3\pi}{2}\right) + \frac{1}{4}\sin\left(\frac{\pi}{2}\right)\right]$$

$$P = \frac{2}{\pi}\left(\frac{\pi}{4} - \frac{1}{4}(-1) + \frac{1}{4}(1)\right) = \frac{1}{2} + \frac{1}{\pi} = 0.818.$$

(Note: The integral formula $\int \sin^2 y\, dy = \frac{1}{2}y - \frac{1}{4}\sin 2y$ was used.)

b) SET UP: The normalized wave function for the first excited state is

$$\psi_2 = \sqrt{\frac{2}{L}}\sin\left(\frac{2\pi x}{L}\right)$$

EXECUTE: $P = \displaystyle\int_{L/4}^{3L/4} |\psi_2|^2\, dx = \frac{2}{L}\int_{L/4}^{3L/4}\sin^2\left(\frac{2\pi x}{L}\right)dx.$

Let $y = 2\pi x/L$; $dx = (L/2\pi)\, dy$ and the integration limits become $\pi/2$ and $3\pi/2$.

$$P = \frac{2}{L}\left(\frac{L}{2\pi}\right)\int_{\pi/2}^{3\pi/2}\sin^2 y\, dy = \frac{1}{\pi}\left[\frac{1}{2}y - \frac{1}{4}\sin 2y\right]_{\pi/2}^{3\pi/2} = \frac{1}{\pi}\left(\frac{3\pi}{4} - \frac{\pi}{4}\right) = 0.500$$

c) EVALUATE: These results are consistent with Fig.40.4b. That figure shows that $|\psi|^2$ is more concentrated near the center of the box for the ground state than for the first excited state; this is consistent with the answer to part (a) being larger than the answer to part (b). Also, this figure shows that for the first excited state half the area under the $|\psi|^2$ curve lies between $L/4$ and $3L/4$, consistent with our answer to part (b).

40.37 IDENTIFY and **SET UP:** The normalized wave function for the $n = 2$ first excited level is $\psi_2 = \sqrt{\dfrac{2}{L}}\sin\left(\dfrac{2\pi x}{L}\right).$

$P = |\psi(x)|^2\, dx$ is the probability that the particle will be found in the interval x to $x + dx$.

EXECUTE:

a) $x = L/4$

$$\psi(x) = \sqrt{\frac{2}{L}}\sin\left(\left(\frac{2\pi}{L}\right)\left(\frac{L}{4}\right)\right) = \sqrt{\frac{2}{L}}\sin\left(\frac{\pi}{2}\right) = \sqrt{\frac{2}{L}}.$$

$P = (2/L)\, dx$

b) $x = L/2$

$$\psi(x) = \sqrt{\frac{2}{L}}\sin\left(\left(\frac{2\pi}{L}\right)\left(\frac{L}{2}\right)\right) = \sqrt{\frac{2}{L}}\sin(\pi) = 0$$

$P = 0$

c) $x = 3L/4$

$$\psi(x) = \sqrt{\frac{2}{L}} \sin\left(\left(\frac{2\pi}{L}\right)\left(\frac{3L}{4}\right)\right) = \sqrt{\frac{2}{L}} \sin\left(\frac{3\pi}{2}\right) = -\sqrt{\frac{2}{L}}.$$

$P = (2/L)\, dx$

EVALUATE: Our results are consistent with the $n = 2$ part of Fig.40.5. $|\psi|^2$ is zero at the center of the box and is symmetric about this point.

40.39 **IDENTIFY** and **SET UP:** The energy levels are given by Eq.(40.9): $E_n = \dfrac{n^2 h^2}{8mL^2}$. Calculate ΔE for the transition and set $\Delta E = hc/\lambda$, the energy of the photon.

EXECUTE:

a) Ground level, $n = 1$, $E_1 = \dfrac{h^2}{8mL^2}$

First excited level, $n = 2$, $E_2 = \dfrac{4h^2}{8mL^2}$

The transition energy is $\Delta E = E_2 - E_1 = \dfrac{3h^2}{8mL^2}$.

Set the transition energy equal to the energy hc/λ of the emitted photon. This gives $\dfrac{hc}{\lambda} = \dfrac{3h^2}{8mL^2}$.

$$\lambda = \frac{8mcL^2}{3h} = \frac{8(9.109 \times 10^{-31}\text{ kg})(2.998 \times 10^8\text{ m/s})(4.18 \times 10^{-9}\text{ m})^2}{3(6.626 \times 10^{-34}\text{ J} \cdot \text{s})}$$

$\lambda = 1.92 \times 10^{-5}$ m $= 19.2$ μm.

b) Second excited level has $n = 3$ and $E_3 = \dfrac{9h^2}{8mL^2}$. The transition energy is

$$\Delta E = E_3 - E_2 = \frac{9h^2}{8mL^2} - \frac{4h^2}{8mL^2} = \frac{5h^2}{8mL^2}.$$

$\dfrac{hc}{\lambda} = \dfrac{5h^2}{8mL^2}$ so $\lambda = \dfrac{8mcL^2}{5h} = \dfrac{3}{5}(19.2$ μm$) = 11.5$ μm.

EVALUATE: The energy spacing between adjacent levels increases with n, and this corresponds to a shorter wavelength and more energetic photon in part (b) than in part (a).

40.41 **IDENTIFY:** Eq.(40.13): $\psi_n = \sqrt{\dfrac{2}{L}} \sin\left(\dfrac{n\pi x}{L}\right)$ for a particle in a box

with walls at $x = 0$ and $x = L$. (This is the wave function for $0 \le x \le L$. For $x < 0$ or $x > L$, $\psi_n = 0$.) We can evaluate $d\psi/dx$ at x slightly greater than 0 and slightly less than L, to find the slope near the walls.

a) SET UP: For $n = 1$, $\psi_1 = \sqrt{\dfrac{2}{L}} \sin\left(\dfrac{\pi x}{L}\right)$

EXECUTE: $\dfrac{d\psi_1}{dx} = \sqrt{\dfrac{2}{L}}\dfrac{\pi}{L}\cos\left(\dfrac{\pi x}{L}\right)$

$\cos\theta = 1 - \theta^2/2 + \ldots$

So for x slightly greater than 0, $\cos\left(\dfrac{\pi x}{L}\right) = 1$ and

$\dfrac{d\psi_1}{dx} = \sqrt{\dfrac{2}{L}}\dfrac{\pi}{L} = \sqrt{\dfrac{2\pi^2}{L^3}}.$

b) SET UP: For $n = 2$, $\psi_2 = \sqrt{\dfrac{2}{L}}\sin\left(\dfrac{2\pi x}{L}\right)$

EXECUTE: $\dfrac{d\psi_2}{dx} = \sqrt{\dfrac{2}{L}}\dfrac{2\pi}{L}\cos\left(\dfrac{2\pi x}{L}\right)$

For x slightly greater than 0, $\cos\left(\dfrac{2\pi x}{L}\right) = 1$ and

$\dfrac{d\psi_2}{dx} = \sqrt{\dfrac{2}{L}}\dfrac{2\pi}{L} = \sqrt{\dfrac{8\pi^2}{L^3}}.$

c) For x very close to L, $\cos\left(\dfrac{\pi x}{L}\right) \approx \cos\pi = -1$ and, from part (a), $\dfrac{d\psi_1}{dx} = -\sqrt{\dfrac{2\pi^2}{L^3}}.$

d) For x very close to L, $\cos\left(\dfrac{2\pi x}{L}\right) \approx \cos 2\pi = 1$ and, from part (b), $\dfrac{d\psi_2}{dx} = \sqrt{\dfrac{8\pi^2}{L^3}}.$

e) The magnitude of the slope of the wavefunction near the walls is greater for the $n = 2$ level.

EVALUATE: These results all agree with Fig.40.4a. For $n = 2$ the slope near both walls is positive, for $n = 1$ the slope is positive near $x = 0$ and negative near $x = L$, and the magnitude of the slope near the walls is larger for $n = 2$ than for $n = 1$.

For $x < 0$ or $x > L$, ψ and $d\psi/dx$ are zero, so $d\psi/dx$ is not continuous at the walls of the box.

40.47 **IDENTIFY** and **SET UP:** When κL is large, then $e^{\kappa L}$ is large and $e^{-\kappa L}$ is small. When κL is small, $\sinh\kappa L \to \kappa L$. Consider both κL large and κL small limits.

EXECUTE:

a) $T = \left[1 + \dfrac{(U_0\sinh\kappa L)^2}{4E(U_0 - E)}\right]^{-1}$

$\sinh\kappa L = \dfrac{e^{\kappa L} - e^{-\kappa L}}{2}$

For $nL \gg 1$, $\sinh \kappa L \to \dfrac{e^{\kappa L}}{2}$ and

$$T \to \left[1 + \frac{U_0^2 e^{2\kappa L}}{16E(U_0 - E)}\right]^{-1} = \frac{16E(U_0 - E)}{16E(U_0 - E) + U_0^2 e^{2\kappa L}}$$

For $\kappa L \gg 1$, $16E(U_0 - E) + U_0^2 e^{2\kappa L} \to U_0^2 e^{2\kappa L}$

$$T \to \frac{16E(U_0 - E)}{U_0^2 e^{2\kappa L}} = 16\left(\frac{E}{U_0}\right)\left(1 - \frac{E}{U_0}\right)e^{-2\kappa L}, \text{ which is Eq.(40.21)}.$$

b) $\kappa L = \dfrac{L\sqrt{2m(U_0 - E)}}{\hbar}$. So $\kappa L \gg 1$ when L is large (barrier is wide) or $U_0 - E$ is large. (E is small compared to U_0.)

c) $\kappa = \dfrac{\sqrt{2m(U_0 - E)}}{\hbar}$; κ becomes small as E approaches U_0.

For κ small, $\sinh \kappa L \to \kappa L$ and

$$T \to \left[1 + \frac{U_0^2 \kappa^2 L^2}{4E(U_0 - E)}\right]^{-1} = \left[1 + \frac{U_0^2 2m(U_0 - E)L^2}{\hbar^2 4E(U_0 - E)}\right]^{-1} \text{ (using the definiton of } \kappa)$$

Thus $T \to \left[1 + \dfrac{2U_0^2 L^2 m}{4E\hbar^2}\right]^{-1}$

$U_0 \to E$ so $\dfrac{U_0^2}{E} \to E$ and $T \to \left[1 + \dfrac{2EL^2 m}{4\hbar^2}\right]^{-1}$

But $k^2 = \dfrac{2mE}{\hbar^2}$, so $T \to \left[1 + \left(\dfrac{kL}{2}\right)^2\right]^{-1}$, as was to be shown.

EVALUATE: When κL is large Eq.(40.20) applies and T is small. When $E \to U_0$, T does not approach unity.

40.49 **IDENTIFY** and **SET UP:** Calculate the angular frequency ω of the pendulum and apply Eq.(40.26) for the energy levels.

EXECUTE: $\omega = \dfrac{2\pi}{T} = \dfrac{2\pi}{0.500 \text{ s}} = 4\pi \text{ s}^{-1}$

The ground-state energy is

$E_0 = \frac{1}{2}\hbar\omega = \frac{1}{2}(1.055 \times 10^{-34} \text{ J} \cdot \text{s})(4\pi \text{ s}^{-1}) = 6.63 \times 10^{-34} \text{ J}.$

$E_0 = 6.63 \times 10^{-34} \text{ J}(1 \text{ eV}/1.602 \times 10^{-19} \text{ J}) = 4.14 \times 10^{-15} \text{ eV}$

$E_n = (n + \frac{1}{2})\hbar\omega$

$E_{n+1} = (n + 1 + \frac{1}{2})\hbar\omega$

The energy difference between the adjacent energy levels is

$\Delta E = E_{n+1} - E_n = \hbar\omega = 2E_0 = 1.33 \times 10^{-33} \text{ J} = 8.30 \times 10^{-15} \text{ eV}$

EVALUATE: These energies are much too small to detect. Quantum effects are not important for ordinary size objects.

40.53 IDENTIFY and **SET UP:** Evaluate $\partial^2\psi/\partial x^2$, $\partial^2\psi/\partial y^2$, and $\partial^2\psi/\partial z^2$ for the proposed ψ and put into Eq.(40.29). Use that ψ_{n_x}, ψ_{n_y}, and ψ_{n_z} are each solutions to Eq.(40.22).

EXECUTE:

a) $-\dfrac{\hbar^2}{2m}\left(\dfrac{\partial^2\psi}{\partial x^2}+\dfrac{\partial^2\psi}{\partial y^2}+\dfrac{\partial^2\psi}{\partial z^2}\right)+U\psi = E\psi$

ψ_{n_x}, ψ_{n_y}, ψ_{n_z} are each solutions of Eq.(40.22), so

$$-\frac{\hbar^2}{2m}\frac{d^2\psi_{n_x}}{dx^2}+\frac{1}{2}k'x^2\psi_{n_x}=E_{n_x}\psi_{n_x}$$

$$-\frac{\hbar^2}{2m}\frac{d^2\psi_{n_y}}{dy^2}+\frac{1}{2}k'y^2\psi_{n_y}=E_{n_y}\psi_{n_y}$$

$$-\frac{\hbar^2}{2m}\frac{d^2\psi_{n_z}}{dz^2}+\frac{1}{2}k'z^2\psi_{n_z}=E_{n_z}\psi_{n_z}$$

$\psi=\psi_{n_x}(x)\psi_{n_y}(y)\psi_{n_z}(z)$, $U=\frac{1}{2}k'x^2+\frac{1}{2}k'y^2+\frac{1}{2}k'z^2$

$$\frac{\partial^2\psi}{\partial x^2}-\left(\frac{d^2\psi_{n_x}}{dx^2}\right)\psi_{n_y}\psi_{n_z},\quad \frac{\partial^2\psi}{\partial y^2}=\left(\frac{d^2\psi_{n_y}}{dy^2}\right)\psi_{n_x}\psi_{n_z},\quad \frac{\partial^2\psi}{\partial z^2}=\left(\frac{d^2\psi_{n_z}}{dz^2}\right)\psi_{n_x}\psi_{n_y}.$$

So $-\dfrac{\hbar^2}{2m}\left(\dfrac{\partial^2\psi}{\partial x^2}+\dfrac{\partial^2\psi}{\partial y^2}+\dfrac{\partial^2\psi}{\partial z^2}\right)+U\psi=\left(-\dfrac{\hbar^2}{2m}\dfrac{d^2\psi_{n_x}}{dx^2}+\dfrac{1}{2}k'x^2\psi_{n_x}\right)\psi_{n_y}\psi_{n_z}$

$$+\left(-\frac{\hbar^2}{2m}\frac{d^2\psi_{n_y}}{dy^2}+\frac{1}{2}k'y^2\psi_{n_y}\right)\psi_{n_x}\psi_{n_z}+\left(-\frac{\hbar^2}{2m}\frac{d^2\psi_{n_z}}{dz^2}+\frac{1}{2}k'z^2\psi_{n_z}\right)\psi_{n_x}\psi_{n_y}$$

$$-\frac{\hbar^2}{2m}\left(\frac{\partial^2\psi}{\partial x^2}+\frac{\partial^2\psi}{\partial y^2}+\frac{\partial^2\psi}{\partial z^2}\right)+U\psi=\left(E_{n_x}+E_{n_y}+E_{n_z}\right)\psi$$

Therefore, we have shown that this ψ is a solution to Eq.(40.29), with energy $E_{n_x n_y n_z}=E_{n_x}+E_{n_y}+E_{n_z}=(n_x+n_y+n_z+\frac{3}{2})\hbar\omega$

b) and **c)** The ground state has $n_x=n_y=n_z=0$, so the energy is $E_{000}=\frac{3}{2}\hbar\omega$. There is only one set of n_x, n_y and n_z that give this energy.

First-excited state: $n_x=1$, $n_y=n_z=0$ or $n_y=1$, $n_x=n_z=0$ or $n_z=1$, $n_x=n_y=0$ and $E_{100}=E_{010}=E_{001}=\frac{5}{2}\hbar\omega$

There are three different sets of n_x, n_y, n_z quantum numbers that give this energy, so there are three different quantum states that have this same energy.

EVALUATE: For the three-dimensional isotropic harmonic oscillator, the wavefunction is a product of one-dimensional harmonic oscillator wavefunctions for each dimension. The energy is a sum of energies for three one-dimensional oscillators. All the excited states are degenerate, with more than one state having the same energy.

CHAPTER 41
ATOMIC STRUCTURE

Exercises

41.1 **IDENTIFY** and **SET UP:** The magnitude of the orbital angular momentum L is related to the quantum number l by Eq.(41.4): $L = \sqrt{l(l+1)}\hbar$, $l = 0, 1, 2, \ldots$

EXECUTE: $l(l+1) = \left(\dfrac{L}{\hbar}\right)^2 = \left(\dfrac{4.716 \times 10^{-34} \text{ kg} \cdot \text{m}^2/\text{s}}{1.055 \times 10^{-34} \text{ J} \cdot \text{s}}\right)^2 = 20$

And then $l(l+1) = 20$ gives that $l = 4$.

EVALUATE: l must be integer.

41.3 **IDENTIFY** and **SET UP:** The angular momentum L is related to the quantum number l by Eq.(41.4), $L = \sqrt{l(l+1)}\hbar$. The maximum l, l_{max}, for a given n is $l_{max} = n - 1$.

EXECUTE:

For $n = 2$, $l_{max} = 1$ and $L = \sqrt{2}\hbar = 1.414\hbar$.

For $n = 20$, $l_{max} = 19$ and $L = \sqrt{(19)(20)}\hbar = 19.49\hbar$.

For $n = 200$, $l_{max} = 199$ and $L = \sqrt{(199)(200)}\hbar = 199.5\hbar$.

EVALUATE: As n increases, the maximum L gets closer to the value $n\hbar$ postulated in the Bohr model.

41.9 **IDENTIFY** and **SET UP:** Eq.(41.8) gives $a = \dfrac{4\pi\epsilon_0\hbar^2}{m_r e^2} = \dfrac{\epsilon_0 h^2}{\pi m_r e^2}$.

EXECUTE:

a) $m_r = m$

$a = \dfrac{\epsilon_0 h^2}{\pi m_r e^2} = \dfrac{(8.854 \times 10^{-12} \text{ C}^2/\text{N} \cdot \text{m}^2)(6.626 \times 10^{-34} \text{ J} \cdot \text{s})^2}{\pi(9.109 \times 10^{-31} \text{ kg})(1.602 \times 10^{-19} \text{ C})^2} = 0.5293 \times 10^{-10} \text{ m}$

b) $m_r = m/2$

$a = 2\left(\dfrac{\epsilon_0 h^2}{\pi m_r e^2}\right) = 1.059 \times 10^{-10} \text{ m}$

c) $m_r = 185.8m$

$$a = \frac{1}{185.8}\left(\frac{\epsilon_0 h^2}{\pi m_r e^2}\right) = 2.849 \times 10^{-13} \text{ m}$$

EVALUATE: a is the radius for the $n = 1$ level in the Bohr model. When the reduced mass m_r increases, a decreases. For positronium and muonium the reduced mass effect is large.

41.13 IDENTIFY and **SET UP:** The interaction energy between an external magnetic field and the orbital angular momentum of the atom is given by Eq.(41.18). The energy depends on m_l with the most negative m_l value having the lowest energy.

EXECUTE:

a) For the $5g$ level, $l = 4$ and there are $2l + 1 = 9$ different m_l states. The $5g$ level is split into 9 levels by the magnetic field.

b) Each m_l level is shifted in energy an amount given by $U = m_l \mu_B B$. Adjacent levels differ in m_l by one, so $\Delta U = \mu_B B$.

$$\mu_B = \frac{e\hbar}{2m} = \frac{(1.602 \times 10^{-19} \text{ C})(1.055 \times 10^{-34} \text{ J} \cdot \text{s})}{2(9.109 \times 10^{-31} \text{ kg})} = 9.277 \times 10^{-24} \text{ A} \cdot \text{m}^2$$

$\Delta U = \mu_B B = (9.277 \times 10^{-24} \text{ A/m}^2)(0.600 \text{ T}) =$

$5.566 \times 10^{-24} \text{ J}(1 \text{ eV}/1.602 \times 10^{-19} \text{ J}) = 3.47 \times 10^{-5} \text{ eV}$

c) The level of highest energy is for the largest m_l, which is $m_l = l = 4$; $U_4 - 4\mu_B B$. The level of lowest energy is for the smallest m_l, which is $m_l = -l = -4$; $U_{-4} = -4\mu_B B$.

The separation between these two levels is $U_4 - U_{-4} = 8\mu_B B = 8(3.47 \times 10^{-5} \text{ eV}) = 2.78 \times 10^{-4} \text{ eV}$.

EVALUATE: The energy separations are proportional to the magnetic field. The energy of the $n = 5$ level in the absence of the external magnetic field is (-13.6) eV$)/5^2 = 0.544$ eV, so the interaction energy with the magnetic field is much less than the binding energy of the state.

41.17 IDENTIFY and **SET UP:** The interaction energy is $U = -\vec{\mu} \cdot \vec{B}$, with μ_z given by Eq.(41.22).

EXECUTE: $U = -\vec{\mu} \cdot \vec{B} = +\mu_z B$, since the magnetic field is in the negative z-direction.

$\mu_z = -(2.00232)\left(\frac{e}{2m}\right)S_z$, so $U = -(2.00232)\left(\frac{e}{2m}\right)S_z B$

$S_z = m_s \hbar$, so $U = -2.00232\left(\frac{e\hbar}{2m}\right)m_s B$

$\frac{e\hbar}{2m} = \mu_B = 5.788 \times 10^{-5} \text{ eV/T}$

$U = -2.00232\mu_B m_s B$

The $m_s = +\frac{1}{2}$ level has lower energy.

$\Delta U = U(m_s = -\frac{1}{2}) - U(m_s = +\frac{1}{2}) = -2.00232\mu_B B(-\frac{1}{2} - (+\frac{1}{2})) = +2.00232\mu_B B$

$\Delta U = +2.00232(5.788 \times 10^{-5} \text{ eV/T})(1.45 \text{ T}) = 1.68 \times 10^{-4} \text{ eV}$

EVALUATE: The interaction energy with the electron spin is the same order of magnitude as the interaction energy with the orbital angular momentum for states with $m_l \neq 0$. But a 1s state has $l = 0$ and $m_l = 0$, so there is no orbital magnetic interaction.

41.19 IDENTIFY and **SET UP:** j can have the values $l + 1/2$ and $l - 1/2$.

EXECUTE: If j takes the values 7/2 and 9/2 it must be that $l - 1/2 = 7/2$ and $l = 8/2 = 4$. The letter that labels this l is g.

EVALUATE: l must be an integer.

41.21 IDENTIFY and **SET UP:** For a classical particle $L = I\omega$. For a uniform sphere with mass m and radius R, $I = \dfrac{2}{5}mR^2$, so $L = \left(\dfrac{2}{5}mR^2\right)\omega$. Solve for ω and then use $v = r\omega$ to solve for v.

EXECUTE:

a) $L = \sqrt{\dfrac{3}{4}}\hbar$ so $\dfrac{2}{5}mR^2\omega = \sqrt{\dfrac{3}{4}}\hbar$

$\omega = \dfrac{5\sqrt{3/4}\hbar}{2mR^2} = \dfrac{5\sqrt{3/4}(1.055 \times 10^{-34} \text{ J} \cdot \text{s})}{2(9.109 \times 10^{-31} \text{ kg})(1.0 \times 10^{-17} \text{ m})^2} = 2.5 \times 10^{30} \text{ rad/s}$

b) $v = r\omega = (1.0 \times 10^{-17} \text{ m})(2.5 \times 10^{30} \text{ rad/s}) = 2.5 \times 10^{13} \text{ m/s}$.

EVALUATE: This is much greater than the speed of light c, so the model cannot be valid.

41.23 IDENTIFY and **SET UP:** The energy of an atomic level is given in terms of n and Z_{eff} by Eq.(41.27), $E_n = -\left(\dfrac{Z_{\text{eff}}^2}{n^2}\right)(13.6 \text{ eV})$. The ionization energy for a level with energy $-E_n$ is $+E_n$.

EXECUTE: $n = 5$ and $Z_{\text{eff}} = 2.771$ gives $E_5 = -\dfrac{(2.771)^2}{5^2}(13.6 \text{ eV}) = -4.18 \text{ eV}$
The ionization energy is 4.18 eV.

EVALUATE: The energy of an atomic state is proportional to Z_{eff}^2.

41.27 IDENTIFY and **SET UP:** Use the exclusion principle to determine the ground-state electron configuration, as in Table 41.3. Estimate the energy by estimating

Z_{eff}, taking into account the electron screening of the nucleus.

EXECUTE:

a) $Z = 7$ for nitrogen so a nitrogen atom has 7 electrons. N^{2+} has 5 electrons: $1s^2 2s^2 2p$.

b) $Z_{\text{eff}} = 7 - 4 = 3$ for the $2p$ level.

$$E_n = -\left(\frac{Z_{\text{eff}}^2}{n^2}\right)(13.6 \text{ eV}) = -\frac{3^2}{2^2}(13.6 \text{ eV}) = -30.6 \text{ eV}$$

c) $Z = 15$ for phosphorus so a phosphorus atom has 15 electrons. P^{2+} has 13 electrons: $1s^2 2s^2 2p^6 3s^2 3p$

d) $Z_{\text{eff}} = 15 - 12 = 3$ for the $3p$ level.

$$E_n = -\left(\frac{Z_{\text{eff}}^2}{n^2}\right)(13.6 \text{ eV}) = -\frac{3^2}{3^2}(13.6 \text{ eV}) = -13.6 \text{ eV}$$

EVALUATE: In these ions there is one electron outside filled subshells, so it is a reasonable approximation to assume full screening by these inner-subshell electrons.

41.29 IDENTIFY and **SET UP:** Estimate Z_{eff} by considering electron screening and use Eq.(41.27) to calculate the energy. Z_{eff} is calculated as in Example 41.8.

EXECUTE:

a) The element Be has nuclear charge $Z = 4$. The ion Be^+ has 3 electrons. The outermost electron sees the nuclear charge screened by the other two electrons so $Z_{\text{eff}} = 4 - 2 = 2$.

$$E_n = -\left(\frac{Z_{\text{eff}}^2}{n^2}\right)(13.6 \text{ eV}) \text{ so } E_2 = -\frac{2^2}{2^2}(13.6 \text{ eV}) = -13.6 \text{ eV}$$

b) The outermost electron in Ca^+ sees a $Z_{\text{eff}} = 2$.

$$E_4 = -\frac{2^2}{4^2}(13.6 \text{ eV}) = -3.4 \text{ eV}$$

EVALUATE: For the electron in the highest l-state it is reasonable to assume full screening by the other electrons, as in Example 41.8. The highest l-states of Be^+, Mg^+, Ca^+, etc. all have a $Z_{\text{eff}} = 2$. But the energies are different because for each ion the outermost sublevel has a different n quantum number.

Problems

41.33 a) IDENTIFY and **SET UP:** The energy is given by Eq.(38.18), which is identical to Eq.(41.3). The potential energy is given by Eq.(23.9), with $q = +Ze$ and $q_0 = -e$.

EXECUTE: $E_{1s} = -\dfrac{1}{(4\pi\epsilon_0)^2}\dfrac{me^4}{2\hbar^2}$; $U(r) = -\dfrac{1}{4\pi\epsilon_0}\dfrac{e^2}{r}$

$E_{1s} = U(r)$ gives $-\dfrac{1}{(4\pi\epsilon_0)^2}\dfrac{me^4}{2\hbar^2} = -\dfrac{1}{4\pi\epsilon_0}\dfrac{e^2}{r}$

$r = \dfrac{(4\pi\epsilon_0)2\hbar^2}{me^2} = 2a$

EVALUATE: The turning point is twice the Bohr radius.

b) IDENTIFY and **SET UP:** For the $1s$ state the probability that the electron is in the classically forbidden region is

$$P(r > 2a) = \int_{2a}^{\infty} |\psi_{1s}|^2\, dV = 4\pi \int_{2a}^{\infty} |\psi_{1s}|^2 r^2\, dr.$$

The normalized wave function of the $1s$ state of hydrogen is given in Example 41.3:

$\psi_{1s}(r) = \dfrac{1}{\sqrt{\pi a^3}} e^{-r/a}$. Evaluate the integral; the integrand is the same as in Example 41.3.

EXECUTE: $P(r > 2a) = 4\pi \left(\dfrac{1}{\pi a^3}\right) \displaystyle\int_{2a}^{\infty} r^2 e^{-2r/a}\, dr$

Use the integral fomula $\int r^2 e^{-\alpha r}\, dr = -e^{-\alpha r}\left(\dfrac{r^2}{\alpha} + \dfrac{2r}{\alpha^2} + \dfrac{2}{\alpha^3}\right)$, with $\alpha = 2/a$.

$P(r > 2a) = -\dfrac{4}{a^3}\left[e^{-2r/a}\left(\dfrac{ar^2}{2} + \dfrac{a^2 r}{2} + \dfrac{a^3}{4}\right)\right]_{2a}^{\infty} = +\dfrac{4}{a^3}e^{-4}(2a^3 + a^3 + a^3/4)$

$P(r > 2a) = 4e^{-4}(13/4) = 13e^{-4} = 0.238.$

EVALUATE: There is a 23.8% probability of the electron being found in the classically forbidden region, where classically its kinetic energy would be negative.

41.35 $\psi_{2s}(r) = \dfrac{1}{\sqrt{32\pi a^3}}\left(2 - \dfrac{r}{a}\right) e^{-r/2a}$

a) IDENTIFY and **SET UP:** Let $I = \displaystyle\int_0^{\infty} |\psi_{2s}|^2\, dV = 4\pi \int_0^{\infty} |\psi_{2s}|^2 r^2\, dr$. If ψ_{2s} is normalized then we will find that $I = 1$.

EXECUTE:

$I = 4\pi \left(\dfrac{1}{32\pi a^3}\right) \displaystyle\int_0^{\infty} \left(2 - \dfrac{r}{a}\right)^2 e^{-r/a} r^2\, dr = \dfrac{1}{8a^3}\int_0^{\infty}\left(4r^2 - \dfrac{4r^3}{a} + \dfrac{r^4}{a^2}\right) e^{-r/a}\, dr$

Use the integral formula $\int_0^{\infty} x^n e^{-\alpha x}\, dx = \dfrac{n!}{\alpha^{n+1}}$, with $\alpha = 1/a$

$I = \dfrac{1}{8a^3}\left(4(2!)(a^3) - \dfrac{4}{a}(3!)(a)^4 + \dfrac{1}{a^2}(4!)(a)^5\right) = \dfrac{1}{8}(8 - 24 + 24) = 1$; this ψ_{2s} is normalized.

b) SET UP: For a spherically symmetric state such as the $2s$, the probability that the electron will be found at $r < 4a$ is $P(r < 4a) = \int_0^{4a} |\psi_{2s}|^2 \, dV =$ $4\pi \int_0^{4a} |\psi_{2s}|^2 r^2 \, dr$.

EXECUTE: $P(r < 4a) = \dfrac{1}{8a^3} \int_0^{4a} \left(4r^2 - \dfrac{4r^3}{a} + \dfrac{r^4}{a^2} \right) e^{-r/a} \, dr$

Let $P(r < 4a) = \dfrac{1}{8a^3}(I_1 + I_2 + I_3)$.

$I_1 = 4 \int_0^{4a} r^2 e^{-r/a} \, dr$

Use the integral formula $\int r^2 e^{-\alpha r} \, dr = -e^{-\alpha r} \left(\dfrac{r^2}{\alpha} + \dfrac{2r}{\alpha^2} + \dfrac{2}{\alpha^3} \right)$ with $\alpha = 1/a$.

$I_1 = -4 \left[e^{-r/a}(r^2 a + 2ra^2 + 2a^3) \right]_0^{4a} = (-104e^{-4} + 8)a^3$.

$I_2 = -\dfrac{4}{a} \int_0^{4a} r^3 e^{-r/a} \, dr$

Use the integral formula

$\int r^3 e^{-\alpha r} \, dr = -e^{-\alpha r} \left(\dfrac{r^3}{\alpha} + \dfrac{3r^2}{\alpha^2} + \dfrac{6r}{\alpha^3} + \dfrac{6}{\alpha^4} \right)$ with $\alpha = 1/a$.

$I_2 = \dfrac{4}{a} \left[e^{-r/a}(r^3 a + 3r^2 a^2 + 6ra^3 + 6a^4) \right]_0^{4a} = (568e^{-4} - 24)a^3$.

$I_3 = \dfrac{1}{a^2} \int_0^{4a} r^4 e^{-r/a} \, dr$

Use the integral formula $\int r^4 e^{-\alpha r} \, dr = -e^{-\alpha r} \left(\dfrac{r^4}{\alpha} + \dfrac{4r^3}{\alpha^2} + \dfrac{12r^2}{\alpha^3} + \dfrac{24r}{\alpha^4} + \dfrac{24}{\alpha^5} \right)$ with $\alpha = 1/a$.

$I_3 = -\dfrac{1}{a^2} \left[e^{-r/a}(r^4 a + 4r^3 a^2 + 12r^2 a^3 + 24ra^4 + 24a^5) \right]_0^{4a} = (-824e^{-4} + 24)a^3$.

Thus $P(r < 4a) = \dfrac{1}{8a^3}(I_1 + I_2 + I_3) = \dfrac{1}{8a^3} a^3([8 - 24 + 24] + e^{-4}[-104 + 568 - 824])$

$P(r < 4a) = \dfrac{1}{8}(8 - 360e^{-4}) = 1 - 45e^{-4} = 0.176$.

EVALUATE: There is a 82.4% probability that the electron will be found at $r > 4a$. In the Bohr model the electron is for certain at $r = 4a$; this is a poor description of the radial probability distribution for this state.

41.37 IDENTIFY: Use Fig.41.1 to relate θ_L to L_z and L:

$$\cos\theta_L = \frac{L_z}{L} \text{ so } \theta_L = \arccos\left(\frac{L_z}{L}\right)$$

a) SET UP: The smallest angle $(\theta_L)_{min}$ is for the state with the largest L and the largest L_z. This is the state with $l = n-1$ and $m_l = l = n-1$.

EXECUTE: $L_z = m_l\hbar = (n-1)\hbar$

$L = \sqrt{l(l+1)}\hbar = \sqrt{(n-1)n}\hbar$

$$(\theta_L)_{min} = \arccos\left(\frac{(n-1)\hbar}{\sqrt{(n-1)n}\hbar}\right) = \arccos\left(\frac{(n-1)}{\sqrt{(n-1)n}}\right) = \arccos\left(\sqrt{\frac{n-1}{n}}\right) =$$
$\arccos(\sqrt{1-1/n})$.

EVALUATE: Note that $(\theta_L)_{min}$ approaches $0°$ as $n \to \infty$.

b) SET UP: The largest angle $(\theta_L)_{max}$ is for $l = n-1$ and $m_l = -l = -(n-1)$.

EXECUTE: A similar calculation to part (a) yields $(\theta_L)_{max} = \arccos(-\sqrt{1-1/n})$

EVALUATE: Note that $(\theta_L)_{max}$ approaches $180°$ as $n \to \infty$.

41.43 IDENTIFY: The ratio according to the Boltzmann distribution is given by Eq.(38.21): $\frac{n_1}{n_0} = e^{-(E_1-E_0)/kT}$, where 1 is the higher energy state and 0 is the lower energy state.

SET UP: The interaction energy with the magnetic field is

$$U = -\mu_z B = 2.00232\left(\frac{e\hbar}{2m}\right)m_s B \text{ (Example 41.5)}.$$

The energy of the $m_s = +\frac{1}{2}$ level is increased and the energy of the $m_s = -\frac{1}{2}$ level is decreased.

$$\frac{n_{1/2}}{n_{-1/2}} = e^{-(U_{1/2}-U_{-1/2})/kT}$$

EXECUTE: $U_{1/2} - U_{-1/2} = 2.00232\left(\frac{e\hbar}{2m}\right)B(\frac{1}{2}-(-\frac{1}{2})) = 2.00232\left(\frac{e\hbar}{2m}\right)B = 2.00232\mu_B B$

$$\frac{n_{1/2}}{n_{-1/2}} = e^{-(2.00232)\mu_B B/kT}$$

a) $B = 5.00 \times 10^{-5}T$

$$\frac{n_{1/2}}{n_{-1/2}} = e^{-2.00232(9.274\times10^{-24} \text{ A/m}^2)(5.00\times10^{-5} \text{ T})/([1.381\times10^{-23} \text{ J/K}][300K])}$$

$$\frac{n_{1/2}}{n_{-1/2}} = e^{-2.24\times10^{-7}} = 0.99999978 = 1 - 2.2 \times 10^{-7}$$

b) $B = 0.500$ T, $\frac{n_{1/2}}{n_{-1/2}} = e^{-2.24\times10^{-3}} = 0.9978$

c) $B = 5.00$ T, $\dfrac{n_{1/2}}{n_{-1/2}} = e^{-2.24 \times 10^{-2}} = 0.978$

EVALUATE: For small fields the energy separation between the two spin states is much less than kT for $T = 300$ K and the states are equally populated. For $B = 5.00$ T the energy spacing is large enough for there to be a small excess of atoms in the lower state.

41.45 IDENTIFY and **SET UP:** m_s can take on 4 different values: $m_s = -\frac{3}{2}, -\frac{1}{2}, +\frac{1}{2}, +\frac{3}{2}$. Each nlm_l state can have 4 electrons, each with one of the four different m_s values. Apply the exclusion principle to determine the electron configurations.

EXECUTE:

a) For a filled $n = 1$ shell, the electron configuration would be $1s^4$; four electrons and $Z = 4$. For a filled $n = 2$ shell, the electron configuration would be $1s^4 2s^4 2p^{12}$; twenty electrons and $Z = 20$.

b) Sodium has $Z = 11$; 11 electrons. The ground-state electron configuration would be $1s^4 2s^4 2p^3$.

EVALUATE: The chemical properties of each element would be very different.

41.47 a) IDENTIFY and **SET UP:** The energy of the photon equals the transition energy of the atom: $\Delta E = hc/\lambda$. The energies of the states are given by Eq.(41.3).

EXECUTE: $E_n = -\dfrac{13.60 \text{ eV}}{n^2}$ so $E_2 = -\dfrac{13.60 \text{ eV}}{4}$ and $E_1 = -\dfrac{13.60 \text{ eV}}{1}$

$\Delta E = E_2 - E_1 = 13.60 \text{ eV}(-\frac{1}{4} + 1) = \frac{3}{4}(13.60 \text{ eV}) = 10.20 \text{ eV} = (10.20 \text{ eV})(1.602 \times 10^{-19} \text{ J/eV}) = 1.634 \times 10^{-18}$ J

$\lambda = \dfrac{hc}{\Delta E} = \dfrac{(6.626 \times 10^{-34} \text{ J} \cdot \text{s})(2.998 \times 10^8 \text{ m/s})}{1.634 \times 10^{-18} \text{ J}} = 1.22 \times 10^{-7}$ m $= 122$ nm

b) IDENTIFY and **SET UP:** Calculate the change in ΔE due to the orbital magnetic interaction energy, Eq.(41.17), and relate this to the shift $\Delta\lambda$ in the photon wavelength.

EXECUTE: The shift of a level due to the energy of interaction with the magnetic field in the z-direction is $U = m_l \mu_B B$.

The ground state has $m_l = 0$ so is unaffected by the magnetic field.

The $n = 2$ initial state has $m_l = -1$ so its energy is shifted downward an amount

$U = m_l \mu_B B = (-1)(9.274 \times 10^{-24} \text{ A/m}^2)(2.20 \text{ T}) = (-2.040 \times 10^{-23} \text{ J})(1 \text{ eV}/1.602 \times 10^{-19} \text{ J}) = 1.273 \times 10^{-4}$ eV

Note that the shift in energy due to the magnetic field is a very small fraction of the 10.2 eV transition energy. Problem 39.54c shows that in this situation

$|\Delta\lambda/\lambda| = |\Delta E/E|$.

This gives $|\Delta\lambda| = \lambda|\Delta E/E| = 122 \text{ nm} \left(\dfrac{1.273 \times 10^{-4} \text{ eV}}{10.2 \text{ eV}}\right) = 1.52 \times 10^{-3} \text{ nm} = 1.52 \text{ pm}$.

EVALUATE: The upper level in the transition is lowered in energy so the transition energy is decreased. A smaller ΔE means a larger λ; the magnetic field increases the wavelength. The fractional shift in wavelength, $\Delta\lambda/\lambda$ is small, only 1.2×10^{-5}.

41.49 IDENTIFY: Estimate the atomic transition energy and use Eq.(38.6) to relate this to the photon wavelength.

a) SET UP: vanadium, $Z = 23$

minimum wavelength; corresponds to largest transition energy

EXECUTE: The highest occupied shell is the N shell ($n = 4$). The highest energy transition is $N \rightarrow K$, with transition energy $\Delta E = E_N - E_K$. Since the shell energies scale like $1/n^2$ neglect E_N relative to E_K, so $\Delta E = E_K = (Z-1)^2(13.6 \text{ eV}) = (23-1)^2(13.6 \text{ eV}) = 6.582 \times 10^3 \text{ eV} = 1.055 \times 10^{-15} \text{ J}$.

The energy of the emitted photon equals this transition energy, so the photon's wavelength is given by $\Delta E = hc/\lambda$ so $\lambda = hc/\Delta E$.

$$\lambda = \frac{(6.626 \times 10^{-34} \text{ J} \cdot \text{s})(2.998 \times 10^8 \text{ m/s})}{1.055 \times 10^{-15} \text{ J}} = 1.88 \times 10^{-10} \text{ m} = 0.188 \text{ nm}.$$

SET UP: maximum wavelength; coresponds to smallest transition energy, so for the K_α transition

EXECUTE: The frequency of the photon emitted in this transition is given by Moseley's law (Eq.41.29):

$f = (2.48 \times 10^{15} \text{ Hz})(Z-1)^2 = (2.48 \times 10^{15} \text{ Hz})(23-1)^2 = 1.200 \times 10^{18} \text{ Hz}$

$\lambda = \dfrac{c}{f} = \dfrac{2.998 \times 10^8 \text{ m/s}}{1.200 \times 10^{18} \text{ Hz}} = 2.50 \times 10^{-10} \text{ m} = 0.250 \text{ nm}$

b) rhenium, $Z = 45$

Apply the analysis of part (a), just with this different value of Z.

minimum wavelength

$\Delta E = E_K = (Z-1)^2(13.6 \text{ eV}) = (45-1)^2(13.6 \text{ eV}) = 2.633 \times 10^4 \text{ eV} = 4.218 \times 10^{-15} \text{ J}$.

$\lambda = hc/\Delta E = \dfrac{(6.626 \times 10^{-34} \text{ J} \cdot \text{s})(2.998 \times 10^8 \text{ m/s})}{4.218 \times 10^{-15} \text{ J}} = 4.71 \times 10^{-11} \text{ m} = 0.0471 \text{ nm}$.

maximum wavelength

$$f = (2.48 \times 10^{15} \text{ Hz})(Z-1)^2 = (2.48 \times 10^{15} \text{ Hz})(45-1)^2 = 4.801 \times 10^{18} \text{ Hz}$$

$$\lambda = \frac{c}{f} = \frac{2.998 \times 10^8 \text{ m/s}}{4.801 \times 10^{18} \text{ Hz}} = 6.24 \times 10^{-11} \text{ m} = 0.0624 \text{ nm}$$

EVALUATE: Our calculated wavelengths have values corresponding to x rays. The transition energies increase when Z increases and the photon wavelengths decrease.

CHAPTER 42
MOLECULES AND CONDENSED MATTER

Exercises 5, 7, 11, 13, 15, 19, 21, 27, 29, 31
Problems 33, 35, 37, 41, 45, 49, 51

Exercises

42.5 **IDENTIFY** and **SET UP:** Set $K = E_1$ from Example 42.2. Use $K = \frac{1}{2}I\omega^2$ to solve for ω and $v = r\omega$ to solve for v.

EXECUTE:

a) From Example 42.2,

$E_1 = 0.479$ meV $= 7.674 \times 10^{-23}$ J and $I = 1.449 \times 10^{-46}$ kg $\cdot$ m^2

$K = \frac{1}{2}I\omega^2$ and $K = E$ gives $\omega = \sqrt{2E_1/I} = 1.03 \times 10^{12}$ rad/s

b) $v_1 = r_1\omega_1 = (0.0644 \times 10^{-9}$ m$)(1.03 \times 10^{12}$ rad/s$) = 66.3$ m/s (carbon)

$v_2 = r_2\omega_2 = (0.0484 \times 10^{-9}$ m$)(1.03 \times 10^{12}$ rad/s$) = 49.8$ m/s (oxygen)

c) $T = 2\pi/\omega = 6.10 \times 10^{-12}$ s

EVALUATE: From the information in Example 42.3 we can calculate the vibrational period to be $T = 2\pi/\omega = 2\pi\sqrt{m_r/k'} = 1.5 \times 10^{-14}$ s. The rotational motion is over an order of magnitude slower than the vibrational motion.

42.7 **IDENTIFY** and **SET UP:** The energy of a rotational level with quantum number l is $E_l = l(l+1)\hbar^2/2I$ (Eq.(42.3)). $I = m_r r^2$, with the reduced mass m_r given by Eq.(42.4). Calculate I and ΔE and then use $\Delta E = hc\lambda$ to find λ.

EXECUTE:

a) $m_r = \dfrac{m_1 m_2}{m_1 + m_2} = \dfrac{m_{Li} m_H}{m_{Li} + m_H} = \dfrac{(1.17 \times 10^{-26}\text{ kg})(1.67 \times 10^{-27}\text{ kg})}{1.17 \times 10^{-26}\text{ kg} + 1.67 \times 10^{-27}\text{ kg}} =$ 1.461×10^{-27} kg

$I = m_r r^2 = (1.461 \times 10^{-27}$ kg$)(0.159 \times 10^{-9}$ m$)^2 = 3.694 \times 10^{-47}$ kg $\cdot$ m^2

$l = 3$: $E = 3(4)\left(\dfrac{\hbar^2}{2I}\right) = 6\left(\dfrac{\hbar^2}{I}\right)$

$l = 4$: $E = 4(5)\left(\dfrac{\hbar^2}{2I}\right) = 10\left(\dfrac{\hbar^2}{I}\right)$

$\Delta E = E_3 - E_2 = 4\left(\dfrac{\hbar^2}{I}\right) = 4\left(\dfrac{(1.055 \times 10^{-34}\text{ J}\cdot\text{s})^2}{3.694 \times 10^{-47}\text{ kg}\cdot\text{m}^2}\right) = 1.20 \times 10^{-21}$ J $=$

7.49×10^{-3} eV

b) $\Delta E = hc/\lambda$ so $\lambda = \dfrac{hc}{\Delta E} = \dfrac{(4.136 \times 10^{-15} \text{ eV})(2.998 \times 10^8 \text{ m/s})}{7.49 \times 10^{-3} \text{ eV}} = 166 \ \mu m$

EVALUATE: LiH has a smaller reduced mass than CO and λ is somewhat smaller here than the λ calculated for CO in Example 42.2.

42.11 IDENTIFY: Find ΔE for the transition and compute λ from $\Delta E = hc/\lambda$.

SET UP: From Example 42.2, $E_l = l(l+1)\dfrac{\hbar^2}{2I}$, with $\dfrac{\hbar^2}{2I} = 0.2395 \times 10^{-3}$ eV.

From Example 42.3, $\Delta E = 0.2690$ eV is the spacing between vibratonal levels. Thus $E_n = (n + \frac{1}{2})\hbar\omega$, with $\hbar\omega = 0.2690$ eV.

By Eq.(42.9), $E = E_n + E_l = (n+\frac{1}{2})\hbar\omega + l(l+1)\dfrac{\hbar^2}{2I}$.

EXECUTE:

a) $n = 0 \to n = 1$ and $l = 1 \to l = 2$

For $n=0$, $l=1$, $E_i = \frac{1}{2}\hbar\omega + 2\left(\dfrac{\hbar^2}{2I}\right)$.

For $n=1$, $l=2$, $E_f = \frac{3}{2}\hbar\omega + 6\left(\dfrac{\hbar^2}{2I}\right)$.

$\Delta E - E_f - E_i = \hbar\omega + 4\left(\dfrac{\hbar^2}{2I}\right) = 0.2690 \text{ eV} + 4(0.2395 \times 10^{-3} \text{ eV}) = 0.2700 \text{ eV}$

$\dfrac{hc}{\lambda} = \Delta E$ so

$\lambda = \dfrac{hc}{\Delta E} = \dfrac{(4.136 \times 10^{-15} \text{ eV}\cdot\text{s})(2.998 \times 10^8 \text{ m/s})}{0.2700 \text{ eV}} = 4.592 \times 10^{-6} \text{ m} = 4.592 \ \mu m$

b) $n = 0 \to n = 1$ and $l = 2 \to l = 1$

For $n=0$, $l=2$, $E_i = \frac{1}{2}\hbar\omega + 6\left(\dfrac{\hbar^2}{2I}\right)$.

For $n=1$, $l=1$, $E_f = \frac{3}{2}\hbar\omega + 2\left(\dfrac{\hbar^2}{2I}\right)$.

$\Delta E = E_f - E_i = \hbar\omega - 4\left(\dfrac{\hbar^2}{2I}\right) = 0.2690 \text{ eV} - 4(0.2395 \times 10^{-3} \text{ eV}) = 0.2680 \text{ eV}$

$\lambda = \dfrac{hc}{\Delta E} = \dfrac{(4.136 \times 10^{-15} \text{ eV}\cdot\text{s})(2.998 \times 10^8 \text{ m/s})}{0.2680 \text{ oV}} = 4.627 \times 10^{-6} \text{ m} = 4.627 \ \mu m$

c) $n = 0 \to n = 1$ and $l = 3 \to l = 2$

For $n=0$, $l=3$, $E_i = \frac{1}{2}\hbar\omega + 12\left(\dfrac{\hbar^2}{2I}\right)$.

For $n=1$, $l=2$, $E_f = \frac{3}{2}\hbar\omega + 6\left(\dfrac{\hbar^2}{2I}\right)$.

$$\Delta E = E_f - E_i = \hbar\omega - 6\left(\frac{\hbar^2}{2I}\right) = 0.2690 \text{ eV} - 6(0.2395 \times 10^{-3} \text{ eV}) = 0.2676 \text{ eV}$$

$$\lambda = \frac{hc}{\Delta E} = \frac{(4.136 \times 10^{-15} \text{ eV}\cdot\text{s})(2.998 \times 10^8 \text{ m/s})}{0.2676 \text{ eV}} = 4.634 \times 10^{-6} \text{ m} = 4.634 \ \mu\text{m}$$

EVALUATE: All three transitions are for $n = 0 \to n = 1$. The spacing between vibrational levels is larger than the spacing between rotational levels, so the difference in λ for the various rotational transitions is small. When the transition is to a larger l, $\Delta E > \hbar\omega$ and when the transition is to a smaller l, $\Delta E < \hbar\omega$.

42.13 a) IDENTIFY and **SET UP:** Use $\omega = \sqrt{k'/m_\text{r}}$ and $\omega = 2\pi f$ to calculate k'. The atomic masses are used in Eq.(42.4) to calculate m_r.

EXECUTE: $f = \dfrac{\omega}{2\pi} = \dfrac{1}{2\pi}\sqrt{\dfrac{k'}{m_\text{r}}}$, so $k' = m_\text{r}(2\pi f)^2$

$$m_\text{r} = \frac{m_1 m_2}{m_1 + m_2} = \frac{m_\text{H} m_\text{F}}{m_\text{H} + m_\text{F}} = \frac{(1.67 \times 10^{-27} \text{ kg})(3.15 \times 10^{-26} \text{ kg})}{1.67 \times 10^{-27} \text{ kg} + 3.15 \times 10^{-26} \text{ kg}} =$$
1.586×10^{-27} kg

$k' = m_\text{r}(2\pi f)^2 = (1.586 \times 10^{-27} \text{ kg})(2\pi[1.24 \times 10^{14} \text{ Hz}])^2 = 963$ N/m

b) IDENTIFY and **SET UP:** The energy levels are given by Eq.(42.7). $E_n = (n + \frac{1}{2})\hbar\omega = (n + \frac{1}{2})hf$, since $\hbar\omega = (h/2\pi)\omega$ and $(\omega/2\pi) = f$. The energy spacing between adjacent levels is $\Delta E = E_{n+1} - E_n = (n + 1 + \frac{1}{2} - n - \frac{1}{2})hf = hf$, independent of n.

EXECUTE: $\Delta E = hf = (6.626 \times 10^{-34} \text{ J}\cdot\text{s})(1.24 \times 10^{14} \text{ Hz}) = 8.22 \times 10^{-20} \text{ J} = 0.513$ eV

c) IDENTIFY and **SET UP:** The photon energy equals the transition energy so $\Delta E = hc/\lambda$.

EXECUTE: $hf = hc/\lambda$ so $\lambda = \dfrac{c}{f} = \dfrac{2.998 \times 10^8 \text{ m/s}}{1.24 \times 10^{14} \text{ Hz}} = 2.42 \times 10^{-6} \text{ m} = 2.42 \ \mu\text{m}$

EVALUATE: This photon is in the infrared, which is typical for vibrational transitions.

42.15 IDENTIFY and **SET UP:** Find the volume occupied by each atom. The density is the average mass of Na and Cl divided by this volume.

EXECUTE: Each atom occupies a cube with side length 0.282 nm. Therefore, the volume occupied by each atom is $V = (0.282 \times 10^{-9} \text{ m})^3 = 2.24 \times 10^{-29} \text{ m}^3$.

In NaCl there are equal numbers of Na and Cl atoms, so the average mass of the atoms in the crystal is

$$m = \tfrac{1}{2}(m_{\mathrm{Na}} + m_{\mathrm{Cl}}) = \tfrac{1}{2}(3.82 \times 10^{-26} \text{ kg} + 5.89 \times 10^{-26} \text{ kg}) = 4.855 \times 10^{-26} \text{ kg}$$

The density then is $\rho = \dfrac{m}{V} = \dfrac{4.855 \times 10^{-26} \text{ kg}}{2.24 \times 10^{-29} \text{ m}^3} = 2.17 \times 10^3 \text{ kg/m}^3$.

EVALUATE: The density of water is $1.00 \times 10^3 \text{ kg/m}^3$, so our result is reasonable.

42.19 **a) IDENTIFY** and **SET UP:** The photon energy must be at least $E = 1.12 \text{ eV} = 1.794 \times 10^{-19} \text{ J}$, the energy required to excite an electron from the valence to the conduction band. The wavelength is given by $E = hc/\lambda$.

EXECUTE: $\lambda = \dfrac{hc}{E} = \dfrac{(6.626 \times 10^{-34} \text{ J} \cdot \text{s})(2.998 \times 10^8 \text{ m/s})}{1.794 \times 10^{-19} \text{ J}} = 1.11 \times 10^{-6} \text{ m} = 1.11 \ \mu\text{m}$; this photon is in the infrared.

b) EVALUATE: Photons of wavelength less than $1.11 \ \mu\text{m}$ have energy greater than 1.12 eV so can be absorbed in transitions from the valence band into the conduction band. This includes the entire visible range of wavelengths so silicon absorbs all visible wavelengths and hence is opaque to visible light.

42.21 **a) IDENTIFY** and **SET UP:** The three-dimensional Schrodinger equation is

$$-\frac{\hbar^2}{2m}\left(\frac{\partial^2\psi}{\partial x^2} + \frac{\partial^2\psi}{\partial y^2} + \frac{\partial^2\psi}{\partial z^2}\right) + U\psi = E\psi \text{ (Eq.40.29)}.$$

For free electrons, $U = 0$. Evaluate $\partial^2\psi/\partial x^2$, $\partial^2\psi/\partial y^2$, and $\partial^2\psi/\partial z^2$ for ψ as given by Eq.(42.10). Put the results into Eq.(40.20) and see if the equation is satisfied.

EXECUTE: $\dfrac{\partial\psi}{\partial x} = \dfrac{n_x\pi}{L} A \cos\left(\dfrac{n_x\pi x}{L}\right) \sin\left(\dfrac{n_y\pi y}{L}\right) \sin\left(\dfrac{n_z\pi z}{L}\right)$

$\dfrac{\partial^2\psi}{\partial x^2} = -\left(\dfrac{n_x\pi}{L}\right)^2 A \sin\left(\dfrac{n_x\pi x}{L}\right) \sin\left(\dfrac{n_y\pi y}{L}\right) \sin\left(\dfrac{n_z\pi z}{L}\right) = -\left(\dfrac{n_x\pi}{L}\right)^2 \psi$

Similarly $\dfrac{\partial^2\psi}{\partial y^2} = -\left(\dfrac{n_y\pi}{L}\right)^2 \psi$ and $\dfrac{\partial^2\psi}{\partial z^2} = -\left(\dfrac{n_z\pi}{L}\right)^2 \psi$.

Therefore, $-\dfrac{\hbar^2}{2m}\left(\dfrac{\partial^2\psi}{\partial x^2} + \dfrac{\partial^2\psi}{\partial y^2} + \dfrac{\partial^2\psi}{\partial z^2}\right) = \dfrac{\hbar^2}{2m}\left(-\dfrac{\pi^2}{L^2}\right)(n_x^2 + n_y^2 + n_z^2)\psi = $

$\dfrac{(n_x^2 + n_y^2 + n_z^2)\pi^2\hbar^2}{2mL^2}\psi$

This equals $E\psi$, with $E = \dfrac{(n_x^2 + n_y^2 + n_z^2)\pi^2\hbar^2}{2mL^2}$, which is Eq.(42.11).

EVALUATE: ψ given by Eq.(42.10) is a solution to Eq.(40.29), with E as given by Eq.(42.11).

b) IDENTIFY and **SET UP:** Find the set of quantum numbers n_x, n_y, and n_z that give the lowest three values of E. The degeneracy is the number of sets of n_x,

n_y, n_z and m_s that give the same E.

EXECUTE:

Ground level: lowest E so $n_x = n_y = n_z = 1$ and $E = \dfrac{3\pi^2\hbar^2}{2mL^2}$.

No other combination of n_x, n_y, and n_z gives this same E, so the only degeneracy is the degeneracy of two due to spin.

First excited level: next lower E so one n equals 2 and the others equal 1.

$$E = (2^2 + 1^2 + 1^2)\frac{\pi^2\hbar^2}{2mL^2} = \frac{6\pi^2\hbar^2}{2mL^2}$$

There are three different sets of n_x, n_y, n_z values that give this E:

$n_x = 2, n_y = 1, n_z = 1$; $n_x = 1, n_y = 2, n_z = 1$; $n_x = 1, n_y = 1, n_z = 2$

This gives a degeneracy of 3 so the total degeneracy, with the factor of 2 from spin, is 6.

Second excited level: next lower E so two of n_x, n_y, n_z equal 2 and the other equals 1.

$$E = (2^2 + 2^2 + 1^2)\frac{\pi^2\hbar^2}{2mL^2} = \frac{9\pi^2\hbar^2}{2mL^2}$$

There are three different sets of n_x, n_y, n_z values that give this E:

$n_x = 2, n_y = 2, n_z = 1$; $n_x = 2, n_y = 1, n_z = 2$; $n_x = 1, n_y = 2, n_z = 2$.

Thus, as for the first excited level, the total degeneracy, including spin, is 6.

EVALUATE: The wavefunction for the 3-dimensional box is a product of the wavefunctions for a 1-dimensional box in the x, y and z coordinates and the energy is the sum of energies for three 1-dimensional boxes. All levels except for the ground level have a degeneracy greater than unity. Compare to the 3-dimensional isotropic harmonic oscillator treated in Problem 40.53.

42.27 a) **IDENTIFY** and **SET UP:** The electron contribution to the molar heat capacity at constant volume of a metal is $C_V = \left(\dfrac{\pi^2 kT}{2E_F}\right) R$.

EXECUTE: $C_V = \dfrac{\pi^2(1.381 \times 10^{-23}\ \text{J/K})(300\ \text{K})}{2(5.48\ \text{eV})(1.602 \times 10^{-19}\ \text{J/eV})} R = 0.0233R$.

b) **EVALUATE:** The electron contribution found in part (a) is $0.0233R = 0.194\ \text{J/mol·K}$. This is $0.194/25.3 = 7.67 \times 10^{-3} = 0.767\%$ of the total C_V.

c) Only a small fraction of C_V is due to the electrons. Most of C_V is due to the vibrational motion of the ions.

42.29 IDENTIFY: Use Eq.(42.17), $f(E) = \dfrac{1}{e^{(E-E_F)/kT} + 1}$. Solve for $E - E_F$.

SET UP: $e^{(E-E_F)/kT} = \dfrac{1}{f(E)} - 1$

The problem states that $f(E) = 4.4 \times 10^{-4}$ for E at the bottom of the conduction band.

EXECUTE: $e^{(E-E_F)/kT} = \dfrac{1}{4.4 \times 10^{-4}} - 1 = 2.272 \times 10^3$.

$E - E_F = kT \ln(2.272 \times 10^3) = (1.3807 \times 10^{-23} \text{ J/T})(300 \text{ K}) \ln(2.272 \times 10^3) = 3.201 \times 10^{-20}$ J $= 0.20$ eV

$E_F = E - 0.20$ eV; the Fermi level is 0.20 eV below the bottom of the conduction band.

EVALUATE: The energy gap between the Fermi level and bottom of the conduction band is large compared to kT at $T = 300$ K and as a result $f(E)$ is small.

42.31 IDENTIFY and **SET UP:** The voltage-current relation is given by Eq.(42.23): $I = I_s\left(e^{eV/kT} - 1\right)$. Use the current for $V = +15.0$ mV to solve for the constant I_s.

EXECUTE:

a) Find I_s: $V = +15.0 \times 10^{-3}$ V gives $I = 9.25 \times 10^{-3}$ A

$\dfrac{eV}{kT} = \dfrac{(1.602 \times 10^{-19} \text{ C})(15.0 \times 10^{-3} \text{ V})}{(1.381 \times 10^{-23} \text{ J/K})(300 \text{ K})} = 0.5800$

$I_s = \dfrac{I}{e^{eV/kT} - 1} = \dfrac{9.25 \times 10^{-3} \text{ A}}{e^{0.5800} - 1} = 1.177 \times 10^{-2} = 11.77$ mA

Then can calculate I for $V = 10.0$ mV:

$\dfrac{eV}{kT} = \dfrac{(1.602 \times 10^{-19} \text{ C})(10.0 \times 10^{-3} \text{ V})}{(1.381 \times 10^{-23} \text{ J/K})(300 \text{ K})} = 0.3867$

$I = I_s\left(e^{eV/kT} - 1\right) = (11.77 \text{ mA})\left(e^{0.3867} - 1\right) = 5.56$ mA

b) $\dfrac{eV}{kT}$ has the same magnitude as in part (a) but now V is negative so $\dfrac{eV}{kT}$ is negative.

$\underline{V = -15.0 \text{ mV}}$: $\dfrac{eV}{kT} = -0.5800$ and

$I = I_s\left(e^{eV/kT} - 1\right) = (11.77 \text{ mA})\left(e^{-0.5800} - 1\right) = -5.18$ mA

$\underline{V = -10.0 \text{ mV}}$: $\dfrac{eV}{kT} = -0.3867$ and

$I = I_s\left(e^{eV/kT} - 1\right) = (11.77 \text{ mA})\left(e^{-0.3867} - 1\right) = -3.77$ mA

EVALUATE: There is a directional asymmetry in the current, with a forward-bias voltage producing more current than a reverse-bias voltage of the same magnitude, but the voltage is small enough for the asymmetry not to be pronounced. Compare to Example 42.11, where more extreme voltages are considered.

Problems

42.33 **IDENTIFY** and **SET UP:** Eq.(21.14) gives the electric dipole moment as $p = qd$, where the dipole consists of charges $\pm q$ separated by distance d.

EXECUTE:

a) Point charges $+e$ and $-e$ separated by distance d, so

$$p = ed = (1.602 \times 10^{-19} \text{ C})(0.24 \times 10^{-9} \text{ m}) = 3.8 \times 10^{-29} \text{ C·m}$$

b) $p = qd$ so $q = \dfrac{p}{d} = \dfrac{3.0 \times 10^{-29} \text{ C} \cdot \text{m}}{0.24 \times 10^{-9} \text{ m}} = 1.3 \times 10^{-19} \text{ C}$

c) $\dfrac{q}{e} = \dfrac{1.3 \times 10^{-19} \text{ C}}{1.602 \times 10^{-19} \text{ C}} = 0.81$

d) $q = \dfrac{p}{d} = \dfrac{1.5 \times 10^{-30} \text{ C} \cdot \text{m}}{0.16 \times 10^{-9} \text{ m}} = 9.37 \times 10^{-21} \text{ C}$

$\dfrac{q}{e} = \dfrac{9.37 \times 10^{-21} \text{ C}}{1.602 \times 10^{-19} \text{ C}} = 0.058$

EVALUATE: The fractional ionic character for the bond in HI is much less than the fractional ionic character for the bond in NaCl. The bond in HI is mostly covalent and not very ionic.

42.35 **a)** **IDENTIFY:** $E(\text{Na}) + E(\text{Cl}) = E(\text{Na}^+) + E(\text{Cl}^-) + U(r)$. Solving for $U(r)$ gives $U(r) = -[E(\text{Na}^+) - E(\text{Na})] + [E(\text{Cl}) - E(\text{Cl}^-)]$.

SET UP: $[E(\text{Na}^+) - E(\text{Na})]$ is the ionization energy of Na, the energy required to remove one electron, and is equal to 5.1 eV. $[E(\text{Cl}) - E(\text{Cl}^-)]$ is the electron affinity of Cl, the magnitude of the decrease in energy when an electron is attached to a neutral Cl atom, and is equal to 3.6 eV.

EXECUTE: $U = -5.1 \text{ eV} + 3.6 \text{ eV} = -1.5 \text{ eV} = -2.4 \times 10^{-19} \text{ J}$, and

$$-\frac{1}{4\pi\epsilon_0}\frac{e^2}{r} = -2.4 \times 10^{-19} \text{ J}$$

$$r = \left(\frac{1}{4\pi\epsilon_0}\right)\frac{e^2}{2.4 \times 10^{-19} \text{ J}} = (8.988 \times 10^9 \text{ N} \cdot \text{m}^2/\text{C}^2)\frac{(1.602 \times 10^{-19} \text{ C})^2}{2.4 \times 10^{-19} \text{ J}}$$

$r = 9.6 \times 10^{-10} \text{ m} = 0.96 \text{ nm}$

b) ionization energy of K = 4.3 eV; electron affinity of Br = 3.5 eV

Thus $U = -4.3$ eV $+ 3.5$ eV $= -0.8$ eV $= -1.28 \times 10^{-19}$ J, and

$$-\frac{1}{4\pi\epsilon_0}\frac{e^2}{r} = -1.28 \times 10^{-19} \text{ J}$$

$$r = \left(\frac{1}{4\pi\epsilon_0}\right)\frac{e^2}{1.28 \times 10^{-19} \text{ J}} = (8.988 \times 10^9 \text{ N} \cdot \text{m}^2/\text{C}^2)\frac{(1.602 \times 10^{-19} \text{ C})^2}{1.28 \times 10^{-19} \text{ J}}$$

$$r = 1.8 \times 10^{-9} \text{ m} = 1.8 \text{ nm}$$

EVALUATE: K has a smaller ionization energy than Na and the electron affinities of Cl and Br are very similar, so it takes less energy to make $K^+ + Br^-$ from K $+$ Br than to make $Na^+ + Cl^-$ from Na $+$ Cl. Thus, the stabilization distance is larger for KBr than for NaCl.

42.37 a) IDENTIFY: The rotational energies of a molecule depend on its moment of inertia, which in turn depends on the separation between the atoms in the molecule.

SET UP: Problem 42.36 gives $I = 2.71 \times 10^{-47}$ kg $\cdot$ m^2. $I = m_r r^2$. Calculate m_r and solve for r.

EXECUTE:

$$m_r = \frac{m_H m_{Cl}}{m_H + m_{Cl}} = \frac{(1.67 \times 10^{-27} \text{ kg})(5.81 \times 10^{-26} \text{ kg})}{1.67 \times 10^{-27} \text{ kg} + 5.81 \times 10^{-26} \text{ kg}} = 1.623 \times 10^{-27} \text{ kg}$$

$$r = \sqrt{\frac{I}{m_r}} = \sqrt{\frac{2.71 \times 10^{-47} \text{ kg} \cdot \text{m}^2}{1.623 \times 10^{-27} \text{ kg}}} = 1.29 \times 10^{-10} \text{ m} = 0.129 \text{ nm}$$

EVALUATE: This is a typical atomic separation for a diatomic molecule; see Example 42.2 for the corresponding distance for CO.

b) IDENTIFY: Each transition is from the level l to the level $l-1$. The rotational energies are given by Eq.(42.3). The transition energy is related to the photon wavelength by $\Delta E = hc/\lambda$.

SET UP: $E_l = l(l+1)\hbar^2/2I$, so

$$\Delta E = E_l - E_{l-1} = [l(l+1) - l(l-1)]\left(\frac{\hbar^2}{2I}\right) = l\left(\frac{\hbar^2}{I}\right).$$

EXECUTE: $l\left(\dfrac{\hbar^2}{I}\right) = \dfrac{hc}{\lambda}$

$$l = \frac{2\pi cI}{\hbar\lambda} = \frac{2\pi(2.998 \times 10^8 \text{ m/s})(2.71 \times 10^{-47} \text{ kg} \cdot \text{m}^2)}{(1.055 \times 10^{-34} \text{ J} \cdot \text{s})\lambda} = \frac{4.843 \times 10^{-4} \text{ m}}{\lambda}$$

For $\lambda = 60.4$ μm, $l = \dfrac{4.843 \times 10^{-4} \text{ m}}{60.4 \times 10^{-6} \text{ m}} = 8$.

For $\lambda = 69.0$ μm, $l = \dfrac{4.843 \times 10^{-4} \text{ m}}{69.0 \times 10^{-6} \text{ m}} = 7$.

For $\lambda = 80.4 \ \mu m$, $l = \dfrac{4.843 \times 10^{-4} \text{ m}}{80.4 \times 10^{-6} \text{ m}} = 6.$

For $\lambda = 96.4 \ \mu m$, $l = \dfrac{4.843 \times 10^{-4} \text{ m}}{96.4 \times 10^{-6} \text{ m}} = 5.$

For $\lambda = 120.4 \ \mu m$, $l = \dfrac{4.843 \times 10^{-4} \text{ m}}{120.4 \times 10^{-6} \text{ m}} = 4.$

EVALUATE: In each case l is an integer, as it must be.

c) IDENTIFY and **SET UP:** Longest λ implies smallest ΔE, and this is for the transition from $l = 1$ to $l = 0$.

EXECUTE: $\Delta E = l \left(\dfrac{\hbar^2}{I} \right) = (1) \dfrac{(1.055 \times 10^{-34} \text{ J} \cdot \text{s})^2}{2.71 \times 10^{-47} \text{ kg} \cdot \text{m}^2} = 4.099 \times 10^{-22} \text{ J}$

$\lambda = \dfrac{hc}{\Delta E} = \dfrac{(6.626 \times 10^{-34} \text{ J} \cdot \text{s})(2.998 \times 10^8 \text{ m/s})}{4.099 \times 10^{-22} \text{ J}} = 4.85 \times 10^{-4} \text{ m} = 485 \ \mu m.$

EVALUATE: This is longer than any of the wavelengths in part (b).

d) IDENTIFY: What changes is m_r, the reduced mass of the molecule.

SET UP: The transition energy is $\Delta E = l \left(\dfrac{\hbar^2}{I} \right)$ and $\Delta E = \dfrac{hc}{\lambda}$, so $\lambda = \dfrac{2 \pi c I}{l \hbar}$ (part (b)).

$I = m_r r^2$, so λ is directly proportional to m_r.

$\dfrac{\lambda(\text{HCl})}{m_r(\text{HCl})} = \dfrac{\lambda(\text{DCl})}{m_r(\text{DCl})}$ so $\lambda(\text{DCl}) = \lambda(\text{HCl}) \dfrac{m_r(\text{DCl})}{m_r(\text{HCl})}$

EXECUTE: The mass of a deuterium atom is approximatey twice the mass of a hydrogen atom, so $m_D = 3.34 \times 10^{-27}$ kg.

$m_r(\text{DCl}) = \dfrac{m_D m_{Cl}}{m_D + m_{Cl}} = \dfrac{(3.34 \times 10^{-27} \text{ kg})(5.81 \times 10^{-26} \text{ kg})}{3.34 \times 10^{-27} \text{ kg} + 5.81 \times 10^{-26} \text{ kg}} = 3.158 \times 10^{-27} \text{ kg}$

$\lambda(\text{DCl}) = \lambda(\text{HCl}) \left(\dfrac{3.158 \times 10^{-27} \text{ kg}}{1.623 \times 10^{-27} \text{ kg}} \right) = (1.946) \lambda(\text{HCl})$

$l = 8 \rightarrow l = 7$; $\lambda = (60.4 \ \mu m)(1.946) = 118 \ \mu m$

$l = 7 \rightarrow l = 6$; $\lambda = (69.0 \ \mu m)(1.946) = 134 \ \mu m$

$l = 6 \rightarrow l = 5$; $\lambda = (80.4 \ \mu m)(1.946) = 156 \ \mu m$

$l = 5 \rightarrow l = 4$; $\lambda = (96.4 \ \mu m)(1.946) = 188 \ \mu m$

$l = 4 \rightarrow l = 3$; $\lambda = (120.4 \ \mu m)(1.946) = 234 \ \mu m$

EVALUATE: The moment of inertia increases when H is replaced by D, so the transition energies decrease and the wavelengths increase. The larger the rotational inertia the smaller the rotational energy for a given l (Eq.42.3).

42.41 **IDENTIFY** and **SET UP:** $E_l = l(l+1)\hbar^2/2I$, so E_l and the transition energy ΔE depends on I. Different isotopic molecules have different I.

EXECUTE:

a) Calculate I for $Na^{35}Cl$:

$$m_r = \frac{m_{Na}m_{Cl}}{m_{Na} + m_{Cl}} = \frac{(3.8176 \times 10^{-26} \text{ kg})(5.8068 \times 10^{-26} \text{ kg})}{3.8176 \times 10^{-26} \text{ kg} + 5.8068 \times 10^{-26} \text{ kg}} = 2.303 \times 10^{-26} \text{ kg}$$

$$I = m_r r^2 = (2.303 \times 10^{-26} \text{ kg})(0.2361 \times 10^{-9} \text{ m})^2 = 1.284 \times 10^{-45} \text{ kg} \cdot \text{m}^2$$

$l = 2 \rightarrow l = 1$ transition

$$\Delta E = E_2 - E_1 = (6-2)\left(\frac{\hbar^2}{2I}\right) = \frac{2\hbar^2}{I} = \frac{2(1.055 \times 10^{-34} \text{ J} \cdot \text{s})^2}{1.284 \times 10^{-45} \text{ kg} \cdot \text{m}^2} = 1.734 \times 10^{-23} \text{ J}$$

$$\Delta E = \frac{hc}{\lambda} \text{ so}$$

$$\lambda = \frac{hc}{\Delta E} = \frac{(6.626 \times 10^{-34} \text{ J} \cdot \text{s})(2.998 \times 10^8 \text{ m/s})}{1.734 \times 10^{-23} \text{ J}} = 1.146 \times 10^{-2} \text{ m} = 1.146 \text{ cm}$$

$l = 1 \rightarrow l = 0$ transition

$$\Delta E = E_1 - E_0 = (2-0)\left(\frac{\hbar^2}{2I}\right) = \frac{\hbar^2}{I} = \frac{1}{2}(1.734 \times 10^{-23} \text{ J}) = 8.67 \times 10^{-24} \text{ J}$$

$$\lambda = \frac{hc}{\Delta E} = \frac{(6.626 \times 10^{-34} \text{ J} \cdot \text{s})(2.998 \times 10^8 \text{ m/s})}{8.67 \times 10^{-24} \text{ J}} = 2.291 \text{ cm}$$

b) Calculate I for $Na^{37}Cl$:

$$m_r = \frac{m_{Na}m_{Cl}}{m_{Na} + m_{Cl}} = \frac{(3.8176 \times 10^{-26} \text{ kg})(6.1384 \times 10^{-26} \text{ kg})}{3.8176 \times 10^{-26} \text{ kg} + 6.1384 \times 10^{-26} \text{ kg}} = 2.354 \times 10^{-26} \text{ kg}$$

$$I = m_r r^2 = (2.354 \times 10^{-26} \text{ kg})(0.2361 \times 10^{-9} \text{ m})^2 = 1.312 \times 10^{-45} \text{ kg} \cdot \text{m}^2$$

$l = 2 \rightarrow l = 1$ transition

$$\Delta E = \frac{2\hbar^2}{I} = \frac{2(1.055 \times 10^{-34} \text{ J} \cdot \text{s})^2}{1.312 \times 10^{-45} \text{ kg} \cdot \text{m}^2} = 1.697 \times 10^{-23} \text{ J}$$

$$\lambda = \frac{hc}{\Delta E} = \frac{(6.626 \times 10^{-34} \text{ J} \cdot \text{s})(2.998 \times 10^8 \text{ m/s})}{1.697 \times 10^{-23} \text{ J}} = 1.171 \times 10^{-2} \text{ m} = 1.171 \text{ cm}$$

$l = 1 \rightarrow l = 0$ transition

$$\Delta E = \frac{\hbar^2}{I} = \frac{1}{2}(1.697 \times 10^{-23} \text{ J}) = 8.485 \times 10^{-24} \text{ J}$$

$$\lambda = \frac{hc}{\Delta E} = \frac{(6.626 \times 10^{-34} \text{ J} \cdot \text{s})(2.998 \times 10^8 \text{ m/s})}{8.485 \times 10^{-24} \text{ J}} = 2.341 \text{ cm}$$

The differences in the wavelengths for the two isotopes are:

$l = 2 \rightarrow l = 1$ transition: $1.171 \text{ cm} - 1.146 \text{ cm} = 0.025 \text{ cm}$

$l = 1 \rightarrow l = 0$ transition: $2.341 \text{ cm} - 2.291 \text{ cm} = 0.050 \text{ cm}$

EVALUATE: Replacing ^{35}Cl by ^{37}Cl increases I, decrases ΔE and increases λ. The effect on λ is small but measurable.

42.45 **IDENTIFY** and **SET UP:** Use Eq.(42.6) to calculate I. The energy levels are given by Eq.(42.9). The transition energy ΔE is related to the photon wavelength by $\Delta E = hc/\lambda$.

EXECUTE:

a) $I = m_r r^2$ $m_r = \dfrac{m_H m_I}{m_H + m_I} = \dfrac{(1.67 \times 10^{-27} \text{ kg})(2.11 \times 10^{-25} \text{ kg})}{1.67 \times 10^{-27} \text{ kg} + 2.11 \times 10^{-25} \text{ kg}} = 1.657 \times 10^{-27}$ kg

$I = m_r r^2 = (1.657 \times 10^{-27} \text{ kg})(0.160 \times 10^{-9} \text{ m})^2 = 4.24 \times 10^{-47} \text{ kg} \cdot \text{m}^2$

b) The energy levels are $E_{nl} = l(l+1)\left(\dfrac{\hbar^2}{2I}\right) + (n + \frac{1}{2})\hbar\sqrt{\dfrac{k'}{m_r}}$ (Eq.(42.9))

$\sqrt{\dfrac{k'}{m}} = \omega = 2\pi f$ so $E_{nl} = l(l+1)\left(\dfrac{\hbar^2}{2I}\right) + (n + \frac{1}{2})hf$

(i) transition $n = 1 \to n = 0$, $l = 1 \to l = 0$

$\Delta E = (2-0)\left(\dfrac{\hbar^2}{2I}\right) + (1 + \frac{1}{2} - \frac{1}{2})hf = \dfrac{\hbar^2}{I} + hf$

$\Delta E = \dfrac{hc}{\lambda}$ so $\lambda = \dfrac{hc}{\Delta E} = \dfrac{hc}{(\hbar^2/I) + hf} = \dfrac{c}{(\hbar/2\pi I) + f}$

$\dfrac{\hbar}{2\pi I} = \dfrac{1.055 \times 10^{-34} \text{ J} \cdot \text{s}}{2\pi(4.24 \times 10^{-47} \text{ kg} \cdot \text{m}^2)} = 3.960 \times 10^{11}$ Hz

$\lambda = \dfrac{c}{(\hbar/2\pi I) + f} = \dfrac{2.998 \times 10^8 \text{ m/s}}{3.960 \times 10^{11} \text{ Hz} + 6.93 \times 10^{13} \text{ Hz}} = 4.30$ μm

(ii) transition $n = 1 \to n = 0$, $l = 2 \to l = 1$

$\Delta E = (6-2)\left(\dfrac{\hbar^2}{2I}\right) + hf = \dfrac{2\hbar^2}{I} + hf$

$\lambda = \dfrac{c}{2(\hbar/2\pi I) + f} = \dfrac{2.998 \times 10^8 \text{ m/s}}{2(3.960 \times 10^{11} \text{ Hz}) + 6.93 \times 10^{13} \text{ Hz}} = 4.28$ μm

(iii) transition $n = 2 \to n = 1$, $l = 2 \to l = 3$

$\Delta E = (6-12)\left(\dfrac{\hbar^2}{2I}\right) + hf = -\dfrac{3\hbar^2}{I} + hf$

$\lambda = \dfrac{c}{-3(\hbar/2\pi I) + f} = \dfrac{2.998 \times 10^8 \text{ m/s}}{-3(3.960 \times 10^{11} \text{ Hz}) + 6.93 \times 10^{13} \text{ Hz}} = 4.40$ μm

EVALUATE: The vibrational energy change for the $n = 1 \to n = 0$ transition is the same as for the $n = 2 \to n = 1$ transition. The rotational energies are much smaller than the vibrational energies, so the wavelengths for all three transitions don't differ by much.

42.49 **IDENTIFY** and **SET UP:** Use the description of the bcc lattice in Fig.42.11c to calculate the number of atoms per unit cell and then the number of atoms per unit volume.

EXECUTE:

a) Each unit cell has one atom at its center and 8 atoms at its corners that are each shared by 8 other unit cells. So there are $1+ 8/8 = 2$ atoms per unit cell.

$$\frac{n}{V} = \frac{2}{(0.35 \times 10^{-9} \text{ m})^3} = 4.66 \times 10^{28} \text{ atoms/m}^3$$

b) $E_{F0} = \dfrac{3^{2/3}\pi^{4/3}\hbar^2}{2m} \left(\dfrac{N}{V}\right)^{2/3}$

In this equation N/V is the number of free electrons per m^3. But the problem says to assume one free electron per atom, so this is the same as n/V calculated in part (a).

$m = 9.109 \times 10^{-31}$ kg (the electron mass), so $E_{F0} = 7.563 \times 10^{-19}$ J $= 4.7$ eV

EVALUATE: Our result for metallic lithium is similar to that calculated for copper in Example 42.8.

42.51 **a)** **IDENTIFY** and **SET UP:** $p = -\dfrac{dE_{tot}}{dV}$. Relate E_{tot} to E_{F0} and evaluate the derivative.

EXECUTE: $E_{tot} = NE_{av} = \dfrac{3N}{5} E_{F0} = \dfrac{3}{5} \left(\dfrac{3^{2/3}\pi^{4/3}\hbar^2}{2m}\right) N^{5/3}V^{-2/3}$

$\dfrac{dE_{tot}}{dV} = \dfrac{3}{5} \left(\dfrac{3^{2/3}\pi^{4/3}\hbar^2}{2m}\right) N^{5/3} \left(-\dfrac{2}{3}V^{-5/3}\right)$ so

$p = \left(\dfrac{3^{2/3}\pi^{4/3}\hbar^2}{5m}\right) \left(\dfrac{N}{V}\right)^{5/3}$, as was to be shown.

b) $N/V = 8.45 \times 10^{28}$ m^{-3}

$p = \left(\dfrac{3^{2/3}\pi^{4/3}(1.055 \times 10^{-34} \text{ J} \cdot \text{s})^2}{5(9.109 \times 10^{-31} \text{ kg})}\right) (8.45 \times 10^{28} \text{ m}^{-3})^{5/3} = 3.81 \times 10^{10}$ Pa $= 3.76 \times 10^5$ atm.

c) **EVALUATE:** Normal atmospheric pressure is about 10^5, so these pressures are exteremly large. The electrons are held in the metal by the attractive force exerted on them by the copper ions.

CHAPTER 43
NUCLEAR PHYSICS

Exercises

43.3 **IDENTIFY:** Calculate the spin magnetic energy shift for each spin state of the $1s$ level. Calculate the energy splitting between these states and relate this to the frequency of the photons.

SET UP: When the spin component is parallel to the field the interaction energy is $U = -\mu_z B$. When the spin component is antiparallel to the field the interaction energy is $U = +\mu_z B$. The transition energy for a transition between these two states is $\Delta E = 2\mu_z B$, where $\mu_z = 2.7928\mu_n$.

The transition energy is related to the photon frequency by $\Delta E = hf$, so $2\mu_z B = hf$.

EXECUTE: $B = \dfrac{hf}{2\mu_z} = \dfrac{(6.626 \times 10^{-34} \text{ J} \cdot \text{s})(22.7 \times 10^6 \text{ Hz})}{2(2.7928)(5.051 \times 10^{-27} \text{ J/T})} = 0.533 \text{ T}$

EVALUATE: This magnetic field is easily achievable. Photons of this frequency have wavelength $\lambda = c/f = 13.2$ m. These are radio waves.

43.5 **IDENTIFY:** Calculate the spin magnetic energy shift for each spin component. Calculate the energy splitting between these states and relate this to the frequency of the photons.

a) SET UP: From Example 43.2, when the z-component of $\vec{S}$ (and $\vec{\mu}$) is parallel to $\vec{B}$, $U = -|\mu_z|B = -2.7928\mu_n B$.

When the z-component of $\vec{S}$ (and $\vec{\mu}$) is antiparallel to $\vec{B}$,
$U = +|\mu_z|B = +2.7928\mu_n B$.

The state with the proton spin component parallel to the field lies lower in energy. The energy difference between these two states is $\Delta E = 2(2.7928\mu_n B)$.

EXECUTE:

$\Delta E = hf$ so $f = \dfrac{\Delta E}{h} = \dfrac{2(2.7928\mu_n B)}{h} = \dfrac{2(2.7928)(5.051 \times 10^{-27} \text{ J/T})(1.65 \text{ T})}{6.626 \times 10^{-34} \text{ J} \cdot \text{s}}$

$f = 7.03 \times 10^7 \text{ Hz} = 70.3 \text{ MHz}$

And then $\lambda = \dfrac{c}{f} = \dfrac{2.998 \times 10^8 \text{ m/s}}{7.03 \times 10^7 \text{ Hz}} = 4.26 \text{ m}$

EVALUATE: From Fig.32.20, these are radio waves.

b) SET UP: From Eqs.(27.27) and (41.22) and Fig.41.13, the state with the z-component of $\vec{\mu}$ parallel to $\vec{B}$ has lower energy. But, since the charge of the electron is negative, this is the state with the electron spin component antiparallel to $\vec{B}$. That is, the $m_s = -\frac{1}{2}$ state lies lower in energy.

EXECUTE: For the $m_s = +\frac{1}{2}$ state,

$$U = +(2.00232)\left(\frac{e}{2m}\right)\left(+\frac{\hbar}{2}\right)B = +\frac{1}{2}(2.00232)\left(\frac{e\hbar}{2m}\right)B = +\frac{1}{2}(2.00232)\mu_{\mathrm{B}}B.$$

For the $m_s = -\frac{1}{2}$ state, $U = -\frac{1}{2}(2.00232)\mu_{\mathrm{B}}B$.

The energy difference between these two states is $\Delta E = (2.00232)\mu_{\mathrm{B}}B$.

$$\Delta E = hf \text{ so } f = \frac{\Delta E}{h} = \frac{2.00232\mu_{\mathrm{B}}B}{h} = \frac{(2.00232)(9.274 \times 10^{-24}\text{ J/T})(1.65\text{ T})}{6.626 \times 10^{-34}\text{ J} \cdot \text{s}} =$$
4.62×10^{10} Hz $= 46.2$ GHz.

And $\lambda = \dfrac{c}{f} = \dfrac{2.998 \times 10^8\text{ m/s)}}{4.62 \times 10^{10}\text{ Hz}} = 6.49 \times 10^{-3}$ m $= 6.49$ mm.

EVALUATE: From Fig.32.20, these are microwaves.

The interaction energy with the magnetic field is inversely proportional to the mass of the particle, so it is less for the proton than for the electron. The smaller transition energy for the proton produces a larger wavelength.

43.7 **IDENTIFY** and **SET UP:** The text calculates that the binding energy of the deuteron is 2.224 MeV. A photon that breaks the deuteron up into a proton and a neutron must have at least this much energy.

$E = \dfrac{hc}{\lambda}$ so $\lambda = \dfrac{hc}{E}$

EXECUTE: $\lambda = \dfrac{(4.136 \times 10^{-15}\text{ eV} \cdot \text{s})(2.998 \times 10^8\text{ m/s})}{2.224 \times 10^6\text{ eV}} = 5.575 \times 10^{-13}$ m $=$ 0.5575 pm.

EVALUATE: This photon has gamma-ray wavelength.

43.9 **a) IDENTIFY:** Find the energy equivalent of the mass defect.

SET UP: A $^{11}_{5}$B atom has 5 protons, $11 - 5 = 6$ neutrons, and 5 electrons. The mass defect therefore is $\Delta M = 5m_{\mathrm{p}} + 6m_{\mathrm{n}} + 5m_{\mathrm{e}} - M(^{11}_{5}\text{B})$.

EXECUTE: $\Delta M = 5(1.0072765\text{ u}) + 6(1.0086649\text{ u}) + 5(0.0005485799\text{ u}) - 11.009305\text{ u} = 0.08181\text{ u}$.

The energy equivalent is $E_{\mathrm{B}} = (0.08181\text{ u})(931.5\text{ MeV/u}) = 76.21$ MeV.

b) IDENTIFY and **SET UP:**

Eq.(43.11): $E_B = C_1 A - C_2 A^{2/3} - C_3 Z(Z-1)/A^{1/3} - C_4(A-2Z)^2/A$

The fifth term is zero since Z is odd but N is even. $A = 11$ and $Z = 5$.

EXECUTE: $E_B = (15.75 \text{ MeV})(11) - (17.80 \text{ MeV})(11)^{2/3} -$
$\qquad (0.7100 \text{ MeV})5(4)/11^{1/3} - (23.69 \text{ MeV})(11-10)^2/11.$

$E_B = +173.25 \text{ MeV} - 88.04 \text{ MeV} - 6.38 \text{ MeV} - 2.15 \text{ MeV} = 76.68 \text{ MeV}$

The percentage difference between the calculated and measured E_B is
$$\frac{76.68 \text{ MeV} - 76.21 \text{ MeV}}{76.21 \text{ MeV}} = 0.6\%.$$

EVALUATE: Eq.(43.11) has a greater percentage accuracy for ^{62}Ni. The semi-empirical mass formula is more accurate for heavier nuclei.

43.13 IDENTIFY: In each case determine how the decay changes A and Z of the nucleus. The β^+ and β^- particles have charge but their nucleon number is $A = 0$.

a) SET UP: α-decay: Z decreases by 2, $A = N + Z$ decreases by 4 (an α particle is a $^4_2$He nucleus)
EXECUTE: $^{239}_{94}$Pu $\rightarrow$ $^4_2$He $+$ $^{235}_{92}$U

b) SET UP: β^- decay: Z increases by 1, $A = N + Z$ remains the same (a β^- particle is an electron, $_{-1}^0$e)
EXECUTE: $^{24}_{11}$Na $\rightarrow$ $_{-1}^0$e $+$ $^{24}_{12}$Mg

c) SET UP: β^+ decay: Z decreases by 1, $A = N + Z$ remains the same (a β^+ particle is a positron, $_{+1}^0$e)
EXECUTE: $^{15}_8$O $\rightarrow$ $_{+1}^0$e $+$ $^{15}_7$N

EVALUATE: In each case the total charge and total number of nucleons for the decay products equals the charge and number of nucleons for the parent nucleus; these two quantities are conserved in the decay.

43.19 IDENTIFY and **SET UP:** Find the mass change in the reaction. If the mass decreases, an equivalent amount of energy is released and the decay is energetically allowed.

EXECUTE:

a) The β^- decay reaction is $^3_1$H $\rightarrow$ $_{-1}^0$e $+$ $^3_2$He. $^3_1$H is unstable with respect to β^- decay since the mass of the $^3_2$He nucleus plus the emitted electron is less than the mass of the $^3_1$H nucleus.

The masses in Table 43.2 are for the neutral atoms, so the mass of the $^3_1$H nucleus is 3.016049 u $-$ 0.0005486 u $=$ 3.0155004 u and the mass of the $^3_2$He nucleus is 3.016029 u $-$ 2(0.0005486 u) $=$ 3.0149318 u.

The mass decrease in the decay is 3.0155004 u $-$ 3.0149318 u $-$ 0.0005486 u $=$

0.000020 u.

b) Find the energy equivalent of the mass decrease found in part (a):

0.000020 u$(931.5$ MeV/u$) = 0.019$ MeV $= 19$ keV.

EVALUATE: Example 43.5 shows that the kinetic energy divides inversely as the masses of the decay products. The emitted electron has a much smaller mass than the $^3_2$He nucleus, so the electron has most of the 19 keV of kinetic energy.

43.21 IDENTIFY and **SET UP:** As discussed in Section 43.4, the activity $A = |dN/dt|$ obeys the same decay equation as Eq.(43.17): $A = A_0 e^{-\lambda t}$. For ^{14}C, $T_{1/2} = 5730$ y and $\lambda = \ln 2/T_{1/2}$ so $A = A_0 e^{-(\ln 2)t/T_{1/2}}$; Calculate A at each t; $A_0 = 180.0$ decays/min.

EXECUTE:

a) $t = 1000$ y, $A = 159$ decays/min

b) $t = 50,000$ y, $A = 0.43$ decays/min

EVALUATE: The time in part (b) is 8.73 half-lives, so the decay rate has decreased by a factor of $(\frac{1}{2})^{8.73}$.

43.27 IDENTIFY and **SET UP:** Calculate the number N of ^{14}C atoms in the sample and then use Eq.(43.17) to find the decay constant λ. Eq.(43.18) then gives $T_{1/2}$.

EXECUTE: Find the total number of carbon atoms in the sample.

$n = m/M$;

$N_{\text{tot}} = nN_A = mN_A/M = (12.0 \times 10^{-3}$ kg$)(6.022 \times 10^{23}$ atoms/mol$)/(12.011 \times 10^{-3}$ kg/mol$)$

$N_{\text{tot}} = 6.016 \times 10^{23}$ atoms, so $(1.3 \times 10^{-12})(6.016 \times 10^{23}) = 7.82 \times 10^{11}$ carbon-14 atoms

$\Delta N/\Delta t = -180$ decays/min $= -3.00$ decays/s

$\Delta N/\Delta t = -\lambda N$; $\lambda = \dfrac{-\Delta N/\Delta t)}{N} = 3.836 \times 10^{-12}$ (s)$^{-1}$

$T_{1/2} = (\ln 2)/\lambda = 1.807 \times 10^{11}$ s $= 5730$ y

EVALUATE: The value we calculated agrees with the value given in Section 43.4.

43.31 IDENTIFY and **SET UP:** Find λ from the half-life and the number N of nuclei from the mass of one nucleus and the mass of the sample. Then use Eq.(43.16) to calculate $|dN/dt|$, the number of decays per second.

EXECUTE:

a) $|dN/dt| = \lambda N$

$$\lambda = \frac{0.693}{T_{1/2}} = \frac{0.693}{(1.28 \times 10^9 \text{ y})(3.156 \times 10^7 \text{ s/1 y})} = 1.715 \times 10^{-17} \text{ s}^{-1}$$

The mass of one ^{40}K atom is approximately 40 u, so the number of ^{40}K nuclei in the sample is

$$N = \frac{1.63 \times 10^{-9} \text{ kg}}{40 \text{ u}} = \frac{1.63 \times 10^{-9} \text{ kg}}{40(1.66054 \times 10^{-27} \text{ kg})} = 2.454 \times 10^{16}.$$

Then $|dN/dt| = \lambda N = (1.715 \times 10^{-17} \text{ s}^{-1})(2.454 \times 10^{16}) = 0.421$ decays/s

b) $|dN/dt| = (0.421 \text{ decays/s})(1 \text{ Ci}/(3.70 \times 10^{10} \text{ decays/s})) = 1.14 \times 10^{-11}$ Ci

EVALUATE: The very small sample still contains a very large number of nuclei. But the half-life is very large, so the decay rate is small.

43.33 IDENTIFY and **SET UP:** Eq.(43.18) relates λ and the half-life. Use Eq.(43.16) to relate N, the number of radioactive nuclei, to the decay rate. The mass of the sample is N times the mass of a single nucleus.

EXECUTE:

a) $\lambda = \dfrac{0.693}{T_{1/2}} = \dfrac{0.693}{(4.47 \times 10^9 \text{ y})(3.156 \times 10^7 \text{ s/1 y})} = 4.91 \times 10^{-18} \text{ s}^{-1}.$

b) Activity of 12.0×10^{-6} Ci implies that $dN/dt = 4.44 \times 10^5$ decays/s

Eq.(43.16) says $|dN/dt| = \lambda N$ so

$$N = \frac{|dN/dt|}{\lambda} = \frac{4.44 \times 10^5 \text{ decays/s}}{4.91 \times 10^{-18} \text{ s}^{-1}} = 9.04 \times 10^{22} \text{ nuclei}$$

The sample must contain 9.04×10^{22} uranium nuclei.

The mass of one uranium ^{238}U atom is approximatey 238 u, so the mass of the sample is

$$m = N(238 \text{ u}) = (9.04 \times 10^{22})(238)(1.66054 \times 10^{-27} \text{ kg}) = 35.7 \text{ g}.$$

c) One α particle is emitted in each decay, so the problem is asking for the activity, in decays/s, of this sample.

Compute N, the number of nuclei in the sample. The mass of one ^{238}U atom is approximately 238 u, so

$$N = \frac{60.0 \times 10^{-3} \text{ kg}}{238 \text{ u}} = \frac{60.0 \times 10^{-3} \text{ kg}}{238(1.66054 \times 10^{-27} \text{ kg})} = 1.518 \times 10^{23} \text{ nuclei}.$$

$|dN/dt| = \lambda N = (4.91 \times 10^{-18} \text{ s}^{-1})(1.518 \times 10^{23}) = 7.45 \times 10^5$ decays/s.

EVALUATE: The decay rate in (c) is about twice what it is in (b), since the mass of the sample is about a factor of two larger.

43.39 a) IDENTIFY and **SET UP:** The total energy absorbed is the number of photons absorbed times the energy of each photon.

EXECUTE: The energy E of each photon is

$$E = \frac{hc}{\lambda} = \frac{(6.626 \times 10^{-34} \text{ J} \cdot \text{s})(2.998 \times 10^8 \text{ m/s})}{0.0200 \times 10^{-9} \text{ m}} = 9.932 \times 10^{-15} \text{ J}.$$

The total energy absorbed is $(6.50 \times 10^{10} \text{ photons})(9.932 \times 10^{-15} \text{ J/photon}) = 6.46 \times 10^{-4}$ J.

b) **IDENTIFY** and **SET UP:** The absorbed dose is the energy absorbed divided by the mass of the absorbing tissue. The equivalent dose in rem equals the RBE times the absorbed dose in rad.

EXECUTE:

$$\text{absorbed dose} = \frac{6.46 \times 10^{-4} \text{ J}}{0.600 \text{ kg}} = (1.08 \times 10^{-3} \text{ J/kg})(1 \text{ rad}/(0.01 \text{ J/kg}))$$

absorbed dose $= 0.108$ rad

For x rays, RBE $=1$, so the equivalent dose is 0.108 rem.

EVALUATE: The equivalent dose is 1.08 mSv. This is about twice the equivalent dose in Example 43.10.

43.41 a) **IDENTIFY** and **SET UP:** Determine X by balancing the charge and nucleon number on the two sides of the reaction equation.

EXECUTE:

X must have $A = +2 + 9 - 4 = 7$ and $Z = +1 + 4 - 2 = 3$. Thus X is $_3^7$Li and the reaction is $_1^2$H $+ {}_4^9$Be $= {}_3^7$Li $+ {}_2^4$He

b) **IDENTIFY** and **SET UP:** Calculate the mass decrease and find its energy equivalent.

EXECUTE: If we use the neutral atom masses then there are the same number of electrons (five) in the reactants as in the products. Their masses cancel, so we get the same mass defect whether we use nuclear masses or neutral atom masses.

The neutral atom masses are given in Table 43.2:

$_1^2$H $+ {}_4^9$Be has mass 2.014102 u $+$ 9.012182 u $=$ 11.026284 u

$_3^7$Li $+ {}_2^4$He has mass 7.016003 u $+$ 4.002603 u $=$ 11.018606 u

The mass decrease is 11.026284 u $-$ 11.018606 u $=$ 0.007678 u.

This corresponds to an energy release of 0.007678 u(931.5 MeV/1 u) $=$ 7.152 MeV.

c) **IDENTIFY** and **SET UP:** Estimate the threshold energy by calculating the Coulomb potential energy when the $_1^2$H and $_4^9$Be nuclei just touch. Obtain the nuclear radii from Eq.(43.1).

EXECUTE:

The radius R_{Be} of the $_4^9$Be nucleus is $R_{Be} = (1.2 \times 10^{-15} \text{ m})(9)^{1/3} = 2.5 \times 10^{-15}$ m.

The radius R_H of the $_1^2$H nucleus is $R_H = (1.2 \times 10^{-15} \text{ m})(2)^{1/3} = 1.5 \times 10^{-15}$ m.

The nuclei touch when their center-to-center separation is

$R = R_{Be} + R_H = 4.0 \times 10^{-15}$ m.

The Coulomb potential energy of the two reactant nuclei at this separation is

$$U = \frac{1}{4\pi\epsilon_0}\frac{q_1 q_2}{r} = \frac{1}{4\pi\epsilon_0}\frac{e(4e)}{r}$$

$$U = (8.988 \times 10^9 \text{ N}\cdot\text{m}^2/\text{C}^2)\frac{4(1.602 \times 10^{-19} \text{ C})^2}{(4.0 \times 10^{-15} \text{ m})(1.602 \times 10^{-19} \text{ J/eV})} = 1.4 \text{ MeV}$$

This is an estimate of the threshold energy for this reaction.

EVALUATE: The reaction releases energy but the total initial kinetic energy of the reactants must be 1.4 MeV in order for the reacting nuclei to get close enough to each other for the reaction of occur. The nuclear force is strong but is very short-range.

43.43 a) IDENTIFY and **SET UP:** Determine X by balancing the charge and nucleon number on the two sides of the reaction equation.

EXECUTE: X must have $A = 2 + 14 - 10 = 6$ and $Z = 1 + 7 - 5 = 3$.

Thus X is ^6_3Li and the reaction is $^2_1\text{H} + {}^{14}_7\text{N} \rightarrow {}^6_3\text{Li} + {}^{10}_5\text{B}$

b) IDENTIFY and **SET UP:** Calculate the mass decrease and find its energy equivalent.

EXECUTE: The neutral atoms on each side of the reaction equation have a total of 8 electrons, so the electron masses cancel when neutral atom masses are used. The neutral atom masses are found in Table 43.2.

mass of $^2_1\text{H} + {}^{14}_7\text{N}$ is 2.014102 u + 14.003074 u = 16.017176 u

mass of $^6_3\text{Li} + {}^{10}_5\text{B}$ is 6.015121 u + 10.012937 u = 16.028058 u

The mass increases, so energy is absorbed by the reaction. The Q value is

$(16.017176 \text{ u} - 16.028058 \text{ u})(931.5 \text{ Mev/u}) = -10.14 \text{ MeV}$

c) IDENTIFY and **SET UP:** The available energy in the collision, the kinetic energy K_{cm} in the center-of-mass reference frame is related to the kinetic energy K of the bombarding particle by Eq.(43.24).

EXECUTE: The kinetic energy that must be available to cause the reaction is 10.14 MeV. Thus $K_{cm} = 10.14$ MeV. The mass M of the stationary target ($^{14}_7\text{N}$) is $M = 14$ u. The mass m of the colliding particle (^2_1H) is 2 u. Then by Eq.(43.24) the minumum kinetic energy K that the ^2_1H must have is

$$K = \left(\frac{M+m}{M}\right)K_{cm} = \left(\frac{14 \text{ u} + 2 \text{ u}}{14 \text{ u}}\right)(10.14 \text{ MeV}) = 11.59 \text{ MeV}$$

EVALUATE: The projectile (^2_1H) is much lighter than the target ($^{14}_7\text{N}$) so K is not much larger than K_{cm}. The K we have calculated is what is required to allow the mass increase. We would also need to check to see if at this energy the projectile can overcome the Coulomb repulsion to get sufficiently close to the target nucleus for the reaction to occur.

43.45 IDENTIFY and **SET UP:** Find the energy equivalent of the mass decrease.

EXECUTE: $^{235}_{92}\text{U} + ^{1}_{0}\text{n} \rightarrow ^{236}_{92}\text{U}$

The mass defect is $\Delta M = M\left(^{235}_{92}\text{U}\right) + M\left(^{1}_{0}\text{n}\right) - M\left(^{236}_{92}\text{U}\right)$.

$\Delta M = 235.043923 \text{ u} + 1.008665 \text{ u} - 236.045562 \text{ u} = +0.007026 \text{ u}$

$Q = (\Delta M)c^2 = (0.007026 \text{ u})(931.5 \text{ MeV}/1 \text{ u}) = 6.545 \text{ MeV}$

EVALUATE: This much energy is liberated in the reaction. By conservaton of linear momentum, since there is essentially zero momentum before the reaction, the product nucleus must be essentially at rest and therefore have zero kinetic energy. All the energy released must go into the internal excitation of the $^{236}_{92}\text{U}$.

Problems

43.53 a) IDENTIFY and **SET UP:** The heavier nucleus will decay into the lighter one.

EXECUTE: $^{25}_{13}\text{Al}$ will decay into $^{25}_{12}\text{Mg}$.

b) IDENTIFY and **SET UP:** Determine the emitted particle by balancing A and Z in the decay reaction.

EXECUTE: This gives $^{25}_{13}\text{Al} \rightarrow ^{25}_{12}\text{Mg} + ^{0}_{+1}\text{e}$. The emitted particle must have charge $+e$ and its nucleon number must be zero. Therefore, it is a β^+ particle, a positron.

c) IDENTIFY and **SET UP:** Calculate the energy defect ΔM for the reaction and find the energy equivalent of ΔM. Use the nuclear masses for $^{25}_{13}\text{Al}$ and $^{25}_{12}\text{Mg}$, to avoid confusion in including the correct number of electrons if neutral atom masses are used.

EXECUTE:

The nuclear mass for $^{25}_{13}\text{Al}$ is $M_{\text{nuc}}\left(^{25}_{13}\text{Al}\right) = 24.990429 \text{ u} - 13(0.000548580 \text{ u}) = 24.983297 \text{ u}$.

The nuclear mass for $^{25}_{12}\text{Mg}$ is $M_{\text{nuc}}\left(^{25}_{12}\text{Mg}\right) = 24.985837 \text{ u} - 12(0.000548580 \text{ u}) = 24.979254 \text{ u}$.

The mass defect for the reaction is

$\Delta M = M_{\text{nuc}}\left(^{25}_{13}\text{Al}\right) - M_{\text{nuc}}\left(^{25}_{12}\text{Mg}\right) - M\left(^{0}_{+1}\text{e}\right) = 24.983297 \text{ u} - 24.979254 \text{ u} - 0.00054858 \text{ u} = 0.003494 \text{ u}$

$Q = (\Delta M)c^2 = 0.003494 \text{ u}(931.5 \text{ MeV}/1 \text{ u}) = 3.255 \text{ MeV}$

EVALUATE: The mass decreases in the decay and energy is released.

Note: $^{25}_{13}\text{Al}$ can also decay into $^{25}_{12}\text{Mg}$ by electron capture.

$^{25}_{13}\text{Al} + _{-1}^{0}\text{e} \rightarrow _{12}^{25}\text{Mg}$

The $_{-1}^{0}\text{e}$ electron in the reaction is an orbital electron in the neutral $_{13}^{25}\text{Al}$ atom. The mass defect can be calculated using the nuclear masses:

$\Delta M = M_{\text{nuc}}\left(_{13}^{25}\text{Al}\right) + M\left(_{-1}^{0}\text{e}\right) - M_{\text{nuc}}\left(_{12}^{25}\text{Mg}\right) = 24.983297$ u $+ 0.00054858$ u $-$ 24.979254 u $= 0.004592$ u.

$Q = (\Delta M)c^2 = (0.004592 \text{ u})(931.5 \text{ MeV}/1 \text{ u}) = 4.277 \text{ MeV}$

The mass decreases in the decay and energy is released.

43.57 **IDENTIFY** and **SET UP:** Find the energy equivalent of the mass decrease. Part of the released energy appears as the emitted photon and the rest as kinetic energy of the electron.

EXECUTE: $^{198}_{79}\text{Au} \rightarrow _{80}^{198}\text{Hg} + _{-1}^{0}\text{e}$

The mass change is 197.968225 u $- 197.966752$ u $= 1.473 \times 10^{-3}$ u

(The neutral atom masses include 79 electrons before the decay and 80 electrons after the decay. This one additional electron in the products accounts correctly for the electron emitted by the nucleus.)

The total energy released in the decay is $(1.473 \times 10^{-3} \text{ u})(931.5 \text{ MeV/u}) = 1.372$ MeV. This energy is divided between the energy of the emitted photon and the kinetic energy of the β^- particle. Thus the β^- particle has kinetic energy equal to 1.372 MeV $- 0.412$ MeV $= 0.960$ MeV.

EVALUATE: The emitted electron is much lighter than the $^{198}_{80}\text{Hg}$ nucleus, so the electron has almost all the final kinetic energy. The final kinetic energy of the ^{198}Hg nucleus is very small.

43.59 **IDENTIFY** and **SET UP:** The decay is energetically possible if the total mass decreases. Determine the nucleus produced by the decay by balancing A and Z on both sides of the decay equation.

$^{13}_{7}\text{N} \rightarrow _{+1}^{0}\text{e} + _{6}^{13}\text{C}$ To avoid confusion in including the correct number of electrons with neutral atom masses, use nuclear masses, obtained by subtracting the mass of the atomic electrons from the neutral atom masses.

EXECUTE:

The nuclear mass for $^{13}_{7}\text{N}$ is $M_{\text{nuc}}\left(_{7}^{13}\text{N}\right) = 13.005739$ u $- 7(0.00054858$ u$) = 13.001899$ u.

The nuclear mass for $^{13}_{6}\text{C}$ is $M_{\text{nuc}}\left(_{6}^{13}\text{C}\right) = 13.003355$ u $- 6(0.00054858$ u$) = 13.000064$ u.

The mass defect for the reaction is $\Delta M = M_{\text{nuc}}\left(_{7}^{13}\text{N}\right) - M_{\text{nuc}}\left(_{6}^{13}\text{C}\right) - M\left(_{+1}^{0}\text{e}\right)$

$\Delta M = 13.001899$ u $- 13.000064$ u $- 0.00054858$ u $= 0.001286$ u.

EVALUATE: The mass decreases in the decay, so energy is released. This decay is energetically possible.

43.63 IDENTIFY: Use Eq.(43.17) to relate the initial number of radioactive nuclei, N_0, to the number, N, left after time t.

SET UP: We have to be careful; after ^{87}Rb has undergone radioactive decay it is no longer a rubidium atom. Let N_{85} be the number of ^{85}Rb atoms; this number doesn't change. Let N_0 be the number of ^{87}Rb atoms on earth when the solar system was formed. Let N be the present number of ^{87}Rb atoms.

EXECUTE: The present measurements say that $0.2783 = N/(N + N_{85})$.
$(N + N_{85})(0.2783) = N$, so $N = 0.3856N_{85}$.
The percentage we are asked to calculate is $N_0/(N_0 + N_{85})$.
N and N_0 are related by $N = N_0 e^{-\lambda t}$ so $N_0 = e^{+\lambda t}N$.

Thus $\dfrac{N_0}{N_0 + N_{85}} = \dfrac{Ne^{\lambda t}}{Ne^{\lambda t} + N_{85}} = \dfrac{(0.3856e^{\lambda t})N_{85}}{(0.3856e^{\lambda t})N_{85} + N_{85}} = \dfrac{0.3856e^{\lambda t}}{0.3856e^{\lambda t} + 1}.$

$t = 4.6 \times 10^9$ y; $\lambda = \dfrac{0.693}{T_{1/2}} = \dfrac{0.693}{4.75 \times 10^{10} \text{ y}} = 1.459 \times 10^{-11} \text{ y}^{-1}$

$e^{\lambda t} = e^{(1.459 \times 10^{-11} \text{ y}^{-1})(4.6 \times 10^9 \text{ y})} = e^{0.06711} = 1.0694$

Thus $\dfrac{N_0}{N_0 + N_{85}} = \dfrac{(0.3856)(1.0694)}{(0.3856)(1.0694) + 1} = 29.2\%.$

EVALUATE: The half-life for ^{87}Rb is a factor of 10 larger than the age of the solar system, so only a small fraction of the ^{87}Rb nuclei initially present have decayed; the percentage of rubidium atoms that are radioactive is only a bit less now than it was when the solar system was formed.

43.65 IDENTIFY and **SET UP:** Find the energy emitted and the energy absorbed each second. Convert the absorbed energy to absorbed dose and to equivalent dose.

EXECUTE:

a) First find the number of decays each second:

$2.6 \times 10^{-4} \text{ Ci} \left(\dfrac{3.70 \times 10^{10} \text{ decays/s}}{1 \text{ Ci}} \right) = 9.6 \times 10^6 \text{ decays/s}$

The average energy per decay is 1.25 MeV, and one-half of this energy is deposited in the tumor. The energy delivered to the tumor per second then is
$\frac{1}{2}(9.6 \times 10^6 \text{ decays/s})(1.25 \times 10^6 \text{ eV/decay})(1.602 \times 10^{-19} \text{ J/eV}) = 9.6 \times 10^{-7}$ J/s.

b) The absorbed dose is the energy absorbed divided by the mass of the tissue:
$\dfrac{9.6 \times 10^{-7} \text{ J/s}}{0.500 \text{ kg}} = (1.9 \times 10^{-6} \text{ J/kg} \cdot \text{s})(1 \text{ rad}/(0.01 \text{ J/kg})) = 1.9 \times 10^{-4} \text{ rad/s}$

c) equivalent dose (REM) = RBE X absorbed dose (rad)

In one second the equivalent dose is $0.70(1.9 \times 10^{-4} \text{ rad}) = 1.3 \times 10^{-4}$ rem.

d) $(200 \text{ rem}/1.3 \times 10^{-4} \text{ rem/s}) = 1.5 \times 10^6 \text{ s}(1 \text{ h}/3600 \text{ s}) = 420 \text{ h} = 17$ days.

EVALUATE: The activity of the source is small so the absorbed energy per second is small and it takes several days for an equivalent dose of 200 rem to be absorbed by the tumor. A 200 rem dose equals 2.00 Sv and this is large enough to damage the tissue of the tumor.

43.67 **IDENTIFY** and **SET UP:** The number of radioactive nuclei left after time t is given by $N = N_0 e^{-\lambda t}$. The problem says $N/N_0 = 0.21$; solve for t.

EXECUTE: $0.21 = e^{-\lambda t}$ so $\ln(0.21) = -\lambda t$ and $t = -\ln(0.21)/\lambda$

Example 43.9 gives $\lambda = 1.209 \times 10^{-4} \text{ y}^{-1}$ for ^{14}C.

Thus $t = \dfrac{-\ln(0.21)}{1.209 \times 10^{-4} \text{ y}} = 1.3 \times 10^4$ y.

EVALUATE: The half-life of ^{14}C is 5730 y, so our calculated t is more than two half-lives, so the fraction remaining is less than $(\frac{1}{2})^2 = \frac{1}{4}$.

43.69 **a)** **IDENTIFY** and **SET UP:** Use Eq.(43.1) to calculate the radius R of a ^2_1H nucleus. Calculate the Coulomb potential energy (Eq.23.9) of the two nuclei when they just touch.

EXECUTE: The radius of ^2_1H is $R = (1.2 \times 10^{-15} \text{ m})(2)^{1/3} = 1.51 \times 10^{-15}$ m. The barrier energy is the Coulomb potential energy of two ^2_1H nuclei with their centers separated by twice this distance:

$$U = \frac{1}{4\pi\epsilon_0} \frac{e^2}{r} = (8.988 \times 10^9 \text{ N} \cdot \text{m}^2/\text{C}^2) \frac{(1.602 \times 10^{-19} \text{ C})^2}{2(1.51 \times 10^{-15} \text{ m})} = 7.64 \times 10^{-14} \text{ J} = 0.48 \text{ MeV}$$

b) **IDENTIFY** and **SET UP:** Find the energy equivalent of the mass decrease.

EXECUTE: $^2_1\text{H} + {^2_1\text{H}} \rightarrow {^3_2\text{He}} + {^1_0\text{n}}$

If we use neutral atom masses there are two electrons on each side of the reaction equation, so their masses cancel. The neutral atom masses are given in Table 43.2.

$^2_1\text{H} + {^2_1\text{H}}$ has mass $2(2.014102 \text{ u}) = 4.028204$ u

$^3_2\text{He} + {^1_0\text{n}}$ has mass $3.016029 \text{ u} + 1.008665 \text{ u} = 4.024694$ u

The mass decrease is $4.028204 \text{ u} - 4.024694 \text{ u} = 3.510 \times 10^{-3}$ u. This corrresponds to a liberated energy of $(3.510 \times 10^{-3} \text{ u})(931.5 \text{ MeV/u}) = 3.270$ MeV, or

$(3.270 \times 10^6 \text{ eV})(1.602 \times 10^{-19} \text{ J/eV}) = 5.239 \times 10^{-13}$ J.

c) IDENTIFY and **SET UP:** We know the energy released when two $_1^2$H nuclei fuse. Find the number of reactions obtained with one mole of $_1^2$H.

EXECUTE: Each reaction takes two $_1^2$H nuclei. Each mole of D_2 has 6.022×10^{23} molecules, so 6.022×10^{23} pairs of atoms. The energy liberated when one more of deuterium undergoes fusion is $(6.022 \times 10^{23})(5.239 \times 10^{-13} \text{ J}) = 3.155 \times 10^{11}$ J/mol.

EVALUATE: The energy liberated per mole is more than a million times larger than from chemical combustion of one mole of hydrogen gas.

43.71 IDENTIFY and **SET UP:** Find the number of ^{40}K nuclei per kg of body tissue and then use Eq.(43.16) to calculate the number of decays per second per kg.

EXECUTE: Consider 1.00 kg of body tissue. The mass of ^{40}K in 1.00 kg of tissue is $(0.21 \times 10^{-2})(0.012 \times 10^{-2})(1.00 \text{ kg}) = 2.52 \times 10^{-7}$ kg.

The mass of a ^{40}K atom is approximately 40 u, so the number of ^{40}K nuclei in 1.00 kg of tissue is

$$\frac{2.52 \times 10^{-7} \text{ kg}}{40 \text{ u}} = \frac{2.52 \times 10^{-7} \text{ kg}}{40 \text{ u}(1.66054 \times 10^{-27} \text{ kg/u})} = 3.794 \times 10^{18}.$$

The activity is $|dN/dt| = \lambda N$. $\lambda = \dfrac{0.693}{T_{1/2}} = \dfrac{0.693}{1.28 \times 10^9 \text{ y}} = 5.414 \times 10^{-10}$ y^{-1}.

Thus $|dN/dt| = (5.414 \times 10^{-10} \text{ y}^{-1})(3.794 \times 10^{18}) = 2.054 \times 10^9$ decays/y.

In 50 y there are $(50 \text{ y})(2.054 \times 10^9 \text{ decays/y}) = 1.027 \times 10^{11}$ decays.

For each decay an average of 0.50 MeV of energy is absorbed. The energy absorbed by 1.00 kg of tissue is $(1.027 \times 10^{11} \text{ decays})(0.50 \text{ MeV/decay}) = 5.14 \times 10^{10}$ MeV $= 5.14 \times 10^{16}$ eV$(1.602 \times 10^{-19} \text{ J/eV}) = 0.0082$ J.

The absobed dose is $(0.0082 \text{ J/kg})(1 \text{ rad}/ 0.01 \text{ J/kg}) = 0.82$ rad.

RBE $= 1.0$, so the equivalent dose is 0.82 rem.

EVALUATE: The dose is 0.16 mSv per year. This is less than the 1.0 mSv per year dose from cosmic rays and natural radioactivity in the environment.

CHAPTER 44
PARTICLE PHYSICS AND COSMOLOGY

Exercises 1, 3, 11, 13, 15, 19, 23, 27, 33, 35, 37, 41
Problems 43, 45, 47, 51, 55

Exercises

44.1 **a) IDENTIFY** and **SET UP:** Use Eq.(37.36) to calculate the kinetic energy K.

EXECUTE: $K = mc^2 \left(\dfrac{1}{\sqrt{1 - v^2/c^2}} - 1 \right) = 0.1547mc^2$

$m = 9.109 \times 10^{-31}$ kg, so $K = 1.27 \times 10^{-14}$ J

b) IDENTIFY and **SET UP:** The total energy of the particles equals the sum of the energies of the two photons. Linear momentum must also be conserved.

EXECUTE: The total energy of each electron or positron is $E = K + mc^2 = 1.1547mc^2 = 9.46 \times 10^{-14}$ J. The total energy of the electron and positron is converted into the total energy of the two photons. The initial momentum of the system in the lab frame is zero (since the equal-mass particles have equal speeds in opposite directions), so the final momentum must also be zero. The photons must have equal wavelengths and must be traveling in opposite directions. Equal λ means equal energy, so each photon has energy 9.46×10^{-14} J.

c) IDENTIFY and **SET UP:** Use Eq.(38.2) to relate the photon energy to the photon wavelength.
EXECUTE: $E = hc/\lambda$ so $\lambda = hc/E = hc/(9.46 \times 10^{-14}$ J$) = 2.10$ pm

EVALUATE: The wavelength calculated in Example 44.1 is 2.43 pm. When the particles also have kinetic energy, the energy of each photon is greater, so its wavelength is less.

44.3 **IDENTIFY** and **SET UP:** By momentum conservation the two photons must have equal and opposite momenta. Then $E = pc$ says the photons must have equal energies. Their total energy must equal the rest mass energy $E = mc^2$ of the pion. Once we have found the photon energy we can use $E = hf$ to calculate the photon frequency and use $\lambda = c/f$ to calculate the wavelength.

EXECUTE: The mass of the pion is $270m_e$, so the rest energy of the pion is $270(0.511$ MeV$) = 138$ MeV. Each photon has half this energy, or 69 MeV.

$E = hf$ so $f = \dfrac{E}{h} = \dfrac{(69 \times 10^6 \text{ eV})(1.602 \times 10^{-19} \text{ J/eV})}{6.626 \times 10^{-34} \text{ J} \cdot \text{s}} = 1.7 \times 10^{22}$ Hz

$$\lambda = \frac{c}{f} = \frac{2.998 \times 10^8 \text{ m/s}}{1.7 \times 10^{22} \text{ Hz}} = 1.8 \times 10^{-14} \text{ m} = 18 \text{ fm}.$$

EVALUATE: These photons are in the gamma ray part of the electromagnetic spectrum.

44.11 a) IDENTIFY and **SET UP:** Eq.(44.7) says $\omega = |q|B/m$ so $B = m\omega/|q|$.
And since $\omega = 2\pi f$, this becomes $B = 2\pi m f/|q|$.

EXECUTE: A deuteron is a deuterium nucleus $\left(_1^2\text{H}\right)$. Its charge is $q = +e$. Its mass is the mass of the neutral $_1^2\text{H}$ atom (Table 43.2) minus the mass of the one atomic electron:

$m = 2.014102 \text{ u} - 0.0005486 \text{ u} = 2.013553 \text{ u}(1.66054 \times 10^{-27} \text{ kg/1 u}) = 3.344 \times 10^{-27} \text{ kg}$

$$B = \frac{2\pi m f}{|q|} = \frac{2\pi(3.344 \times 10^{-27} \text{ kg})(9.00 \times 10^6 \text{ Hz})}{1.602 \times 10^{-19} \text{ C}} = 1.18 \text{ T}$$

b) Eq.(44.8): $K = \dfrac{q^2 B^2 R^2}{2m} = \dfrac{[(1.602 \times 10^{-19} \text{ C})(1.18 \text{ T})(0.320 \text{ m})]^2}{2(3.344 \times 10^{-27} \text{ kg})}.$

$K = 5.471 \times 10^{-13} \text{ J} = (5.471 \times 10^{-13} \text{ J})(1 \text{ eV}/1.602 \times 10^{-19} \text{ J}) = 3.42 \text{ MeV}$

$$K = \tfrac{1}{2}mv^2 \text{ so } v = \sqrt{\frac{2K}{m}} = \sqrt{\frac{2(5.471 \times 10^{-13} \text{ J})}{3.344 \times 10^{-27} \text{ kg}}} = 1.81 \times 10^7 \text{ m/s}$$

EVALUATE: $v/c = 0.06$, so it is ok to use the nonrelativistic expression for kinetic energy.

44.13 a) IDENTIFY and **SET UP:** The masses of the target and projectile particles are equal, so Eq.(44.10) can be used.
$E_a^2 = 2mc^2(E_m + mc^2)$. E_a is specified; solve for the energy E_m of the beam particle.

EXECUTE: $E_m = \dfrac{E_a^2}{2mc^2} - mc^2$

The mass of the alpha particle can be calculated by subtracting two electron masses from the $_2^4\text{He}$ atomic mass:

$m = m_\alpha = 4.002603 \text{ u} - 2(0.0005486 \text{ u}) = 4.001506 \text{ u}$

Then $mc^2 = (4.001506 \text{ u})(931.5 \text{ MeV/u}) = 3.727 \text{ GeV}.$

$$E_m = \frac{E_a^2}{2mc^2} - mc^2 = \frac{(16.0 \text{ GeV})^2}{2(3.727 \text{ GeV})} - 3.727 \text{ GeV} = 30.6 \text{ GeV}.$$

b) Each beam must have $\tfrac{1}{2}E_a = 8.0 \text{ GeV}$.

EVALUATE: For a stationary target the beam energy is nearly twice the available energy. In a colliding beam experiment all the energy is available and each beam needs to have just half the required available energy.

44.15 a) IDENTIFY and **SET UP:** For a proton beam on a stationary proton target and since E_a is much larger than the proton rest energy we can use Eq.(44.11): $E_a^2 = 2mc^2 E_m$.

EXECUTE: $E_m = \dfrac{E_a^2}{2mc^2} = \dfrac{(77.4 \text{ GeV})^2}{2(0.938 \text{ GeV})} = 3200 \text{ GeV}$

b) IDENTIFY and **SET UP:** For colliding beams the total momentum is zero and the available energy E_a is the total energy of the two colliding particles.

EXECUTE: For proton-proton collisions the colliding beams each have the same energy, so the total energy of each beam is $\frac{1}{2}E_a = 38.7 \text{ GeV}$.

EVALUATE: For a stationary target less than 3% of the beam energy is available for conversion into mass. The beam energy for a colliding beam experiment is a factor of (1/83) times smaller than the required energy for a stationary target experiment.

44.19 IDENTIFY and **SET UP:** Find the energy equivalent of the mass decrease.

EXECUTE: The mass decrease is $m(\sum^+) - m(p) - m(\pi^0)$ and the energy released is

$mc^2(\sum^+) - mc^2(p) - mc^2(\pi^0) = 1189 \text{ MeV} - 938.3 \text{ MeV} - 135.0 \text{ MeV} = 116 \text{ MeV}$.

(The mc^2 values for each particle were taken from Table 44.3.)

EVALUATE: The mass of the decay products is less than the mass of the original particle, so the decay is energetically allowed and energy is released.

44.23 IDENTIFY and **SET UP:** Compare the sum of the strangeness quantum numbers for the particles on each side of the decay equation. The strangeness quantum numbers for each particle are given in Table 44.3.

EXECUTE:

a) $K^+ \to \mu^+ + \nu_\mu$; $S_{K^+} = +1$, $S_{\mu^+} = 0$, $S_{\nu_\mu} = 0$

$S = 1$ initially; $S = 0$ for the products; S is <u>not conserved</u>

b) $n + K^+ \to p + \pi^0$; $S_n = 0$, $S_{K^+} = +1$, $S_p = 0$, $S_{\pi^0} = 0$

$S = 1$ initially; $S = 0$ for the products; S is <u>not conserved</u>

c) $K^+ + K^- \to \pi^0 + \pi^0$; $S_{K^+} = +1$; $S_{K^-} = -1$; $S_{\pi^0} = 0$

$S = +1 - 1 = 0$ initially; $S = 0$ for the products; S <u>is conserved</u>

d) $p + K^- \to \Lambda^0 + \pi^0$; $S_p = 0$, $S_{K^-} = -1$, $S_{\Lambda^0} = -1$, $S_{\pi^0} = 0$.

$S = -1$ initially; $S = -1$ for the products; S <u>is conserved</u>

EVALUATE: Strangeness is not a conserved quantity in weak interactions and strangeness non-conserving reactions or decays can occur.

44.27 IDENTIFY and **SET UP:** Each value for the combination is the sum of the values for each quark. Use Table 44.4.

EXECUTE:

a) uds

$Q = \frac{2}{3}e - \frac{1}{3}e - \frac{1}{3}e = 0$
$B = \frac{1}{3} + \frac{1}{3} + \frac{1}{3} = 1$
$S = 0 + 0 - 1 = -1$
$C = 0 + 0 + 0 = 0$

b) c$\bar{\text{u}}$

The values for $\bar{\text{u}}$ are the negative of those for **u**.

$Q = \frac{2}{3}e - \frac{2}{3}e = 0$
$B = \frac{1}{3} - \frac{1}{3} = 0$
$S = 0 + 0 = 0$
$C = +1 + 0 = +1$

c) ddd

$Q = -\frac{1}{3}e - \frac{1}{3}e - \frac{1}{3}e = -e$
$B = \frac{1}{3} + \frac{1}{3} + \frac{1}{3} = +1$
$S = 0 + 0 + 0 = 0$
$C = 0 + 0 + 0 = 0$

d) d$\bar{\text{c}}$

$Q = -\frac{1}{3}e - \frac{2}{3}e = -e$
$B = \frac{1}{3} - \frac{1}{3} = 0$
$S = 0 + 0 = 0$
$C = 0 - 1 = -1$

EVALUATE: The charge, baryon number, strangeness and charm quantum numbers of a particle are determined by the particle's quark composition.

44.33 a) IDENTIFY and **SET UP:** Hubble's law is Eq.(44.15), with $H_0 = 71$ (km/s)/(Mpc). 1 Mpc= 3.26 Mly.

EXECUTE: $r = 5210$ Mly so $v = H_0 r = ((71 \text{ km/s})/\text{Mpc})(1 \text{ Mpc}/3.26 \text{ Mly})(5210 \text{ Mly}) = 1.1 \times 10^5$ km/s

b) IDENTIFY and **SET UP:** Use v from part (a) in Eq.(44.13).

EXECUTE: $\dfrac{\lambda_0}{\lambda_S} = \sqrt{\dfrac{c+v}{c-v}} = \sqrt{\dfrac{1+v/c}{1-v/c}}$

$\dfrac{v}{c} = \dfrac{1.1 \times 10^8 \text{ m/s}}{2.9980 \times 10^8 \text{ m/s}} = 0.367$ so $\dfrac{\lambda_0}{\lambda_S} = \sqrt{\dfrac{1+0.367}{1-0.367}} = 1.5$

EVALUATE: The galaxy in Examples 44.9 and 44.10 is 710 Mly away so has a smaller recession speed and redshift than the galaxy in this problem.

44.35 **a) IDENTIFY** and **SET UP:** Use Eq.(44.14) to calculate v.

EXECUTE: $v = \left[\dfrac{(\lambda_0/\lambda_S)^2 - 1}{(\lambda_0/\lambda_s)^2 + 1}\right]c = \left[\dfrac{(658.5 \text{ nm}/590 \text{ nm})^2 - 1}{(658.5 \text{ nm}/590 \text{ nm})^2 + 1}\right]c = 0.1094c$

$v = (0.1094)(2.998 \times 10^8 \text{ m/s}) = 3.28 \times 10^7 \text{ m/s}$

b) IDENTIFY and **SET UP:** Use Eq.(44.15) to calculate r.

EXECUTE: $r = \dfrac{v}{H_0} = \dfrac{3.28 \times 10^4 \text{ km/s}}{(71 \text{ (km/s)/Mpc})(1 \text{ Mpc}/3.26 \text{ Mly})} = 1510 \text{ Mly}$

EVALUATE: The red shift $\lambda_0/\lambda_S - 1$ for this galaxy is 0.116. It is therefore about twice as far from earth as the galaxy in Examples 44.9 and 44.10, that had a red shift of 0.053.

44.37 **IDENTIFY** and **SET UP:** Find the energy equivalent of the mass decrease.

EXECUTE:

a) $p + {}^2_1\text{H} \rightarrow {}^3_2\text{He}$ or can write as ${}^1_1\text{H} + {}^2_1\text{H} \rightarrow {}^3_2\text{He}$

If neutral atom masses are used then the masses of the two atomic electrons on each side of the reaction will cancel.

Taking the atomic masses from Table 43.2, the mass decrease is

$m({}^1_1\text{H}) + m({}^2_1\text{H}) - m({}^3_2\text{He}) = 1.007825 \text{ u} + 2.014102 \text{ u} - 3.016029 \text{ u} = 0.005898 \text{ u}.$

The energy released is the energy equivalent of this mass decrease:

$(0.005898 \text{ u})(931.5 \text{ MeV/u}) = 5.494 \text{ MeV}$

b) ${}^1_0\text{n} + {}^3_2\text{He} \rightarrow {}^4_2\text{He}$

If neutral helium masses are used then the masses of the two atomic electrons on each side of the reaction equation will cancel. The mass decrease is

$m({}^1_0\text{n}) + m({}^3_2\text{He}) - m({}^4_2\text{He}) = 1.008665 \text{ u} + 3.016029 \text{ u} - 4.002603 \text{ u} = 0.022091 \text{ u}.$

The energy released is the energy equivalent of this mass decrease:

$(0.022091 \text{ u})(931.5 \text{ MeV/u}) = 20.58 \text{ MeV}$

EVALUATE: These are important nucleosynthesis reactions, discussed in Section 44.7.

44.41 IDENTIFY and **SET UP:** The Wien displacement law (Eq.38.30) says $\lambda_m T$ equals a constant. Use this to relate $\lambda_{m,1}$ at T_1 to $\lambda_{m,2}$ at T_2.

EXECUTE: $\lambda_{m,1} T_1 = \lambda_{m,2} T_2$

$$\lambda_{m,1} = \lambda_{m,2} \left(\frac{T_2}{T_1} \right) = 1.062 \times 10^{-3} \text{ m} \left(\frac{2.728 \text{ K}}{3000 \text{ K}} \right) = 966 \text{ nm}$$

EVALUATE: The peak wavelength was much less when the temperature was much higher.

Problems

44.43 IDENTIFY and **SET UP:** For colliding beams the available energy is twice the beam energy. For a fixed-target experiment only a portion of the beam energy is available energy (Eqs.44.9 and 44.10).

EXECUTE:

a) $E_a = 2(7.0 \text{ TeV}) = 14.0 \text{ TeV}$

b) Need $E_a = 14.0 \text{ TeV} = 14.0 \times 10^6 \text{ MeV}$.

Since the target and projectile particles are both protons Eq.(44.10) can be used:

$E_a^2 = 2mc^2(E_m + mc^2)$

$E_m = \dfrac{E_a^2}{2mc^2} - mc^2 = \dfrac{(14.0 \times 10^6 \text{ MeV})^2}{2(938.3 \text{ MeV})} - 938.3 \text{ MeV} = 1.0 \times 10^{11} \text{ MeV} =$

$1.0 \times 10^5 \text{ TeV}$.

EVALUATE: This shows the great advantage of colliding beams at relativistic energies.

44.45 IDENTIFY and **SET UP:** $e^- + e^- \rightarrow e^- + e^- + \pi^0$. The mass increase is the mass of the π^0 that is produced.

$Q = m_{\pi^0} c^2 = 135.0 \text{ MeV}$

The available energy E_a in the collision must be $E_a = Q + 2m_e c^2 = 135.0 \text{ MeV} + 2(0.511 \text{ MeV}) = 136.0 \text{ MeV}$.

Since the beam and target particles are the same we can use Eq.(44.10):

$E_a^2 = 2mc^2(E_m + mc^2)$, where m is the electron mass m_e.

EXECUTE: $E_m = \dfrac{E_a^2}{2mc^2} - mc^2 = \dfrac{(136.0 \text{ MeV})^2}{2(0.511 \text{ MeV})} - 0.511 \text{ MeV} = 1.81 \times 10^4 \text{ MeV}$

$E_m = K + m_e c^2$, so $K = E_m - m_e c^2 = 1.81 \times 10^4 \text{ MeV} - 0.511 \text{ MeV} = 1.81 \times 10^4 \text{ MeV} = 18.1 \text{ GeV}$

EVALUATE: To produce a particle with rest mass energy 135 MeV the kinetic energy of the beam particle must 18.1 GeV. Most of the kinetic energy of the collision is not available for conversion into mass of created particles.

44.47 IDENTIFY and **SET UP:** The total available energy E_a must be at least the total rest energy of the product particles. Since the target and projectile particles are different we must use Eq.(44.9) to relate the beam energy E_m to the required available energy.

EXECUTE: $E_a = mc^2(\Lambda^0) + mc^2(K^+) + mc^2(K^-) = 1116$ MeV $+ 2(493.7$ MeV$)$ $= 2103.4$ MeV

$E_a^2 = 2Mc^2E_m + (Mc^2)^2 + (mc^2)^2$, with $M = m_p$ and $m = m_{K^-}$

$E_a^2 = 2m_pc^2E_{K^-} + (m_pc^2)^2 + (m_{K^-}c^2)^2$

$E_{K^-} = \dfrac{E_a^2 - (m_pc^2)^2 - (m_{K^-}c^2)^2}{2m_pc^2}$

$E_{K^-} = \dfrac{(2103.4 \text{ MeV})^2 - (938.3 \text{ MeV})^2 - (493.7 \text{ MeV})^2}{2(938.3 \text{ MeV})} = 1758.6$ MeV

This is the total energy of the K^- particle. Its kinetic energy is

$K = E_{K^-} - (m_{K^-})c^2 = 1758.6$ MeV $- 493.7$ MeV $= 1265$ MeV

EVALUATE: Q for the reaction is $mc^2(p) - mc^2(K^+) - mc^2(\Lambda^0) = 938.3$ MeV $- 493.7$ MeV $- 1116$ MeV $= -671$ MeV.

44.51 IDENTIFY and **SET UP:** $\phi \rightarrow K^+ + K^-$. The total energy released is the energy equivalent of the mass decrease.

a) EXECUTE: The mass decrease is $m(\phi) - m(K^+) - m(K^-)$. The energy equivalent of the mass decrease is $mc^2(\phi) - mc^2(K^+) - mc^2(K^-)$. The rest mass energy mc^2 for the ϕ meson is given in Problem 44.50, and the values for K^+ and K^- are given in Table 44.3. The energy released then is 1019.4 MeV $- 2(493.7$ MeV$) = 32.0$ MeV. The K^+ gets half this, 16.0 MeV.

EVALUATE:

b) Does the decay $\phi \rightarrow K^+ + K^- + \pi^0$ occur?

The energy equivalent of the $K^+ + K^- + \pi^0$ mass is 493.7 MeV $+ 493.7$ MeV $+ 135.0$ MeV $= 1122$ MeV. This is greater than the energy equivalent of the ϕ mass. The mass of the decay products would be greater than the mass of the parent particle; the decay is energetically forbidden.

c) Does the decay $\phi \rightarrow K^+ + \pi^-$ occur?

The reaction $\phi \rightarrow K^+ + K^-$ is observed. K^+ has strangeness $+1$ and K^- has strangeness -1, so the total strangeness of the decay products is zero. If strangeness must conserved we deduce that the ϕ particle has strangeness zero.

π^- has strangeness 0, so the products $K^+ + \pi^-$ has strangeness -1. The decay $\phi \rightarrow K^+ + \pi^-$ violates consevation of strangeness.

Does the decay $\phi \rightarrow K^+ + \mu^-$ occur?

μ^- has strangeness 0, so this decay would also violate conservation of strangeness.

44.55 **IDENTIFY** and **SET UP:** The total released energy is the equivalent of the mass decrease. Use conservation of linear momentum to relate the kinetic energies of the decay particles.

EXECUTE:

a) The energy equivalent of the mass decrease is $mc^2(\Xi^-) - mc^2(\Lambda^0) - mc^2(\pi^-)$
= 1321 MeV - 1116 MeV - 139.6 MeV = 65 MeV

b) The Ξ^- is at rest means that the linear momentum is zero. Conservation of linear momentum then says that the Λ^0 and π^- must have equal and opposite momenta·

$$m_{\Lambda^0} v_{\Lambda^0} = m_{\pi^-} v_{\pi^-}$$

$$v_{\pi^-} = \left(\frac{m_{\Lambda^0}}{m_{\pi^-}} \right) v_{\Lambda^0}$$

Also, the sum of the kinetic energies of the Λ^0 and π^- must equal the total kinetic energy $K_{\text{tot}} = 65$ MeV calculated in part (a):

$$K_{\text{tot}} = K_{\Lambda^0} + K_{\pi^-}$$

$$K_{\Lambda^0} + \tfrac{1}{2} m_{\pi^-} v_{\pi^-}^2 = K_{\text{tot}}$$

Use the momentum conservation result:

$$K_{\Lambda^0} + \tfrac{1}{2} m_{\pi^-} \left(\frac{m_{\Lambda^0}}{m_{\pi^-}} \right)^2 v_{\Lambda^0}^2 = K_{\text{tot}}$$

$$K_{\Lambda^0} + \left(\frac{m_{\Lambda^0}}{m_{\pi^-}} \right) \left(\tfrac{1}{2} m_{\Lambda^0} v_{\Lambda^0}^2 \right) = K_{\text{tot}}$$

$$K_{\Lambda^0} \left(1 + \frac{m_{\Lambda^0}}{m_{\pi^-}} \right) = K_{\text{tot}}$$

$$K_{\Lambda^0} = \frac{K_{\text{tot}}}{1 + m_{\Lambda^0}/m_{\pi^-}} = \frac{65 \text{ MeV}}{1 + (1116 \text{ MeV})/(139.6 \text{ MeV})} = 7.2 \text{ MeV}$$

$K_{\Lambda^0} + K_{\pi^-} = K_{\text{tot}}$ so

$K_{\pi^-} = K_{\text{tot}} - K_{\Lambda^0} = 65 \text{ MeV} - 7.2 \text{ MeV} = 57.8 \text{ MeV}$

The fraction for the Λ^0 is $\dfrac{7.2 \text{ MeV}}{65 \text{ MeV}} = 11\%$.

The fraction for the π^- is $\dfrac{57.8 \text{ MeV}}{65 \text{ MeV}} = 89\%$.

EVALUATE: The lighter particle carries off more of the kinetic energy that is released in the decay than the heavier particle does.